Student Solutions Manual to Accompany
CHEMISTRY

By

Stanley R. Radel
City College of the City University of New York

Marjorie H. Navidi
Queens College of the City University of New York

Prepared by
Alan Tchernoff

WEST PUBLISHING COMPANY
St. Paul New York Los Angelos San Francisco

COPYRIGHT © 1990   by WEST PUBLISHING CO.
610 Opperman Drive
P.O. Box 64526
St. Paul, MN 55164–0526

97 96 95 94 93 92   8 7 6 5 4 3 2

ISBN 0-314-67574-4

Table of Contents

Preface

To The Student:

Once you have completed study of a chapter you should then attempt to work the final exercises. Do not give in to the temptation to look up answers before you complete the problems, because then you will lose the opportunity of discovering for yourself the thought process involved in problem solving and will greatly reduce your confidence level. Because problem solving is critical for the study of chemistry, you will be doing yourself a disservice. Rather, you should complete your problem selection and only then check your solutions against the solutions manual. This process will help you spot weaknesses in your problem solving technique and thereby improve your skills.

I wish to thank Dr. Marjorie Navidi for her assistance in checking this manual. I also wish to thank Dr. David Adams for his checking of the manual. My many talks with Dr. Stanley Radel were enlightening and very helpful. Finally, I would like to thank my wife Rachel and daughter Rebecca for their support.

Dr. Alan Tchernoff

CHAPTER 1
CHEMISTRY AND MEASUREMENT

Solutions To Practice Exercises

PE 1.7 (a) The measurement 6.8 mL has one decimal place; therefore, the sum will have one decimal place.

```
  6.8│  mL
 71.3│5 mL
 78.1│5 mL = 78.2 mL after rounding off to one decimal place.
```

(b) The measurement 3.43 cm has two decimal places; therefore, the difference will have two decimal places.

```
   9.22│41 cm
 − 3.43│   cm
   5.79│41 cm = 5.79 cm after rounding off to the second decimal place.
```

(c) The measurement 21.33 g has two decimal places; therefore, the sum will have two decimal places.

```
   0.00│41 g
 + 21.33│   g
  21.33│41 g
 − 7.08│44 g
  14.24│97 g = 14.25 g after rounding off to the second decimal place.
```

PE 1.8 (a) The number 5.0003 has five significant figures, 2.100 has four significant figures, and 0.0104 has three significant figures; the product will have three significant figures.

5.0003 x 2.100 x 0.0104 = 0.10920 = 0.109 after rounding off to three significant figures.

(b) Both 0.024 and 0.0015 have two significant figures; the quotient will have two significant figures.

0.024/0.0015 = 16

(c) 3.005×10^{-5} has four significant figures while 1.1×10^6 has two significant figures; the quotient will have two significant figures.

$3.005 \times 10^{-5}/1.1 \times 10^6 = 2.7318 \times 10^{-11} = 2.7 \times 10^{-11}$ after rounding off to two significant figures.

PE 1.9 The number of objects in a dozen is exactly 12 by definition. The average weight of one orange is 3.10 kg/12 = 0.258 kg. The answer has three significant figures because 3.10 is given to three significant figures.

PE 1.11 The conversion factor we need is

$$\frac{3 \text{ ft}}{1 \text{ yard}} \times \frac{12 \text{ in}}{1 \text{ ft}} \times \frac{2.54 \text{ cm}}{1 \text{ in}} \times \frac{1 \text{ m}}{100 \text{ cm}} = 0.9144 \text{ m/yard}$$

Area = length x width = 100 yards x 53.33 yards x $\left(\frac{0.9144 \text{ m}}{1 \text{ yard}}\right)^2 = 4.46 \times 10^3 \text{ m}^2$

PE 1.14 (a) For this part we use the conversion factor 5.00 g alloy/3.00 g gold

$$0.500 \text{ kg gold} \times \frac{10^3 \text{ g}}{1 \text{ kg}} \times \frac{5.00 \text{ g alloy}}{3.00 \text{ g gold}} = 833 \text{ g alloy}$$

(b) For this part we use the conversion factor 2.00 g platinum/5.00 g alloy.

$$833 \text{ g alloy} \times \frac{2.00 \text{ g platinum}}{5.00 \text{ g alloy}} = 333 \text{ g platinum}$$

or by difference, 833 g alloy – 500 g gold = 333 g platinum.

PE 1.17 The density of aluminum = 2.70 g/mL; density of lead = 11.35 g/mL.

$$\text{volume } 100.0 \text{ g aluminum} = 100.0 \text{ g} \times \frac{1 \text{ mL}}{2.70 \text{ g}} = 37.0 \text{ mL or } 37.0 \text{ cm}^3$$

$$\text{volume } 100.0 \text{ g lead} = 100.0 \text{ g} \times \frac{1 \text{ mL}}{11.35 \text{ g}} = 8.811 \text{ mL or } 8.811 \text{ cm}^3$$

Aluminum occupies a little more than four times the volume of an equal mass of lead.

PE 1.18 First we must convert the speed into m/s.

$$v = \frac{80 \text{ km}}{1 \text{ h}} \times \frac{10^3 \text{ m}}{1 \text{ km}} \times \frac{1 \text{ h}}{3600 \text{ s}} = 22 \text{ m/s}$$

Then,

$$KE = \frac{m \times v^2}{2} = \frac{1680 \text{ kg} \times (22 \text{ m/s})^2}{2} = 4.1 \times 10^5 \text{ kg m}^2/\text{s}^2$$

$$= 4.1 \times 10^5 \text{ Nm} = 4.1 \times 10^5 \text{ J} = 4.1 \times 10^2 \text{ kJ}$$

Remember: $1 \text{ N} = 1 \text{ kg m/s}^2$; $1 \text{ J} = 1 \text{ Nm}$.

PE 1.19 (a) Work must be done to lift the book against the gravitational force. Therefore, the potential energy increases.

(b) Work must be done to stretch a rubber band; the energy is stored as potential energy in the rearranged internal structure of the rubber. As the rubber band returns to its original shape, the potential energy converts to kinetic energy and/or heat energy. The potential energy decreases.

(c) Depending on the conditions, some or all of the kinetic energy of the billiard balls converts into compression potential energy upon collision. The potential energy increases at the instant of collision.

(d) Oppositely charged particles attract each other. Work must be done to separate them. Consequently, the potential energy decreases as they come together.

PE 1.20 Imagine splitting the 100 mL of water at 95°C into two identical 50-mL portions, each at 95°C. Obviously, they each must contain the same amount of heat energy and together twice as much energy as another identical 50-mL portion at 95°C. Since the 100-mL portion contains twice as much heat energy, it can provide more heat energy.

PE 1.21 (a) One calorie raises the temperature of 1 g of water by about 1°C. The temperature rise is 100°C − 0°C = 100°C.

$$5.00 \text{ kg} \times \frac{10^3 \text{ g}}{1 \text{ kg}} \times 100°C \times \frac{1 \text{ cal}}{1 \text{ g} \times 1°C} = 500 \times 10^3 \text{ cal} = 500 \text{ kcal}$$

(b) In terms of joules

$$500 \times 10^3 \text{ cal} \times \frac{4.184 \text{ J}}{1 \text{ cal}} = 2.09 \times 10^6 \text{ J} = 2.09 \times 10^3 \text{ kJ}$$

Solutions To Final Exercises

1.4 No. A field of investigative inquiry can only be called a science when its experimental results can be reproduced by other experimenters working in different laboratories. Consequently, fields that have no quantitative aspects are not true or pure sciences, since purely qualitative results are not universally reproducible.

1.5 The answer depends on the choice of definition for the term *measurement*. Any experiment (like the flipping of a coin) that has a finite number of outcomes (heads or tails in this case) employs counting as a form of measurement. In this case, counting measures the number of heads and tails obtained in the flipping experiment.

If, on the other hand, the definition of measurement is restricted to finding the magnitude of some quantity in terms of a previously defined unit that serves as a standard, then counting is not a measurement in this sense.

1.10 There are 1968/2 = 984 leaves. The thickness is

$$\frac{5.74 \text{ cm}}{984 \text{ leaves}} = 5.83 \times 10^{-3} \text{ cm/leaf}.$$

(a)
$$5.83 \times 10^{-3} \text{ cm} \times \frac{10 \text{ mm}}{1 \text{ cm}} = 5.83 \times 10^{-2} \text{ mm}$$

(b)
$$5.83 \times 10^{-3} \text{ cm} \times \frac{1 \text{ m}}{10^2 \text{ cm}} \times \frac{1 \text{ } \mu m}{10^{-6} \text{ m}} = 58.3 \text{ } \mu m$$

1.11 (a) $$\frac{60 \text{ miles}}{1 \text{ h}} \times \frac{1.609 \text{ km}}{1 \text{ mile}} = 97 \text{ km/h}$$

(b) $$\frac{60 \text{ miles}}{1 \text{ h}} \times \frac{1.609 \text{ km}}{1 \text{ mile}} \times \frac{10^3 \text{ m}}{1 \text{ km}} \times \frac{10^2 \text{ cm}}{1 \text{ m}} \times \frac{1 \text{ h}}{3600 \text{ s}} = 2.7 \times 10^3 \text{ cm/s}$$

1.12

$$\text{length} = 78 \text{ ft} \times \frac{12 \text{ in}}{1 \text{ ft}} \times \frac{1 \text{ m}}{39.37 \text{ in}} = 23.77 \text{ m} = 24 \text{ m} \text{ (two significant figures)}$$

$$\text{width} = 36 \text{ ft} \times \frac{12 \text{ in}}{1 \text{ ft}} \times \frac{1 \text{ m}}{39.37 \text{ in}} = 10.97 \text{ m} = 11 \text{ m} \text{ (two significant figures)}$$

$$\text{area} = \text{length} \times \text{width} = 23.77 \text{ m} \times 10.97 \text{ m} = 261 \text{ m}^2 = 2.6 \times 10^2 \text{ m}^2$$
$$\text{(two significant figures)}$$

1.13

The volume of a sphere of radius r is given by the formula $V = (4/3) \pi r^3$.

$$r = \frac{d}{2} = \frac{2.50 \text{ in}}{2} = 1.25 \text{ in} \; ; \; V = \frac{4}{3} \times 3.14 \times (1.25 \text{ in})^3 = 8.18 \text{ in}^3$$

Converting to cubic centimeters, we get $V = 8.18 \text{ in}^3 \times \frac{(2.54 \text{ cm})^3}{1 \text{ in}^3} = 134 \text{ cm}^3$

1.15

The volume of a cylinder is given by the formula $V = \pi r^2 \times h$

$r = d/2 = 0.5 \; \mu\text{m}; \; h = 2 \; \mu\text{m}$

$V = 3.14 \times (0.5 \; \mu\text{m})^2 \times 2 \; \mu\text{m} = 1.6 \; \mu\text{m}^3 = 2 \; \mu\text{m}^3$ (one significant figure)

1.20　(a) $\frac{3.0 \times 22.4}{1.120} = 60$

(b)
$$\begin{array}{r} 56.85 \\ - 9.9 \\ \hline \end{array}$$
$46.95 = 47.0$ after rounding off to one decimal place.

(c) $\frac{4.38 \times 10^4}{5.1 \times 10^{-3}} = 8.6 \times 10^6$ after rounding off to two significant figures.

(d)
$$\begin{array}{r} 22.22 \\ 2.71828 \\ 2001. \\ + \quad 0.03 \\ \hline \end{array}$$
$2025.96828 = 2026$ after rounding off to zero decimal places.

(e)
$$\begin{array}{r} 3.61 \times 10^5 \\ + \quad 0.275 \times 10^5 \\ \hline 3.885 \times 10^5 \end{array}$$
$= 3.88 \times 10^5$ after rounding off to two decimal places.

(f) $9.1095 \times 10^{-28} \times 6.022 \times 10^{23} = 5.486 \times 10^{-4}$ after rounding off to four significant figures.

1.23 Systematic errors are caused mainly by inaccurate instruments, problems or inaccuracies inherent in the method employed, and personal tendencies in the experimenter's technique and analysis. Random errors are small variations and accidental errors over which the experimenter has little control.
(a) Random. The volume readings should be randomly scattered about the fuzzy markings.
(b) Random. The increases and decreases should cancel each other out.
(c) Systematic. Poor personal technique here leads to each weight being higher than it actually is.

(d) Random. This falls into the category of small variations of instrument performance.

(e) Systematic. Since the value of the gravitational acceleration at the equator is different from that of the south pole, all measurements on the spring balance will be off by a constant factor.

1.25 (a)

$$2000 \text{ lb} \times \frac{453.6 \text{ g}}{1 \text{ lb}} \times \frac{1 \text{ kg}}{10^3 \text{ g}} \times \frac{1 \text{ metric ton}}{10^3 \text{ kg}} = 0.9072 \text{ metric tons}$$

(b)

$$9.29 \times 10^7 \text{ miles} \times \frac{1 \text{ km}}{0.6214 \text{ mile}} = 15.0 \times 10^7 \text{ km}$$

(c)

$$\frac{55 \text{ miles}}{1 \text{ h}} \times \frac{1 \text{ h}}{3600 \text{ s}} \times \frac{1 \text{ km}}{0.6214 \text{ mile}} = 2.5 \times 10^{-2} \text{ km/s}$$

(d)

$$\frac{1.00 \text{ g}}{1 \text{ cm}^3} \times \frac{1 \text{ lb}}{453.6 \text{ g}} \times \frac{10^3 \text{ cm}^3}{1 \text{ L}} \times \frac{3.785 \text{ L}}{1 \text{ gal}} = \frac{8.34 \text{ lb}}{1 \text{ gal}}$$

(e)

$$\frac{9.81 \text{ m}}{1 \text{ s}^2} \times \frac{(3600 \text{ s})^2}{1 \text{ h}^2} \times \frac{1 \text{ km}}{10^3 \text{ m}} \times \frac{0.6214 \text{ mile}}{1 \text{ km}} = \frac{79.0 \times 10^3 \text{ mile}}{1 \text{ h}^2}$$

(f)

$$50.0 \text{ kcal} \times \frac{4.184 \text{ kJ}}{1 \text{ kcal}} = 209 \text{ kJ}$$

1.26 The weight of a body is the force exerted on it by another body's (earth, moon, etc.) gravitational attraction. The weight is equal to the mass of the body times the gravitational acceleration of the other body or system.

weight = mass x gravitational acceleration

The weight of a body is not a constant since the value of the gravitational acceleration is variable. However, at any given spot the gravitational acceleration is constant and the weights at that spot are directly proportional to the masses. Thus you can lose weight without losing mass by moving to a spot where the gravitational acceleration has a lower value.

1.28 The balance is the instrument used in science for determining the mass of an object. The balance makes use of the fact that the gravitational attraction on objects of equal mass is the same. In other words, it makes use of the fact that equal masses have equal weights. The double-pan balance measures the mass of an object by comparing its mass (placed in one pan of the balance) with that of "weights" of known mass, which are placed on the other pan of the balance.

A single-pan balance measures the mass of an object by comparing its mass (placed on the single pan) against "weights" of known mass within the balance.

A spring scale measures the weight of an object by comparing its deflection to that of known weights whose deflections were recorded. (Some spring scales have both weight and mass calibrations, and these can be used to measure either the weight or mass of the object. However, the mass calibration will strictly hold only for the location where the spring scale was calibrated.)

1.35 Since there are 24 hours in a day, the person will take four teaspoonfuls or approximately 20 mL of cough medicine in one day. The number of grams of glyceryl guaiacolate taken in one day is

$$20 \text{ mL} \times \frac{2 \text{ g}}{100 \text{ mL}} = 0.4 \text{ g}$$

1.37   Density is defined as mass per unit volume.

$$density = \frac{mass}{volume}$$

To solve this problem we must first calculate the volume of the cylindrical metal rod. From Table 1.5 we get V (cylinder) = π x r^2 x h, where r is the radius of the cylinder, h the altitude or height of the cylinder, and the constant π = 3.14. So,

V = 3.14 x $(0.25\ cm)^2$ x 3.0 cm = 0.59 cm^3, and density = $\frac{1.55\ g}{0.59\ cm^3}$ = 2.6 g/cm^3

1.39   Rearrangement of the density equation gives volume = mass/density. The masses are all 5.0 g. The densities are found in Table 1.7.

for lead, volume = 5.0 g/11.35 g/mL = 0.44 mL
for water, volume = 5.0 g/0.99823 g/mL = 5.0 mL
for air, volume = 5.0 g/0.001205 g/mL = 4.1 x 10^3 mL

1.41   We first find the number of cubic centimeters of boric acid and then convert the volume to liters.

$$\underbrace{\frac{1\ cm^3}{1.435\ g} \times \frac{10^3\ g}{1\ kg}}_{\substack{\text{volume of 1 kg of}\\ \text{boric acid in } cm^3}} \times \underbrace{\frac{1\ L}{10^3\ cm^3}}_{\substack{\text{converts}\\ \text{to liters}}} = 0.6969\ L/1\ kg$$

Any bottle holding 0.70 L or more will hold 1 kg of boric acid.

1.42   The weight is converted from ounces to grams and the volume is calculated in cubic centimeters.

21 oz x $\frac{1\ lb}{16\ oz}$ x $\frac{453.6\ g}{1\ lb}$ = 595 g (keep extra significant figures)

The volume of a sphere is given by the formula V = 4/3 πr^3 and the circumference of a circle is given by C = 2πr. So, r = C/2π = 30 in/2 x 3.14 = 4.78 in.

V = $\frac{4}{3}$ x 3.14 x $(4.78\ in)^3$ x $\frac{(2.54\ cm)^3}{1\ in^3}$ = 7493 cm^3

and d = 595 g/7493 cm^3 = 7.9 x 10^{-2} g/cm^3 (two significant figures)

1.44   To solve this problem we first have to calculate the volume of the cylinder. Once we have that, we can use the density formula to calculate the mass.
(a) volume of cylinder = area of base x height = 1.00 cm^2 x 76.0 cm = 76.0 cm^3

mass = density x volume = $\frac{13.6\ g}{1\ cm^3}$ x 76.0 cm^3 = 1.03 x 10^3 g mercury

(b) volume = mass/density = 1.03 x 10^3 g/0.99823 g/mL = 1.03 x 10^3 mL or 1.03 L water

1.45   A metric ton is equal to 1000 kg.

10,000 gal x $\frac{3.785\ L}{1\ gal}$ x $\frac{879\ g}{1\ L}$ x $\frac{1\ metric\ ton}{1000 \times 10^3\ g}$ = 33.3 metric tons of benzene

1.48   Work is the product of a force (f) and the distance (d) through which it operates, w = f x d. The joule (J) or newton meter (Nm) is the SI unit of work and energy. The newton is the SI unit of force, $1 N = 1 kg\ m/s^2$. The calorie is an alternative energy unit often used by chemists, 1 cal = 4.184 J. Using these definitions we get

(a)
$$w = f\ x\ d = 10.0\ N\ x\ 300\ cm\ x\ \frac{1\ m}{10^2\ cm} = 30.0\ Nm = 30.0\ J$$

(b)
$$w = 30.0\ J\ x\ \frac{1\ cal}{4.184\ J} = 7.17\ cal$$

1.49   To calculate the amount of work it takes to lift the lemon, we must first calculate the magnitude of the downward gravitational force acting on the lemon, i.e., the weight of the lemon. From Equation 1.1 of the text we have f = m x g, where g is the gravitational acceleration, $9.80665\ m/s^2$.

$$f = 85\ g\ x\ \frac{1\ kg}{10^3\ g}\ x\ 9.80665\ m/s^2 = 0.83\ N$$

We can now calculate the work required to lift the lemon.

$$w = f\ x\ d = 0.83\ N\ x\ 4\ ft\ x\ \frac{12\ in}{1\ ft}\ x\ \frac{1\ m}{39.37\ in} = 1.0\ J$$

Comment: The value of g is actually a variable of the distance from the center of the earth. For small changes in that distance the g value can be treated as a constant.

1.50   One calorie of energy raises the temperature of 1 g of water by $1°C$. This relation gives rise to the conversion factor $1\ cal/g_{water}°C$. The amount of energy needed to change the temperature of a mass of water is therefore

$$energy\ required = mass\ water\ x\ \frac{1\ cal}{g_{water}°C}\ x\ temperature\ change$$

$$temperature\ change = \frac{energy\ required}{mass\ water\ x\ 1\ cal/g_{water}°C}$$

Assuming the density of water to be 1.0 g/mL,

$$mass\ water = 1.0\ L\ x\ \frac{10^3\ mL}{1\ L}\ x\ \frac{1.0\ g}{1\ mL} = 1000\ g$$

$$temperature\ change = \frac{5000\ cal}{1000\ g\ x\ 1\ cal/g°C} = 5°C$$

The final temperature is $30°C$.

1.52
$$v = \sqrt{2KE/m}$$

$$v = \sqrt{\frac{2\ x\ 1.1\ x\ 10^{-19}\ J}{9.0\ x\ 10^{-31}\ kg}} = \sqrt{0.2444\ x\ 10^{12}\ m^2/s^2} = 4.9\ x\ 10^5\ m/s$$

1.54   No. When matter changes temperature, it absorbs or releases energy. The amount of energy absorbed or released depends on the amount and kind of matter and on the initial and final temperatures. For instance, 2 kg of water requires twice as much heat as 1 kg of water to raise it from $0°C$ to $50°C$. Also, different kinds of matter have different capacities for holding or containing heat energy. For example, 1 g of water (specific heat = 1 cal/g°C) will contain an additional calorie of heat energy when raised from $20°C$ to $21°C$, while 1 g of mercury (specific heat = 0.033 cal/g$^\circ$C) will only contain an additional 0.033 cal of heat energy when raised from 20°C to 21°C.

Comment: See text for definition of specific heat.

1.60   Each 5-mL teaspoonful contains 4 mg phenobarbital, 65 mg theophylline, and 12 mg ephedrine hydrochloride, giving us the conversion factors:

$$\frac{4 \text{ mg phenobarbital}}{5 \text{ mL}} \; ; \; \frac{65 \text{ mg theophylline}}{5 \text{ mL}} \; ; \; \frac{12 \text{ mg ephedrine hydrochloride}}{5 \text{ mL}}$$

The label recommends one teaspoonful four times daily per 60 lb of body weight, giving us the conversion factor:

$$\frac{20 \text{ mL}}{1 \text{ day x 60 lb}}$$

Combining these conversion factors we get

$$\frac{16 \text{ mg phenobarbital}}{1 \text{ day x 60 lb}} \; ; \; \frac{260 \text{ mg theophylline}}{1 \text{ day x 60 lb}} \; ; \; \frac{48 \text{ mg ephedrine hydrochloride}}{1 \text{ day x 60 lb}}$$

(a)
$$1 \text{ day x 90 lb x } \frac{16 \text{ mg phenobarbital}}{1 \text{ day x 60 lb}} = 24 \text{ mg phenobarbital}$$

$$1 \text{ day x 90 lb x } \frac{260 \text{ mg theophylline}}{1 \text{ day x 60 lb}} = 390 \text{ mg theophylline}$$

$$1 \text{ day x 90 lb x } \frac{48 \text{ mg ephedrine hydrochloride}}{1 \text{ day x 60 lb}} = 72 \text{ mg ephedrine hydrochloride}$$

(b)
$$24 \text{ mg phenobarbital x } \frac{1 \text{ grain}}{64.80 \text{ mg}} = 0.37 \text{ grains phenobarbital}$$

(c)
$$\frac{44 \text{ mL}}{\text{bottle}} \text{ x } \frac{4 \text{ mg phenobarbital}}{5 \text{ mL}} \text{ x } \frac{1 \text{ day}}{24 \text{ mg phenobarbital}} = 1.5 \text{ days/bottle}$$

1.62   The densities of gold and copper are 19.32 g/mL and 8.96 g/mL, respectively (Table 1.7).
(a) Less. The density of gold is greater than that of copper; therefore, a mass of pure gold equal to that of the adulterated gold would have a smaller volume. Since both objects would be totally submerged, the one with the smaller volume, the gold, would displace less water.
(b) The statuette contains x g gold and $(210 - x)$g copper. According to the exercise

$$x \text{ g gold x } \frac{1 \text{ mL}}{19.32 \text{ g gold}} + (210 - x)\text{g copper x } \frac{1 \text{ mL}}{8.96 \text{ g copper}} = 14.0 \text{ mL}$$

$0.05176x + 23.44 - 0.1116x = 14.0$
$0.05984x = 9.44$
$x = 9.44/0.05984 = 157.8 \text{ g gold}$

$$\text{gold percent} = \frac{157.8 \text{ g x } 100\%}{210 \text{ g}} = 75.1\%$$

1.64   (a) See the solution to Exercise 1.49 for a comment about g value.

w = f x d and f = m x g

f = 70 kg x 9.80665 m/s^2 = 686.5 N

w = 686.5 N x 10 m = 6865 J = 6.9 kJ (two significant figures)

(b) The potential energy of the object is equal to the work required to raise the object to the specified height. So PE = w = f x d; f = m x g and d = h; therefore, PE = m x g x h.

1.65   One gram of water requires one calorie of energy in order to raise its temperature $1°C$. Therefore, the potential energy of each gram of water is one calorie higher at the top of the falls than at the bottom. Therefore,

$$h = \frac{PE}{m \times g} = \frac{1 \text{ cal } \times 4.184 \text{ J/cal}}{1.00 \times 10^{-3} \text{ kg } \times 9.80665 \text{ m/s}^2} = 427 \text{ m}$$

CHAPTER 2
ATOMS, MOLECULES, AND IONS

Solutions To Practice Exercises

PE 2.2 (a) The mass number (A) is equal to the total number of protons and neutrons in the nucleus of an atom. A = number of protons + number of neutrons. A = 26 + 30 = 56.
  (b) The symbol for iron is Fe. To obtain the atomic symbol of a given isotope, attach the mass number A as a left superscript and the atomic number Z as a left subscript to the symbol. The atomic symbol for this iron isotope is therefore

$^{56}_{26}\text{Fe}$

PE 2.3 The symbol for chlorine is Cl. The number of protons = Z = 17. Mass number A = number of protons + number of neutrons = 17 + 18 = 35. The atomic symbol is therefore

$^{35}_{17}\text{Cl}^-$

The – sign means that the neutral chlorine atom has gained an additional negative charge, i.e., an additional electron, and is now a negative ion, the chloride ion.

PE 2.4 Let x = fractional abundance of lithium-6 and $(1 - x)$ = fractional abundance of lithium-7. Then $6.01512x + 7.01600(1 - x) = 6.941$ from the definition of the chemical atomic weight.

$6.01512x + 7.01600 - 7.01600x = 6.941$

$1.00088x = 0.075$

$x = 0.075/1.00088 = 0.075$ and $(1 - x) = 1 - 0.075 = 0.925$

The percent abundance is equal to 100 times the fractional abundance. Hence, percent abundance of lithium-6 = 7.5%; percent abundance of lithium-7 = 92.5%.

PE 2.5 The charge of one hydrogen ion (proton) is 1.6022×10^{-19} C. One mole of hydrogen ions contains Avogadro's number of hydrogen ions, i.e., 1 mol of hydrogen ions = 6.0221×10^{23} H$^+$ ions. The charge of 1 mol of hydrogen ions is

$$6.0221 \times 10^{23} \text{ H}^+ \text{ ions} \times \frac{1.6022 \times 10^{-19} \text{ C}}{1 \text{ H}^+ \text{ ion}} = 9.6486 \times 10^4 \text{ C}$$

PE 2.8   The atomic weight of calcium to three significant figures is 40.1 u; therefore, the mass of 1 mol of calcium is 40.1 g. The mass in grams of 1.55 mol of calcium is

$$1.55 \text{ mol Ca} \times \frac{40.1 \text{ g}}{1 \text{ mol Ca}} = 62.2 \text{ g}$$

PE 2.9   The atomic weight of helium is 4.00 u, and its molar mass is 4.00 g. Using conversion factors:

$$2.00 \times 10^{21} \text{ helium atoms} \times \frac{4.00 \text{ u}}{1 \text{ helium atom}} \times \frac{1 \text{ g}}{6.022 \times 10^{23} \text{ u}} = 1.33 \times 10^{-2} \text{ g}$$

This problem could also be solved by using the definition of a mole. One mole of any substance contains Avogadro's number of particles = 6.022×10^{23} particles. The mass of 1 mol, called the molar mass, in grams is numerically equal to the atomic weight in atomic mass units. So,

$$1 \text{ mol of helium atoms} = 6.022 \times 10^{23} \text{ helium atoms} = 4.00 \text{ g}$$

$$2.00 \times 10^{21} \text{ helium atoms} \times \frac{4.00 \text{ g}}{6.022 \times 10^{23} \text{ helium atoms}} = 1.33 \times 10^{-2} \text{ g}$$

PE 2.13 (a)   Eleven elements are gases at room temperature: helium (He), neon (Ne), argon (Ar), krypton (Kr), xenon (Xe), radon (Rn), hydrogen (H_2), nitrogen (N_2), oxygen (O_2), fluorine (F_2), and chlorine (Cl_2).

(b)   Two elements are liquids at room temperature: bromine (Br_2) and mercury (Hg).

PE 2.14 (a)   One mole of calcium chloride ($CaCl_2$) contains 1 mol of calcium ions (Ca^{2+}) and 2 mol of chloride ions (Cl^-), so 3.5 mol of calcium chloride will contain 3.5 x 1 = 3.5 mol of Ca^{2+} and 3.5 x 2 = 7.0 mol of Cl^-.

(b)   Each mole of ions contains 6.022×10^{23} ions.

$$3.5 \text{ mol Ca}^{2+} \times \frac{6.022 \times 10^{23} \text{ Ca}^{2+} \text{ ions}}{1 \text{ mol Ca}^{2+}} = 2.1 \times 10^{24} \text{ Ca}^{2+} \text{ ions}$$

$$7.0 \text{ mol Cl}^- \times \frac{6.022 \times 10^{23} \text{ Cl}^- \text{ ions}}{1 \text{ mol Cl}^-} = 4.2 \times 10^{24} \text{ Cl}^- \text{ ions}$$

PE 2.16 (a)   One mole of C_4H_{10} contains 4 mol of C atoms and 10 mol of H atoms. The molar masses of C and H are 12.01 g and 1.008 g, respectively. The total mass is

C: 4 mol x 12.01 g/mol = 48.04 g
H: 10 mol x 1.008 g/mol = <u>10.08 g</u>
      Total molar mass = 58.12 g

(b)   One mole of butane contains 6.022×10^{23} molecules and has a mass of 58.12 g. The mass of one molecule is

$$\frac{58.12 \text{ g}}{1 \text{ mol butane}} \times \frac{1 \text{ mol butane}}{6.022 \times 10^{23} \text{ molecules}} = 9.651 \times 10^{-23} \text{ g/molecule}$$

PE 2.17 (a)   The molar masses of sulfur and oxygen are 32.07 g and 16.00 g, respectively. The molar mass of sulfur dioxide is

S: 1 mol x 32.07 g/mol   = 32.07 g
O: 2 mol x 16.00 g/mol   = <u>32.00 g</u>
      Total molar mass = 64.07 g

The number of moles of SO_2 is

$$1000 \text{ g } SO_2 \times \frac{1 \text{ mol } SO_2}{64.07 \text{ g } SO_2} = 15.61 \text{ mol } SO_2$$

(b)
$$15.61 \text{ mol } SO_2 \times \frac{6.022 \times 10^{23} \text{ molecules}}{1 \text{ mol } SO_2} = 9.400 \times 10^{24} \text{ molecules}$$

PE 2.18 (a) From the table we see that the sodium ion is Na^+ and the carbonate ion is CO_3^{2-}. A total charge of zero is obtained from two sodium ions ($2 \times 1+ = 2+$) and one carbonate ion ($1 \times 2- = 2-$). The formula is $(Na^+)_2CO_3^{2-}$ or Na_2CO_3.

(b) From the table we see that the magnesium ion is Mg^{2+} and the chloride ion is Cl^-. A total charge of zero is obtained from one magnesium ion ($1 \times 2+ = 2+$) and two chloride ions ($2 \times 1- = 2-$). The formula is $Mg^{2+}(Cl^-)_2$ or $MgCl_2$.

(c) From the table we see that the iron(III) ion is Fe^{3+} and the bromide ion is Br^-. A total charge of zero is obtained from one iron(III) ion ($1 \times 3+ = 3+$) and three bromide ions ($3 \times 1- = 3-$). The formula is $Fe^{3+}(Br^-)_3$ or $FeBr_3$.

Solutions to Final Exercises

2.4   Millikan assumed that the electron charge is the smallest unit of charge and that all other charges are some integral whole number multiple of the electron charge. If this is so, then the numerical value of the charge on the positively charged air fragments picked up by the oil droplets must be equal to the electron charge or some integral multiple of it. If we divide the oil drop charges by the electron charge determined by Millikan, $e = 1.602 \times 10^{-19}$ C, we get

1.60×10^{-18} C / 1.602×10^{-19} C $= 9.99$
1.76×10^{-18} C / 1.602×10^{-19} C $= 11.0$
1.12×10^{-18} C / 1.602×10^{-19} C $= 6.99$

The oil drop charges are all equal (within experimental error) to an integral multiple of the basic electron charge and, therefore, support Millikan's contentions and the value given for the electron charge.

2.10   A narrow beam of alpha (α) particles is aimed at a thin metal foil (gold, platinum, silver, etc.). A zinc sulfide fluorescent screen is used to detect the alpha particles after they are scattered by the foil.

The observers didn't expect to find any alpha particles deflected through large angles, since they had in mind a Thomson's pudding model for the atom. When they performed the experiment, they were surprised to find that some alpha particles were indeed deflected through rather large angles and that a few were even going backward toward the source.

(a) The deflection of alpha particles through large angles was interpreted as a head–on or near head–on collision of the α particle with a small, massive, positively charged core or nucleus.

(b) The fact that most of the α particles were not appreciably deflected was interpreted to mean that most of the atom was empty space, since α particles not encountering a nucleus would continue in nearly straight paths.

2.11   Both the Rutherford and Thomson atoms are distinct neutral entities of the same size. In both of these atoms, there exist a number of electrons and some form of offsetting positive charge such that the whole atom is neutral. The differences between them are in the way the mass, the positive charge, and the electrons are distributed.

In the Thomson atom, the positive charge is distributed uniformly throughout a sphere and the electrons are embedded in the positive charge like raisins in pudding. The mass of the atom is distributed uniformly throughout the sphere.

In the Rutherford atom, the positive charge and almost all the mass are concentrated in a dense central core called the nucleus, which is very small compared to the total size of an atom. The Rutherford atom is mostly empty space, while the Thomson atom has very little or none. In the Rutherford atom, the electrons reside outside the nucleus in the remainder (practically all) of the atom's volume; they are separated or away from the protons.

2.13 To solve this problem we have to calculate the factor or multiplier needed to make the nuclear diameter equal to the diameter of a U.S. penny.

The nuclear diameter is 2×10^{-15} m, the diameter of a U.S. penny is 1.9 cm = 0.019 m, and the factor is

$$2 \times 10^{-15} \text{ m} \times x = 0.019 \text{ m}$$

$$x = \frac{0.019 \text{ m}}{2 \times 10^{-15} \text{ m}} = 9.5 \times 10^{12}$$

The atomic diameter is 200 pm = 2×10^{-10} m. If it is expanded by the same factor, i.e., by the same proportion as the nuclear diameter, it would equal 2×10^{-10} m $\times 9.5 \times 10^{12} = 1.9 \times 10^{3}$ m or about 2 km.

2.18 Atomic number Z = number of protons = number of electrons in the neutral atom. Mass number A = Z + number of neutrons.

Atom	Z	A	Protons	Neutrons	Electrons
Zn	30	64	30	34	30
Eu	63	153	63	90	63
U	92	235	92	143	92
Pd	46	106	46	60	46

2.19 The symbol for a specific atom or ion is

$_{Z}^{A}X^{charge}$, where A = mass number and Z = atomic number

(a)

$_{82}^{208}Pb^{2+}$

Since Z = 82 there are 82 protons. There are A - Z = 208 - 82 = 126 neutrons. Since there is a charge of 2+ on the ion there must be 2 fewer electrons than protons; 82 - 2 = 80 electrons.

Answer: 82 protons, 126 neutrons, and 80 electrons.

(b)

$_{7}^{14}N^{3-}$

Since Z = 7 there are 7 protons. There are 14 - 7 = 7 neutrons. Since there is a charge of 3- on the ion there must be 3 more electrons than protons; 7 + 3 = 10 electrons.

Answer: 7 protons, 7 neutrons, and 10 electrons.

(c)

$_{1}^{3}H^{+}$

Z = 1; 1 proton. A - Z = 3 - 1 = 2; 2 neutrons. Charge 1+, there must be 1 fewer electrons than protons; 1 - 1 = 0 electrons.

Answer: 1 proton, 2 neutrons, and 0 electrons.

2.21   Isotopes are atoms with the same atomic number but different mass numbers.
(a)

$^{32}_{16}X$ and $^{33}_{16}X$ are isotopes because each has Z = 16 and a different mass number.

Note: $^{32}_{16}X^{2-}$ has the same nucleus as $^{32}_{16}X$ and, therefore, is not a different isotope.

$^{40}_{18}X$ and $^{39}_{18}X$ are isotopes because each has Z = 18 and a different mass number (A).

(b) To solve the problem, we first have to determine how many electrons each atom has. A neutral atom has the same number of electrons as protons; number of electrons = Z.

$^{32}_{16}X$ neutral, has 16 electrons; $^{35}_{17}X$ neutral, has 17 electrons;

$^{40}_{18}X$ neutral, has 18 electrons;

$^{32}_{16}X^{2-}$ negative ion, gained 2 electrons, has 18 electrons;

$^{39}_{18}X$ neutral, has 18 electrons; $^{33}_{16}X$ neutral, has 16 electrons;

$^{39}_{19}X^+$ positive ion, lost 1 electron, has 18 electrons.

Answer:

$^{32}_{16}X$ and $^{33}_{16}X$ are isoelectronic both having 16 electrons.

$^{40}_{18}X$, $^{32}_{16}X^{2-}$, $^{39}_{18}X$, and $^{39}_{19}X^+$ are isoelectronic, each having 18 electrons.

(c)

$^{32}_{16}X$ is $^{32}_{16}S$; $^{35}_{17}X$ is $^{35}_{17}Cl$; $^{40}_{18}X$ is $^{40}_{18}Ar$; $^{32}_{16}X^{2-}$ is $^{32}_{16}S^{2-}$; $^{39}_{18}X$ is $^{39}_{18}Ar$;

$^{33}_{16}X$ is $^{33}_{16}S$; and $^{39}_{19}X^+$ is $^{39}_{19}K^+$.

2.26

total mass of coins = 250 dimes x $\frac{2.27\ g}{1\ dime}$ + 45 quarters x $\frac{5.67\ g}{1\ quarter}$ = 822.65 g

average mass of a coin = $\frac{822.65\ g}{295\ coins}$ = 2.79 g/coin

This average is a weighted average. A simple average confers equal abundance for all types of items. A weighted average takes into account the different abundances and multiplies each weight by the abundance.

A chemical atomic weight is a weighted average. The contribution to the average mass from each isotope is in proportion to its abundance.

Comment: If abundance values are accurate, a weighted average gives the same result as an average where the contribution from each of the n individual objects is summed up and the total is divided by the total number of objects n. In chemistry the number of objects is much too large for such an averaging process, and therefore a weighted average must be taken.

2.27   Chemists use a weighted average mass because the isotopes of an element have different abundances. A number of elements have one or two isotopes that are in much greater abundance than any of the others. A simple average in which each isotope is assigned an equal abundance value would give an inaccurate and useless value for the chemical atomic weight.

2.28   The chemical atomic weight is found by multiplying each isotopic mass by its fractional abundance and adding the products. The fractional abundance equals the abundance/100%.

$$0.7870 \times 23.98504 \text{ u} = \qquad 18.876 \text{ u}$$
$$0.1013 \times 24.98584 \text{ u} = \qquad 2.531 \text{ u}$$
$$0.1117 \times 25.98259 \text{ u} = \qquad \underline{2.902 \text{ u}}$$

Chemical atomic weight Mg = 24.309 u = 24.31 u

2.30   The abundances must add up to 1, and the weighted average must equal the chemical atomic weight. Let x be the abundance of the boron isotope of mass 10.0129 u and let $(1 - x)$ be the abundance of the boron isotope of 11.00931 u. Then

$10.0129x + 11.00931(1 - x) = 10.81$
$0.99641x = 0.19931$
$x = 0.2000$
$(1 - x) = 1 - 0.2000 = 0.8000$
Answer: percent abundance $^{10}_{5}\text{B} = 20.00\%$

percent abundance $^{11}_{5}\text{B} = 80.00\%$

2.31   The sum of the mass of each isotope times its fractional abundance equals 12.011 u. Remember that the mass of the carbon-12 isotope is exactly 12.0000 u.

$(0.9889)(12.0000 \text{ u}) + (0.0111)(\text{mass carbon-13}) = 12.011 \text{ u}$

$$\text{mass carbon-13} = \frac{0.1442 \text{ u}}{0.0111} = 13.0 \text{ u}$$

2.40   (a) $\dfrac{1.6022 \times 10^{-19} \text{ C}}{1 \text{ electron}} \times \dfrac{6.0221367 \times 10^{23} \text{ electrons}}{1 \text{ mol}} = 96,487 \text{ C/mol}$

(b) $\dfrac{3.2044 \times 10^{-19} \text{ C}}{1 \text{ alpha particle}} \times \dfrac{6.0221367 \times 10^{23} \text{ alpha particles}}{1 \text{ mol}} = 192,970 \text{ C/mol}$

2.43   (a) The molar mass of aluminum is 26.98 g/mol.

$$2.55 \text{ mol Al} \times \frac{26.98 \text{ g}}{1 \text{ mol Al}} = 68.8 \text{ g}$$

(b) A millimole (abbreviated mmol) is a thousandth $(1/1000 = 10^{-3})$ of a mole. The molar mass of krypton is 83.80 g/mol. The mass of 1 mmol of krypton is therefore

$$\frac{83.80 \text{ g}}{1 \text{ mol}} \times \frac{1 \text{ mol}}{1000 \text{ mmol}} = \frac{0.08380 \text{ g}}{1 \text{ mmol}} \text{ or } \frac{83.80 \text{ mg}}{1 \text{ mmol}}$$

Note that the conversion factor mg/mmol is numerically the same as the conversion factor g/mol. The millimole is a convenient size for many chemical investigations and is used quite frequently.

$$3.44 \text{ millimoles Kr} \times \frac{83.80 \text{ mg}}{1 \text{ millimole Kr}} = 288 \text{ mg or } 0.288 \text{ g}$$

2.44   (a) One platinum atom has a mass of 195.09 u. The mass in grams is

$$195.09 \text{ u } \times \frac{1 \text{ g}}{6.022 \times 10^{23} \text{ u}} = 3.240 \times 10^{-22} \text{ g}$$

(b) One neon atom has a mass of 20.179 u. The mass in grams is

$$20.179 \text{ u } \times \frac{1 \text{ g}}{6.022 \times 10^{23} \text{ u}} = 3.351 \times 10^{-23} \text{ g}$$

(c) One atom of iodine has a mass of 126.9045 u. The mass in grams is

$$126.9045 \text{ u } \times \frac{1 \text{ g}}{6.022 \times 10^{23} \text{ u}} = 2.107 \times 10^{-22} \text{ g}$$

2.46   (a) One mole of potassium contains 6.022×10^{23} atoms. The number of atoms in 1.88 mol is

$$1.88 \text{ mol } \times \frac{6.022 \times 10^{23} \text{ atoms}}{1 \text{ mol}} = 1.13 \times 10^{24} \text{ atoms}$$

(b) The molar mass of chromium is 51.996 g/mol. The number of atoms in 100 g is

$$100 \text{ g } \times \frac{1 \text{ mol}}{51.996 \text{ g}} \times \frac{6.022 \times 10^{23} \text{ atoms}}{1 \text{ mol}} = 1.16 \times 10^{24} \text{ atoms}$$

(c) The mass of 1.00 L of gold is

$$\text{mass of gold} = 1.00 \text{ L } \times \frac{10^3 \text{ cm}^3}{1 \text{ L}} \times \frac{19.32 \text{ g}}{1 \text{ cm}^3} = 1.93 \times 10^4 \text{ g}$$

The molar mass of gold is 196.97 g/mol. The number of atoms in 1.00 L is

$$1.93 \times 10^4 \text{ g } \times \frac{1 \text{ mol}}{196.97 \text{ g}} \times \frac{6.022 \times 10^{23} \text{ atoms}}{1 \text{ mol}} = 5.90 \times 10^{25} \text{ atoms}$$

2.47   (a) Carbon–12 has $Z = 6$, $A = 12$. Therefore, it has 6 protons, 6 neutrons, and 6 electrons in each atom. The number of protons in 2.35 mol is

$$2.35 \text{ mol } \times \frac{6.022 \times 10^{23} \text{ atoms}}{1 \text{ mol}} \times \frac{6 \text{ protons}}{1 \text{ atom}} = 8.49 \times 10^{24} \text{ protons}$$

Likewise, there are 8.49×10^{24} neutrons and 8.49×10^{24} electrons.

(b)

$^{17}_{8}O^{2-}$ has 8 protons, $17 - 8 = 9$ neutrons, and $8 + 2 = 10$ electrons.

The number of protons in 1.2 mol is

$$1.2 \text{ mol } \times \frac{6.022 \times 10^{23} \text{ atoms}}{1 \text{ mol}} \times \frac{8 \text{ protons}}{1 \text{ atom}} = 5.8 \times 10^{24} \text{ protons}$$

The number of neutrons in 1.2 mol is

$$1.2 \text{ mol } \times \frac{6.022 \times 10^{23} \text{ atoms}}{1 \text{ mol}} \times \frac{9 \text{ neutrons}}{1 \text{ atom}} = 6.5 \times 10^{24} \text{ neutrons}$$

The number of electrons in 1.2 mol is

$$1.2 \text{ mol } \times \frac{6.022 \times 10^{23} \text{ atoms}}{1 \text{ mol}} \times \frac{10 \text{ electrons}}{1 \text{ atom}} = 7.2 \times 10^{24} \text{ electrons}$$

Comment: Once you calculate the number of protons, you can use the conversion factors 9 neutrons/8 protons and 10 electrons/8 protons to calculate the number of neutrons and electrons, respectively. This is an alternative approach.

(c)

$_{20}^{40}Ca^{2+}$ has 20 protons, 40 − 20 = 20 neutrons, and 20 − 2 = 18 electrons.

The number of protons in 3.55 millimoles is

$$3.55 \text{ millimoles } x \frac{1 \text{ mol}}{10^3 \text{ millimoles}} x \frac{6.022 \times 10^{23} \text{ atoms}}{1 \text{ mol}} x \frac{20 \text{ protons}}{1 \text{ atom}}$$

$$= 4.28 \times 10^{22} \text{ protons}$$

Likewise, there are 4.28 x 10^{22} neutrons.

The number of electrons can be calculated using the conversion factor 18 electrons/20 protons.

$$4.28 \times 10^{22} \text{ protons } x \frac{18 \text{ electrons}}{20 \text{ protons}} = 3.85 \times 10^{22} \text{ electrons}$$

2.51 (a) $Hg_2(NO_3)_2$; count NO_3 twice. There are 2 mercury atoms, 2 nitrogen atoms, and 6 oxygen atoms.
(b) $(NH_4)_2SO_4$; count NH_4 twice. There are 2 nitrogen atoms, 8 hydrogen atoms, 1 sulfur atom, and 4 oxygen atoms.
(c) $CH_3(CH_2)_4CH_3$; count CH_2 four times. There are 6 carbon atoms and 14 hydrogen atoms.
(d) $Fe_2(SO_4)_3$; count SO_4 three times. There are 2 iron atoms, 3 sulfur atoms, and 12 oxygen atoms.

2.53 The formulas for molecular elements have a subscript showing the number of atoms in the molecule. The formulas of nonmolecular elements are simply their atomic symbols.
(a) Hydrogen consists of diatomic molecules; H_2.
(b) Oxygen consists of diatomic molecules; O_2.
(c) Nitrogen consists of diatomic molecules; N_2.
(d) Ozone consists of triatomic molecules; O_3.
(e) Bromine consists of diatomic molecules; Br_2.
(f) Iodine consists of diatomic molecules; I_2.
(g) Argon consists of separate atoms; Ar.
(h) White phosphorus consists of four-atom molecules; P_4.
(i) Copper is a metallic element; Cu.

2.58 (a) One mole of ammonia (NH_3) contains 1 mol of nitrogen atoms and 3 mol of hydrogen atoms. Therefore, 2.5 mol of ammonia will contain 2.5 x 1 = 2.5 mol of nitrogen atoms and 2.5 x 3 = 7.5 mol of hydrogen atoms.
(b) 4.0 mol of NH_3 will contain 4.0 x 1 = 4.0 mol of nitrogen atoms and 4.0 x 3 = 12 mol of hydrogen atoms. The number of nitrogen atoms in 4.0 mol of NH_3 is

$$4.0 \text{ mol N } x \frac{6.022 \times 10^{23} \text{ N atoms}}{1 \text{ mol N}} = 2.4 \times 10^{24} \text{ N atoms}$$

The number of H atoms in 4.0 mol of NH_3 is

$$2.4 \times 10^{24} \text{ N atoms } x \frac{3 \text{ H atoms}}{1 \text{ N atom}} = 7.2 \times 10^{24} \text{ H atoms}$$

2.61   A "mole of hydrogen" might mean a mole of hydrogen atoms (H) or a mole of hydrogen molecules (H_2). Similarly, a "mole of oxygen" might mean a mole of oxygen atoms (O) or a mole of oxygen molecules (O_2). In most cases it is self-evident which form is intended. However, in certain circumstances it might be necessary to specify the form by using the clarifying adjectives *atomic* and *molecular*, or the nouns *atoms* and *molecules*.

Comment: This problem could also arise with the other molecular elements. It should be clearly stated, though generally it isn't, whether the atomic form or the molecular form of the element is under consideration. In most cases it is obvious which one applies, and that is why, in general, only the element's name is mentioned.

No. Under ordinary conditions lead is a metal and therefore nonmolecular. Lead always has 1 mol of atoms per mole and no ambiguity can arise. Water is a molecular compound. One mole of water always contains 1 mol of water molecules.

2.62   The molar mass of a compound is the sum of the molar masses of the atoms in its formula.
(a) One mole of $C_6H_{12}O_6$ contains 6 mol of carbon atoms, 12 mol of hydrogen atoms, and 6 mol of oxygen atoms. The molar masses of carbon, hydrogen, and oxygen are 12.01 g, 1.008 g, and 16.00 g, respectively. The total mass is

```
Carbon:      6 mol x 12.01 g/mol  =   72.06  g
Hydrogen:   12 mol x 1.008 g/mol  =   12.096 g
Oxygen:      6 mol x 16.00 g/mol  =   96.00  g
                                     _____
Total molar mass                   = 180.156 g = 180.16 g
```

(b) One mole of sulfur trioxide contains 1 mol of sulfur atoms and 3 mol of oxygen atoms. The molar masses of sulfur and oxygen are 32.07 g and 16.00 g, respectively. The total mass is

```
Sulfur:      1 mol x 32.07 g/mol  =   32.07 g
Oxygen:      3 mol x 16.00 g/mol  =   48.00 g
                                     _____
Total molar mass                   =   80.07 g
```

(c) One mole of ethanol contains 2 mol of carbon atoms, 6 mol of hydrogen atoms, and 1 mol of oxygen atoms. The molar masses of C, H, and O are 12.01 g, 1.01 g, and 16.00 g, respectively. The total mass is

```
Carbon:      2 mol x 12.01 g/mol  =   24.02 g
Hydrogen:    6 mol x 1.01 g/mol   =    6.06 g
Oxygen:      1 mol x 16.00 g/mol  =   16.00 g
                                     _____
Total molar mass                   =   46.08 g
```

(d) One mole of isopropyl alcohol contains 3 mol of C atoms, 8 mol of H atoms and 1 mol of O atoms. The molar masses of C, H, and O are 12.01 g, 1.01 g, and 16.00 g, respectively. The total mass is

```
Carbon:      3 mol x 12.01 g/mol  =   36.03 g
Hydrogen:    8 mol x 1.01 g/mol   =    8.08 g
Oxygen:      1 mol x 16.00 g/mol  =   16.00 g
                                     _____
Total molar mass                   =   60.11 g
```

2.63   (a) The mass of one molecule of a molecular compound in atomic mass units is numerically equal to the molar mass in grams. Therefore, one molecule of glucose has a mass of 180.16 u, one molecule of sulfur trioxide = 80.07u, one molecule of ethanol = 46.08 u, and one molecule of isopropyl alcohol = 60.11 u.

(b) To convert atomic mass units to grams we use the conversion factor 1 g/6.022 x 10^{23} u.

Glucose: $\dfrac{180.16 \text{ u}}{1 \text{ molecule}} \times \dfrac{1 \text{ g}}{6.022 \times 10^{23} \text{ u}} = \dfrac{2.992 \times 10^{-22} \text{ g}}{1 \text{ molecule}}$

Sulfur trioxide: $\dfrac{80.07 \text{ u}}{1 \text{ molecule}} \times \dfrac{1 \text{ g}}{6.022 \times 10^{23} \text{u}} = \dfrac{1.330 \times 10^{-22} \text{ g}}{1 \text{ molecule}}$

Ethanol: $\dfrac{46.08 \text{ u}}{1 \text{ molecule}} \times \dfrac{1 \text{ g}}{6.022 \times 10^{23} \text{ u}} = \dfrac{7.652 \times 10^{-23} \text{ g}}{1 \text{ molecule}}$

Isopropyl alcohol: $\dfrac{60.11 \text{ u}}{1 \text{ molecule}} \times \dfrac{1 \text{ g}}{6.022 \times 10^{23} \text{ u}} = \dfrac{9.982 \times 10^{-23} \text{ g}}{1 \text{ molecule}}$

2.64 (a) One mole of silicon carbide contains 1 mol of silicon atoms and 1 mol of carbon atoms. The molar masses of Si and C are 28.09 g and 12.01 g, respectively. The total mass is

Si: 1 mol x 28.09 g/mol = 28.09 g
C: 1 mol x 12.01 g/mol = 12.01 g

Total molar mass = 40.10 g

(b) One mole of $NaPO_3$ contains 1 mol of sodium atoms, 1 mol of phosphorus atoms, and 3 mol of oxygen atoms. The molar masses of Na, P, and O are 22.99 g, 30.97 g, and 16.00 g, respectively. The total mass is

Na: 1 mol x 22.99 g/mol = 22.99 g
P: 1 mol x 30.97 g/mol = 30.97 g
O: 3 mol x 16.00 g/mol = 48.00 g

Total molar mass = 101.96 g

(c) One mole of Al_2O_3 contains 2 mol of aluminum atoms and 3 mol of oxygen atoms. The molar masses of Al and O are 26.98 g and 16.00 g, respectively. The total mass is

Al: 2 mol x 26.98 g/mol = 53.96 g
O: 3 mol x 16.00 g/mol = 48.00 g

Total molar mass = 101.96 g

2.66 (a) One mole of N_2O_5 contains 2 mol of nitrogen atoms and 5 mol of oxygen atoms; therefore, 1.5 mol of N_2O_5 will contain 1.5 x 2 = 3.0 mol of nitrogen atoms and 1.5 x 5 = 7.5 mol of oxygen atoms.

(b) One mole of H_3PO_4 contains 3 mol of hydrogen atoms, 1 mol of phosphorus atoms, and 4 mol of oxygen atoms. The molar masses of H, P, and O are 1.01 g, 30.97 g, and 16.00 g, respectively. The molar mass of H_3PO_4 is

H: 3 mol x 1.01 g/mol = 3.03 g
P: 1 mol x 30.97 g/mol = 30.97 g
O: 4 mol x 16.00 g/mol = 64.00 g

Total molar mass = 98.00 g

The number of moles of H_3PO_4 is

$65 \text{ g } H_3PO_4 \times \dfrac{1 \text{ mol } H_3PO_4}{98.00 \text{ g } H_3PO_4} = 0.66 \text{ mol } H_3PO_4$

0.66 mol H_3PO_4 will contain 0.66 x 3 = 2.0 mol of hydrogen atoms, 0.66 x 1 = 0.66 mol of phosphorus atoms, and 0.66 x 4 = 2.6 mol of oxygen atoms.

(c) The molar mass of ethanol was found to be 46.08 g in Exercise 2.62 (c). The number of moles of ethanol is

$$750 \text{ mL} \times 0.789 \text{ g/mL} \times \frac{1 \text{ mol ethanol}}{46.08 \text{ g}} = 12.8 \text{ mol ethanol}$$

12.8 mol C_2H_5OH will contain 12.8 x 2 = 25.6 mol of carbon atoms, 12.8 x 6 = 76.8 mol of hydrogen atoms, and 12.8 x 1 = 12.8 mol of oxygen atoms.

2.68   (a) The molar masses of C, H, and O are 12.01 g, 1.01 g, and 16.00 g, respectively. The molar mass of CH_3COOH is 2 x 12.01 g + 4 x 1.01 g + 2 x 16.00 g = 60.06 g.

The number of moles of CH_3COOH is

$$25.0 \text{ g } CH_3COOH \times \frac{1 \text{ mol } CH_3COOH}{60.06 \text{ g } CH_3COOH} = 0.416 \text{ mol } CH_3COOH$$

(b) The molar masses of C, H, and O are 12.01 g, 1.01 g, and 16.00 g, respectively. The molar mass of C_2H_5OH is 2 x 12.01 g + 6 x 1.01 g + 16.00 g = 46.08 g.

The mass of 0.56 mol of ethanol is

$$0.56 \text{ mol } C_2H_5OH \times \frac{46.08 \text{ g}}{1 \text{ mol } C_2H_5OH} = 26 \text{ g}$$

(c) We first convert millimoles to moles.

$$35.0 \text{ millimoles } O_3 \times \frac{1 \text{ mol}}{10^3 \text{ millimoles}} = 0.0350 \text{ mol } O_3$$

The number of O_3 molecules in 0.0350 mol of O_3 is

$$0.0350 \text{ mol } O_3 \times \frac{6.022 \times 10^{23} O_3 \text{ molecules}}{1 \text{ mol } O_3} = 2.11 \times 10^{22} O_3 \text{ molecules}$$

(d) The molar mass of $C_6H_{12}O_6$ is 180.16 g from Exercise 2.62 (a). The number of moles of $C_6H_{12}O_6$ is

$$100 \text{ mg} \times \frac{1 \text{ g}}{10^3 \text{ mg}} \times \frac{1 \text{ mol } C_6H_{12}O_6}{180.16 \text{ g}} = 5.55 \times 10^{-4} \text{ mol } C_6H_{12}O_6$$

The number of $C_6H_{12}O_6$ molecules in 5.55 x 10^{-4} mol $C_6H_{12}O_6$ is

$$5.55 \times 10^{-4} \text{ mol } C_6H_{12}O_6 \times \frac{6.022 \times 10^{23} C_6H_{12}O_6 \text{ molecules}}{1 \text{ mol } C_6H_{12}O_6}$$

$$= 3.34 \times 10^{20} C_6H_{12}O_6 \text{ molecules}$$

(e) One mole of K_2SO_4 contains 2 mol of K^+ ions and 1 mol of SO_4^{2-} ions, so 0.75 mol of K_2SO_4 will contain 0.75 x 2 = 1.5 mol of K^+ ions and 0.75 x 1 = 0.75 mol of SO_4^{2-} ions.

The number of K^+ and SO_4^{2-} ions in 0.75 mol of K_2SO_4 is

$$1.5 \text{ mol } K^+ \times \frac{6.022 \times 10^{23} \text{ } K^+ \text{ ions}}{1 \text{ mol } K^+} = 9.0 \times 10^{23} \text{ } K^+ \text{ ions}$$

$$0.75 \text{ mol } SO_4^{2-} \times \frac{6.022 \times 10^{23} \text{ } SO_4^{2-} \text{ ions}}{1 \text{ mol } SO_4^{2-}} = 4.5 \times 10^{23} \text{ } SO_4^{2-} \text{ ions}$$

2.70   (a) There are 454 x 0.00010 = 0.045 g of KI in the container. The molar masses of K and I are 39.10 g and 126.90 g, respectively. The molar mass of KI is 1 x 39.10 g + 1 x 126.90 g = 166.00 g.

The number of moles of KI in the container is

$$0.045 \text{ g } \times \frac{1 \text{ mol KI}}{166.00 \text{ g}} = 2.7 \times 10^{-4} \text{ mol KI}$$

(b) One mole of KI contains 1 mol of K^+ ions and 1 mol of I^- ions; therefore, 2.7 x 10^{-4} mol of KI contains 2.7 x 10^{-4} mol I^- ions. The number of I^- ions is

$$2.7 \times 10^{-4} \text{ mol } I^- \times \frac{6.022 \times 10^{23} \text{ } I^- \text{ ions}}{1 \text{ mol } I^-} = 1.6 \times 10^{20} \text{ } I^- \text{ ions}$$

2.72   Ionic compounds when melted (liquid) conduct electricity, while covalent compounds in the liquid state do not. A simple experimental arrangement of an electric lamp connected in series with a battery, a switch, and a pair of platinum electrodes to dip into the liquid under investigation could be used to distinguish between ionic and covalent compounds. If the liquid tested is a conductor of electricity, the lamp filament will glow when the switch is closed.

(a) If the electrodes are lowered into a beaker of methyl chloride, the filament will not glow. Methyl chloride is a nonconductor and, therefore, a covalent compound.

(b) If the electrodes are lowered into melted (liquid) KI, the filament will light up. KI is a conductor and, therefore, an ionic compound.

Comment: Certain substances are covalent in their pure states and ionic in solution. For instance, sulfuric acid (H_2SO_4) in its pure liquid state doesn't conduct appreciable electricity, while an aqueous solution of sulfuric acid does. In its pure liquid state sulfuric acid is covalent, while in aqueous solution it is ionic. Most covalent compounds do not ionize (do not break up into ions or ionic parts) in solution. Ionization is discussed in subsequent chapters of the text.

2.73   (a) Li^+; S^{2-}; I^-; Ba^{2+}; N^{3-}; Al^{3+}; F^-; Sr^{2+}; O^{2-}.
Li is in Group 1A. All elements in Group 1A form 1+ ions; Li^+.
Sulfur and oxygen in Group 6A form 2– ions; S^{2-} and O^{2-}.
The halogens in Group 7A form 1– ions; I^- and F^-.
Ba and Sr are in Group 2A. The Group 2A elements form 2+ ions; Ba^{2+} and Sr^{2+}.
Aluminum is in Group 3A. Group 3A elements form 3+ ions; Al^{3+}.
Nitrogen is in Group 5A and forms a 3– ion; N^{3-}.

(b) The noble gases in Group 8A do not form any ions under natural conditions.

2.74   Cesium (Cs) is in Group 1A. Group 1A elements form 1+ ions.
Strontium (Sr) is in Group 2A. Group 2A elements form 2+ ions.
Bromine (Br) is in Group 7A. Group 7A elements form 1– ions.

(a) To maintain electrical neutrality in the binary ionic compound formed from cesium and bromine, we need a 1-to-1 relationship between the cesium and bromine ions. The formula is therefore CsBr.

(b) To maintain electrical neutrality in the binary ionic compound formed from strontium and bromine, we need two bromine ions for every strontium ion. The formula is therefore $SrBr_2$.

2.84   The atomic numbers Z are obtained from the periodic table.

(a) $^{131}_{53}I$, (b) $^{201}_{181}Tl$, (c) $^{99}_{43}Tc$, (d) $^{60}_{27}Co$, and (e) $^{24}_{11}Na$.

2.86   (a) The molar masses of the elements needed for this problem are Na, 22.99 g; Cl, 35.45 g; C, 12.01 g; H, 1.01 g; O, 16.00 g; K, 39.10 g; and Ca, 40.08 g.

The molar mass of NaCl is 1 x 22.99 g + 1 x 35.45 g = 58.44 g

The molar mass of sodium lactate is 1 x 22.99 g + 3 x 12.01 g + 5 x 1.01 g + 3 x 16.00 g = 112.07 g

The molar mass of KCl is 1 x 39.10 g + 1 x 35.45 g = 74.55 g

The molar mass of $CaCl_2$ is 1 x 40.08 g + 2 x 35.45 g = 110.98 g

The number of moles of NaCl in 1 L of solution is

$$5.96 \text{ g} \times \frac{1 \text{ mol NaCl}}{58.44 \text{ g}} = 0.102 \text{ mol NaCl}$$

The number of moles of sodium lactate is

$$3.1 \text{ g} \times \frac{1 \text{ mol } NaC_3H_5O_3}{112.07 \text{ g}} = 0.028 \text{ mol } NaC_3H_5O_3$$

The number of moles of KCl is $0.3 \text{ g} \times \dfrac{1 \text{ mol KCl}}{74.55 \text{ g}} = 0.004 \text{ mol KCl}$

The number of moles of $CaCl_2$ is $0.2 \text{ g} \times \dfrac{1 \text{ mol } CaCl_2}{110.98 \text{ g}} = 0.002 \text{ mol } CaCl_2$

(b) 0.102 mol NaCl contributes 0.102 mol Na^+ ions and 0.102 mol Cl^- ions.
0.028 mol $NaC_3H_5O_3$ contributes 0.028 mol Na^+ ions and 0.028 mol $C_3H_5O_3^-$ ions.
0.004 mol KCl contributes 0.004 mol K^+ ions and 0.004 mol Cl^- ions.
0.002 mol $CaCl_2$ contributes 0.002 mol Ca^{2+} ions and 0.002 x 2 = 0.004 mol Cl^- ions.
The total number of moles of Na^+ ions is 0.102 + 0.028 = 0.130 mol.
The total number of moles of Cl^- ions is 0.102 + 0.004 + 0.004 = 0.110 mol.
Answer: Na^+, 0.130 mol; Ca^{2+}, 0.002 mol; Cl^-, 0.110 mol; and $C_3H_5O_3^-$, 0.028 mol.

2.88   To solve this problem we have to calculate the factor or multiplier needed to make the atomic diameter equal to 100 yards (the length of a football field). The atomic diameter is 200 pm = 2×10^{-10} m. Let the factor = x.

$$(2 \times 10^{-10} \text{ m})(x) = 100 \text{ yards} \times \frac{0.9144 \text{ m}}{1 \text{ yd}} = 91.44 \text{ m}$$

$$x = \frac{91.44 \text{ m}}{2 \times 10^{-10} \text{ m}} = 4.572 \times 10^{11}$$

The nuclear diameter is 2×10^{-15} m. If it is expanded by the same factor, i.e., by the same proportion as the atomic diameter, it would equal

$$2 \times 10^{-15} \text{ m} \times \frac{10^2 \text{ cm}}{1 \text{ m}} \times \frac{1 \text{ in}}{2.54 \text{ cm}} \times 4.572 \times 10^{11} = 0.036 \text{ in or } 0.04 \text{ in}$$
(rounded off to one significant figure)

2.89   The percent of the total atomic volume occupied by the nucleus is

$$\frac{V_{nucleus}}{V_{atom}} \times 100\% = \frac{(4/3)\pi r^3_{nucleus}}{(4/3)\pi r^3_{atom}} \times 100\% = \frac{r^3_{nucleus}}{r^3_{atom}} \times 100\%$$

$$= \frac{(10^{-15}\ m)^3}{(10^{-10}\ m)^3} \times 100\% = \frac{10^{-45}\ m^3}{10^{-30}\ m^3} \times 100\% = 10^{-13}\%$$

2.90   The masses of the proton and neutron are 1.67265×10^{-24} g and 1.67495×10^{-24} g, respectively. The volume of a sphere of radius 5×10^{-15} m is

$$V_{nucleus} = (4/3) \times 3.1416 \times (5 \times 10^{-15}\ m)^3 = 5 \times 10^{-43}\ m^3 \times \frac{10^6\ cm^3}{1\ m^3}$$

$$= 5 \times 10^{-37}\ cm^3$$

The total mass of the nucleus is $2 \times 1.67265 \times 10^{-24}$ g $+ 2 \times 1.67495 \times 10^{-24}$ g $= 6.6952 \times 10^{-24}$ g

The density of the nucleus is

$$d = \frac{mass}{V} = \frac{6.6952 \times 10^{-24}\ g}{5 \times 10^{-37}\ cm^3} = 1 \times 10^{13}\ g/cm^3$$

2.91   If the sun had a density of 1×10^{13} g/cm^3 its volume would be

$$V = mass/d = \frac{1.991 \times 10^{33}\ g}{1 \times 10^{13}\ g/cm^3} = 1.991 \times 10^{20}\ cm^3.$$

Since $V = 4/3\ \pi r^3$, its radius would be

$$r = \sqrt[3]{\frac{3V}{4\pi}} = \sqrt[3]{\frac{(3)(1.991 \times 10^{20}\ cm^3)}{(4)(3.1416)}} = \sqrt[3]{0.04753 \times 10^{21}\ cm^3}$$

$$= \sqrt[3]{0.04753} \times \sqrt[3]{10^{21}\ cm^3} = 3.62 \times 10^6\ cm = 36.2\ km$$

or 4×10 km to one significant figure.

Math Reminder: In general, if a and b are nonnegative numbers and n is a natural number (a positive integer), then

$$\sqrt[n]{ab} = \sqrt[n]{a} \times \sqrt[n]{b}$$

CHAPTER 3
CHEMICAL REACTIONS, EQUATIONS, AND STOICHIOMETRY

Solutions To Practice Exercises

PE 3.1   (a) Chemical reaction; souring is caused by microorganisms that break down the proteins and sugars in milk, forming new substances.
(b) Physical change; no new substances are formed.
(c) Chemical change; the interaction of the moisture, carbon dioxide, and sulphur oxides present in air with the copper in bronze causes the bronze statue to turn green; new substances are formed.

PE 3.5   (a) The molar mass of chromite ($FeCr_2O_4$) is 223.84 g. The percentages of Fe, Cr, and O are

$$\text{percent Fe} = \frac{55.85 \text{ g}}{223.84 \text{ g}} \times 100\% = 24.95\%$$

$$\text{percent Cr} = \frac{103.99 \text{ g}}{223.84 \text{ g}} \times 100\% = 46.46\%$$

$$\text{percent O} = \frac{64.00 \text{ g}}{223.84 \text{ g}} \times 100\% = 28.59\%$$

(b) Chromite is 46.46% chromium, so any sample of chromite will contain 46.46 kg of chromium for every 100 kg of sample. The number of kilograms of chromium in 1000 kg of chromite is

$$1000 \text{ kg chromite} \times \frac{46.46 \text{ kg chromium}}{100 \text{ kg chromite}} = 464.6 \text{ kg chromium}$$

PE 3.6   The atomic weight of sulfur is 32.07 u. The molecular weight divided by the atomic weight is 256.5 u/32.07 u = 8.00. Therefore, there must be eight atoms of sulfur in one molecule of sulfur. The formula is S_8.

PE 3.7   The atomic weights of S and H are 32.1 u and 1.0 u, respectively. Since the molecular weight of hydrogen sulfide is 34.1 u, the hydrogen sulfide molecule can only contain one sulfur atom. The remaining mass, 34.1 − 32.1 = 2.0 u, is due to hydrogen. Since each hydrogen is 1.0 u, there must be two atoms of hydrogen in the molecule. The formula is H_2S.

PE 3.9   A 100-g sample of chloroform would contain 89.10 g of chlorine, 0.84 g of hydrogen, and 100 – 89.10 – 0.84 = 10.06 g of carbon. The number of moles of each element in 100 g is

$$89.10 \text{ g Cl} \times \frac{1 \text{ mol Cl atoms}}{35.45 \text{ g Cl}} = 2.51 \text{ mol Cl atoms}$$

$$0.84 \text{ g H} \times \frac{1 \text{ mol H atoms}}{1.01 \text{ g H}} = 0.83 \text{ mol H atoms}$$

$$10.06 \text{ g C} \times \frac{1 \text{ mol C atoms}}{12.01 \text{ g C}} = 0.84 \text{ mol C atoms}$$

By inspection we see that there are 3 mol of Cl atoms for every 1 mol of H atoms and 1 mol of C atoms; the ratio is 3:1:1. The atom ratio in the formula is the same as the mole ratio. The formula is $CHCl_3$.

PE 3.10   The sample contained 8.98 g of Al and 25.0 g – 8.98 g = 16.0 g of S. The number of moles of each element in the sample is

$$8.98 \text{ g Al} \times \frac{1 \text{ mol Al atoms}}{26.98 \text{ g Al}} = 0.333 \text{ mol Al atoms}$$

$$16.0 \text{ g S} \times \frac{1 \text{ mol S atoms}}{32.07 \text{ g S}} = 0.499 \text{ mol S atoms}$$

To find the simplest whole-number mole ratio we have to divide through by the number of moles of Al.

Al: $\frac{0.333}{0.333} = 1.00$ $1.00 \times 2 = 2$

S: $\frac{0.499}{0.333} = 1.50$ $1.50 \times 2 = 3$

We then mutiply by 2 to obtain a whole number ratio. Therefore, there are 2 mol of Al for every 3 mol of S, and the formula is Al_2S_3.

PE 3.11   One mole of CH_2 units has a mass of $12.01 + (2 \times 1.01) = 14.03$ g. One mole of molecules has a molar mass of 56.10 g. If we divide the molar mass by 14.03 g we get 56.10 g/14.03 g = 4.0, so 1 mol of molecules contains 4 mol of CH_2 units. The molecular formula is $(CH_2)_4$ or C_4H_8.

PE 3.12   To solve this problem we have to calculate the number of moles of nitrogen atoms and selenium atoms present in 1 mol of nitrogen selenide. The number of grams of nitrogen in 1 mol (371.9 g) of nitrogen selenide is

$$371.9 \text{ g nitrogen selenide} \times \frac{15.07 \text{ g N}}{100 \text{ g nitrogen selenide}} = 56.0 \text{ g N}$$

The mass of selenium in 1 mol of compound is 371.9 g – 56.0 g = 315.9 g Se. The number of moles of N and Se in 1 mol of nitrogen selenide is

$$56.0 \text{ g N} \times \frac{1 \text{ mol N atoms}}{14.0 \text{ g N}} = 4.00 \text{ mol N atoms}$$

$$315.9 \text{ g Se} \times \frac{1 \text{ mol Se atoms}}{78.96 \text{ g Se}} = 4.00 \text{ mol Se atoms}$$

The atom ratio is the same as the mole ratio, and the formula is N_4Se_4.

PE 3.13 (a) To calculate the empirical formula, we have to calculate the number of moles of each element present in the vitamin A sample. We know from Example 3.13 that there are 24.02 mg of C, 3.025 mg of H, and 1.60 mg of O in 28.64 mg of vitamin A. The number of moles of each element is

$$24.02 \text{ mg C} \times \frac{1 \text{ g}}{10^3 \text{ mg}} \times \frac{1 \text{ mol C atoms}}{12.01 \text{ g C}} = 0.0020 \text{ mol C atoms}$$

$$3.025 \text{ mg H} \times \frac{1 \text{ g}}{10^3 \text{ mg}} \times \frac{1 \text{ mol H atoms}}{1.01 \text{ g H}} = 0.0030 \text{ mol H atoms}$$

$$1.60 \text{ mg O} \times \frac{1 \text{ g}}{10^3 \text{ mg}} \times \frac{1 \text{ mol O atoms}}{16.00 \text{ g O}} = 0.00010 \text{ mol O atoms}$$

To find the simplest whole-number ratio we will divide through by the number of moles of O. This gives us 20 mol of C for every 30 mol of H and 1 mol of O; the ratio is 20:30:1. The empirical formula is $C_{20}H_{30}O$.

(b) To find the molecular formula, we have to determine how many empirical unit masses there are in the molar mass of the compound. One mole of $C_{20}H_{30}O$ units has a mass of $(20 \times 12.01) + (30 \times 1.01) + 16.00 = 286.5$ g. The molar mass of vitamin A is 286.5 g, so the molecular formula is the same as the empirical formula. The molecular formula is $C_{20}H_{30}O$.

PE 3.14 (a) To get the percentage composition, we need the mass of each element in the original sample. After combustion the carbon is all in the carbon dioxide and the hydrogen is all in the water. The masses of C and H in the sample are

C: $\quad 81.36 \text{ mg } CO_2 \times \frac{12.01 \text{ mg C}}{44.01 \text{ mg } CO_2} = 22.20 \text{ mg C}$

H: $\quad 24.98 \text{ mg } H_2O \times \frac{2.016 \text{ mg H}}{18.02 \text{ mg } H_2O} = 2.795 \text{ mg H}$

The percentages are C: $\dfrac{22.20 \text{ mg}}{25.00 \text{ mg}} \times 100\% = 88.80\%$; H: $\dfrac{2.795 \text{ mg}}{25.00 \text{ mg}} \times 100\% = 11.18\%$

(b) When both the molar mass and the percentage composition are known, the molecular formula can be determined directly by calculating the number of moles of each element present in the molar mass. The atom ratio in the formula is the same as the mole ratio. The number of moles of C and H in 1 mol of compound is

$$54.09 \text{ g compound} \times \frac{88.80 \text{ g C}}{100 \text{ g compound}} \times \frac{1 \text{ mol C atoms}}{12.01 \text{ g C}} = 4.00 \text{ mol C atoms}$$

$$54.09 \text{ g compound} \times \frac{11.18 \text{ g H}}{100 \text{ g compound}} \times \frac{1 \text{ mol H atoms}}{1.008 \text{ g H}} = 6.00 \text{ mol H atoms}$$

In 1 mol of compound there are 4 mol of C atoms and 6 mol of H atoms. The formula is C_4H_6.

PE 3.17 The ions involved in this reaction are: potassium, K^+; chromate, CrO_4^{2-}; silver, Ag^+; and nitrate, NO_3^-.

potassium chromate + silver nitrate $\longrightarrow$ silver chromate + potassium nitrate
$\quad K_2CrO_4(aq) \quad + AgNO_3(aq) \quad \longrightarrow \quad Ag_2CrO_4(s) \quad + KNO_3(aq)$

The CrO_4^{2-} and NO_3^- ions remain intact in this reaction and can be treated as units for the purposes of balancing the equation. Two K^+ ions on the left require two KNO_3 formula units on the right, and two Ag^+ ions on the right require two $AgNO_3$ formula units on the left. The balanced equation is $K_2CrO_4(aq) + 2AgNO_3(aq) \longrightarrow Ag_2CrO_4(s) + 2KNO_3(aq)$.

PE 3.19 $F_2(g) + H_2O(l) \longrightarrow O_2(g) + HF(aq)$ (unbalanced)

$F_2(g) + H_2O(l) \longrightarrow \frac{1}{2} O_2(g) + 2HF(aq)$ (balanced)

$2F_2(g) + 2H_2O(l) \longrightarrow O_2(g) + 4HF(aq)$ (balanced - integral coefficients)

PE 3.22 $C_3H_8(g) + 5O_2(g) \longrightarrow 3CO_2(g) + 4H_2O(g)$

From the balanced equation we see that 4 mol of H_2O are produced for every mole of C_3H_8 consumed. The conversion factor 4 mol H_2O/1 mol C_3H_8 gives

$$2.00 \text{ mol } C_3H_8 \times \frac{4 \text{ mol } H_2O}{1 \text{ mol } C_3H_8} = 8.00 \text{ mol } H_2O$$

PE 3.23 $\underset{\substack{50.0 \text{ kg}}}{SnO_2(s)} + 2C(s) \longrightarrow \underset{\substack{kg = ?}}{Sn(s)} + 2CO(g)$

The steps in the calculation are: kg $SnO_2 \longrightarrow$ mol $SnO_2 \longrightarrow$ mol Sn $\longrightarrow$ kg Sn.

$$50.0 \times 10^3 \text{ g } SnO_2 \times \frac{1 \text{ mol } SnO_2}{151 \text{ g } SnO_2} \times \frac{1 \text{ mol } Sn}{1 \text{ mol } SnO_2} \times \frac{119 \text{ g } Sn}{1 \text{ mol } Sn}$$

$= 39.4 \times 10^3$ g Sn = 39.4 kg Sn

PE 3.25 $\underset{\substack{g = ?}}{2KClO_3(s)} \longrightarrow 2KCl(s) + \underset{\substack{5.00 \text{ g}}}{3O_2(g)}$

The steps in the calculation are: g $O_2 \longrightarrow$ mol $O_2 \longrightarrow$ mol $KClO_3 \longrightarrow$ g $KClO_3$.

$$5.00 \text{ g } O_2 \times \frac{1 \text{ mol } O_2}{32.00 \text{ g } O_2} \times \frac{2 \text{ mol } KClO_3}{3 \text{ mol } O_2} \times \frac{122.55 \text{ g } KClO_3}{1 \text{ mol } KClO_3} = 12.8 \text{ g } KClO_3$$

PE 3.26 To solve this problem, we first have to calculate the theoretical yield of Cu_2S.

$$\text{theoretical yield} = \frac{\text{actual yield}}{\text{percent yield}} \times 100\%$$

Since we want an actual yield of 50.0 g Cu_2S, the theoretical yield is

$$\text{theoretical yield} = \frac{50.0 \text{ g} \times 100\%}{40.0\%} = 125 \text{ g } Cu_2S$$

$\underset{\substack{g = ?}}{2Cu(s)} + S(s) \longrightarrow \underset{\substack{125 \text{ g}}}{Cu_2S(s)}$

The remaining steps in the calculation are: g $Cu_2S \longrightarrow$ mol $Cu_2S \longrightarrow$ mol Cu $\longrightarrow$ g Cu.

$$125 \text{ g } Cu_2S \times \frac{1 \text{ mol } Cu_2S}{159.1 \text{ g } Cu_2S} \times \frac{2 \text{ mol } Cu}{1 \text{ mol } Cu_2S} \times \frac{63.5 \text{ g } Cu}{1 \text{ mol } Cu} = 99.8 \text{ g } Cu$$

PE 3.28 (a) The equation for the reaction is

$\underset{\substack{50.0 \text{ g}}}{3CaCl_2(aq)} + \underset{\substack{100.0 \text{ g}}}{2Na_3PO_4(aq)} \longrightarrow Ca_3(PO_4)_2(s) + 6NaCl(aq)$

To solve this problem we first have to convert the known masses to moles. The number of moles of each is

$$50.0 \text{ g CaCl}_2 \text{ x } \frac{1 \text{ mol CaCl}_2}{111 \text{ g CaCl}_2} = 0.450 \text{ mol CaCl}_2$$

$$100.0 \text{ g Na}_3\text{PO}_4 \text{ x } \frac{1 \text{ mol Na}_3\text{PO}_4}{164 \text{ g Na}_3\text{PO}_4} = 0.610 \text{ mol Na}_3\text{PO}_4$$

From the equation we see that 3 mol of $CaCl_2$ are needed for every 2 mol of Na_3PO_4. Since the mixture contains fewer moles of $CaCl_2$ than Na_3PO_4, $CaCl_2$ must be the limiting reactant and Na_3PO_4 the excess reactant.

(b) The number of grams of Na_3PO_4 consumed is

$$0.450 \text{ mol CaCl}_2 \text{ x } \frac{2 \text{ mol Na}_3\text{PO}_4}{3 \text{ mol CaCl}_2} \text{ x } \frac{164.0 \text{ g Na}_3\text{PO}_4}{1 \text{ mol Na}_3\text{PO}_4} = 49.2 \text{ g Na}_3\text{PO}_4$$

Since there was originally 100.0 g of Na_3PO_4, there are 100.0 g − 49.2 g = 50.8 g Na_3PO_4 remaining.

PE 3.29 $S(s) + O_2(g) \longrightarrow SO_2(g)$
100.0 g   200.0 g   g = ?

The numbers of moles of S and O_2 are

$$100.0 \text{ g S x } \frac{1 \text{ mol S}}{32.07 \text{ g S}} = 3.118 \text{ mol S}$$

$$200.0 \text{ g O}_2 \text{ x } \frac{1 \text{ mol O}_2}{32.00 \text{ g O}_2} = 6.25 \text{ mol O}_2$$

From the equation we see that 1 mol of S reacts with 1 mol of O_2. Since we have 6.25 mol O_2 and only 3.119 mol S, S is the limiting reactant. The mass of SO_2 formed is calculated as follows: mol S $\longrightarrow$ mol $SO_2 \longrightarrow$ g SO_2.

$$3.118 \text{ mol S x } \frac{1 \text{ mol SO}_2}{1 \text{ mol S}} \text{ x } \frac{64.07 \text{ g SO}_2}{1 \text{ mol SO}_2} = 199.8 \text{ g SO}_2$$

Solutions to Final Exercises

3.2   (a) Physical change; no new substances are formed. The poker returns to its original state on cooling.
  (b) Chemical change; the smoke and brown material consist of new substances that result from the breakdown (decomposition) of the oil molecules.
  (c) Chemical change; most greases are organic compounds that are combustible and form $CO_2(g)$ and $H_2O(g)$ when they undergo combustion. New substances are formed.
  (d) Physical change; the grease is just dissolved away by the cleansing fluid. No new substances are formed.

3.4   (a) Physical property; only the state of oxygen has changed.

    (b) Physical property; when substances enter the nose and stimulate certain receptors we experience the sensation of smell. No new substances are formed, therefore, this is a physical property.

    (c) Chemical property; new substances are formed from the lye and vinegar. A chemical reaction has taken place.

    (d) Physical change; no new substances are formed.

Comment: Dissolving should not be thought of exclusively as a physical change, since many substances form new compounds when they are dissolved in certain fluids.

3.6   (a) Using the law of conservation of mass, mass oxygen = mass mercury(II) oxide – mass mercury = 35.0 g – 32.4 g = 2.6 g.

    (b) The percentage composition of a compound is the percent of each element by mass.

$$\text{percent Hg} = \frac{32.4 \text{ g}}{35.0 \text{ g}} \times 100\% = 92.6\%$$

$$\text{percent O} = \frac{2.6 \text{ g}}{35.0 \text{ g}} \times 100\% = 7.4\%$$

3.8   Since there is an excess of fluorine, all the calcium metal reacts in forming the calcium fluoride.

$$\text{percent Ca} = \frac{0.842 \text{ g}}{1.64 \text{ g}} \times 100\% = 51.3\%$$

$$\text{percent F} = 100\% - \text{percent Ca} = 100\% - 51.3\% = 48.7\%$$

3.10   The law of multiple proportions states that in different compounds containing the same elements, the masses of one element combined with a fixed mass of the other element are in the ratio of small whole numbers. To see if these facts comply with this law, we first calculate the masses of nitrogen and oxygen in a 100.00-g sample of each compound. We then calculate the mass of one of the elements per gram of the other in each compound and calculate the ratios of those masses.

Compound 1:   mass nitrogen = 46.7 g
                     mass oxygen = 100.00 – 46.7 = 53.3 g

Compound 2:   mass nitrogen = 30.45 g
                     mass oxygen = 100.00 – 30.45 = 69.55 g

Compound 3:   mass nitrogen = 25.9 g
                     mass oxygen = 100.00 – 25.9 = 74.1 g

The mass of oxygen per gram of nitrogen in each compound is

Compound 1: $\dfrac{53.3 \text{ g oxygen}}{46.7 \text{ g nitrogen}} = \dfrac{1.14 \text{ g oxygen}}{1.00 \text{ g nitrogen}}$

Compound 2: $\dfrac{69.55 \text{ g oxygen}}{30.45 \text{ g nitrogen}} = \dfrac{2.28 \text{ g oxygen}}{1.00 \text{ g nitrogen}}$

Compound 3: $\dfrac{74.1 \text{ g oxygen}}{25.9 \text{ g nitrogen}} = \dfrac{2.86 \text{ g oxygen}}{1.00 \text{ g nitrogen}}$

The masses of oxygen involved are 1.14 g, 2.28 g, and 2.86 g. Dividing through by 1.14 g we get 1, 2, 2.5, or the whole-number proportion 2:4:5 between the oxygen masses.

Comment: You could choose to fix the mass of oxygen instead of nitrogen, and the overall result would be the same.

3.12   (a) The molar mass of oxalic acid ($H_2C_2O_4$) is (2 x 1.01) + (2 x 12.01) + (4 x 16.00) = 90.04 g.

$$\text{percent carbon} = \frac{24.02 \text{ g}}{90.04 \text{ g}} \times 100\% = 26.68\%$$

$$\text{percent oxygen} = \frac{64.00 \text{ g}}{90.04 \text{ g}} \times 100\% = 71.08\%$$

$$\text{percent hydrogen} = \frac{2.02 \text{ g}}{90.04 \text{ g}} \times 100\% = 2.24\%$$

(b) The molar mass of $C_6H_4Cl_2$ is (6 x 12.01) + (4 x 1.01) + (2 x 35.45) = 147.00 g.

$$\text{percent carbon} = \frac{72.06 \text{ g}}{147.00 \text{ g}} \times 100\% = 49.02\%$$

$$\text{percent hydrogen} = \frac{4.04 \text{ g}}{147.00 \text{ g}} \times 100\% = 2.75\%$$

$$\text{percent chlorine} = \frac{70.90 \text{ g}}{147.00 \text{ g}} \times 100\% = 48.23\%$$

(c) The molar mass of SnF_2 is 118.69 + (2 x 19.00) = 156.69 g.

$$\text{percent tin} = \frac{118.69 \text{ g}}{156.69 \text{ g}} \times 100\% = 75.75\%$$

$$\text{percent fluorine} = \frac{38.00 \text{ g}}{156.69 \text{ g}} \times 100\% = 24.25\%$$

3.14   (a) The molar masses of quartz (SiO_2) and limestone ($CaCO_3$) are 28.09 + (2 x 16.00) = 60.09 g and 40.08 + 12.01 + (3 x 16.00) = 100.09 g, respectively.

$$SiO_2: \text{percent oxygen} = \frac{32.00 \text{ g}}{60.09 \text{ g}} \times 100\% = 53.25\%$$

$$CaCO_3: \text{percent oxygen} = \frac{48.00 \text{ g}}{100.09 \text{ g}} \times 100\% = 47.96\%$$

(b) The number of grams of oxygen in 1.00 kg of each of these materials is

$$SiO_2: 1.00 \text{ kg } SiO_2 \times \frac{10^3 \text{ g}}{1 \text{ kg}} \times \frac{53.25 \text{ g O}}{100 \text{ g } SiO_2} = 532 \text{ g oxygen}$$

$$CaCO_3: 1.00 \text{ kg } CaCO_3 \times \frac{10^3 \text{ g}}{1 \text{ kg}} \times \frac{47.96 \text{ g O}}{100 \text{ g } CaCO_3} = 480 \text{ g oxygen}$$

Note: Each answer was rounded to three significant figures.

3.16   The molar mass of CH_2O is 12.01 + (2 x 1.01) + 16.00 = 30.03 g. The milligram ratios will be the same as the gram ratios. The mass of CH_2O that contains 72.5 mg C is

$$72.5 \text{ mg C} \times \frac{30.03 \text{ mg } CH_2O}{12.01 \text{ mg C}} = 181 \text{ mg } CH_2O$$

3.18   (a) The molar mass of water (H_2O) is (2 x 1.01) + 16.00 = 18.02 g; 1.00 kg water contains

$$1.00 \text{ kg } H_2O \times \frac{10^3 \text{ g}}{1 \text{ kg}} \times \frac{2.02 \text{ g H}}{18.02 \text{ g } H_2O} = 112 \text{ g H}$$

       (b) 1.00 mg water contains

$$1.00 \text{ mg } H_2O \times \frac{2.02 \text{ mg H}}{18.02 \text{ mg } H_2O} = 0.112 \text{ mg H} = 1.12 \times 10^{-4} \text{ g H}$$

       (c) 75 g water contains

$$75 \text{ g } H_2O \times \frac{2.02 \text{ g H}}{18.02 \text{ g } H_2O} = 8.4 \text{ g H}$$

3.23   (a) The masses of arsenic and sulfur in the sample are 6.09 g and 10.00 − 6.09 = 3.91 g, respectively. The numbers of moles of arsenic and sulfur are

$$6.09 \text{ g As } \times \frac{1 \text{ mol As atoms}}{74.92 \text{ g As}} = 0.0813 \text{ mol As atoms}$$

$$3.91 \text{ g S } \times \frac{1 \text{ mol S atoms}}{32.07 \text{ g S}} = 0.122 \text{ mol S atoms}$$

To find the simplest whole-number mole ratio, we divide through by the number of moles of arsenic. This gives us 1 mol As to 0.122/0.0813 = 1.50 mol S. To obtain a whole-number ratio we multiply by 2. There are 2 mol of arsenic for every 3 mol of S, and the empirical formula is As_2S_3.

       (b) No. To determine if this is the molecular formula, you must know the molar mass of the molecule.

3.24   (a) A 100-g sample of the compound would contain 43.18 g K, 39.15 g Cl, and 17.67 g O. The numbers of moles of each element in a 100-g sample are

$$43.18 \text{ g K } \times \frac{1 \text{ mol K atoms}}{39.10 \text{ g K}} = 1.104 \text{ mol K atoms}$$

$$39.15 \text{ g Cl } \times \frac{1 \text{ mol Cl atoms}}{35.45 \text{ g Cl}} = 1.104 \text{ mol Cl atoms}$$

$$17.67 \text{ g O } \times \frac{1 \text{ mol O atoms}}{16.00 \text{ g O}} = 1.104 \text{ mol O atoms}$$

From inspection we see that there is 1 mol of each element. The empirical formula is KClO.

       (b) A 100-g sample of the compound would contain 31.90 g K, 28.93 g Cl, and 39.17 g O. The numbers of moles of each element in 100 g of the compound are

$$31.90 \text{ g K } \times \frac{1 \text{ mol K atoms}}{39.10 \text{ g K}} = 0.8159 \text{ mol K atoms} \qquad \frac{0.8159}{0.8159} = 1.00$$

$$28.93 \text{ g Cl } \times \frac{1 \text{ mol Cl atoms}}{35.45 \text{ g Cl}} = 0.8161 \text{ mol Cl atoms} \qquad \frac{0.8161}{0.8159} = 1.00$$

$$39.17 \text{ g O } \times \frac{1 \text{ mol O atoms}}{16.00 \text{ g O}} = 2.448 \text{ mol O atoms} \qquad \frac{2.448}{0.8159} = 3.00$$

After dividing through by the number of moles of K, we see that the resulting numbers are 1, 1, and 3. There is 1 mol of K for every 1 mol of Cl and 3 mol of O. The empirical formula is $KClO_3$.

(c) A 100-g sample of the compound would contain 28.22 g K, 25.59 g Cl, and 46.19 g O. The numbers of moles of each element in 100 g of the compound are

$$28.22 \text{ g K} \times \frac{1 \text{ mol K atoms}}{39.10 \text{ g K}} = 0.7217 \text{ mol K atoms} \qquad \frac{0.7217}{0.7217} = 1.00$$

$$25.59 \text{ g Cl} \times \frac{1 \text{ mol Cl atoms}}{35.45 \text{ g Cl}} = 0.7218 \text{ mol Cl atoms} \qquad \frac{0.7218}{0.7217} = 1.00$$

$$46.19 \text{ g O} \times \frac{1 \text{ mol O atoms}}{16.00 \text{ g O}} = 2.887 \text{ mol O atoms} \qquad \frac{2.887}{0.7217} = 4.00$$

After dividing through by the number of moles of K, we see that the resulting ratio is 1:1:4. The empirical formula is $KClO_4$.

3.26   The masses of phosphorus and oxygen in the sample are 9.29 g and 21.29 − 9.29 = 12.00 g, respectively. The numbers of moles of phosphorus and oxygen are

$$9.29 \text{ g P} \times \frac{1 \text{ mol P atoms}}{30.97 \text{ g P}} = 0.300 \text{ mol P atoms}$$

$$12.00 \text{ g O} \times \frac{1 \text{ mol O atoms}}{16.00 \text{ g O}} = 0.7500 \text{ mol O atoms}$$

To find the simplest whole-number ratio we divide through by the number of moles of P. This gives us a phosphorus-to-oxygen ratio of 1:2.5. Multiplying by 2 gives us the whole-number ratio 2:5. The empirical formula is P_2O_5.

3.29   The number of moles of C, H, and O in the molar mass are

$$\text{C:} \quad 180.2 \text{ g fructose} \times \frac{40.00 \text{ g C}}{100 \text{ g fructose}} \times \frac{1 \text{ mol C atoms}}{12.01 \text{ g C}} = 6.00 \text{ mol C atoms}$$

$$\text{H:} \quad 180.2 \text{ g fructose} \times \frac{6.72 \text{ g H}}{100 \text{ g fructose}} \times \frac{1 \text{ mol H atoms}}{1.01 \text{ g H}} = 12.0 \text{ mol H atoms}$$

$$\text{O:} \quad 180.2 \text{ g fructose} \times \frac{53.28 \text{ g O}}{100 \text{ g fructose}} \times \frac{1 \text{ mol O atoms}}{16.00 \text{ g O}} = 6.00 \text{ mol O atoms}$$

The molecular formula is $C_6H_{12}O_6$.

3.31   The numbers of moles of carbon, oxygen, and hydrogen in the molar mass are

$$\text{C:} \quad 194 \text{ g acid} \times \frac{37.12 \text{ g C}}{100 \text{ g acid}} \times \frac{1 \text{ mol C atoms}}{12.01 \text{ g C}} = 6.00 \text{ mol C atoms}$$

$$\text{O:} \quad 194 \text{ g acid} \times \frac{57.69 \text{ g O}}{100 \text{ g acid}} \times \frac{1 \text{ mol O atoms}}{16.00 \text{ g O}} = 6.99 \text{ mol O atoms}$$

$$\text{H:} \quad 194 \text{ g acid} \times \frac{5.188 \text{ g H}}{100 \text{ g acid}} \times \frac{1 \text{ mol H atoms}}{1.008 \text{ g H}} = 9.98 \text{ mol H atoms}$$

The molecular formula is $C_6H_{10}O_7$.

3.33   After combustion of the hydrocarbon, all the carbon is in the carbon dioxide (CO_2) and all the hydrogen is in the water (H_2O). The numbers of moles of carbon and hydrogen in the sample are

$$\text{C:} \quad 6.60 \text{ g } CO_2 \times \frac{1 \text{ mol } CO_2}{44.01 \text{ g } CO_2} \times \frac{1 \text{ mol C atoms}}{1 \text{ mol } CO_2} = 0.150 \text{ mol C atoms}$$

$$\text{H:} \quad 4.10 \text{ g } H_2O \times \frac{1 \text{ mol } H_2O}{18.02 \text{ g } H_2O} \times \frac{2 \text{ mol H atoms}}{1 \text{ mol } H_2O} = 0.455 \text{ mol H atoms}$$

To find the simplest whole number ratio, we divide through by the number of moles of H. This gives us a carbon-to-hydrogen ratio of 1:3. The empirical formula is CH_3.

3.35   After combustion, all the carbon is in the CO_2 and all the hydrogen is in the H_2O. The masses of C, H, and O in the sample are

$$\text{C:} \quad 1.50 \text{ mg } CO_2 \times \frac{12.01 \text{ mg C}}{44.01 \text{ mg } CO_2} = 0.409 \text{ mg C}$$

$$\text{H:} \quad 0.408 \text{ mg } H_2O \times \frac{2.02 \text{ mg H}}{18.02 \text{ mg } H_2O} = 0.0457 \text{ mg H}$$

O: 1.00 mg − 0.409 mg − 0.0457 mg = 0.545 mg O (carry an extra significant figure)

The numbers of moles of C, H, and O in the molar mass are

$$\text{C:} \quad 176.12 \text{ g Vit. C} \times \frac{0.409 \text{ g C}}{1.00 \text{ g Vit. C}} \times \frac{1 \text{ mol C atoms}}{12.01 \text{ g C}} = 6.00 \text{ mol C atoms}$$

$$\text{H:} \quad 176.12 \text{ g Vit. C} \times \frac{0.0457 \text{ g H}}{1.00 \text{ g Vit. C}} \times \frac{1 \text{ mol H atoms}}{1.01 \text{ g H}} = 7.97 \text{ mol H atoms}$$

$$\text{O:} \quad 176.12 \text{ g Vit. C} \times \frac{0.545 \text{ g O}}{1.00 \text{ g Vit. C}} \times \frac{1 \text{ mol O atoms}}{16.00 \text{ g O}} = 6.00 \text{ mol O atoms}$$

The molecular formula is $C_6H_8O_6$.

3.39   (a) $C_6H_6(l) + O_2(g) \longrightarrow CO_2(g) + H_2O(g)$ (unbalanced)
            $C_6H_6(l) + 7\ 1/2\ O_2(g) \longrightarrow 6CO_2(g) + 3H_2O(g)$ (balanced)
            $2C_6H_6(l) + 15O_2(g) \longrightarrow 12CO_2(g) + 6H_2O(g)$ (balanced – integral coefficients)
     (b) $ZnS(s) + O_2(g) \longrightarrow ZnO(s) + SO_2(g)$ (unbalanced)
            $ZnS(s) + 1\ 1/2\ O_2(g) \longrightarrow ZnO(s) + SO_2(g)$ (balanced)
            $2ZnS(s) + 3O_2(g) \longrightarrow 2ZnO(s) + 2SO_2(g)$ (balanced – integral coefficients)
     (c) $CaCl_2(aq) + Na_3PO_4(aq) \longrightarrow Ca_3(PO_4)_2(s) + NaCl(aq)$ (unbalanced)
            $3CaCl_2(aq) + 2Na_3PO_4(aq) \longrightarrow Ca_3(PO_4)_2(s) + 6NaCl(aq)$ (balanced)

3.41   (a) $N_2(g) + H_2(g) \longrightarrow NH_3(g)$ (unbalanced)
            $N_2(g) + 3H_2(g) \longrightarrow 2NH_3(g)$ (balanced)
     (b) $Na(s) + H_2O(l) \longrightarrow H_2(g) + NaOH(aq)$ (unbalanced)
            $2Na(s) + 2H_2O(l) \longrightarrow H_2(g) + 2NaOH(aq)$ (balanced)
     (c) $C_2H_2(g) + O_2(g) \longrightarrow CO_2(g) + H_2O(g)$ (unbalanced)
            $C_2H_2(g) + 5/2\ O_2(g) \longrightarrow 2CO_2(g) + H_2O(g)$ (balanced)
            $2C_2H_2(g) + 5O_2(g) \longrightarrow 4CO_2(g) + 2H_2O(g)$ (balanced – integral coefficients)
     (d) $AgNO_3(aq) + CaCl_2(aq) \longrightarrow AgCl(s) + Ca(NO_3)_2(aq)$ (unbalanced)
            $2AgNO_3(aq) + CaCl_2(aq) \longrightarrow 2AgCl(s) + Ca(NO_3)_2(aq)$ (balanced)

3.43   (a) $P_4O_{10}(s) + H_2O(l) \longrightarrow H_3PO_4(aq)$ (unbalanced)
              $P_4O_{10}(s) + 6H_2O(l) \longrightarrow 4H_3PO_4(aq)$ (balanced)
        (b) $H_2(g) + I_2(g) \longrightarrow 2HI(g)$ (balanced)
        (c) $PbS(s) + 1\ 1/2\ O_2(g) \longrightarrow PbO(s) + SO_2(g)$ (balanced)
              $2PbS(s) + 3O_2(g) \longrightarrow 2PbO(s) + 2SO_2(g)$ (balanced - integral coefficients)
        (d) $TiCl_4(l) + 2Mg(s) \longrightarrow Ti(s) + 2MgCl_2(s)$ (balanced)
        (e) $Pb(NO_3)_2(aq) + 2KCl(aq) \longrightarrow PbCl_2(s) + 2KNO_3(aq)$ (balanced)
        (f) $KClO_3(s) \longrightarrow KClO_4(s) + KCl(s)$ (unbalanced)
              $4KClO_3(s) \longrightarrow 3KClO_4(s) + KCl(s)$ (balanced)
        (g) $2NaBr(aq) + Cl_2(aq) \longrightarrow 2NaCl(aq) + Br_2(aq)$ (balanced)
        (h) $XeF_6(s) + 3H_2O(l) \longrightarrow XeO_3(s) + 6HF(g)$ (balanced)

3.51   (a) $PbO(s) + C(s) \longrightarrow Pb(l) + CO(g)$. Carbon is taking the place of lead in the compound; displacement reaction.
        (b) $2K(s) + Cl_2(g) \longrightarrow 2KCl(s)$. Potassium chloride is formed from its elements; formation reaction.
        (c) $2AgBr(s) \longrightarrow 2Ag(s) + Br_2(l)$. Silver bromide is breaking down into its elements; decomposition reaction.
        (d) $2Na(s) + 2H_2O(l) \longrightarrow H_2(g) + 2NaOH(aq)$. Sodium is displacing hydrogen from water; displacement reaction.

3.56   (a) $Cr_2O_3(s) + 2Al(s) \longrightarrow 2Cr(l) + Al_2O_3(s)$
        (b) $Fe_2O_3(s) + 3H_2(g) \longrightarrow 2Fe(l) + 3H_2O(g)$
        (c) $Bi_2O_3(s) + 3C(s) \longrightarrow 2Bi(l) + 3CO(g)$

        Note: The metals are liquid because high temperatures are used.

3.58   (a) $4Al(s) + 3O_2(g) \longrightarrow 2Al_2O_3(s)$
        (b) $4Al(s) + 3O_2(g) \longrightarrow 2Al_2O_3(s)$
           30.0 g   g = ?

        The steps in the calculation are: g Al $\longrightarrow$ mol Al $\longrightarrow$ mol O_2 $\longrightarrow$ g O_2.

$$30.0 \text{ g Al} \times \frac{1 \text{ mol Al}}{26.98 \text{ g Al}} \times \frac{3 \text{ mol } O_2}{4 \text{ mol Al}} \times \frac{32.00 \text{ g } O_2}{1 \text{ mol } O_2} = 26.7 \text{ g } O_2$$

3.60   (a) $C_6H_{12}O_6(s) + 6O_2(g) \longrightarrow 6CO_2(g) + 6H_2O(g)$
           20.0 g   mol = ?

        The steps in the calculation are: g glucose $\longrightarrow$ mol glucose $\longrightarrow$ mol CO_2.

$$20.0 \text{ g } C_6H_{12}O_6 \times \frac{1 \text{ mol } C_6H_{12}O_6}{180.18 \text{ g } C_6H_{12}O_6} \times \frac{6 \text{ mol } CO_2}{1 \text{ mol } C_6H_{12}O_6} = 0.666 \text{ mol } CO_2$$

        (b)

$$0.666 \text{ mol } CO_2 \times \frac{44.01 \text{ g } CO_2}{1 \text{ mol } CO_2} = 29.3 \text{ g } CO_2$$

3.62   (a) $3Cl_2(g) + 6KOH(aq) \longrightarrow 5KCl(aq) + KClO_3(aq) + 3H_2O(l)$
           1.86 mol   mol = ?

$$1.86 \text{ mol } Cl_2 \times \frac{1 \text{ mol } KClO_3}{3 \text{ mol } Cl_2} = 0.62 \text{ mol } KClO_3$$

        (b)

$$0.45 \text{ mol KCl} \times \frac{6 \text{ mol KOH}}{5 \text{ mol KCl}} = 0.54 \text{ mol KOH}$$

3.63

$$2NaHCO_3(s) \longrightarrow Na_2CO_3(s) + CO_2(g) + H_2O(g)$$
$$mg = ? \qquad\qquad\qquad\qquad 8.22 \text{ mg}$$

To solve this problem, we first calculate the number of moles of either CO_2 or H_2O driven off during heating. Let $x = $ mol $CO_2 = $ mol H_2O driven off (in vapor) during heating. Then

$$x \text{ mol } CO_2 \times \frac{44.01 \text{ g}}{1 \text{ mol } CO_2} + x \text{ mol } H_2O \times \frac{18.02 \text{ g}}{1 \text{ mol } H_2O} = 8.22 \times 10^{-3} \text{ g}$$

$$62.03x = 8.22 \times 10^{-3}$$
$$x = 1.325 \times 10^{-4} \text{ mol } CO_2 \text{ (carry an extra significant figure)}$$

The remaining steps in the calculation are:
mol $CO_2 \longrightarrow$ mol $NaHCO_3 \longrightarrow$ mass $NaHCO_3 \longrightarrow$ % $NaHCO_3$.

$$1.325 \times 10^{-4} \text{ mol } CO_2 \times \frac{2 \text{ mol } NaHCO_3}{1 \text{ mol } CO_2} \times \frac{84.01 \text{ g } NaHCO_3}{1 \text{ mol } NaHCO_3}$$

$$= 223 \times 10^{-4} \text{ g or } 22.3 \text{ mg } NaHCO_3.$$

The original sample contained 22.3 mg of $NaHCO_3$, so the percentage of $NaHCO_3$ in the sample is

$$\% \text{ NaHCO}_3 = \frac{22.3 \text{ mg}}{25.0 \text{ mg}} \times 100\% = 89.2\%$$

3.66

(a) $$2NaCl(aq) + 2H_2O(l) \longrightarrow 2NaOH(aq) + H_2(g) + Cl_2(g)$$
100 kg $\qquad\qquad\qquad\qquad$ kg = ?

The steps in the calculation of the theoretical yield are:
kg NaCl $\longrightarrow$ g NaCl $\longrightarrow$ mol NaCl $\longrightarrow$ mol NaOH $\longrightarrow$ kg NaOH.

$$100 \text{ kg NaCl} \times \frac{10^3 \text{ g}}{1 \text{ kg}} \times \frac{1 \text{ mol NaCl}}{58.44 \text{ g NaCl}} \times \frac{2 \text{ mol NaOH}}{2 \text{ mol NaCl}} \times \frac{40.00 \text{ g NaOH}}{1 \text{ mol NaOH}} = 68.4 \text{ kg NaOH}$$

(b)

$$\text{percent yield} = \frac{55 \text{ kg}}{68.4 \text{ kg}} \times 100\% = 80\%$$

3.68

Hematite reduction: $Fe_2O_3(s) + C(s) \longrightarrow 2Fe(l) + 3CO(g)$
$\qquad\qquad\qquad\qquad$ 1000 kg $\qquad\qquad\qquad\qquad$ kg = ?

The molar mass of Fe_2O_3 is 159.70 g, of which 111.70 g is Fe. The ratio of Fe to Fe_2O_3 is therefore 111.70 g Fe/159.70 g Fe_2O_3 or 111.70 kg Fe/159.70 kg Fe_2O_3. The road map for obtaining the actual mass of iron from hematite is: kg $Fe_2O_3 \longrightarrow$ theoretical kg Fe $\longrightarrow$ actual kg Fe.

$$1000 \text{ kg Fe}_2O_3 \times \frac{111.70 \text{ kg Fe}}{159.70 \text{ kg Fe}_2O_3} \times \frac{78\%}{100\%} = 5.5 \times 10^2 \text{ kg Fe}$$

Magnetite reduction: $Fe_3O_4(s) + 4C(s) \longrightarrow 3Fe(l) + 4CO(g)$
$\qquad\qquad\qquad\qquad$ 1000 kg $\qquad\qquad\qquad\qquad$ kg = ?

The molar mass of Fe_3O_4 is 231.55 g, of which 167.55 g is Fe. The ratio of Fe to Fe_3O_4 is therefore 167.55 g Fe/231.55 g Fe_3O_4 or 167.55 kg Fe/231.55 kg Fe_3O_4. The road map for obtaining the actual mass of iron from magnetite is: kg $Fe_3O_4 \longrightarrow$ theoretical kg Fe $\longrightarrow$ actual kg Fe.

$$1000 \text{ kg Fe}_3O_4 \times \frac{167.55 \text{ kg Fe}}{231.55 \text{ kg Fe}_3O_4} \times \frac{72\%}{100\%} = 5.2 \times 10^2 \text{ kg Fe}$$

Answer: Hematite yields the greatest amount of iron per metric ton.

3.70 $4Al(s) + 3O_2(g) \longrightarrow 2Al_2O_3(s)$
         100.0 g   100.0 g

     (a) The numbers of moles of oxygen and aluminum are

$$100.0 \text{ g } O_2 \text{ x } \frac{1 \text{ mol } O_2}{32.00 \text{ g } O_2} = 3.125 \text{ mol } O_2$$

$$100.0 \text{ g Al x } \frac{1 \text{ mol Al}}{26.98 \text{ g Al}} = 3.706 \text{ mol Al}$$

The number of moles of oxygen needed to react with 3.706 mol of Al is

$$3.706 \text{ mol Al x } \frac{3 \text{ mol } O_2}{4 \text{ mol Al}} = 2.780 \text{ mol } O_2$$

The amount of O_2 in the original mixture, 3.125 mol, is greater than 2.780 mol; hence, Al is the limiting reactant.

     (b) $4Al(s) + 3O_2(g) \longrightarrow 2Al_2O_3(s)$
           100.0 g   g = ?

The mass of Al_2O_3 formed is calculated as follows: g Al $\longrightarrow$ mol Al $\longrightarrow$ mol Al_2O_3 $\longrightarrow$ g Al_2O_3.

$$100.0 \text{ g Al x } \frac{1 \text{ mol Al}}{26.98 \text{ g Al}} \text{ x } \frac{2 \text{ mol } Al_2O_3}{4 \text{ mol Al}} \text{ x } \frac{101.96 \text{ g } Al_2O_3}{1 \text{ mol } Al_2O_3} = 189.0 \text{ g } Al_2O_3$$

     (c) The mass of oxygen consumed in the reaction is equal to the mass of Al_2O_3 formed minus the mass of Al consumed, which is 189.0 g – 100.0 g = 89.0 g oxygen. The mass of O_2 remaining is equal to the initial amount minus the amount consumed: 100.0 g – 89.0 g = 11.0 g O_2.

3.72 $N_2(g) + 3H_2(g) \longrightarrow 2NH_3(g)$
         35.0 g   25.0 g

The numbers of moles of N_2 and H_2 are

$$35.0 \text{ g } N_2 \text{ x } \frac{1 \text{ mol } N_2}{28.02 \text{ g } N_2} = 1.25 \text{ mol } N_2$$

$$25.0 \text{ g } H_2 \text{ x } \frac{1 \text{ mol } H_2}{2.02 \text{ g } H_2} = 12.4 \text{ mol } H_2$$

Nitrogen is the limiting reagent. The maximum amount of ammonia is found by using the strategy: g N_2 $\longrightarrow$ mol N_2 $\longrightarrow$ mol NH_3 $\longrightarrow$ g NH_3.

$$35.0 \text{ g } N_2 \text{ x } \frac{1 \text{ mol } N_2}{28.02 \text{ g } N_2} \text{ x } \frac{2 \text{ mol } NH_3}{1 \text{ mol } N_2} \text{ x } \frac{17.04 \text{ g } NH_3}{1 \text{ mol } NH_3} = 42.6 \text{ g } NH_3$$

3.74   (a) The molar mass of sulfadiazine ($C_{10}H_{10}N_4O_2S$) is (10 x 12.011) + (10 x 1.008) + (4 x 14.01) + (2 x 16.00) + 32.07 = 250.30 g. The fraction of sulfur in sulfadiazine is 32.07 g/250.30 g = 0.1281. The number of milligrams of S in a 500-mg tablet of sulfadiazine is 500 mg x 0.1281 = 64.0 mg sulfur.

(b) The molar mass of hydroxyapatite ($Ca_{10}(PO_4)_6(OH)_2$) is $(10 \times 40.08) + (6 \times 30.97) + (26 \times 16.00) + (2 \times 1.01) = 1004.6$ g, of which $10 \times 40.08 = 400.8$ g are calcium The fraction of calcium in hydroxyapatite is 400.8 g/1004.6 g = 0.3990. The number of milligrams of Ca in 1.00 g of hydroxyapatite is

$$1.00 \text{ g} \times \frac{10^3 \text{ mg}}{1 \text{ g}} \times 0.3990 = 399 \text{ mg Ca}$$

3.77   The molar mass of H_2O is 18.02 g, of which 2.02 g is H. The ratio of H to H_2O is therefore 2.02 g H/18.02 g H_2O or 2.02 kg H/18.02 kg H_2O. The mass of deuterium (^2H) per metric ton of water is

$$1000 \text{ kg } H_2O \times \frac{2.02 \text{ kg H}}{18.02 \text{ kg } H_2O} \times \frac{0.015 \text{ kg } ^2H}{100 \text{ kg H}} = 1.7 \times 10^{-2} \text{ kg } ^2H$$

3.80 $H_2SO_4(aq) + 2NH_3(g) \longrightarrow (NH_4)_2SO_4(aq)$
          g = ?

The calculation of the number of grams of ammonia follows the scheme:
V x d (of acid mixture) $\longrightarrow$ g acid mixture $\longrightarrow$ g H_2SO_4 $\longrightarrow$ mol H_2SO_4 $\longrightarrow$ mol NH_3 $\longrightarrow$ g NH_3.

$$35.5 \text{ mL} \times \frac{1.84 \text{ g acid mixture}}{1 \text{ mL}} \times \frac{98.0 \text{ g } H_2SO_4}{100 \text{ g acid mixture}} \times \frac{1 \text{ mol } H_2SO_4}{98.08 \text{ g } H_2SO_4}$$

$$\times \frac{2 \text{ mol } NH_3}{1 \text{ mol } H_2SO_4} \times \frac{17.04 \text{ g } NH_3}{1 \text{ mol } NH_3} = 22.2 \text{ g } NH_3$$

3.81 $CH_3COOH(aq) + NaHCO_3(s) \longrightarrow CH_3COONa(aq) + CO_2(g) + H_2O(l)$
          5.00 g   5.00 g   g = ?

First we have to find the limiting reagent. The number of moles of acetic acid and sodium hydrogen carbonate are

$$5.00 \text{ g } CH_3COOH \times \frac{1 \text{ mol } CH_3COOH}{60.06 \text{ g } CH_3COOH} = 0.0833 \text{ mol } CH_3COOH$$

$$5.00 \text{ g } NaHCO_3 \times \frac{1 \text{ mol } NaHCO_3}{84.01 \text{ g } NaHCO_3} = 0.0595 \text{ mol } NaHCO_3$$

From the equation we see that acetic acid and sodium hydrogen carbonate react on a 1 mol to 1 mol basis; therefore, $NaHCO_3$ is a limiting reactant. The number of grams of CO_2 produced is calculated as follows: mol $NaHCO_3$ $\longrightarrow$ mol CO_2 $\longrightarrow$ g CO_2.

$$0.0595 \text{ mol } NaHCO_3 \times \frac{1 \text{ mol } CO_2}{1 \text{ mol } NaHCO_3} \times \frac{44.01 \text{ g } CO_2}{1 \text{ mol } CO_2} = 2.62 \text{ g } CO_2$$

CHAPTER 4
SOLUTIONS AND SOLUTION
STOICHIOMETRY

Solutions To Practice Exercises

PE 4.4   (a)   When lead nitrate ($PbNO_3$) and potassium bromide (KBr) are mixed in aqueous solution, the ions initially present are Pb^{2+}, NO_3^-, K^+, and Br^-. The possible products of a precipitation reaction are lead bromide ($PbBr_2$) and potassium nitrate (KNO_3). The solubility rules state that $PbBr_2$ is sparingly soluble (Rule 3) and KNO_3 is soluble (Rule 2). A precipitate of $PbBr_2$ will form.

$$Pb(NO_3)_2(aq) + 2KBr(aq) \longrightarrow PbBr_2(s) + 2KNO_3(aq)$$
$$Pb^{2+}(aq) + 2Br^-(aq) \longrightarrow PbBr_2(s)$$

   (b)   After mixing $Na_2S(aq)$ and $ZnCl_2(aq)$, the ions momentarily present are Na^+, S^{2-}, Zn^{2+}, and Cl^-. The possible products of a precipitation reaction are NaCl and ZnS. NaCl is soluble (Rule 2); ZnS is sparingly soluble (Rule 6). A precipitate of ZnS will form.

$$Na_2S(aq) + ZnCl_2(aq) \longrightarrow ZnS(s) + 2NaCl(aq)$$
$$S^{2-}(aq) + Zn^{2+}(aq) \longrightarrow ZnS(s)$$

PE 4.5   Silver phosphate (Ag_3PO_4) is sparingly soluble (Rule 6). Silver nitrate ($AgNO_3$) is soluble (Rule 1); sodium phosphate (Na_3PO_4) is soluble (Rule 2). They can be used as reactants.

$$3AgNO_3(aq) + Na_3PO_4(aq) \longrightarrow Ag_3PO_4(s) + 3NaNO_3(aq)$$

Sodium nitrate ($NaNO_3$) is soluble (Rules 1 and 2).

PE 4.6   All the chloride ions (Cl^-) initially in the solution are now in the form of AgCl. The steps in the calculation are: 0.3050 g AgCl $\longrightarrow$ g Cl^- $\longrightarrow$ % Cl^-.

One mole of AgCl (143.321 g) contains 1 mol of Cl (35.453 g). The mass of chloride in 0.3050 g AgCl is

$$0.3050 \text{ g AgCl } \times \frac{35.453 \text{ g Cl}^-}{143.321 \text{ g AgCl}} = 0.07545 \text{ g Cl}^-$$

The percent of chloride in the original mixture is

$$\frac{\text{mass of Cl}^-}{\text{mass of sample}} \times 100\% = \frac{0.07545 \text{ g}}{0.2501 \text{ g}} \times 100\% = 30.17\%$$

PE 4.11 (a) Magnesium (Mg) is above silver (Ag) in the activity series and will displace silver from aqueous $AgNO_3$. Magnesium will dissolve according to the equation

$$Mg(s) + 2AgNO_3(aq) \longrightarrow Mg(NO_3)_2(aq) + 2Ag(s)$$

(b) Lead (Pb) is above copper (Cu) in the activity series and will displace copper from aqueous $CuSO_4$. It will react according to the equation

$$Pb(s) + CuSO_4(aq) \longrightarrow PbSO_4(s) + Cu(s)$$

PE 4.12

$$\text{mass of solution} = \frac{\text{mass of sulfuric acid x 100\%}}{\text{\% sulfuric acid}} = \frac{308.4 \text{ g x 100\%}}{26.00\%} = 1186 \text{ g}$$

The mass of the water is the total mass minus the H_2SO_4 mass.

$$\text{volume of water} = \frac{\text{mass water}}{\text{density water}} = \frac{1186 \text{ g} - 308.4 \text{ g}}{1.00 \text{ g/mL}} = 878 \text{ mL}$$

PE 4.13 A dioxin level of 50 ppt by mass means 50 g of dioxin in one trillion (1.0×10^{12}) grams of fish. The amount of dioxin in 100 g of fish is

$$100 \text{ g fish} \times \frac{50 \text{ g dioxin}}{1.0 \times 10^{12} \text{ g fish}} = 5.0 \times 10^{-9} \text{ g dioxin}$$

PE 4.15 The steps in the calculation are: g $AgNO_3$/mL $\longrightarrow$ g $AgNO_3$/L $\longrightarrow$ mol $AgNO_3$/L $\longrightarrow$ M $AgNO_3$.

$$\text{molarity} = \frac{5.25 \text{ g } AgNO_3}{125 \text{ mL}} \times \frac{10^3 \text{ mL}}{1 \text{ L}} \times \frac{1 \text{ mol } AgNO_3}{169.87 \text{ g } AgNO_3} = 0.247 \text{ mol } AgNO_3/L$$

$$= 0.247 \text{ M } AgNO_3$$

PE 4.16 The calculation will proceed as follows: g soln/mL $\longrightarrow$ g soln/L $\longrightarrow$ g HNO_3/L $\longrightarrow$ moles HNO_3/L $\longrightarrow$ M HNO_3.

$$\frac{1.424 \text{ g soln}}{1 \text{ mL}} \times \frac{1000 \text{ mL}}{1 \text{ L}} \times \frac{70.9 \text{ g } HNO_3}{100 \text{ g soln}} \times \frac{1 \text{ mol } HNO_3}{63.02 \text{ g } HNO_3}$$

$$= 16.0 \text{ mol } HNO_3/L = 16.0 \text{ M } HNO_3$$

The solution is 16.0 M in HNO_3.

PE 4.18 The calculation will proceed as follows: V x M (of $NaNO_3$) $\longrightarrow$ mol $NaNO_3$ $\longrightarrow$ g $NaNO_3$.

$$0.250 \text{ L} \times \frac{1.45 \text{ mol } NaNO_3}{1 \text{ L}} \times \frac{85.00 \text{ g } NaNO_3}{1 \text{ mol } NaNO_3} = 30.8 \text{ g } NaNO_3$$

PE 4.19 The number of grams of Na_2CO_3 needed is

$$100.0 \text{ mL} \times \frac{0.250 \text{ mol } Na_2CO_3}{1000 \text{ mL}} \times \frac{106.0 \text{ g } Na_2CO_3}{1 \text{ mol } Na_2CO_3} = 2.65 \text{ g } Na_2CO_3$$

Put 2.65 g Na_2CO_3 in a 100–mL volumetric flask. Dissolve and bring solution up to mark.

PE 4.20   One mole of $Fe_2(SO_4)_3$ dissociates into 2 mol of Fe^{3+} and 3 mol of SO_4^{2-}. A 0.750 M $Fe_2(SO_4)_3$ solution will be 2 x 0.750 M = 1.50 M in Fe^{3+} and 3 x 0.750 M = 2.25 M in SO_4^{2-}. The number of moles of SO_4^{2-} and Fe^{3+} in 250 mL of solution is

(a)

$$0.250 \text{ L} \times \frac{2.25 \text{ mol } SO_4^{2-}}{1 \text{ L}} = 0.562 \text{ mol } SO_4^{2-}$$

(b)

$$0.250 \text{ L} \times \frac{1.50 \text{ mol } Fe^{3+}}{1 \text{ L}} = 0.375 \text{ mol } Fe^{3+}$$

PE 4.21   The total number of moles of chloride ion (Cl^-) is the sum of the moles of chloride ion in each of the separate solutions.

$$0.250 \text{ L } MgCl_2 \times \frac{0.125 \text{ mol } MgCl_2}{1 \text{ L}} \times \frac{2 \text{ mol } Cl^-}{1 \text{ mol } MgCl_2} + 0.800 \text{ L}$$

$$\times \frac{0.350 \text{ mol } FeCl_3}{1 \text{ L}} \times \frac{3 \text{ mol } Cl^-}{1 \text{ mol } FeCl_3} = 0.9025 \text{ mol } Cl^- \text{ (carry an extra significant figure)}$$

The volume of the mixed solution = 0.250 L + 0.800 L = 1.050 L. The molarity of the chloride ion is

$$\text{molarity} = \frac{0.9025 \text{ mol } Cl^-}{1.050 \text{ L}} = 0.860 \text{ mol } Cl^-/L$$

The solution is 0.860 M in chloride ion.

PE 4.24   The balanced equation for the neutralization is

$$H_2SO_4(aq) + 2NaOH(aq) \longrightarrow Na_2SO_4(aq) + 2H_2O(l)$$
$$M = ?$$

The steps in the calculation are: V x M (of NaOH) $\longrightarrow$ mmol NaOH $\longrightarrow$ mmol H_2SO_4 $\longrightarrow$ molarity of H_2SO_4 solution.

$$40.0 \text{ mL} \times \frac{0.750 \text{ mmol NaOH}}{1 \text{ mL}} \times \frac{1 \text{ mmol } H_2SO_4}{2 \text{ mmol NaOH}} \times \frac{1}{10.0 \text{ mL}}$$

$$= \frac{1.50 \text{ mmol } H_2SO_4}{1 \text{ mL}} = 1.50 \text{ M } H_2SO_4$$

PE 4.25   The balanced equation is

$$NaHCO_3(s) + HNO_3(aq) \longrightarrow NaNO_3(aq) + H_2O(l) + CO_2(g)$$
$$5.23 \text{ g} \qquad mL = ?$$

The steps in the calculation are: g $NaHCO_3$ $\longrightarrow$ mol $NaHCO_3$ $\longrightarrow$ mol HNO_3 $\longrightarrow$ mL HNO_3.

$$5.23 \text{ g } NaHCO_3 \times \frac{1 \text{ mol } NaHCO_3}{84.09 \text{ g } NaHCO_3} \times \frac{1 \text{ mol } HNO_3}{1 \text{ mol } NaHCO_3} \times \frac{1 \text{ L}}{1.25 \text{ mol } HNO_3}$$

$$= 0.0498 \text{ L} = 49.8 \text{ mL}$$

PE 4.26   The balanced equation is $BaCl_2(aq) + H_2SO_4(aq) \longrightarrow BaSO_4(s) + 2HCl(aq)$
$$\underset{5.55\ g}{} \qquad \underset{mL\ =\ ?}{}$$

The steps in the calculation are: g $BaCl_2 \longrightarrow$ mol $BaCl_2 \longrightarrow$ mol $H_2SO_4 \longrightarrow$ mL H_2SO_4.

$$5.55 \text{ g } BaCl_2 \text{ x } \frac{1 \text{ mol } BaCl_2}{208.2 \text{ g } BaCl_2} \text{ x } \frac{1 \text{ mol } H_2SO_4}{1 \text{ mol } BaCl_2} \text{ x } \frac{1 \text{ L}}{2.00 \text{ mol } H_2SO_4}$$

$$= 0.0133 \text{ L} = 13.3 \text{ mL}$$

PE 4.27   The balanced equation is $H_3PO_4(aq) + 3KOH(aq) \longrightarrow K_3PO_4(aq) + 3H_2O(l)$
$$\underset{M\ =\ ?}{}$$

The steps in the calculation are: V x M (of KOH) $\longrightarrow$ mmol KOH $\longrightarrow$ mmol $H_3PO_4 \longrightarrow$ molarity H_3PO_4 solution.

$$25.54 \text{ mL x } \frac{2.111 \text{ mmol KOH}}{1 \text{ mL}} \text{ x } \frac{1 \text{ mmol } H_3PO_4}{3 \text{ mmol KOH}} \text{ x } \frac{1}{40.00 \text{ mL}} = \frac{0.4493 \text{ mmol } H_3PO_4}{1 \text{ mL}}$$

$$= 0.4493 \text{ M } H_3PO_4$$

PE 4.28   The balanced equation for the reaction is

$$Na_2CO_3(s) + 2HCl(aq) \longrightarrow 2NaCl(aq) + H_2O(l) + CO_2(g)$$
$$\underset{g\ =\ ?}{} \qquad \underset{\substack{33.75 \text{ mL of} \\ 0.4150 \text{ M}}}{}$$

The steps in the calculation are: V x M (of HCl) $\longrightarrow$ mol HCl $\longrightarrow$ mol $Na_2CO_3 \longrightarrow$ g $Na_2CO_3 \longrightarrow$ % Na_2CO_3.

$$0.03375 \text{ L x } \frac{0.4150 \text{ mol HCl}}{1 \text{ L}} \text{ x } \frac{1 \text{ mol } Na_2CO_3}{2 \text{ mol HCl}} \text{ x } \frac{106.0 \text{ g } Na_2CO_3}{1 \text{ mol } Na_2CO_3} = 0.7423 \text{ g } Na_2CO_3$$

The percent by weight of Na_2CO_3 in the sample is

$$\text{\% } Na_2CO_3 = \frac{0.7423 \text{ g}}{2.9929 \text{ g}} \text{ x } 100\% = 24.80\%$$

Solutions To Final Exercises

4.8   If the solution is saturated, then 50 mL of water will contain no more than

$$50 \text{ mL x } \frac{79.4 \text{ g thiosulfate}}{100 \text{ mL}} = 39.7 \text{ g thiosulfate}$$

This supersaturated solution contains 500 g – 39.7 g = 460 g of excess thiosulfate in a metastable state. The addition of a crystal of sodium thiosulfate should cause the crystallization of this 460 g of excess thiosulfate.

4.19   (a) The ions initially present in an aqueous solution are Na^+, Cl^-, Ag^+, and NO_3^-. The possible products of a precipitation reaction are AgCl and $NaNO_3$. AgCl is sparingly soluble (Rule 3), while $NaNO_3$ is soluble (Rules 1 and 2). A precipitate of AgCl will form.

$$NaCl(aq) + AgNO_3(aq) \longrightarrow AgCl(s) + NaNO_3(aq)$$
$$Cl^-(aq) + Ag^+(aq) \longrightarrow AgCl(s)$$

(b) The ions initially present in aqueous solution are Ba^{2+}, NO_3^-, Na^+, and SO_4^{2-}. The possible products of a precipitation reaction are $BaSO_4$ and $NaNO_3$. $BaSO_4$ is sparingly soluble (Rule 4), while $NaNO_3$ is soluble (Rules 1 and 2). A precipitate of $BaSO_4$ will form.

$$Ba(NO_3)_2(aq) + Na_2SO_4(aq) \longrightarrow BaSO_4(s) + 2NaNO_3(aq)$$
$$Ba^{2+}(aq) + SO_4^{2-}(aq) \longrightarrow BaSO_4(s)$$

(c) The ions initially present in aqueous solution are Cu^{2+}, SO_4^{2-}, Ca^{2+}, and Cl^-. The possible products of a precipitation reaction are $CuCl_2$ and $CaSO_4$. $CuCl_2$ is soluble (Rule 3), while $CaSO_4$ is sparingly soluble (Rule 4). A precipitate of $CaSO_4$ will form.

$$CuSO_4(aq) + CaCl_2(aq) \longrightarrow CaSO_4(s) + CuCl_2(aq)$$
$$SO_4^{2-}(aq) + Ca^{2+}(aq) \longrightarrow CaSO_4(s)$$

(d) The ions initially present in aqueous solution are Cu^{2+}, Cl^-, Ca^{2+}, and NO_3^-. The possible products of a precipitation reaction are $Cu(NO_3)_2$ and $CaCl_2$. $Cu(NO_3)_2$ is soluble (Rule 1), and $CaCl_2$ is soluble (Rule 3). No precipitate will form.

(e) The ions initially present in aqueous solution are Pb^{2+}, NO_3^-, K^+, and S^{2-}. The possible products of a precipitation reaction are PbS and KNO_3. PbS is sparingly soluble (Rule 6), while KNO_3 is soluble (Rules 1 and 2). A precipitate of PbS will form.

$$Pb(NO_3)_2(aq) + K_2S(aq) \longrightarrow PbS(s) + 2KNO_3(aq)$$
$$Pb^{2+}(aq) + S^{2-}(aq) \longrightarrow PbS(s)$$

4.20   Yes. At the moment of mixing the ions present are 1.00 mol Ca^{2+}, 2.00 mol NO_3^-, 1.00 mol Na^+, and 1.00 mol OH^- in 2.00 L of solution. Since the formula of calcium hydroxide is $Ca(OH)_2$, the 1.00 mol OH^- can form only 0.500 mol $Ca(OH)_2$. The number of grams of $Ca(OH)_2$ per 100 mL of solution at the instant of mixing is therefore

$$\frac{0.500 \text{ mol } Ca(OH)_2}{2.00 \text{ L}} \times \frac{74.10 \text{ g } Ca(OH)_2}{1 \text{ mol } Ca(OH)_2} \times \frac{0.100 \text{ L}}{100 \text{ mL}} = \frac{1.85 \text{ g } Ca(OH)_2}{100 \text{ mL}}$$

Since the amount present is 10 times greater than the amount needed for saturation, a precipitate of $Ca(OH)_2$ will form.

4.21   The mass of chromium in 0.2748 g of Cr_2O_3 is

$$0.2748 \text{ g } Cr_2O_3 \times \frac{104.0 \text{ g } Cr}{152.0 \text{ g } Cr_2O_3} = 0.1880 \text{ g } Cr$$

$$\% \text{ chromium} = \frac{\text{mass chromium}}{\text{mass sample}} \times 100\% = \frac{0.1880 \text{ g}}{1.4312 \text{ g}} \times 100\% = 13.14\%$$

4.32   (a), (c), (d), and (e) will release gases.

(a) $Mg(HCO_3)_2(s) + 2HCl(aq) \longrightarrow MgCl_2(aq) + 2H_2O(l) + 2CO_2(g)$
   $Mg(HCO_3)_2(s) + 2H^+(aq) \longrightarrow Mg^{2+}(aq) + 2H_2O(l) + 2CO_2(g)$
(c) $Ca(CN)_2(s) + 2HCl(aq) \longrightarrow CaCl_2(aq) + 2HCN(g)$
   $Ca(CN)_2(s) + 2H^+(aq) \longrightarrow Ca^{2+}(aq) + 2HCN(g)$
(d) $CdS(s) + 2HCl(aq) \longrightarrow CdCl_2(aq) + H_2S(g)$
   $CdS(s) + 2H^+(aq) \longrightarrow Cd^{2+}(aq) + H_2S(g)$
(e) $K_2SO_3(s) + 2HCl(aq) \longrightarrow 2KCl(aq) + H_2O(l) + SO_2(g)$
   $K_2SO_3(s) + 2H^+(aq) \longrightarrow 2K^+(aq) + H_2O(l) + SO_2(g)$

4.34   Each element in the activity series is able to displace the elements below it, but not the elements above it.
   (a) From the activity series we see that zinc is above lead. Therefore, a lead pipe will not react with aqueous zinc chloride.
   (b) From the activity series we see that silver is below lead. Therefore, a lead pipe will react with aqueous silver nitrate. Some of the lead pipe will dissolve and solid silver will precipitate.

4.35   (a) No, the silver coin will not dissolve. Silver is below copper in the activity series and therefore cannot displace copper from its compounds.
   (b) Yes, the copper coin will dissolve. Since copper is above silver in the activity series, it can displace silver from its compounds.
   (c) Yes, the aluminum foil will dissolve. Aluminum is above iron in the activity series and therefore can displace iron from its compounds.
   (d) No, the tin foil will not dissolve. Tin (Sn) is below iron in the activity series and therefore cannot displace iron from its compounds.

4.39   The mass of 1.00 mL of peroxide solution is

   $$mass = volume \times density = 1.00 \text{ mL} \times 1.0 \text{ g/mL} = 1.0 \text{ g} = 1.0 \times 10^3 \text{ mg}$$

   The number of milligrams of H_2O_2 in 1.00 mL of the solution is

   $$1.0 \times 10^3 \text{ mg soln} \times \frac{3.0 \text{ mg } H_2O_2}{100 \text{ mg soln}} = 30 \text{ mg } H_2O_2$$

4.40   (a) The solubility of DDT expressed in parts per thousand means the number of grams of DDT per 10^3 g of water. This can be calculated from the given solubility as follows:

   $$\frac{5.0 \times 10^{-5} \text{ g DDT}}{10^2 \text{ g } H_2O} \times \frac{10}{10} = \frac{5.0 \times 10^{-4} \text{ g DDT}}{10^3 \text{ g } H_2O}$$

   Answer: Solubility is 5.0×10^{-4} parts per thousand by mass.

   (b) The solubility expressed in parts per million means the number of grams of DDT per 10^6 g of water. This can be calculated from the given solubility as follows:

   $$\frac{5.0 \times 10^{-5} \text{ g DDT}}{10^2 \text{ g } H_2O} \times \frac{10^4}{10^4} = \frac{5.0 \times 10^{-1} \text{ g DDT}}{10^6 \text{ g } H_2O}$$

   Answer: Solubility is 0.50 ppm by mass.

4.42   (a) A carbon dioxide concentration of 480.0 ppm by mass means that there is 480.0 g of CO_2 in one million (1.0×10^6) grams of air. The percent, the number of grams of CO_2 in 100 g of air, will be smaller by a factor of 10^{-4} or

   $$\frac{480.0 \text{ g } CO_2}{10^6 \text{ g air}} \times \frac{10^{-4}}{10^{-4}} = \frac{0.0480 \text{ g } CO_2}{10^2 \text{ g air}}$$

   Answer: Air contains 0.0480% CO_2 by mass.

   (b) A liter of air has a mass of 1.29 g and would therefore contain

   $$\frac{1.29 \text{ g air}}{1 \text{ L}} \times \frac{0.0480 \text{ g } CO_2}{100 \text{ g air}} \times \frac{1000 \text{ mg } CO_2}{1 \text{ g } CO_2} = 0.619 \text{ mg } CO_2/L$$

4.43   The percentage by weight of ethanol is

$$\% \text{ ethanol} = \frac{\text{mass ethanol}}{\text{mass of solution}} \times 100\% = \frac{20.0 \text{ g} \times 100\%}{100.0 \text{ g}} = 20.0\%$$

The number of grams of ethanol in 1.00 L of solution is calculated as follows:
V x density ——> g solution ——> g ethanol.

$$1.00 \text{ L} \times \frac{10^3 \text{ mL}}{1 \text{ L}} \times \frac{0.9687 \text{ g}}{1 \text{ mL}} \times 0.200 = 194 \text{ g ethanol}$$

4.44   (a)

$$\text{mass of solution} = \frac{\text{mass of solute} \times 100\%}{\text{percent by weight}} = \frac{100 \text{ g} \times 100\%}{15.0\%}$$

$$= 667 \text{ g of glucose solution}$$

(b) mass water = mass solution – mass glucose = 667 g – 100 g = 567 g.

(c)

$$\text{volume} = \frac{\text{mass}}{\text{density}} = \frac{667 \text{ g}}{1.06 \text{ g/mL}} = 629 \text{ mL}$$

(d) Place the solid glucose in a 1–L volumetric cylinder calibrated in 1-mL increments. Dissolve the glucose in some water and then bring the solution up to the 629–mL mark with additional water.

4.46   number of moles = V(L) x M(mol/L)
(a) 2.00 L x 3.00 mol/L = 6.00 mol NaCl
(b) 0.175 L x 1.30 x 10^{-3} mol/L = 2.28 x 10^{-4} mol $(NH_4)_2SO_4$
(c) 0.250 L x 0.100 mol/L = 2.50 x 10^{-2} mol NaOH
(d) 1.55 L x 1.2 mol/L = 1.86 mol = 1.9 mol $BaCl_2$ (two significant figures)

4.47   The number of grams of solute needed is equal to the number of moles of solute in the solution times the molar mass of the solute.

(a)

$$6.00 \text{ mol NaCl} \times \frac{58.44 \text{ g NaCl}}{1 \text{ mol NaCl}} = 351 \text{ g NaCl}$$

(b)

$$2.28 \times 10^{-4} \text{ mol} (NH_4)_2SO_4 \times \frac{132.14 \text{ g } (NH_4)_2SO_4}{1 \text{ mol } (NH_4)_2SO_4} = 3.01 \times 10^{-2} \text{ g } (NH_4)_2SO_4$$

(c)

$$2.50 \times 10^{-2} \text{ mol NaOH} \times \frac{40.0 \text{ g NaOH}}{1 \text{ mol NaOH}} = 1.00 \text{ g NaOH}$$

(d) Use unrounded answer (1.86 mol $BaCl_2$) in this calculation and round off at the end.

$$1.86 \text{ mol } BaCl_2 \times \frac{208 \text{ g } BaCl_2}{1 \text{ mol } BaCl_2} = 386.88 \text{ g } BaCl_2 = 3.9 \times 10^2 \text{ g } BaCl_2$$
$$\text{(two significant figures)}$$

4.48

$$\text{molarity} = \frac{\text{number of moles of solute}}{\text{volume of solution in liters}}$$

(a)

$$\text{molarity} = \frac{40.0 \text{ g NaCl}}{0.250 \text{ L}} \times \frac{1 \text{ mol NaCl}}{58.44 \text{ g NaCl}} = 2.74 \text{ mol NaCl/L}$$

The solution is 2.74 M in NaCl.

(b)

$$\text{molarity} = \frac{49.0 \text{ g H}_2\text{SO}_4}{2.00 \text{ L}} \times \frac{1 \text{ mol H}_2\text{SO}_4}{98.1 \text{ g H}_2\text{SO}_4} = 0.250 \text{ mol H}_2\text{SO}_4/\text{L}$$

The solution is 0.250 M in H_2SO_4.

(c)

$$\text{molarity} = \frac{2.00 \text{ g Ba(OH)}_2}{0.125 \text{ L}} \times \frac{1 \text{ mol Ba(OH)}_2}{171 \text{ g Ba(OH)}_2} = 9.36 \times 10^{-2} \text{ mol Ba(OH)}_2/\text{L}$$

The solution is 9.36×10^{-2} M in $Ba(OH)_2$.

4.49

$$\text{molarity} = \frac{\text{number of moles of solute}}{\text{volume of solution in liters}}$$

(a) The ratio of grams ethanol to grams solution is 6.00 g ethanol/81.0 g solution. The remaining steps in the calculation are:

d x 10^3 mL/L $\longrightarrow$ g soln/L $\longrightarrow$ g ethanol/L $\longrightarrow$ mol ethanol/L $\longrightarrow$ M ethanol.

$$\frac{0.986 \text{ g soln}}{1 \text{ mL}} \times \frac{10^3 \text{ mL}}{1 \text{ L}} \times \frac{6.00 \text{ g ethanol}}{81.0 \text{ g soln}} \times \frac{1 \text{ mol ethanol}}{46.08 \text{ g ethanol}} = \frac{1.59 \text{ mol ethanol}}{1 \text{ L}}$$

$$= 1.59 \text{ M ethanol}$$

(b) The steps in the calculation are:

d x 10^3 mL/L $\longrightarrow$ g soln/L $\longrightarrow$ g NaCl/L $\longrightarrow$ mol NaCl/L $\longrightarrow$ M NaCl.

$$\frac{1.01 \text{ g soln}}{1 \text{ mL}} \times \frac{10^3 \text{ mL}}{1 \text{ L}} \times \frac{2.00 \text{ g NaCl}}{100 \text{ g soln}} \times \frac{1 \text{ mol NaCl}}{58.44 \text{ g NaCl}} = \frac{0.346 \text{ mol NaCl}}{1 \text{ L}}$$

$$= 0.346 \text{ M NaCl}$$

(c) The number of grams of glucose in a liter of serum is

$$\frac{109 \text{ mg glucose}}{1 \text{ dL}} \times \frac{10 \text{ dL}}{1 \text{ L}} \times \frac{1 \text{ g}}{10^3 \text{ mg}} = \frac{1.09 \text{ g glucose}}{1 \text{ L}}$$

The molarity is

$$\text{molarity} = \frac{1.09 \text{ g glucose}}{1 \text{ L}} \times \frac{1 \text{ mol glucose}}{180.18 \text{ g glucose}}$$

$$= 6.05 \times 10^{-3} \text{ mol glucose/L} = 6.05 \times 10^{-3} \text{ M glucose}$$

4.51   (a)

$$0.30 \text{ mol HCl} \times \frac{1.0 \text{ L}}{0.15 \text{ mol HCl}} = 2.0 \text{ L} = 2.0 \times 10^3 \text{ mL}$$

(b)

$$0.30 \text{ mmol HCl} \times \frac{1.0 \text{ mL}}{0.15 \text{ mmol HCl}} = 2.0 \text{ mL}$$

(c)

$$0.30 \text{ g HCl} \times \frac{1 \text{ mol HCl}}{36.46 \text{ g HCl}} = 0.0082 \text{ mol HCl} = 8.2 \text{ mmol HCl}$$

$$8.2 \text{ mmol HCl} \times \frac{1.0 \text{ mL}}{0.15 \text{ mmol HCl}} = 55 \text{ mL}$$

4.53 (a) The steps in the calculation are: density (g/mL) ——> g H_2SO_4 soln/L
——> g H_2SO_4/L ——> mol H_2SO_4/L ——> M H_2SO_4.

$$\frac{1.29 \text{ g soln}}{1 \text{ mL}} \times \frac{1000 \text{ mL}}{1 \text{ L}} \times \frac{38.0 \text{ g } H_2SO_4}{100 \text{ g soln}} \times \frac{1 \text{ mol } H_2SO_4}{98.1 \text{ g } H_2SO_4}$$

$$= 5.00 \text{ mol } H_2SO_4/\text{L} = 5.00 \text{ M } H_2SO_4$$

(b) number of mmol = V (mL) x M (mmol/mL) = 10 mL x 5.00 mmol H_2SO_4/mL = 50 mmol H_2SO_4

4.55 (a) The steps in the calculation are: V (mL) x d (g/mL) ——> g acetic acid solution
——> g acetic acid ——> moles acetic acid.

$$250 \text{ mL} \times \frac{1.00 \text{ g soln}}{1 \text{ mL}} \times \frac{4.93 \text{ g acetic acid}}{100 \text{ g soln}} \times \frac{1 \text{ mol acetic acid}}{60.05 \text{ g acetic acid}}$$

$$= 0.205 \text{ mol acetic acid}$$

(b) Use the percent by mass to calculate the mass of solution; then use the density to calculate the volume of solution.

$$10.0 \text{ g acetic acid} \times \frac{100 \text{ g soln}}{4.93 \text{ g acetic acid}} = 203 \text{ g soln}$$

$$203 \text{ g soln} \times \frac{1.00 \text{ mL}}{1.00 \text{ g}} = 203 \text{ mL soln}$$

4.58 (a) The number of moles of Cl^- needed is 0.300 L x 0.55 mol Cl^-/L = 0.165 mol Cl^-. Since each mole of $CaCl_2$ supplies 2 mol of Cl^-, we need only 0.165/2 = 0.0825 mol of $CaCl_2$. The number of grams of $CaCl_2$ needed is

$$0.0825 \text{ mol } CaCl_2 \times \frac{110.99 \text{ g } CaCl_2}{1 \text{ mol } CaCl_2} = 9.2 \text{ g } CaCl_2$$

(b) There are half as many moles of Ca^{2+} as Cl^-. Therefore, the molarity of Ca^{2+} will be

$$\frac{0.55 \text{ mol } Cl^-}{1 \text{ L}} \times \frac{1 \text{ mol } Ca^{2+}}{2 \text{ mol } Cl^-} = 0.275 \text{ M } Ca^{2+} \text{ or } 0.28 \text{ M } Ca^{2+} \text{ (to two significant figures)}$$

4.59 The amount of sulfate ion in the $Cr_2(SO_4)_3$ solution is

$$0.100 \text{ L} \times \frac{0.120 \text{ mol } Cr_2(SO_4)_3}{1 \text{ L}} \times \frac{3 \text{ mol } SO_4^{2-}}{1 \text{ mol } Cr_2(SO_4)_3} = 0.0360 \text{ mol } SO_4^{2-}$$

The amount of sulfate ion in the Na_2SO_4 solution is

$$0.150 \text{ L} \times \frac{0.200 \text{ mol } Na_2SO_4}{1 \text{ L}} \times \frac{1 \text{ mol } SO_4^{2-}}{1 \text{ mol } Na_2SO_4} = 0.0300 \text{ mol } SO_4^{2-}$$

The total sulfate ion in the mixed solution is 0.0360 mol + 0.0300 mol = 0.0660 mol SO_4^{2-}.

The total volume of the mixed solution is 0.100 L + 0.150 L = 0.250 L.

The final molarity of the sulfate ion is

$$\text{molarity} = \frac{0.0660 \text{ mol } SO_4^{2-}}{0.250 \text{ L}} = 0.264 \text{ mol } SO_4^{2-}/\text{L} = 0.264 \text{ M } SO_4^{2-}$$

4.61   (a) The steps in the calculation are: d (g/mL) soln $\longrightarrow$ g soln/L $\longrightarrow$ g HCl/L
$\longrightarrow$ mol HCl/L $\longrightarrow$ M HCl.

$$\frac{1.19 \text{ g soln}}{1 \text{ mL}} \times \frac{1000 \text{ mL}}{1 \text{ L}} \times \frac{37.0 \text{ g HCl}}{100 \text{ g soln}} \times \frac{1 \text{ mol HCl}}{36.46 \text{ g}} = 12.1 \text{ mol HCl/L} = 12.1 \text{ M HCl}$$

(b) $V_C \times M_C = V_D \times M_D$

$$V_C = \frac{100 \text{ mL} \times 0.30 \text{ mmol/mL}}{12.1 \text{ mmol/mL}} = 2.5 \text{ mL}$$

4.63   First find the molarity of the concentrated NH_3 solution. Then use the dilution formula to calculate the volume of concentrated NH_3 needed. The steps in the molarity calculation are: d (g/mL) x 1000 mL/L $\longrightarrow$ g soln/L $\longrightarrow$ g NH_3/L $\longrightarrow$ mol NH_3/L $\longrightarrow$ M NH_3.

$$\frac{0.900 \text{ g soln}}{1 \text{ mL}} \times \frac{1000 \text{ mL}}{1 \text{ L}} \times \frac{28.0 \text{ g } NH_3}{100 \text{ g soln}} \times \frac{1 \text{ mol } NH_3}{17.0 \text{ g } NH_3} = 14.8 \text{ mol } NH_3\text{/L} = 14.8 \text{ M } NH_3$$

The volume of concentrated NH_3 solution needed to make the dilute solution is

$$V_C = \frac{1.50 \text{ L} \times 3.00 \text{ mol/L}}{14.8 \text{ mol/L}} = 0.304 \text{ L} = 304 \text{ mL}$$

4.64   Yes; $\text{molarity} = \dfrac{\text{moles of solute}}{1 \text{ L}} = \dfrac{\text{g solute/molar mass}}{1 \text{ L}}$

Substituting this expression into the dilution formula, $V_C \times M_C = V_D \times M_D$, we get

$$V_C \times \frac{g_C/\text{molar mass}}{1 \text{ L}} = V_C \times \frac{g_D/\text{molar mass}}{1 \text{ L}}$$

Since the molar mass on each side of the equation is the same, it can be canceled out, giving us

$V_C \times g_C/L = V_D \times g_D/L$

If we let $C_C = g_C/L$ and $C_D = g_D/L$ stand for the concentrations in grams of solute per liter of solution in the concentrated and dilute solutions, respectively, then by substituting these expressions into the previous equation we get

$V_C \times C_C = V_D \times C_D$

Therefore, the dilution formula retains its same form or validity in these concentration units.

Comment: An alternative approach is to derive this formula directly using the same argument as in the text, except that you would equate equal masses of solute in both solutions instead of equal numbers of moles of solute in both solutions. Try it.

4.65 $2AgNO_3(aq) + K_2CrO_4(aq) \longrightarrow Ag_2CrO_4(s) + 2KNO_3(aq)$
      mL of 0.10 M = ? 2.0×10^{-4} mol

(a) From the equation we see that for every mole of K_2CrO_4 consumed, 1 mol of Ag_2CrO_4 is produced; therefore, we need 2.0×10^{-4} mol of K_2CrO_4. The number of milliliters of 0.10 M K_2CrO_4 required is

$$2.0 \times 10^{-4} \text{ mol } K_2CrO_4 \times \frac{1.0 \text{ L}}{0.10 \text{ mol } K_2CrO_4} = 2.0 \times 10^{-3} \text{ L} = 2.0 \text{ mL}$$

(b) The steps in the calculation are: g $Ag_2CrO_4 \longrightarrow$ mol $Ag_2CrO_4 \longrightarrow$ mol $AgNO_3$
$\longrightarrow$ mL $AgNO_3$ soln.

$$3.0 \text{ g } Ag_2CrO_4 \times \frac{1 \text{ mol } Ag_2CrO_4}{331.7 \text{ g } Ag_2CrO_4} \times \frac{2 \text{ mol } AgNO_3}{1 \text{ mol } Ag_2CrO_4} \times \frac{1.0 \text{ L soln}}{0.60 \text{ mol } AgNO_3}$$

$= 0.030 \text{ L soln} = 30 \text{ mL soln}$

(c) The steps in the calculations are: $V \times M$ (of K_2CrO_4) $\longrightarrow$ mmol K_2CrO_4 $\longrightarrow$ mmol $AgNO_3$ $\longrightarrow$ mL $AgNO_3$.

$$50 \text{ mL} \times \frac{0.10 \text{ mmol } K_2CrO_4}{1 \text{ mL}} \times \frac{2 \text{ mmol } AgNO_3}{1 \text{ mmol } K_2CrO_4} \times \frac{1 \text{ mL}}{0.60 \text{ mmol } AgNO_3} = 17 \text{ mL}$$

(d) The steps in the calculation are: $V \times M$ (of K_2CrO_4) $\longrightarrow$ mol K_2CrO_4 $\longrightarrow$ mol Ag_2CrO_4.

$$0.050 \text{ L} \times \frac{0.10 \text{ mol } K_2CrO_4}{1 \text{ L}} \times \frac{1 \text{ mol } Ag_2CrO_4}{1 \text{ mol } K_2CrO_4} = 5.0 \times 10^{-3} \text{ mol } Ag_2CrO_4$$

4.68 $H_2SO_4(aq) + 2NaOH(aq) \longrightarrow Na_2SO_4(aq) + 2H_2O(l)$

(a) The steps in the calculation are: $V \times M$ (of NaOH) $\longrightarrow$ mol NaOH $\longrightarrow$ mol H_2SO_4 $\longrightarrow$ M H_2SO_4.

$$0.04000 \text{ L} \times \frac{0.1000 \text{ mol NaOH}}{1 \text{ L}} \times \frac{1 \text{ mol } H_2SO_4}{2 \text{ mol NaOH}} = 2.000 \times 10^{-3} \text{ mol } H_2SO_4$$

$$\text{molarity A} = \frac{\text{moles solute}}{\text{liter soln}} = \frac{2.000 \times 10^{-3} \text{ mol } H_2SO_4}{4.000 \times 10^{-2} \text{ L}}$$

$$= 5.000 \times 10^{-2} \text{ mol } H_2SO_4/L = 5.000 \times 10^{-2} \text{ M } H_2SO_4$$

(b) mol H_2SO_4 = 2.000 x 10^{-3} mol; see (a)

$$\text{molarity B} = \frac{2.000 \times 10^{-3} \text{ mol } H_2SO_4}{2.000 \times 10^{-2} \text{ L}} = \frac{0.1000 \text{ mol } H_2SO_4}{1 \text{ L}} = 0.1000 \text{ M } H_2SO_4$$

(c)

$$0.02832 \text{ L} \times \frac{0.1000 \text{ mol NaOH}}{1 \text{ L}} \times \frac{1 \text{ mol } H_2SO_4}{2 \text{ mol NaOH}} = 1.416 \times 10^{-3} \text{ mol } H_2SO_4$$

$$\text{molarity C} = \frac{1.416 \times 10^{-3} \text{ mol } H_2SO_4}{3.184 \times 10^{-2} \text{ L}}$$

$$= 4.447 \times 10^{-2} \text{ mol } H_2SO_4/L = 4.447 \times 10^{-2} \text{ M } H_2SO_4$$

4.69 $MgCO_3 \cdot CaCO_3(s) + 4HCl(aq) \longrightarrow MgCl_2(aq) + CaCl_2(aq) + 2CO_2(g) + 2H_2O(l)$

The steps in the calculation are: $V \times M$ (of HCl) $\longrightarrow$ mol HCl $\longrightarrow$ mol dolomite $\longrightarrow$ g dolomite $\longrightarrow$ % dolomite.

$$0.0500 \text{ L} \times \frac{0.260 \text{ mol HCl}}{1 \text{ L}} \times \frac{1 \text{ mol dolomite}}{4 \text{ mol HCl}} \times \frac{184.41 \text{ g dolomite}}{1 \text{ mol dolomite}}$$

$$= 0.599 \text{ g dolomite}$$

$$\% \text{ dolomite} = \frac{\text{mass dolomite}}{\text{mass sample}} \times 100\% = \frac{0.599 \text{ g}}{1.00 \text{ g}} \times 100\% = 59.9\%$$

4.71

$$2AgNO_3(aq) + CaI_2(aq) \longrightarrow 2AgI(s) + Ca(NO_3)_2(aq)$$
$$M = ? \qquad 26 \text{ mL of}$$
$$0.250 \text{ M}$$

The steps in the calculation are: V x M (of CaI_2) $\longrightarrow$ mol CaI_2 $\longrightarrow$ mol $AgNO_3$ $\longrightarrow$ M $AgNO_3$.

$$0.0260 \text{ L x } \frac{0.250 \text{ mol } CaI_2}{1 \text{ L}} \text{ x } \frac{2 \text{ mol } AgNO_3}{2 \text{ mol } CaI_2} = 0.0130 \text{ mol } AgNO_3$$

$$\text{molarity} = \frac{\text{moles } AgNO_3}{1 \text{ L soln}} = \frac{0.0130 \text{ mol } AgNO_3}{0.0450 \text{ L}} = 0.289 \text{ mol } AgNO_3/L = 0.289 \text{ M } AgNO_3$$

4.72

The steps in the calculation are: V x M (of Co^{2+}) $\longrightarrow$ mol Co^{2+} $\longrightarrow$ g Co $\longrightarrow$ % Co.

$$0.0500 \text{ L x } \frac{0.073 \text{ mol } Co^{2+}}{1 \text{ L}} \text{ x } \frac{58.93 \text{ g Co}}{1 \text{ mol } Co^{2+}} = 0.215 \text{ g Co}$$

$$\% \text{ Co} = \frac{\text{mass Co}}{\text{mass sample}} \text{ x } 100\% = \frac{0.215 \text{ g}}{2.216 \text{ g}} \text{ x } 100\% = 9.7\%$$

4.75

$$CaCO_3(s) + 2HCl(aq) \longrightarrow CaCl_2(aq) + CO_2(g) + H_2O(l)$$
$$1.110 \text{ g} \qquad M = ?$$

The steps in the calculation are: g $CaCO_3$ $\longrightarrow$ mol $CaCO_3$ $\longrightarrow$ mol HCl $\longrightarrow$ M HCl.

$$1.110 \text{ g } CaCO_3 \text{ x } \frac{1 \text{ mol } CaCO_3}{100.09 \text{ g } CaCO_3} \text{ x } \frac{2 \text{ mol HCl}}{1 \text{ mol } CaCO_3} = 0.02218 \text{ mol HCl}$$

The molarity of the HCl solution is

$$\text{molarity HCl} = \frac{0.02218 \text{ mol HCl}}{0.03545 \text{ L}} = \frac{0.6257 \text{ mol HCl}}{1 \text{ L}} = 0.6257 \text{ M HCl}$$

4.77

$$CaCO_3(s) + 2HCl(aq) \longrightarrow CaCl_2(aq) + CO_2(g) + H_2O(l)$$

First we find the quantity of HCl used up. The number of millimoles of HCl reacted is equal to the total number in the original solution minus the number remaining after reaction. The original solution contained 20.00 mL x 1.052 mmol/mL = 21.04 mmol HCl. The resulting solution contained

$$15.85 \text{ mL x } \frac{0.09850 \text{ mmol NaOH}}{1 \text{ mL}} \text{ x } \frac{1 \text{ mmol HCl}}{1 \text{ mmol NaOH}} = 1.561 \text{ mmol HCl}$$

The number of millimoles of HCl reacted is 21.04 – 1.561 = 19.48 mmol HCl.

From the equation we see that the number of millimoles of $CaCO_3$ in the limestone rock is equal to half the number of millimoles of HCl that reacted. The remaining steps in the calculation are: mmol HCl reacted $\longrightarrow$ mmol $CaCO_3$ $\longrightarrow$ g $CaCO_3$ $\longrightarrow$ % $CaCO_3$.

$$19.48 \text{ mmol HCl x } \frac{1 \text{ mmol } CaCO_3}{2 \text{ mmol HCl}} \text{ x } \frac{100.09 \text{ mg } CaCO_3}{1 \text{ mmol } CaCO_3} = 974.9 \text{ mg } CaCO_3$$

The percent by weight of $CaCO_3$ is

$$\% \text{ } CaCO_3 = \frac{\text{mass } CaCO_3}{\text{mass sample}} \text{ x } 100\% = \frac{974.9 \text{ mg}}{1500 \text{ mg}} \text{ x } 100\% = 64.99\%$$

4.80

$$150\text{-lb body x } \frac{1 \text{ kg}}{2.205 \text{ lb}} \text{ x } \frac{43 \text{ mL plasma}}{1 \text{ kg body}} \text{ x } \frac{0.1 \text{ g glucose}}{100 \text{ mL plasma}} = 3 \text{ g glucose}$$

4.82   A density of 1.05 g/mL is the same as 1.05 kg/1000 mL.

$$70\text{-kg body} \times \frac{7.7 \text{ kg blood}}{100 \text{ kg body}} \times \frac{1000 \text{ mL blood}}{1.05 \text{ kg blood}} \times \frac{15.5 \text{ g hemoglobin}}{100 \text{ mL blood}}$$

$$= 8.0 \times 10^2 \text{ g hemoglobin}$$

4.84 $CaCO_3(s) + H_2SO_4(aq) \longrightarrow CaSO_4(aq) + H_2O(l) + CO_2(g)$

One metric ton (1000 kg) of high sulfur coal contains

$$1000 \text{ kg coal} \times \frac{10^3 \text{ g}}{1 \text{ kg}} \times \frac{3 \text{ g sulfur}}{100 \text{ g coal}} = 3 \times 10^4 \text{ g sulfur}$$

All the S is converted into sulfuric acid. The equation for that reaction is not needed for the calculation; only the mass fraction of S in H_2SO_4 is needed. The rest of the steps in the calculation are: g S $\longrightarrow$ g H_2SO_4 $\longrightarrow$ mol H_2SO_4 $\longrightarrow$ mol $CaCO_3$ $\longrightarrow$ kg $CaCO_3$.

$$3 \times 10^4 \text{ g S} \times \frac{98 \text{ g } H_2SO_4}{32 \text{ g S}} \times \frac{1 \text{ mol } H_2SO_4}{98 \text{ g } H_2SO_4} \times \frac{1 \text{ mol } CaCO_3}{1 \text{ mol } H_2SO_4} \times \frac{100 \text{ g } CaCO_3}{1 \text{ mol } CaCO_3}$$

$$= 93750 \text{ g } CaCO_3 = 90 \text{ kg } CaCO_3 \text{ (to one significant figure)}$$

Answer: The rain could dissolve 90 kg of marble.

4.86   (a) The number of moles of HCl in the original solution is

$$0.0500 \text{ L} \times \frac{0.500 \text{ mol HCl}}{1 \text{ L}} = 0.0250 \text{ mol HCl}$$

The number of moles of HCl remaining after the tablet reacted equals the number of moles of NaOH needed to neutralize it.

$$0.0265 \text{ L} \times \frac{0.377 \text{ mol NaOH}}{1 \text{ L}} \times \frac{1 \text{ mol HCl}}{1 \text{ mol NaOH}} = 0.00999 \text{ mol HCl}$$

The difference is the number of moles of HCl neutralized by the tablet.

0.0250 mol HCl – 0.00999 mol HCl = 0.0150 mol HCl

Answer: There was 0.0150 mol OH^- in the tablet, since it takes 1 mol of OH^- to neutralize 1 mol of HCl.

(b) Each mole of $Al(OH)_3$ supplies 3 mol of OH^-, and each mole of $Mg(OH)_2$ supplies 2 mol of OH^-. Let x = number of moles of $Al(OH)_3$ and y = number of moles of $Mg(OH)_2$ in the tablet. Then

$3x + 2y = 0.0150$

$x \times$ (molar mass $Al(OH)_3$) = $y \times$ (molar mass $Mg(OH)_2$)

and

$$x = \frac{y(\text{molar mass } Mg(OH)_2)}{\text{molar mass } Al(OH)_3} = \frac{y(58.32 \text{ g})}{78.00 \text{ g}} = 0.7477y$$

Solving for x and y

$3(0.7477y) + 2y = 0.0150$
$4.2431y = 0.0150$
$y = 0.00354$
$x = 0.7477y = (0.7477)(0.00354) = 0.00265$

Answer: The tablet contained 0.00265 mol $Al(OH)_3$ and 0.00354 mol $Mg(OH)_2$.

4.88   (a) We have seen (Exercise 4.64) that a valid dilution formula is $V_C \times C_C = V_D \times C_D$, where C_C and C_D are the concentrations of the concentrated and dilute solutions in units of mass/volume, respectively. V_C is the original volume and V_D is the final volume.

5.0 mL x 5.00 mg/mL = V_D x 0.0080 mg/mL

$$V_D = \frac{5.0 \text{ mL} \times 5.00 \text{ mg/mL}}{0.0080 \text{ mg/mL}} = 3125 \text{ mL or } 3.1 \times 10^3 \text{ mL (to two significant figures)}$$

(b) Less. The dye concentration measured, C_D, is less than it should be because some dye was lost to surrounding tissues. From the equation we see that a higher C_D value gives a lower V_D value and vice versa. Therefore, the true V_D value should be smaller than the calculated one.

CHAPTER 5
Gases and Their Properties

Solutions To Practice Exercises

PE 5.1   The weight of the cylindrical mercury column is equal to the volume of the cylinder x density of mercury x g.

$$\text{weight} = 76.0 \text{ cm x } 1.00 \text{ cm}^2 \text{ x } 13.6 \text{ g/cm}^3 \text{ x } 9.81 \text{ m/s}^2 \text{ x } \frac{1 \text{ kg}}{10^3 \text{ g}}$$

$$= 10.1 \text{ kg m/s}^2 = 10.1 \text{ N}$$

The pressure exerted by the cylindrical mercury column is

$$\text{pressure} = \frac{\text{force}}{\text{area}} = \frac{10.1 \text{ N}}{1.00 \text{ cm}^2} \text{ x } \left(\frac{10^2 \text{ cm}}{1 \text{ m}} \right)^2 = 1.01 \text{ x } 10^5 \text{ N/m}^2$$

PE 5.4   The pressure of the gas is equal to the sum of the atmospheric pressure, P_{atm} = 770 torr, and the pressure exerted by 110 mm of mercury. Hence,

$$P_{gas} = P_{atm} + 110 \text{ torr} = 770 \text{ torr} + 110 \text{ torr} = 880 \text{ torr}$$

PE 5.6   The initial gas pressure is 1.5 atm. The volume decreases by a factor of 18.5/25.9. Hence, the gas pressure increases by the inverse of this factor. The final pressure will be 1.5 atm x 25.9/18.5 = 2.1 atm.

PE 5.8   (a) Increase. A decrease in pressure will cause the volume to increase.
          (b) The factor must be greater than unity; 780 torr/760 torr = 1.03.

PE 5.9   (a) Decrease. The pressure varies inversely with the volume. If the volume increases, the pressure must decrease.
          (b) The pressure decreases, so the volume factor must be less than unity; 4.0 L/6.0 L = 0.67.

PE 5.12   (a) Increase. The volume is directly proportional to the Kelvin temperature. If the temperature increases, the volume must increase.
          (b) The initial and final Kelvin temperatures are T_i = 273 – 83 = 190 K and T_f = 273 + 30 = 303 K. The volume increases, so the temperature factor must be greater than unity; 303 K/190 K = 1.59.

PE 5.13 The decrease in temperature from $75°C = 348$ K to $-10°C = 263$ K tends to decrease the volume; the temperature factor will be less than unity, or 263 K/348 K. The increase in pressure from 620 torr to 745 torr also tends to decrease the volume; the pressure factor will be less than unity, or 620 torr/745 torr.

$V_f = V_i$ x temperature factor x pressure factor

$$= 55.0 \text{ mL } \times \frac{263 \text{ K}}{348 \text{ K}} \times \frac{620 \text{ torr}}{745 \text{ torr}} = 34.6 \text{ mL}$$

PE 5.14 The density increases as the temperature goes down from 303 K to 273 K; therefore, the temperature factor must be greater than unity, or 303 K/273 K. The density increases as the pressure goes up from 750 torr to 760 torr; therefore, the pressure factor must be greater than unity, or 760 torr/750 torr.

$d_f = d_i$ x temperature factor x pressure factor

$$= 0.635 \text{ g/L } \times \frac{303 \text{ K}}{273 \text{ K}} \times \frac{760 \text{ torr}}{750 \text{ torr}} = 0.714 \text{ g/L}$$

PE 5.15 The molar volume (volume per mole) of any gas is approximately 22.4 L at standard conditions, 1.00 atm and $0°C = 273$ K. The volume increases as the temperature goes up from 273 K to 373 K; therefore, the temperature factor must be greater than unity, or 373 K/273 K. The volume increases as the pressure goes down from 760 torr to 740 torr; therefore, the pressure factor must be greater than unity, or 760 torr/740 torr.

$$22.4 \text{ L/mol } \times \frac{373 \text{ K}}{273 \text{ K}} \times \frac{760 \text{ torr}}{740 \text{ torr}} = 31.4 \text{ L/mol}$$

PE 5.19 $V = 0.100$ L, $T = 301$ K, and $P = 770$ torr x 1 atm/760 torr $= 1.01$ atm.

$$n = \frac{PV}{RT} = \frac{1.01 \text{ atm x } 0.100 \text{ L}}{0.0821 \text{ L atm/mol K x } 301 \text{ K}} = 4.09 \text{ x } 10^{-3} \text{ mol}$$

Thus, 4.09×10^{-3} mol of the unknown gas has a mass of 0.360 g. The mass of 1 mol (the molar mass) is 0.360 g/4.09 x 10^{-3} mol = 88.0 g/mol.

PE 5.21 $CH_4(g) + 2O_2(g) \longrightarrow CO_2(g) + 2H_2O(g)$
0.250 mol   L = ?

From the equation we see that 0.250 mol CO_2 will be produced from 0.250 mol CH_4. $T = 293$ K, $P = 1.00$ atm.

$$V = \frac{nRT}{P} = \frac{0.250 \text{ mol x } 0.821 \text{ L atm/mol K x } 293 \text{ K}}{1.00 \text{ atm}} = 6.01 \text{ L}$$

PE 5.23 (a) $P_{total} = P_{hydrogen} + P_{water vapor}$

$P_{hydrogen} = P_{total} - P_{water vapor} = 740 \text{ torr} - 23.8 \text{ torr} = 716 \text{ torr}$

(b)
$$X_{hydrogen} = \frac{P_{hydrogen}}{P_{total}} = \frac{716 \text{ torr}}{740 \text{ torr}} = 0.968$$

(c) mole percent hydrogen = 100% x $X_{hydrogen}$ = 100% x 0.968 = 96.8%

PE 5.25 $2HgO(s) \longrightarrow 2Hg(l) + O_2(g)$
The vapor pressure of water is 18.65 torr at 21°C. The partial pressure of oxygen is

$$P_{oxygen} = P_{total} - P_{water} = 765 \text{ torr} - 18.65 \text{ torr} = 746 \text{ torr} \times \frac{1 \text{ atm}}{760 \text{ torr}}$$

$$= 0.982 \text{ atm}$$

V = 0.250 L, T = 294 K. Substituting these values into the ideal gas law gives the number of moles of oxygen produced:

$$n_{oxygen} = \frac{PV}{RT} = \frac{0.982 \text{ atm} \times 0.250 \text{ L}}{0.0821 \text{ L atm/mol K} \times 294 \text{ K}} = 0.0102 \text{ mol}$$

The remainder of the calculation is: $\text{mol } O_2 \longrightarrow \text{mol HgO} \longrightarrow \text{g HgO.}$

$$0.0102 \text{ mol } O_2 \times \frac{2 \text{ mol HgO}}{1 \text{ mol } O_2} \times \frac{216.59 \text{ g HgO}}{1 \text{ mol HgO}} = 4.42 \text{ g HgO}$$

PE 5.26 $r_{CO_2} \times \sqrt{M_{CO_2}} = r_x \times \sqrt{M_x}$, $r_x = 1.66 \times r_{CO_2}$, and $M_{CO_2} = 44.0 \text{ g/mol}$.

$$\sqrt{M_x} = \frac{r_{CO_2}}{1.66 r_{CO_2}} \times \sqrt{44.0 \text{ g/mol}}$$

$$M_x = \left(\frac{1}{1.66}\right)^2 \times 44.0 \text{ g/mol} = 16.0 \text{ g/mol}$$

PE 5.30   V = 0.750 L, T = 293 K, n = 1.10 mol, a = 3.667 L² atm/mol², and b = 0.04081 L/mol.

(a)
$$P = \frac{nRT}{V} = \frac{1.10 \text{ mol} \times 0.0821 \text{ L atm/mol K} \times 293 \text{ K}}{0.750 \text{ L}} = 35.3 \text{ atm}$$

(b)
$$P = \frac{nRT}{V - nb} - \frac{an^2}{V^2}$$

$$P = \frac{1.10 \text{ mol} \times 0.0821 \text{ L atm/mol K} \times 293 \text{ K}}{0.750 \text{ L} - (1.10 \text{ mol} \times 0.04081 \text{ L/mol})}$$

$$- \frac{3.667 \text{ L}^2 \text{ atm/mol}^2 \times (1.10 \text{ mol})^2}{(0.750 \text{ L})^2} = 37.5 \text{ atm} - 7.89 \text{ atm} = 29.6 \text{ atm}$$

PE 5.31

(a) The proportionality constant *a* is a measure of the intrinsic strength of the attractive forces in the gas. The larger the value, the greater the attractive forces in the gas. In order of increasing attractive force: He, H_2, O_2, N_2, CO_2, and HCl.
(b) The magnitude of *b* is a measure of the size of the molecules making up the gas. In order of increasing molecular size: He, H_2, O_2, N_2, HCl, and CO_2.

Solutions To Final Exercises

5.1   (a) 1. Finely divided particles suspended in a liquid are seen to be in continuous random motion. This observation is evidence that the much smaller liquid molecules themselves are in incessant and random motion. This phenomenon is called *Brownian motion.*
2. The spontaneous spreading of one substance through another, called *diffusion*, is evidence that the molecules are in continuous motion. It is the continuous random motion of the molecules that causes one substance's molecules to intermingle with those of another.

3. Gases have neither a definite volume nor a definite shape, but expand and completely fill any container. This is evidence that the gas molecules are in continuous random motion. The continuous random motion of the gas molecules brings them to every part of the container.

4. Gases exert continuous pressure equally in all directions. This is evidence that the gas molecules are in incessant random motion, since they are bombarding each square centimeter of the container walls equally.

5. The experimentally observed relationships between temperature and the rates of many molecular processes are explainable in terms of molecular motion. For instance, liquids flow more freely when hot, and the rate of diffusion increases with increasing temperature.

(b) 1. The pressure of gases in a confined space increases with increasing temperature. The molecules move more rapidly at the higher temperatures. They collide with the container walls more frequently and with a greater force and therefore exert a greater pressure on the container walls.

2. The rate of diffusion increases with temperature, showing that the molecules are moving faster.

3. Liquids flow more easily when hot, showing that the cohesion of the molecules is disrupted by the increased molecular motion.

5.4 (a) According to the kinetic theory of gases, the molecules of gases are in continuous random motion and intermolecular attractions that would impede the motion are very weak. These motions bring the molecules to every part of the container, so the entire container is eventually filled uniformly with the gas. Therefore, the fact that intermolecular attractions in gases are very weak allows gases to expand and fill their containers.

(b) According to the kinetic theory of gases, the attractive forces between gas molecules are weak and usually negligible. Furthermore, the gas molecules are in rapid constant random motion and are separated by distances that are large compared to their own size, except at low temperatures and high pressures. Therefore, at normal temperatures and pressures, the attractive forces are too weak to overcome the molecular motion and the relatively large intermolecular distances to form molecular aggregates that are large or massive enough for the relatively weak gravitational force to pull down to the earth.

(c) The friction between the tire and the road causes heat energy to be produced. The heat energy produced causes the temperature of the gas in the tire to rise. According to the kinetic theory of gases, the average kinetic energy of the gas molecules increases with the increasing temperature. The pressure increases because the more rapidly moving molecules make more frequent collisions with the walls of the tire and the average collision imparts a greater force.

5.10 The pressure of 1 atm supports a column of mercury 760 mm (0.760 m) high. Therefore, 90 atm can support a mercury column of 90 atm x 0.76 m/1 atm = 68 m.

5.11 One torr supports 1 mm Hg; therefore, 760 torr supports a column of Hg 760 mm in height. Since Hg is 13.6 times as dense as water, the same pressure can support a column of water 13.6 times higher than that of Hg.

13.6 x 0.760 m x 1 ft/0.3048 m = 33.9 ft

5.12

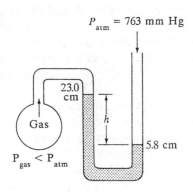

$P_{atm} = 763$ mm Hg

23.0 cm

Gas

h

5.8 cm

$P_{gas} < P_{atm}$

(a) $P_{gas} = P_{atm} - P_{Hg}$; $P_{Hg} = 23.0$ cm $- 5.8$ cm $= 172$ mm $= 172$ torr

$P_{gas} = 763$ torr $- 172$ torr $= 591$ torr

(b) 591 torr x 1 atm/760 torr = 0.778 atm

5.14 The Kelvin degree and the Celsius degree are the same size. The Celsius temperature can be converted to a Kelvin temperature by adding 273.15. For general purposes, 273 is sufficiently accurate. So, T = 273.15 + C for accurate or detailed calculations; T = 273 + C for general purpose calculations.

(a) T = 273.15 + 84.3 = 357.4 K
   T = 273.15 − 112.36 = 160.79 K
   T = 273 + 39 = 312 K

(b) $C = T - 273.15$ (accurate) or $C = T - 273$ (general purpose)
   C = 2.74 − 273.15 = −270.41°C
   C = 5386 − 273 = 5113°C
   C = 397.2 − 273.15 = 124.0°C

5.16 Standard conditions (STP) are 0°C and 1 atm pressure.
(a) The temperature remains constant; the pressure decreases from 760 torr to 700 torr. Since the volume increases, the pressure factor must be greater than unity, or 760 torr/700 torr.

$V_f = V_i$ x pressure factor = 2.4 L x 760 torr/700 torr = 2.6 L

(b) The pressure remains constant; the temperature decreases from 273 K to 253 K. Since the volume decreases, the temperature factor must be less than unity, or 253 K/273 K.

$V_f = V_i$ x temperature factor = 2.4 L x 253 K/273 K = 2.2 L

5.18 (a) The temperature goes up from 273 K to 303 K; therefore, the temperature factor must be less than unity, or 273 K/303 K. The pressure goes down from 760 torr to 700 torr; therefore, the pressure factor must be less than unity, or 700 torr/760 torr.

$d_f = d_i$ x temperature factor x pressure factor

$$= 1.29 \text{ g/L} \times \frac{273 \text{ K}}{303 \text{ K}} \times \frac{700 \text{ torr}}{760 \text{ torr}} = 1.07 \text{ g/L}$$

(b) The temperature factor must be greater than unity, or 273 K/258 K. The pressure factor must be greater than unity, or 1.25 atm/1.00 atm.

$$d_f = 1.29 \text{ g/L} \times \frac{273 \text{ K}}{258 \text{ K}} \times \frac{1.25 \text{ atm}}{1.00 \text{ atm}} = 1.71 \text{ g/L}$$

5.20   Assuming constant temperature, we can use Boyle's law: $P_i \times V_i = P_f \times V_f$.
$V_i = 200$ mL, $V_f = 6.60$ mL, $P_f = 30$ torr, and $P_i = ?$

$$P_i = P_f \times \frac{V_f}{V_i} = 30 \text{ torr} \times \frac{6.60 \text{ mL}}{200 \text{ mL}} = 0.99 \text{ torr}$$

5.22

$$T_f = T_i \times \frac{P_f}{P_i} \times \frac{V_f}{V_i}$$

$P_i = 1.60$ atm, $V_i = 30.0$ mL, $T_i = 223$ K; $P_f = 1.75$ atm, $V_f = 35.0$ mL, and $T_f = ?$

$$T_f = 223 \text{ K} \times \frac{1.75 \text{ atm}}{1.60 \text{ atm}} \times \frac{35.0 \text{ mL}}{30.0 \text{ mL}} = 285 \text{ K}$$

5.23   Since the pressure decreases from 2.1 atm to 1.0 atm, the bubble increases by a factor of 2.1 atm/1.0 atm. The volume of the bubble is originally

$$V_{bubble} = (4/3)\pi r^3_{bubble} = (4/3) \times 3.1416 \times (1.5 \text{ cm})^3 = 14 \text{ cm}^3 = 14 \text{ mL}$$

$$V_f = V_i \times \text{pressure factor} = 14 \text{ mL} \times 2.1 \text{ atm}/1.0 \text{ atm} = 29 \text{ mL}$$

5.25   The ideal gas law is $PV = nRT$, where R is a constant.
(a) When n and T are also constant, then $PV = \text{constant}$ (Boyle's law).
(b) When n and P are also constant, then $V = (nR/P) \times T = \text{constant} \times T$ (Charles' law).
(c) When P and T are also constant; then $V = (RT/P) \times n = \text{constant} \times n$ (Avogadro's law).

5.29   The molar volume of an ideal gas is given by the equation

$$\text{molar volume ideal gas} = \frac{V}{n} = \frac{RT}{P}$$

At standard conditions, $T = 273$ K and $P = 1.00$ atm. The molar volume in liters of an ideal gas at standard conditions is

$$\frac{V}{n} = \frac{0.0821 \text{ L atm/mol K} \times 273 \text{ K}}{1.00 \text{ atm}} = 22.4 \text{ L/mol}$$

This result is consistent with Table 5.1. The molar volumes at STP of the real gases listed in Table 5.1 are all fairly close to 22.4 L/mol.

5.32   The number of moles of gas is constant.

$$\frac{P_i V_i}{T_i} = \frac{P_f V_f}{T_f}$$

$P_i = 1.00$ atm, $V_i = 1.00$ L, $T_i = 273$ K; $P_f = 0.300$ atm, $V_f = 5.00$ L, and $T_f = ?$
The temperature the gas must have when $V = 5.00$ L and $P = 0.300$ atm is

$$T_f = T_i \times \frac{P_f}{P_i} \times \frac{V_f}{V_i} = 273 \text{ K} \times \frac{0.300 \text{ atm}}{1.00 \text{ atm}} \times \frac{5.00 \text{ L}}{1.00 \text{ L}} = 410 \text{ K} = 137°C$$

The initial temperature was $0°C$, therefore it requires a temperature change of $137°C$ to bring the final pressure to 0.300 atm.

5.34 (a) At STP, 1 mol of oxygen occupies 22.4 L. Therefore, 10.0 g of O_2 will occupy

$$10.0 \text{ g } O_2 \text{ x } \frac{1 \text{ mol } O_2}{32.00 \text{ g } O_2} \text{ x } \frac{22.4 \text{ L}}{1 \text{ mol } O_2} = 7.00 \text{ L}$$

(b) The temperature decreases from 273 K to 255 K; therefore, the temperature factor must be less than unity, or 255 K/273 K. The pressure increases from 760 torr to 775 torr; therefore, the pressure factor must be less than unity, or 760 torr/775 torr. The volume at $-18°C$ and 775 torr is

$$V_f = 7.00 \text{ L } \text{ x } \frac{255 \text{ K}}{273 \text{ K}} \text{ x } \frac{760 \text{ torr}}{775 \text{ torr}} = 6.41 \text{ L}$$

Comment: You could also use the ideal gas law (PV = nRT) to calculate the volume in parts (a) and (b).

5.35 $1.00 \text{ cm}^3 = 1.00 \text{ mL} = 0.00100 \text{ L}$
(a) V = 0.00100 L, P = 1.00 atm, T = 298 K.

$$n = \frac{PV}{RT} = \frac{1.00 \text{ atm x } 0.00100 \text{ L}}{0.0821 \text{ L atm/mol K x } 298 \text{ K}} = 4.09 \text{ x } 10^{-5} \text{ mol air}$$

The number of air molecules is 4.09 x 10^{-5} mol x 6.022 x 10^{23} molecules/mol = 2.46 x 10^{19} molecules.

(b) V = 0.00100 L, P = 0.60 atm, T = 273 K.

$$n = \frac{0.60 \text{ atm x } 0.00100 \text{ L}}{0.0821 \text{ L atm/mol K x } 273 \text{ K}} = 2.7 \text{ x } 10^{-5} \text{ mol air}$$

The number of air molecules is 2.7 x 10^{-5} mol x 6.022 x 10^{23} molecules/mol = 1.6 x 10^{19} molecules.

(c) V = 0.00100 L, P = 1.0 x 10^{-6} torr x 1 atm/760 torr = 1.3 x 10^{-9} atm, T = 293 K.

$$n = \frac{1.3 \text{ x } 10^{-9} \text{ atm x } 1.00 \text{ x } 10^{-3} \text{ L}}{0.0821 \text{ L atm/mol K x } 293 \text{ K}} = 5.4 \text{ x } 10^{-14} \text{ mol air}$$

The number of air molecules is 5.4 x 10^{-14} mol x 6.022 x 10^{23} molecules/mol = 3.3 x 10^{10} molecules.

Note: Parts (b) and (c) could also be calculated by applying temperature and pressure factors to the answers in (a).

5.37 One mole of any gas occupies approximately 22.4 L at STP. Therefore, its approximate molar mass is

$$\frac{5.86 \text{ g}}{1 \text{ L}} \text{ x } \frac{22.4 \text{ L}}{1 \text{ mol}} = 131 \text{ g/mol}$$

5.40 (a) M = 153.8 g/mol, T = 273 K, and P = 800 torr x 1 atm/760 torr = 1.05 atm.

$$d = \frac{MP}{RT} = \frac{153.8 \text{ g/mol x } 1.05 \text{ atm}}{0.0821 \text{ L atm/mol K x } 273 \text{ K}} = 7.21 \text{ g/L}$$

(b) M = 44.0 g/mol, T = 310 K, and P = 1.2 atm.

$$d = \frac{MP}{RT} = \frac{44.0 \text{ g/mol x } 1.2 \text{ atm}}{0.0821 \text{ L atm/mol K x } 310 \text{ K}} = 2.07 \text{ g/L}$$

5.42   Rearrangement of the density equation gives M = dRT/P; d = 3.76 g/L, T = 298 K, and P = 1.00 atm.

$$M = \frac{dRT}{P} = \frac{3.76 \text{ g/L x } 0.0821 \text{ L atm/mol K x } 298 \text{ K}}{1.00 \text{ atm}} = 92.0 \text{ g/mol}$$

5.44   (a) V = 0.600 L, P = 427 torr x 1 atm/760 torr = 0.562 atm, T = 343 K.

$$n = \frac{PV}{RT} = \frac{0.562 \text{ atm x } 0.600 \text{ L}}{0.0821 \text{ L atm/mol K x } 343 \text{ K}} = 0.0120 \text{ mol}$$

The molar mass is 1.430 g/0.0120 mol = 119 g/mol.

(b) The number of moles of C, H, and Cl in the molar mass is

C: 119 g compound x $\frac{10.1 \text{ g C}}{100 \text{ g compound}}$ x $\frac{1 \text{ mol C atoms}}{12.0 \text{ g C}}$ = 1.00 mol C atoms

H: 119 g compound x $\frac{0.84 \text{ g H}}{100 \text{ g compound}}$ x $\frac{1 \text{ mol H atoms}}{1.01 \text{ g H}}$ = 0.990 mol H atoms

Cl: 119 g compound x $\frac{89.1 \text{ g Cl}}{100 \text{ g compound}}$ x $\frac{1 \text{ mol Cl atoms}}{35.45 \text{ g Cl}}$ = 2.99 mol Cl atoms

There is 1 mol of C atoms and 1 mol of H atoms for every 3 mol of Cl atoms. The atom ratio is the same as the mole ratio. The formula is $CHCl_3$.

5.45   The mass of C and H in the sample is

$$\text{mass C} = 20.5 \text{ mg } CO_2 \text{ x } \frac{12.0 \text{ mg C}}{44.0 \text{ mg } CO_2} = 5.59 \text{ mg C}$$

mass H = mass sample – mass C = 6.54 mg – 5.59 mg = 0.95 mg H

The molar mass of the compound is (d = 1.215 g/L, T = 298 K, and P = 800 torr x 1 atm/760 torr = 1.053 atm):

$$M = \frac{dRT}{P} = \frac{1.215 \text{ g/L x } 0.0821 \text{ L atm/mol K x } 298 \text{ K}}{1.053 \text{ atm}} = 28.2 \text{ g/mol}$$

The number of moles of C and H in the molar mass is

C: 28.2 g compound x $\frac{5.59 \text{ g C}}{6.54 \text{ g compound}}$ x $\frac{1 \text{ mol C atom}}{12.0 \text{ g C}}$ = 2.01 mol C atoms

H: 28.2 g compound x $\frac{0.95 \text{ g H}}{6.54 \text{ g compound}}$ x $\frac{1 \text{ mol H atoms}}{1.01 \text{ g H}}$ = 4.06 mol H atoms

There are 2 mol of C atoms and 4 mol of H atoms in 1 mol of compound. The formula is C_2H_4.

5.47 $2CH_3OH(l) + 3O_2(g) \longrightarrow 2CO_2(g) + 4H_2O(g)$
1.00 g

The steps in the calculation are: g $CH_3OH \longrightarrow$ mol $CH_3OH \longrightarrow$ mol $O_2 \longrightarrow$ mL O_2.

1.00 g CH_3OH x $\frac{1 \text{ mol } CH_3OH}{32.04 \text{ g } CH_3OH}$ x $\frac{3 \text{ mol } O_2}{2 \text{ mol } CH_3OH}$ = 0.0468 mol O_2

The number of milliliters occupied by 0.0468 mol O_2 at STP is

0.0468 mol O_2 x 22.4 L/1 mol O_2 = 1.05 L or 1.05 x 10^3 mL O_2

Answer: 1.05 x 10^3 mL of O_2 measured at STP.

5.49 $2H_2(g) + O_2(g) \longrightarrow 2H_2O(g)$

Under identical conditions, the volume ratio of the gases consumed and produced in a chemical reaction is the same as the mole ratio. The mole ratio is 2 mol hydrogen to 1 mol O_2, or 2:1. The volume of H_2 needed to combine with 12 mL O_2 is

$$12 \text{ mL } O_2 \text{ x } \frac{2 \text{ mL } H_2}{1 \text{ mL } O_2} = 24 \text{ mL } H_2$$

5.51 $\underset{\substack{50.0 \text{ g}}}{Mg(s)} + 2HCl(aq) \longrightarrow MgCl_2(aq) + \underset{\substack{L = ?}}{H_2(g)}$

(a) The steps in the calculation are: g Mg $\longrightarrow$ mol Mg $\longrightarrow$ mol $H_2 \longrightarrow$ L H_2.

$$50.0 \text{ g Mg x } \frac{1 \text{ mol Mg}}{24.3 \text{ g Mg}} \text{ x } \frac{1 \text{ mol } H_2}{1 \text{ mol Mg}} = 2.06 \text{ mol } H_2$$

At STP, 2.06 mol H_2 occupies 2.06 mol x 22.4 L/mol = 46.1 L.

(b) P = 780 torr x 1 atm/760 torr = 1.26 atm, T = 303 K, n = 2.06 mol, and

$$V = \frac{nRT}{P} = \frac{2.06 \text{ mol x } 0.0821 \text{ L atm/mol K x } 303 \text{ K}}{1.026 \text{ atm}} = 49.9 \text{ L}$$

Answer: 46.1 L at STP; 49.9 L at 30°C and 780 torr.

5.53 $2H_2S(g) + 3O_2(g) \longrightarrow 2SO_2(g) + 2H_2O(l)$

From the coefficients of the equation we see that 3 L $O_2(g)$ are required for every 2 L $H_2S(g)$. Assuming that the gases are measured under identical conditions, the volume of O_2 required for the oxidation of 100 mL of H_2S is

$$100 \text{ mL } H_2S \text{ x } \frac{3 \text{ mL } O_2}{2 \text{ mL } H_2S} = 150 \text{ mL } O_2$$

Notice that this volume relationship is valid under all temperature and pressure conditions, including standard conditions. According to Avogadro's law (see the solution to Exercise 5.66), the volume percent in a gas mixture is the same as the mole percent. Therefore,

$$150 \text{ mL } O_2 \text{ x } \frac{100 \text{ mL dry air}}{20.95 \text{ mL } O_2} = 716 \text{ mL dry air}$$

Answer: 716 mL of dry air at STP.

5.56 $P_i = P_T \text{ x } n_i/n_T$; $P_{CO_2} = 90 \text{ atm x } 0.96 = 86 \text{ atm}$; $P_{N_2} = P_T - P_{CO_2} = 90 \text{ atm} - 86 \text{ atm} = 4 \text{ atm}$

5.58 $P_i = P_T \text{ x } X_i$

$P_{O_2} = P_T \text{ x } X_{O_2} = 720 \text{ torr x } 1 \text{ mol}/3 \text{ mol} = 240 \text{ torr}$

$P_{N_2} = P_T - P_{O_2} = 720 \text{ torr} - 240 \text{ torr} = 480 \text{ torr}$

5.60   To solve this problem, we have to find the partial pressure of hydrogen. The gas sample consists of hydrogen and water vapor. The vapor pressure of water at $30°C$ is 31.8 torr. The partial pressure of H_2 is

$$P_{H_2} = P_T - P_{water} = 770 \text{ torr} - 31.8 \text{ torr} = 738 \text{ torr}$$

To obtain the volume occupied by the hydrogen at STP we use $P_iV_i/T_i = P_fV_f/T_f$ with $V_i = 250$ mL, $P_i = 738$ torr, $T_i = 303$ K; $P_f = 760$ torr, $T_f = 273$ K, and $V_f = ?$

$$V_f = 250 \text{ mL} \times \frac{738 \text{ torr}}{760 \text{ torr}} \times \frac{273 \text{ K}}{303 \text{ K}} = 219 \text{ mL}$$

5.61 $2KClO_3(s) \longrightarrow 2KCl(s) + 3O_2(g)$

The number of moles of oxygen gas can be calculated from the ideal gas law, but the partial pressure of oxygen must first be determined. The vapor pressure of water is 23.8 torr at $25°C$ (Table 5.3). The partial pressure of oxygen is

$$P_{O_2} = P_T - P_{water} = 764 \text{ torr} - 23.8 \text{ torr} = 740 \text{ torr} \times 1 \text{ atm}/760 \text{ torr} = 0.974 \text{ atm}$$

Substituting the values of $V = 1.90$ L, $T = 298$ K, and $P = 0.974$ atm into the ideal gas law gives the number of moles of oxygen:

$$n_{oxygen} = \frac{PV}{RT} = \frac{0.974 \text{ atm} \times 1.90 \text{ L}}{0.0821 \text{ L atm/mol K} \times 298 \text{ K}} = 0.0756 \text{ mol}$$

The remaining steps in the calculation are: mol $O_2 \longrightarrow$ mol $KClO_3 \longrightarrow$ g $KClO_3 \longrightarrow$ % $KClO_3$.

$$0.0756 \text{ mol } O_2 \times \frac{2 \text{ mol } KClO_3}{3 \text{ mol } O_2} \times \frac{122.55 \text{ g } KClO_3}{1 \text{ mol } KClO_3} = 6.18 \text{ g } KClO_3$$

The percent by weight of $KClO_3$ in the mixture is

$$\text{percent } KClO_3 = \frac{\text{mass } KClO_3}{\text{mass mixture}} \times 100\% = \frac{6.18 \text{ g}}{10.0 \text{ g}} \times 100\% = 61.8\%$$

5.65   (a) The molar masses of N_2O and $C_4H_{10}O$ are 44.0 g and 74.1 g, respectively. Therefore, N_2O effuses more rapidly than $C_4H_{10}O$.

(b) To compare the rates, we use Graham's law.

$$r_{nitrous\ oxide} \times \sqrt{44.0 \text{ g/mol}} = r_{diethylether} \times \sqrt{74.1 \text{ g/mol}}$$

$$r_{nitrous\ oxide} = r_{diethylether} \times \sqrt{\frac{74.1}{44.0}} = 1.30 \times r_{diethylether}$$

Nitrous oxide should effuse 1.30 times more rapidly than diethylether.

5.66 $P_TV_T = n_TRT$ and $V_T = n_TRT/P_T$; $P_TV_i = n_iRT$ and $V_i = n_iRT/P_T$

Dividing the expression for V_i by the expression for V_T and multiplying by 100% we get

$$\frac{V_i}{V_T} \times 100\% = \frac{n_iRT/P_T}{n_TRT/P_T} \times 100\% = \frac{n_i}{n_T} \times 100\%$$

This shows that for an ideal gas mixture the volume percent is equal to the mole percent.

5.67   (a)

$$\text{average speed} = \frac{375 \text{ m/s} + 420 \text{ m/s} + 480 \text{ m/s}}{3} = 425 \text{ m/s}$$

$$\text{mean square speed} = \frac{(375 \text{ m/s})^2 + (420 \text{ m/s})^2 + (480 \text{ m/s})^2}{3} = 1.82 \times 10^5 \text{ m}^2/\text{s}^2$$

$$\text{root mean square speed} = \sqrt{1.82 \times 10^5 \text{ m}^2/\text{s}^2} = 427 \text{ m/s}$$

(b) The mean square speed ($\overline{u^2}$) is obtained by finding the squares of the speeds of all the molecules, adding these squares together, and taking the average. The square of the average speed ($\overline{u}^2$) is obtained by evaluating the average speed of all the molecules and then squaring the result. Since $\overline{u^2}$ is not numerically equal to $\overline{u}^2$, the root mean square speed ($\sqrt{\overline{u^2}}$) is not equal to the average speed ($\overline{u} = \sqrt{\overline{u}^2}$).

5.71   First we use the ideal gas law to calculate the temperature of the gas. n = 2 mol, V = 20.0 L, P = 1.00 atm, and

$$T = \frac{PV}{nR} = \frac{1.00 \text{ atm} \times 20.0 \text{ L}}{2 \text{ mol} \times 0.0821 \text{ L atm/mol K}} = 122 \text{ K}$$

(a) The kinetic energy per mole is $E_k = (3/2)RT$. The total kinetic energy of the argon atoms is
total kinetic energy = 2 mol $\times E_k$ = 2 mol $\times$ (3/2)RT = 2 mol $\times$ (3/2) $\times$ 8.314 J/mol K $\times$ 122 K = 3.04×10^3 J

(b)

$$u_{rms} = \sqrt{\frac{3RT}{M}} = \sqrt{\frac{3 \times 8.314 \text{ kg m}^2/\text{s}^2 \text{ mol K} \times 122 \text{ K}}{0.03995 \text{ kg/mol}}} = 276 \text{ m/s}$$

5.73   (a) Greater than. All gases have the same molar kinetic energy at the same temperature. Since there is an approximate nitrogen to oxygen mole ratio of 4:1 in air, the nitrogen molecules should possess a total of four times more kinetic energy than the oxygen molecules.
(b) Greater than. At constant temperature, the root mean square speed varies inversely with the square root of the molar mass; $u_{rms} = \sqrt{3RT/M} = k \times \sqrt{1/M}$, where $k = \sqrt{3RT}$. The larger the mass, the smaller the u_{rms}. The molar masses of N_2 and O_2 are 28.0 g/mol and 32.0 g/mol, respectively. Since $M_{nitrogen} < M_{oxygen}$, the u_{rms} of the nitrogen molecules is greater than that of the oxygen molecules.

5.77   (a) As T $\longrightarrow \infty$ the distribution curve continues to flatten out and eventually joins or becomes indistinguishable from the molecular speed axis. Thus the molecules are evenly distributed among all the speeds at very high temperatures. The root mean square speed and most probable speed increase without limit.

(b) As T $\longrightarrow 0$ the distribution curve bunches up toward the relative distribution axis and eventually joins or becomes indistinguishable from it. The fraction of molecules having the most probable speed increases and eventually becomes 1.0 on this scale, while the value of the most probable speed decreases and becomes zero at the same time. Thus all the molecules have zero speed and therefore zero kinetic energy at T = 0, the absolute zero of temperature.

5.82   (a) n = 1.00 mol, V = 5.00 L, T = 473 K, and

$$P = \frac{nRT}{V} = \frac{1.00 \text{ mol} \times 0.0821 \text{ L atm/mol K} \times 473 \text{ K}}{5.00 \text{ L}} = 7.77 \text{ atm}$$

(b)

$$P = \frac{nRT}{V - nb} - \frac{an^2}{V^2} \; ; \; a = 5.464 \text{ L}^2 \text{ atm/mol}^2 \text{ and } b = 0.03049 \text{ L/mol}$$

$$P = \frac{1.00 \text{ mol} \times 0.0821 \text{ L atm/mol K} \times 473 \text{ K}}{5.00 \text{ L} - (1.00 \text{ mol} \times 0.03049 \text{ L/mol})} - \frac{5.464 \text{ L}^2 \text{ atm/mol}^2 \times (1.00 \text{ mol})^2}{(5.00 \text{ L})^2}$$

$$= 7.81 \text{ atm} - 0.219 \text{ atm} = 7.59 \text{ atm}$$

The van der Waals equation is more accurate than the ideal gas law; therefore, the van der Waals value of 7.59 atm should be closer to the actual pressure.

5.84 (a) V = 50.0 L, T = 273 K, n = 31.25 mol, and

$$P = \frac{nRT}{V} = \frac{31.25 \text{ mol} \times 0.0821 \text{ L atm/mol K} \times 273 \text{ K}}{50.0 \text{ L}} = 14.0 \text{ atm}$$

(b)

$$P = \frac{nRT}{V - nb} - \frac{an^2}{V^2} \; ; \; a = 1.360 \text{ L}^2 \text{ atm/mol}^2 \text{ and } b = 0.03183 \text{ L/mol.}$$

$$P = \frac{31.25 \text{ mol} \times 0.0821 \text{ L atm/mol K} \times 273 \text{ K}}{50.0 \text{ L} - (31.25 \text{ mol} \times 0.03183 \text{ L/mol})} - \frac{1.360 \text{ L}^2 \text{ atm/mol}^2 \times (31.25 \text{ mol})^2}{(50.0 \text{ L})^2}$$

$$= 14.3 \text{ atm} - 0.531 \text{ atm} = 13.8 \text{ atm}$$

5.85 (a) Real gases have attractive interactions, i.e., there are attractive forces between their molecules. When expanding, work must be performed to overcome these attractive forces. The energy to perform the work comes from the heat energy of the gas. According to the kinetic molecular theory of gases, when heat energy is lost, the average kinetic energy of the gas molecules decreases and the temperature drops. Therefore, gases cool (their temperatures drop) upon expansion.

(b) When a tire is inflated, the pressure of the incoming air pushes back the existing air. This physical moving of the air by a force is a form of work (work = force x distance = pressure x volume change); sometimes called pressure-volume work or PV work. The energy used to perform the work winds up as heat energy of the gas. According to the kinetic molecular theory of gases, when heat energy is gained, the average kinetic energy of the gas molecules increases and the temperature rises. Therefore, the gas warms up (temperature rises) and the tire becomes warm by heat conduction when air is pumped in.

These effects wouldn't occur if the gases were ideal, because ideal gas molecules have no attractive interactions and zero volume (a gas moving into a vacuum performs no work).

5.86 $NaHCO_3(aq) + HCl(aq) \longrightarrow NaCl(aq) + H_2O(l) + CO_2(g)$
520 mg Na   L = ?

According to the equation, for every mole of sodium consumed in the form of $NaHCO_3$, 1 mol CO_2 gas is evolved. The steps in the calculation are: g Na $\longrightarrow$ mol Na $\longrightarrow$ mol CO_2 $\longrightarrow$ L CO_2.

$$0.520 \text{ g Na} \times \frac{1 \text{ mol Na}}{22.99 \text{ g Na}} \times \frac{1 \text{ mol } CO_2}{1 \text{ mol Na}} = 0.0226 \text{ mol } CO_2$$

The volume of CO_2 at T = 310 K and P = 1.00 atm can be calculated using the ideal gas equation.

$$V = \frac{nRT}{P} = \frac{0.0226 \text{ mol} \times 0.0821 \text{ L atm/mol K} \times 310 \text{ K}}{1.00 \text{ atm}} = 0.575 \text{ L}$$

5.89   Since all the balloons are identical, we can use Boyle's law: $P_{tank} \times V_{tank} = P_{balloons} \times V_{balloons}$

$100 \text{ atm} \times 1.5 \text{ L} = \frac{765}{760} \text{ atm} \times V_{balloons}$

$V_{balloons} = 149 \text{ L}$

The number of balloons that can be filled is

$149 \text{ L} \times 1 \text{ balloon}/1.2 \text{ L} = 124 \text{ or } 1.2 \times 10^2$ balloons (to two significant figures)

5.91   (a) 1 mol hemoglobin + 4 mol $O_2 \longrightarrow$ 1 mol oxyhemoglobin. The steps in the calculation are:
g hemoglobin $\longrightarrow$ mol hemoglobin $\longrightarrow$ mol $O_2 \longrightarrow$ mL O_2.

$1.00 \text{ g hemoglobin} \times \dfrac{1 \text{ mol hemoglobin}}{6.80 \times 10^4 \text{ g hemoglobin}} \times \dfrac{4 \text{ mol } O_2}{1 \text{ mol hemoglobin}}$

$= 5.88 \times 10^{-5} \text{ mol } O_2$

The number of milliliters of O_2 at STP combined with 1.00 g of hemoglobin can be calculated using the ideal gas equation

$V = \dfrac{nRT}{P} = \dfrac{5.88 \times 10^{-5} \text{ mol} \times 0.0821 \text{ L atm/mol K} \times 273 \text{ K}}{1.00 \text{ atm}} = 1.32 \times 10^{-3} \text{ L or } 1.32 \text{ mL}$

(b)

$\dfrac{1.32 \text{ mL } O_2}{1.00 \text{ g hemoglobin}} \times \dfrac{15 \text{ g hemoglobin}}{100 \text{ mL blood}} = \dfrac{20 \text{ mL } O_2}{100 \text{ mL blood}}$

5.94   The volume of the air in the flask before heating is ($V_i = 200$ mL, $T_i = 273$ K; $T_f = 293$ K, $V_f = ?$):

$V_f = V_i \times \text{temperature factor} = 200 \text{ mL} \times \dfrac{293 \text{ K}}{273 \text{ K}} = 215 \text{ mL}$

The volume of the air in the flask after heating is ($V_i = 200$ mL, $T_i = 273$ K; $T_f = 313$ K, $V_f = ?$):

$V_f = 200 \text{ mL} \times \dfrac{313 \text{ K}}{273 \text{ K}} = 229 \text{ mL}$

The increase in volume in going from 20°C to 40°C is

$V_{40°C} - V_{20°C} = 229 \text{ mL} - 215 \text{ mL} = 14 \text{ mL} = 14 \text{ cm}^3$

The volume of any section of the tube is $V = h \times$ cross sectional area $= h \times \pi d^2/4$; h is the amount the liquid will rise in the tube when the air volume increase by 14 cm³.

$h \times \pi d^2/4 = h \times 3.14 \times (0.60 \text{ cm})^2/4 = h \times 0.28 \text{ cm}^2 = 14 \text{ cm}^3$

$h = 14 \text{ cm}^3/0.28 \text{ cm}^2 = 50 \text{ cm}$

5.96 $Zn(s) + 2HCl(aq) \longrightarrow ZnCl_2(aq) + H_2(g)$
$2Al(s) + 6HCl(aq) \longrightarrow 2AlCl_3(aq) + 3H_2(g)$

The number of moles of hydrogen gas produced can be calculated from the ideal gas equation once we know the partial pressure of the hydrogen. The vapor pressure of water at 22°C is 19.8 torr.

$P_{H_2} = P_T - P_{water} = (760 \text{ torr} - 19.8 \text{ torr}) \times 1 \text{ atm}/760 \text{ torr} = 0.974 \text{ atm}$

The number of moles of hydrogen is (P = 0.974 atm, V = 3.78 L, T = 295 K):

$$n = \frac{PV}{RT} = \frac{0.974 \text{ atm x } 3.78 \text{ L}}{0.0821 \text{ L atm/mol K x } 295 \text{ K}} = 0.152 \text{ mol}$$

The molar masses of Zn and Al are 65.38 g and 26.98 g, respectively. Let x = g of Zn and y = g of Al in the mixture. Then

$x + y = 5.00$, $y = 5.00 - x$.

The total moles of H_2 are:

$$x \text{ g Zn x } \frac{1 \text{ mol Zn}}{65.38 \text{ g Zn}} \text{ x } \frac{1 \text{ mol } H_2}{1 \text{ mol Zn}} + y \text{ g Al x } \frac{1 \text{ mol Al}}{26.98 \text{ g Al}} \text{ x } \frac{3 \text{ mol } H_2}{2 \text{ mol Al}} = 0.152 \text{ mol } H_2$$

$0.01530x + 0.05560y = 0.152$

Substituting $y = 5.00 - x$ gives

$0.01530x + 0.05560(5.00 - x) = 0.152$

$0.04030x = 0.126$

$x = 3.13$

There were 3.13 g Zn in the mixture, so the percent by weight of zinc in the original mixture is

$$\text{weight \% Zn} = \frac{3.13 \text{ g}}{5.00 \text{ g}} \text{ x } 100\% = 62.6\%$$

5.97   (a) Let a = $^{235}UF_6$ and b = $^{238}UF_6$.

$$r_a \text{ x } \sqrt{M_a} = r_b \text{ x } \sqrt{M_b}; \quad r_a = r_b \text{ x } \sqrt{\frac{M_b}{M_a}}$$

The molar masses of $^{235}UF_6$ and $^{238}UF_6$ are 349.03 g and 352.04 g, respectively.

$r_a = r_b \text{ x } \sqrt{352.04/349.03} = 1.0043 \text{ x } r_b$

Therefore, the separation or enrichment factor is 1.0043.

(b) Let n be the number of effusion stages needed for a tenfold enrichment. Each stage contributes an enrichment factor of 1.0043; therefore, we need n multiples of 1.0043.

$10 = (1.0043)_1 \text{ x } (1.0043)_2 \text{ x } (1.0043)_3 \text{ x } \cdots \text{ x } (1.0043)_n$

$10 = (1.0043)^n$

$n \log 1.0043 = \log 10 = 1$

and n = 537

Answer: The gas has to pass through 537 effusion stages.

5.98   No. $P(V - nb) = nRT$
        $PV - Pnb = nRT$

$\dfrac{PV}{nRT} - \dfrac{Pnb}{nRT} = 1$ and $\dfrac{PV}{nRT} = 1 + \dfrac{Pnb}{nRT} = 1 + \dfrac{b}{RT} \times P = 1 + k \times P$

Since b is a positive constant, k is a positive constant at constant T. This is the equation of a straight line with an intercept of 1.0 on the PV/nRT axis and a positive slope of k.

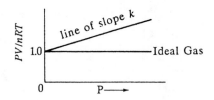

This line never goes below the ideal gas value of 1.0. Therefore, a law of this form cannot account for the dip below 1.0 that occurs for many real gases.

CHAPTER 6
THERMOCHEMISTRY

Solutions To Practice Exercises

PE 6.3 The liquid water absorbs 2600 J of heat; q = +2600 J. The steam does 170 J of work; w = –170 J. $\Delta E = q + w = 2600$ J – 170 J = +2430 J.

PE 6.5 (a) q = ΔH, q is negative because heat is being given off. Therefore, ΔH is negative.

(b) Since the system is colder than the surroundings, heat will flow into the system. q is positive and, therefore, ΔH is positive.

PE 6.6 The number of moles of methane burned can be calculated using the ideal gas equation. V = 10.0 L, T = 298 K, P = 1 atm, and

$$n = \frac{PV}{RT} = \frac{1.00 \text{ atm x } 10.0 \text{ L}}{0.0821 \text{ L atm/mol K x } 298 \text{ K}} = 0.409 \text{ mol } CH_4$$

The amount of heat given off by the combustion of 0.409 mol CH_4 is

$$0.409 \text{ mol } CH_4 \text{ x } \frac{802.3 \text{ kJ}}{1 \text{ mol } CH_4} = 328 \text{ kJ}$$

PE 6.7 To find the number of moles in 1.00 L: V x d (of compound) ——> g compound ——> mol compound.

$$1000 \text{ mL x } \frac{0.692 \text{ g}}{1 \text{ mL}} \text{ x } \frac{1 \text{ mol}}{114.23 \text{ g}} = 6.06 \text{ mol}$$

The number of kilojoules of heat given off during the combustion is 6.06 mol x 5455.6 kJ/1 mol = 3.31×10^4 kJ.

PE 6.8 (a) Fe_2O_3 forms from iron and oxygen. Iron and rust are solids and oxygen is a gas at 1 atm and 25°C.

$$2Fe(s) + 3/2 \text{ } O_2(g) \longrightarrow Fe_2O_3(s) \qquad \Delta H_f^o = -824.2 \text{ kJ}$$

(b) The sign of the enthalpy change shows that 824.2 kJ are given off when 2 mol of Fe reacts with oxygen. The steps in the calculation are: 50.0 kg Fe ⟶ mol Fe ⟶ kJ.

$$50{,}000 \text{ g Fe} \times \frac{1 \text{ mol Fe}}{55.85 \text{ g Fe}} \times \frac{824.2 \text{ kJ}}{2.00 \text{ mol Fe}} = 3.69 \times 10^5 \text{ kJ}$$

PE 6.10   The combustion reactions are

$$\Delta H°$$

(1) $CH_3COOH(1) + 2O_2(g) \longrightarrow 2CO_2(g) + 2H_2O(1)$ −874.2 kJ

(2) $H_2(g) + 1/2 \ O_2(g) \longrightarrow H_2O(1)$ −285.8 kJ

(3) $C(\text{graphite}) + O_2(g) \longrightarrow CO_2(g)$ −393.5 kJ

The thermochemical equation for the formation of CH_3COOH is

(4) $2C(\text{graphite}) + 2H_2(g) + O_2(g) \longrightarrow CH_3COOH(1)$ $\Delta H_f° = ?$

Reversing and multiplying as needed gives us the steps that add up to 4.

$$\Delta H°$$

(1a) $2CO_2(g) + 2H_2O(1) \longrightarrow CH_3COOH(1) + 2O_2(g)$ +874.2 kJ

(2a) $2H_2(g) + O_2(g) \longrightarrow 2H_2O(1)$ $2 \times −285.8$ kJ

(3a) $2C(\text{graphite}) + 2O_2(g) \longrightarrow 2CO_2(g)$ $2 \times −393.5$ kJ

The enthalpy change for equation 4 is obtained by adding the enthalpy changes of the three steps: $\Delta H_f° = 874.2 \text{ kJ} − 2 \times 285.8 \text{ kJ} − 2 \times 393.5 \text{ kJ} = −484.4 \text{ kJ}$

PE 6.11

$$FeCr_2O_4(s) + 4C(\text{graphite}) \longrightarrow Fe(s) + 2Cr(s) + 4CO(g) \quad \Delta H° = +988.4 \text{ kJ}$$
$$\Delta H_f°: \quad ? \qquad 4 \times 0 \text{ kJ} \qquad 1 \times 0 \text{ kJ} \quad 2 \times 0 \text{ kJ} \quad 4 \times −110.5 \text{ kJ}$$

$\Delta H° = 1 \times 0 \text{ kJ} + 2 \times 0 \text{ kJ} + 4 \times −110.5 \text{ kJ} − \Delta H_f° \ FeCr_2O_4 − (4 \times 0 \text{ kJ}) = 988.4 \text{ kJ}$
$\Delta H_f° \ FeCr_2O_4 = −988.4 \text{ kJ} − 442.0 \text{ kJ} = −1430.4 \text{ kJ}$
Answer: The enthalpy of formation of $FeCr_2O_4$ is $\Delta H_f° = −1430.4$ kJ/mol.

PE 6.13   q = mass x specific heat x ΔT

q = −3.0 kJ; the sign is negative since heat is lost, m = 200 g, and specific heat = 4.2 J/g°C. ΔT is

$\Delta T = q/\text{mass} \times \text{specific heat} = −3000 \text{ J}/200 \text{ g} \times 4.2 \text{ J/g°C} = −3.6°C$
$\Delta T = T_{final} − T_{initial}$
$T_{final} = \Delta T + T_{initial} = −3.6°C + 80.0°C = 76.4°C$

PE 6.14   The amount of heat given off during the combustion is

$$q = \text{heat capacity calorimeter} \times \Delta T = \frac{5200 \text{ J}}{1°C} \times 2.93°C = 1.52 \times 10^4 \text{ J} = 15.2 \text{ kJ}$$

Hence, 0.555 g mayonnaise gives off 15.2 kJ on combustion. The heat given off in kilocalories per gram is

$$\frac{15.2 \text{ kJ}}{0.555 \text{ g}} \times \frac{1 \text{ kcal}}{4.184 \text{ kJ}} = 6.55 \text{ kcal/g}$$

A dietary Calorie is equal to one kilocalorie; hence, the caloric content of 1 g of mayonnaise is 6.55 Calories. The number of dietary Calories in a 10.0–g helping of mayonnaise is therefore 10.0 g x 6.55 Calories/1 g = 65.5 Calories.

PE 6.15 If the reaction doesn't involve gases or there is no change in the number of moles of gas, then the constant volume heat of reaction equals (approximately) the enthalpy change.

(a) $S(s) + O_2(g) \longrightarrow SO_2(g)$. Equal number of gas moles before and after reaction; therefore, there will be no difference.

(b) $CaO(s) + H_2O(l) \longrightarrow Ca(OH)_2(s)$. The reaction doesn't involve gases; therefore, there will be no difference.

(c) $ZnO(s) + H_2(g) \longrightarrow Zn(s) + H_2O(l)$. The number of moles of gas decreases; therefore, there will be a difference.

Answer: (a) no; (b) no; (c) yes.

PE 6.16 $\quad NH_3(aq) + HCl(aq) \longrightarrow NH_4Cl(aq) \quad \Delta H = -52.0 \text{ kJ}$

The number of moles of NH_3 that reacts is 0.100 L x 0.50 mol NH_3/L = 0.050 mol NH_3. The heat given off by the reaction of 0.050 mol NH_3 is 0.050 mol NH_3 x 52.0 kJ/1 mol NH_3 = 2.6 kJ. The mass of the solution is 400 mL x 1.00 g/mL = 400 g. The temperature change is

$$\Delta T = \frac{q}{\text{mass x specific heat}} = \frac{2600 \text{ J}}{400 \text{ g x } 4.18 \text{ J/g}^\circ\text{C}} = 1.6^\circ\text{C}$$

Solutions To Final Exercises

6.5 The internal energy of the system comprises the total chemical bond potential energy, the total internal potential energy of other forms (intermolecular forces, electrical and magnetic interactions with the surroundings, etc.), and the total internal motional energy of the system's substances or components.

(a) When the temperature changes, the motional energy component of the internal energy changes the most.

(b) Changes of state, like melting, disrupts or radically changes the internal arrangement of the particles composing the substance. The rearranged particles have a totally different intermolecular force relationship than before and, therefore, the intermolecular potential energy component of the internal energy is primarily affected. It should be pointed out that the nature of the intermolecular forces does not change, only their strengths and the number of each type of interaction. The motional energy component, on the other hand, does not change during a phase change.

(c) Chemical changes have the greatest effect on the chemical bond potential energy of the system. Therefore, the chemical bond potential energy component of the internal energy changes for the most part.

6.7 $\Delta E = q + w$. q is positive when heat flows in and negative when heat flows out of the system. w is positive when work is done on the system by the surroundings and negative when work is done by the system on the surroundings.

(a) $\Delta E = +4.9 \text{ J} + 7.8 \text{ J} = +12.7 \text{ J}$

(b) $\Delta E = -55.8 \text{ J} - 17.3 \text{ J} = -73.1 \text{ J}$

(c) $\Delta E = +254 \text{ J} - 13 \text{ J} = +241 \text{ J}$

(d) $\Delta E = -12.8 \text{ J} + 6.4 \text{ J} = -6.4 \text{ J}$

6.9 The battery is the system; the rest of the universe is the surroundings.

(a) For the battery: $q_{batt} = -2 \text{ J}$, $w_{batt} = -15 \text{ J}$ and $\Delta E_{batt} = -2 \text{ J} - 15 \text{ J} = -17 \text{ J}$.

(b) For the surroundings: $q_{surr} = +2 \text{ J}$, $w_{surr} = +15 \text{ J}$ and $\Delta E_{surr} = +2 \text{ J} + 15 \text{ J} = +17 \text{ J}$.

6.14   When heat is absorbed, q is positive and ΔH is positive. When heat is given off, q is negative and ΔH is negative. Endothermic reactions have positive ΔH. Exothermic reactions have negative ΔH.

(a) Heat must be absorbed to vaporize the bromine. Therefore, ΔH is positive and the change is endothermic.

(b) The reaction produces heat; heat is given off. Therefore, q is negative, ΔH is negative, and the reaction is exothermic.

(c) It requires energy to decompose water into hydrogen and oxygen. Therefore, q is positive, ΔH is positive, and the reaction is endothermic.

(d) When liquid mercury freezes it gives off heat. Therefore, q is negative, ΔH is negative, and the change is exothermic.

6.15   A substance is said to be in a standard state when its pressure is 1 atm. The standard state of an element is its most stable form at 1 atm.

(a) No. At 1 atm and 25°C, the standard state would be gaseous nitrogen.

(b) Yes. Helium is a gas at 1 atm and 25°C.

(c) No. The most stable form of carbon at 1 atm and 25°C is graphite.

(d) No. Solid iodine is the most stable form at 1 atm and 25°C.

(e) No. Diatomic molecular oxygen gas, O_2, is the more stable form.

(f) Yes. Liquid bromine is the most stable form at 1 atm and 25°C.

(g) Yes. Sodium is a metal at 1 atm and 25°C.

6.16   A thermochemical equation is a chemical equation that includes the enthalpy change. For standard enthalpies of combustion to apply, all reactants and all products must be in their standard states.

(a) $C_2H_2(g) + 5/2\ O_2(g) \longrightarrow 2CO_2(g) + H_2O(l)$ $\Delta H° = -1299.6$ kJ

(b) $C_6H_5COOH(s) + 15/2\ O_2(g) \longrightarrow 7CO_2(g) + 3H_2O(l)$ $\Delta H° = -3226.9$ kJ

(c) $CH_3OH(l) + 3/2\ O_2(g) \longrightarrow CO_2(g) + 2H_2O(l)$ $\Delta H° = -726.5$ kJ

(d) $C_{21}H_{22}O_2N_2(s) + 51/2\ O_2(g) \longrightarrow 21CO_2(g) + 11H_2O(l) + N_2(g)$ $\Delta H°_{293} = -11237$ kJ

6.18   A standard enthalpy of formation ($\Delta H_f°$) is the standard enthalpy change accompanying the formation of 1 mol of a substance from its elements, each in its most stable (lowest energy) form.

(a) $2Hg(l) + Cl_2(g) \longrightarrow Hg_2Cl_2(s)$ $\Delta H_f° = -265.2$ kJ

(b) $Ca(s) + O_2(g) + H_2(g) \longrightarrow Ca(OH)_2(s)$ $\Delta H_f° = -986.1$ kJ

(c) $2C\ (graphite) + 2H_2(g) \longrightarrow C_2H_4(g)$ $\Delta H_f° = +52.3$ kJ

(d) $Hg(l) \longrightarrow Hg(g)$ $\Delta H_f° = +61.3$ kJ

(e) $2C\ (graphite) + 1/2\ O_2(g) + 3H_2(g) \longrightarrow C_2H_5OH(l)$ $\Delta H_f° = -277.7$ kJ

6.20 $CS_2(l) + 3O_2(g) \longrightarrow CO_2(g) + 2SO_2(g)$ $\Delta H° = -1076.9$ kJ

The steps are: g CS_2 ⟶ mol CS_2 ⟶ kJ.

$$25.0\ g\ CS_2 \times \frac{1\ mol\ CS_2}{76.14\ g\ CS_2} \times \frac{1076.9\ kJ}{1\ mol\ CS_2} = 354\ kJ$$

6.23 $Na(s) + 1/2\ Cl_2(g) \longrightarrow NaCl(s)$ $\Delta H_f° = -411.2$ kJ

(a) The steps are: g Na ⟶ mol Na ⟶ kJ.

$$5.00\ g\ Na \times \frac{1\ mol\ Na}{22.99\ g\ Na} \times \frac{411.2\ kJ}{1\ mol\ Na} = 89.4\ kJ$$

(b) The steps are: g NaCl ⟶ mol NaCl ⟶ kJ.

$$100.0\ g\ NaCl \times \frac{1\ mol\ NaCl}{58.44\ g\ NaCl} \times \frac{411.2\ kJ}{1\ mol\ NaCl} = 703.6\ kJ$$

6.25

$$C \text{ (graphite)} + O_2(g) \longrightarrow CO_2(g) \quad \Delta H_f^\circ = -393.5 \text{ kJ}$$

$$X \text{ g C} \times \frac{1 \text{ mol C}}{12.01 \text{ g C}} \times \frac{393.5 \text{ kJ}}{1 \text{ mol C}} = 5.00 \times 10^5 \text{ kJ}$$

$$X \text{ g} = \frac{12.01 \text{ g} \times 5.00 \times 10^5}{393.5} = 1.53 \times 10^4 \text{ g} = 15.3 \text{ kg}$$

Answer: 15.3 kg of coke.

6.27

Twenty-five percent efficient means that only one-quarter of the heat produced is actually used in melting the ice. The steps in the calculation are: $1 \text{ mol H}_2 \longrightarrow \text{kJ} \longrightarrow$ effective kJ $\longrightarrow$ mol ice $\longrightarrow$ g ice.

$$1 \text{ mol H}_2 \times \frac{285.8 \text{ kJ}}{1 \text{ mol H}_2} \times 0.25 \times \frac{1 \text{ mol ice}}{6.02 \text{ kJ}} \times \frac{18.0 \text{ g ice}}{1 \text{ mol ice}} = 214 \text{ g ice}$$

or 2.1×10^2 g ice (to two significant figures).

6.29

Reversing an equation changes the sign of its enthalpy change, and multiplying an equation by a factor multiplies the enthalpy change by the same factor.

$$CO(g) + 1/2 \; O_2(g) \longrightarrow CO_2(g) \quad \Delta H^\circ = -283.0 \text{ kJ}$$

(a) $2CO(g) + O_2(g) \longrightarrow 2CO_2(g) \quad \Delta H^\circ = -566.0 \text{ kJ}$
Original equation multiplied by a factor of two.

(b) $CO_2(g) \longrightarrow CO(g) + 1/2 \; O_2(g) \quad \Delta H^\circ = +283.0 \text{ kJ}$
Original equation reversed.

6.31

$$C_2H_2(g) + 2H_2(g) \longrightarrow C_2H_6(g) \quad \Delta H^\circ = ?$$
Reversing and multiplying the original equation as needed, we get the following steps that add up to the desired equation.

$$C_2H_2(g) + 5/2 \; O_2(g) \longrightarrow 2CO_2(g) + H_2O(l) \qquad \Delta H^\circ = -1300 \text{ kJ}$$
$$2H_2(g) + O_2(g) \longrightarrow 2H_2O(l) \qquad \Delta H^\circ = 2 \times -286 \text{ kJ}$$
$$2CO_2(g) + 3H_2O(l) \longrightarrow 7/2 \; O_2(g) + C_2H_6(g) \qquad \Delta H^\circ = +1560 \text{ kJ}$$

The enthalpy change is obtained by adding the enthalpy changes of the three steps:
$$\Delta H^\circ = -1300 \text{ kJ} - 572 \text{ kJ} + 1560 \text{ kJ} = -312 \text{ kJ}$$

6.32

The standard enthalpy change for a reaction is given by the following equation.

$$\Delta H^\circ = \sum_{\substack{\text{all} \\ \text{products}}} n_p \times (\Delta H_f^\circ)_p - \sum_{\substack{\text{all} \\ \text{reactants}}} n_r \times (\Delta H_f^\circ)_r,$$

where n_p is the number of moles of a given product and $(\Delta H_f^\circ)_p$ is its standard enthalpy of formation; n_r is the number of moles of a given reactant and $(\Delta H_f^\circ)_r$ is its standard enthalpy of formation.

(a) $CO(g) + 1/2 \; O_2(g) \longrightarrow CO_2(g)$; $\Delta H^\circ = 1 \times -393.5 \text{ kJ} - (1 \times -110.5 \text{ kJ}) - (1/2 \times 0 \text{ kJ}) = -283.0 \text{ kJ}$; exothermic

(b) $N_2(g) + 3H_2(g) \longrightarrow 2NH_3(g)$; $\Delta H^\circ = 2 \times -46.1 \text{ kJ} - (1 \times 0 \text{ kJ}) - (3 \times 0 \text{ kJ}) = -92.2 \text{ kJ}$; exothermic

(c) $2O_3(g) \longrightarrow 3O_2(g)$; $\Delta H^\circ = 3 \times 0 \text{ kJ} - (2 \times 142.7 \text{ kJ}) = -285.4 \text{ kJ}$; exothermic

(d) $2KClO_3(s) \longrightarrow 2KCl(s) + 3O_2(g)$; $\Delta H^\circ = 2 \times -436.7 \text{ kJ} + 3 \times 0 \text{ kJ} - (2 \times -397.7 \text{ kJ}) = -78.0 \text{ kJ}$; exothermic

(e) $CO(g) + 2H_2(g) \longrightarrow CH_3OH(l)$; $\Delta H^\circ = 1 \times -238.7 \text{ kJ} - (1 \times -110.5 \text{ kJ}) - (2 \times 0 \text{ kJ}) = -128.2 \text{ kJ}$; exothermic

6.34 (a) $CH_4(g) + 2O_2(g) \longrightarrow CO_2(g) + 2H_2O(l)$; $\Delta H° = 2$ x -285.8 kJ + 1 x -393.5 kJ $- (1$ x -74.8 kJ)
$- (2$ x 0 kJ) $= -890.3$ kJ; value in Table 6.2 is $\Delta H° = -890.4$ kJ

(b) $C_3H_8(g) + 5O_2(g) \longrightarrow 3CO_2(g) + 4H_2O(l)$; $\Delta H° = 4$ x -285.8 kJ + 3 x -393.5 kJ $- (1$ x -104.9 kJ)
$- (5$ x 0 kJ) $= -2218.8$ kJ; value in Table 6.2 is $\Delta H° = -2218.8$ kJ

(c) $C_8H_{18}(l) + 25/2\ O_2(g) \longrightarrow 8CO_2(g) + 9H_2O(l)$; $\Delta H° = 9$ x -285.8 kJ + 8 x -393.5 kJ $- (1$ x -269.8
kJ) $- (25/2$ x 0 kJ) $= -5450.4$ kJ; value in Table 6.2 is $\Delta H° = -5450.5$ kJ

6.38 (a) q = mass x specific heat x $\Delta T = 15.0$ g x 0.900 J/g°C x $(30°C - 20°C) = 135$ J
(b) q = mass x specific heat x ΔT

$$= 1.50 \text{ mol Cu} \times \frac{63.55 \text{ g}}{1 \text{ mol Cu}} \times \frac{0.387 \text{ J}}{\text{g}°\text{C}} \times (30°C - 20°C) = 369 \text{ J}$$

6.40 ΔT = q/mass x specific heat

For copper: ΔT = 100 J/1.00 g x 0.387 J/g°C = 258°C
For gold: ΔT = 100 J/1.00 g x 0.128 J/g°C = 781°C

Gold has a lower specific heat than copper and, therefore, a greater temperature change. Gold will have the higher final temperature.

6.42 The heat lost by the iron is equal to the heat gained by the water. The final temperature is the same for both the iron and the water. The specific heats of iron and water are in Table 6.6.

Iron: q_{iron} = 13.0 g x 0.451 J/g°C x $(T_{final} - 95°C)$
Water: q_{water} = 80.0 g x 4.18 J/g°C x $(T_{final} - 15.0°C)$
$q_{iron} = -q_{water}$
13.0 g x 0.451 J/g°C x $(T_{final} - 95°C)$ = -80.0 g x 4.18 J/g°C x $(T_{final} - 15.0°C)$
5.86 J/°C x $T_{final} - 557$ J = -334 J/°C x T_{final} + 5016 J
340 J/°C x T_{final} = 5573 J
T_{final} = 5573 J/340 J/°C = 16.4°C

6.44 (a) The heat lost by the copper is equal to the heat gained by the water. The final temperature is the same for both the copper and the water. The specific heats are in Table 6.6.

Copper: q_{copper} = 100 g x 0.387 J/g°C x $(T_{final} - 75°C)$
Water: q_{water} = 500 g x 4.18 J/g°C x $(T_{final} - 15°C)$
$q_{copper} = -q_{water}$
100 g x 0.387 J/g°C x $(T_{final} - 75°C)$ = -500 g x 4.18 J/g°C x $(T_{final} - 15°C)$
38.7 J/°C x $T_{final} - 2902.5$ J = -2090.0 J/°C x T_{final} + 31350 J
2128.7 J/°C x T_{final} = 34252.5 J

$$T_{final} = \frac{34252.5 \text{ J}}{2128.7 \text{ J}/°C} = 16°C$$

(b) q_{copper} = 100 g x 0.387 J/g°C x $(16°C - 75°C)$ = -2.3 x 10^3 J
(c) q_{water} = +2.3 x 10^3 J

6.47

$$q = 500 \text{ W} \times \frac{1 \text{ J/s}}{1 \text{ W}} \times 60.0 \text{ s} = 3.00 \times 10^4 \text{ J}; \text{ mass water} = 250 \text{ g}$$

$$\Delta T = \frac{q}{\text{mass water} \times \text{specific heat}} = \frac{3.00 \times 10^4 \text{ J}}{250 \text{ g} \times 4.18 \text{ J/g}°\text{C}} = 28.7°C$$

6.48   The constant volume heat of combustion is the heat given off when 1 mol of the substance is burned at constant volume. 29.6 kJ were given off by the combustion of 1.50 g of morphine. The combustion of 1 mol, 303.36 g, would give off

$$\frac{29.6 \text{ kJ}}{1.50 \text{ g morphine}} \times \frac{303.36 \text{ g morphine}}{1 \text{ mol morphine}} = 5.99 \times 10^3 \text{ kJ/mol}$$

The combustion is exothermic. Hence, the constant volume heat of combustion of morphine is -5.99×10^3 kJ/mol.

6.51   (a) The heat capacity of the calorimeter is the amount of heat that would produce a one degree rise in the temperature of the calorimeter, or 15.0 kJ / 2.00°C = 7.50 kJ/$^\circ$C.

      (b) The combustion causes the temperature of the calorimeter to increase by 1.54°C. The amount of heat given off during the combustion of 0.300 g of camphor is 1.54°C x 7.50 kJ/$^\circ$C = 11.6 kJ. The combustion of 1 mol, 152 g, would give off

$$\frac{11.6 \text{ kJ}}{0.300 \text{ g}} \times \frac{152 \text{ g}}{1 \text{ mol}} = 5.88 \times 10^3 \text{ kJ/mol}$$

The constant volume heat of combustion of camphor is -5.88×10^3 kJ/mol.

6.54   (a) C (graphite) $\longrightarrow$ C (diamond). No. There are no gases produced or consumed.

      (b) C (graphite) + O_2(g) $\longrightarrow$ CO_2(g). No. The number of moles of gas consumed equals the number of moles of gas produced; Δn gas = 0.

      (c) 2C (graphite) + O_2(g) $\longrightarrow$ 2CO(g). Yes. For each mole of oxygen gas consumed 2 mol of carbon monoxide gas is produced; Δn gas does not equal zero.

6.57 $CaCO_3$(s) $\longrightarrow$ CaO(s) + CO_2(g); $\Delta H^\circ = \Delta E^\circ + RT\Delta n$; $\Delta E^\circ = \Delta H^\circ - RT\Delta n$
ΔH° = +178.3 kJ, T = 298 K, and Δn = 1 mol – 0 mol = 1 mol. Substituting into the equation gives ΔE° = +178.3 kJ – (8.314 x 10^{-3} kJ/mol K) (298 K) (1 mol) = +178.3 kJ – 2.48 kJ = + 175.8 kJ.

6.59 $KClO_3$(s) $\longrightarrow$ KCl(s) + 3/2 O_2(g); $\Delta E = \Delta H - RT\Delta n$. ΔH = –39.0 kJ, T = 298 K, and Δn = 1.5 mol – 0 mol = 1.5 mol. Substituting into the equation gives ΔE = –39.0 kJ – (8.314 x 10^{-3} kJ/mol K) (298 K) (1.5 mol) = –39.0 kJ – 3.72 kJ = –42.7 kJ.

6.61 NH_3(g) + HCl(g) $\longrightarrow$ NH_4Cl(s); $w = -P\Delta V = -RT\Delta n$. For the gaseous reactants and products $\Delta n = n_{products} - n_{reactants}$ = 0 mol – 2 mol = –2 mol. The PV work done on the system is w = –(8.314 x 10^{-3} kJ/mol K) (298 K) (–2 mol) = +4.96 kJ. The surroundings do 4.96 kJ of work on the system.

6.62   More. Since the volume decreases, work is performed on the system by the surroundings during a constant pressure hydrocarbon combustion reaction. This work adds heat energy to the system and, therefore, more heat has to flow out of the system in order to bring it back to the original starting temperature.

6.66   (a) w = force x distance = 120 lb x 5000 ft = 6.00×10^5 ft·lb

$$w = 6.00 \times 10^5 \text{ ft·lb} \times \frac{0.239 \text{ cal}}{0.738 \text{ ft·lb}} = 1.94 \times 10^5 \text{ calories} = 194 \text{ kcal}$$

      (b) X x 0.250 = 194 kcal, X = 194 kcal/0.250 = 776 kcal

6.68   For the man to lose the 30 lb in 20 weeks, he must take in 30 x 3500 = 105,000 kcal less than required for normal maintenance over that period. On a per day basis, he would have to take in 105,000/140 = 750 kcal less than required for normal maintenance. A complication arises in the fact that the amount of calories required for normal maintenance per day decreases as the person loses weight. In other words, as the person begins to lose weight, he needs less calories to maintain his lower weight and his daily caloric intake would likewise be lowered.

To maintain the present weight of 180 lb he would have to take in 15 x 180 = 2700 kcal per day. But to maintain the final weight of 150 lb he only needs 2250 kcal per day. Therefore, on the first day of the diet the person should have a caloric intake of no more than 2700 − 750 = 1950 kcal per day, while on the last day of the diet the person should have a caloric intake of no more than 2250 − 750 = 1500 kcal per day. The average of the two extreme daily intakes (1950 + 1500)/2 = 1725 kcal per day provides an estimate of the daily caloric intake he would need in order to lose the 30 lb in 20 weeks. Therefore, in the beginning of the diet he would be losing more weight per day than at the end of the diet, but overall he should lose approximately 30 lb.

Answer: 1725 kcal/day.

6.70   (a) $w = -P\Delta V = -P \times (V_{final} - V_{initial})$; $w = -1.25$ atm $\times$ (8.50 L − 3.75 L) = −5.94 L atm

(b) $w = -5.94$ L atm $\times$ 101.3 J/1 L atm = −602 J. w is the PV work done on the gas. Since the system does work on the surroundings, w is negative.

6.72   The volume change per mole is

$$\Delta V = V_{final} - V_{initial} = 18.016 \text{ g} \times \frac{1 \text{ cm}^3}{0.9999 \text{ g/cm}^3} - 18.016 \text{ g} \times \frac{1 \text{ cm}^3}{0.9168 \text{ g/cm}^3}$$

= 18.018 cm^3 − 19.651 cm^3 = −1.633 cm^3 $\times$ 1 L/10^3 cm^3 = −1.633 $\times$ 10^{-3} L

$w = -P\Delta V = -1$ atm $\times$ (−1.633 $\times$ 10^{-3} L) = 1.633 $\times$ 10^{-3} L atm $\times$ 101.3 J/1 L atm = +0.1654 J

Work is done on the system (the system's volume decreases); therefore, w is positive.

6.73   For constant pressure changes $q = \Delta H$; therefore $q = \Delta H$ = +1.50 kJ. The initial volume of the sample is 100 g/0.820 g/cm^3 = 122 cm^3 = 0.122 L. The change in volume, ΔV, is 0.100 x 0.122 L = 0.0122 L. The work done on the system is $w = -P\Delta V = -1$ atm x 0.0122 L = −0.0122 L atm; w = −0.0122 L atm x 101.3 J/L atm = −1.24 J. w is negative because the substance expands and does work on the surroundings; i.e., the surroundings do negative work on the system, and $\Delta E = \Delta H - P\Delta V$ = +1.50 kJ − 0.00124 kJ = +1.50 kJ to three significant figures.

6.74   Warming it at constant pressure. Gases expand when heated (at constant pressure). Therefore, the gas does work on the surroundings (and in so doing loses energy to the surroundings) when heated under constant pressure and, consequently, requires more heat in order to bring it up to the final temperature.

6.76   (a) $CO(g) + 1/2 \ O_2(g) \longrightarrow CO_2(g)$. The total number of moles of gas decreases and, consequently, work is done on the system by the surroundings.

(b) $S(s) + O_2(g) \longrightarrow SO_2(g)$. The total number of moles of gas doesn't change and, consequently, no work is performed.

(c) $2 \ Mg(s) + O_2(g) \longrightarrow 2MgO(s)$. Gas is consumed during the reaction. Therefore, work will be performed on the system by the surroundings.

CHAPTER 7
QUANTUM THEORY AND THE
HYDROGEN ATOM

Solutions To Practice Exercises

PE 7.2 $E = h\nu$ and $\nu \times \lambda = c$. So $\nu = c/\lambda = E/h$ and

$$\lambda = \frac{c \times h}{E} = \frac{2.9979 \times 10^8 \text{ m/s} \times 6.626 \times 10^{-34} \text{ Js}}{1.50 \times 10^{-18} \text{ J}} = 1.32 \times 10^{-7} \text{ m} = 132 \text{ nm}$$

PE 7.3 $KE = h\nu - W$ and $\nu_o = W/h$.

$$\nu = c/\lambda = \frac{3.00 \times 10^8 \text{ m/s}}{500 \times 10^{-9} \text{ m}} = 6.00 \times 10^{14} \text{ s}^{-1}$$

$W = h\nu - KE = 6.63 \times 10^{-34} \text{ J s} \times 6.00 \times 10^{14} \text{ s}^{-1} - 1.08 \times 10^{-19} \text{ J}$

$\quad = 3.98 \times 10^{-19} \text{ J} - 1.08 \times 10^{-19} \text{ J} = 2.90 \times 10^{-19} \text{ J}$

$\nu_o = 2.90 \times 10^{-19} \text{ J}/6.63 \times 10^{-34} \text{ J s} = 4.37 \times 10^{14} \text{ s}^{-1}$

PE 7.4

$$n^2 = \frac{-2.179 \times 10^{-18} \text{ J}}{E_n} = \frac{-2.179 \times 10^{-18} \text{ J}}{-8.716 \times 10^{-20} \text{ J}} = 25; \quad n = 5$$

Answer: The fourth excited state.

PE 7.6   The energy of the electron before emission is equal to the ground-state energy plus the energy of the photon. The energy of the photon is

$$E = h\nu = \frac{hc}{\lambda} = \frac{6.6261 \times 10^{-34} \text{ Js} \times 2.9979 \times 10^8 \text{ m/s}}{97.25 \times 10^{-9} \text{ m}} = 2.043 \times 10^{-18} \text{ J}$$

$E_n = -2.179 \times 10^{-18} \text{ J}/n^2$. The energy of the ground state, $n = 1$, is
$E_1 = -2.179 \times 10^{-18}$ J. The energy of the electron before emission is
$E_{electron} = E_1 + E_{photon} = -2.179 \times 10^{-18}$ J $+ 2.043 \times 10^{-18}$ J $= -1.36 \times 10^{-19}$ J

The energy level the electron was in is

$$n^2 = \frac{-2.179 \times 10^{-18} \text{ J}}{E_n} = \frac{-2.179 \times 10^{-18} \text{ J}}{-1.36 \times 10^{-19} \text{ J}} = 16.0; \quad n = 4$$

Answer: The electron had an energy of -1.36×10^{-19} J and was in the fourth energy level (third excited state).

PE 7.7 The first Balmer line is caused by the electron transition from the $n = 3$ level to the $n = 2$ level.

$$E_{photon} = -2.179 \times 10^{-18} \text{ J}(\frac{1}{n_H^2} - \frac{1}{n_L^2})$$

$$= -2.179 \times 10^{-18} \text{ J}(\frac{1}{3^2} - \frac{1}{2^2}) = 3.026 \times 10^{-19} \text{ J}$$

$$\lambda = \frac{hc}{E_{photon}} = \frac{6.626 \times 10^{-34} \text{ Js} \times 2.998 \times 10^8 \text{ m/s}}{3.026 \times 10^{-19} \text{ J}} = 6.565 \times 10^{-7} \text{ m} = 656.5 \text{ nm}$$

The first Balmer line thus appears as an orange-red line (Fig. 7.3) in the emission spectrum of hydrogen.

PE 7.8 100 miles/h = 44.7 m/s

$$\lambda = \frac{h}{mv} = \frac{6.626 \times 10^{-34} \text{ Js}}{0.140 \text{ kg} \times 44.7 \text{ m/s}} = 1.06 \times 10^{-34} \text{ m}$$

The wavelength of the baseball is approximately $1/10^{29}$ that of the electron. The wavelength of the baseball is extremely small compared to that of the electron.

PE 7.9 For an f subshell, $l = 3$ and $2l + 1 = 7$. Any f subshell will always contain seven orbitals regardless of its n value. These correspond to the seven possible m_l values: $-3, -2, -1, 0, 1, 2, 3$.

Solutions to Final Exercises

7.6 The signal was in the form of electromagnetic radiation and, therefore, moved at the speed of light (c).

$$time = \frac{distance}{speed} = \frac{1.69 \times 10^{12} \text{ miles} \times 1609 \text{ m/mile}}{3.00 \times 10^8 \text{ m/s} \times 3600 \text{ s/h}} = 2.52 \times 10^3 \text{ h}$$

7.7 (a)
$$\nu = \frac{c}{\lambda} = \frac{3.00 \times 10^8 \text{ m/s}}{650 \times 10^{-9} \text{ m}} = 4.62 \times 10^{14} \text{ s}^{-1}$$

(b)
$$\lambda = \frac{c}{\nu} = \frac{3.00 \times 10^8 \text{ m/s}}{6.00 \times 10^{16}/\text{s}} = 5.00 \times 10^{-9} \text{ m} = 5.00 \text{ nm}$$

7.11 (a)
$$\nu = \frac{c}{\lambda} = \frac{2.9979 \times 10^8 \text{ m/s}}{589.0 \times 10^{-9} \text{ m}} = 5.090 \times 10^{14} \text{ Hz}$$

$$\nu = \frac{2.9979 \times 10^8 \text{ m/s}}{589.6 \times 10^{-9} \text{ m}} = 5.085 \times 10^{14} \text{ Hz}$$

(b) The visible region.

7.14   In certain physical interactions light behaves like a wave. In other physical interactions light behaves like a particle. The properties of waves and particles are not compatible with one another. True particles do not have wave properties and true waves do not exhibit particle properties. Since electromagnetic radiation exhibits both wave and particle properties at different times, it is said to have a "dual nature."

7.18 $E = h\nu = hc/\lambda$ and $\lambda\nu = c$.

Range In Which Wave Is Found	Frequency, ν	Wavelength, λ	Energy, E
Ultraviolet	1×10^{16} Hz	30 nm	7×10^{-18} J
Radio	1×10^{6} Hz	300 m	7×10^{-28} J
Infrared	5×10^{13} Hz	6 microns	3×10^{-20} J
Visible (green)	6×10^{14} Hz	500 nm	4×10^{-19} J
Visible (red)	4×10^{14} Hz	7000 A	3×10^{-19} J
X-rays	9×10^{16} Hz	3 nm	6×10^{-17} J

7.20   (a)
$$\nu = \frac{c}{\lambda} = \frac{2.9979 \times 10^8 \text{ m/s}}{589.2 \times 10^{-9} \text{ m}} = 5.088 \times 10^{14} \text{ Hz}$$

$E = h\nu = 6.6261 \times 10^{-34}$ J s $\times 5.088 \times 10^{14}$/s $= 3.371 \times 10^{-19}$ J

(b) From Fig 7.3 we see that radiation with wavelengths in the region of 600 nm lie in the orange-yellow portion of the visible spectrum. Therefore, objects will appear to be orange-yellow when they reflect this light.

7.22   The energy of one photon is
$$E = \frac{hc}{\lambda} = \frac{6.63 \times 10^{-34} \text{ Js} \times 3.00 \times 10^8 \text{ m/s}}{675 \times 10^{-9} \text{ m}} = 2.95 \times 10^{-19} \text{ J}$$

The energy of 1 mol of 675–nm photons is
$$\frac{2.95 \times 10^{-19} \text{ J}}{1 \text{ photon}} \times \frac{6.022 \times 10^{23} \text{ photons}}{1 \text{ mol}} = 1.78 \times 10^5 \text{ J/mol}$$

7.25   (a) The energy of one photon is
$$E = \frac{hc}{\lambda} = \frac{6.6261 \times 10^{-34} \text{ Js} \times 2.9979 \times 10^8 \text{ m/s}}{285.2 \times 10^{-9} \text{ m}} = 6.965 \times 10^{-19} \text{ J}$$

The number of photons required to provide 1 J of energy is
$$1 \text{ J} \times \frac{1 \text{ photon}}{6.965 \times 10^{-19} \text{ J}} = 1.436 \times 10^{18} \text{ photons}$$

(b) The energy of one photon is
$$E = \frac{6.6261 \times 10^{-34} \text{ Js} \times 2.9979 \times 10^8 \text{ m/s}}{501.5 \times 10^{-9} \text{ m}} = 3.961 \times 10^{-19} \text{ J}$$

The number of photons required to provide 1 J of energy is
$$1 \text{ J} \times \frac{1 \text{ photon}}{3.961 \times 10^{-19} \text{ J}} = 2.525 \times 10^{18} \text{ photons}$$

(c) The energy of one photon is

$$E = \frac{hc}{\lambda} = \frac{6.63 \times 10^{-34} \text{ Js} \times 3.00 \times 10^8 \text{ m/s}}{45 \times 10^{-6} \text{ m}} = 4.4 \times 10^{-21} \text{ J}$$

The number of photons required to provide 1 J of energy is

$$1 \text{ J} \times \frac{1 \text{ photon}}{4.4 \times 10^{-21} \text{ J}} = 2.3 \times 10^{20} \text{ photons}$$

(d) The energy of one photon is (1 gigahertz = 10^9 Hz; 1 GHz = 10^9 s^{-1}).

$$E = h\nu = 6.63 \times 10^{-34} \text{ J s} \times 8.4 \times 10^9/\text{s} = 5.6 \times 10^{-24} \text{ J}$$

The number of photons required to provide 1 J of energy is

$$1 \text{ J} \times \frac{1 \text{ photon}}{5.6 \times 10^{-24} \text{ J}} = 1.8 \times 10^{23} \text{ photons}$$

7.26 Based on the wave theory one would expect the release of some electrons at every frequency of radiation employed, since according to wave theory the energy of the radiation beam depends on the intensity and, therefore, a sufficiently intense beam of any frequency should supply enough energy to cause the ejection of electrons. However, no electrons are ejected until a threshold frequency is reached, no matter how intense the beam employed. This implies that the radiation energy is contained in tiny bundles or packets, called photons, and, therefore, supports the concept of the quantization of electromagnetic radiation.

Also, based on the wave theory one would expect the kinetic energy of the released electrons to depend on the intensity of the radiation. The more intense the radiation, the greater the kinetic energy of the ejected electrons. However, it is found that the kinetic energy of an ejected electron is independent of the intensity and just depends on the frequency of the radiation employed. This also implies that the radiation energy is quantized.

7.28 For the light to eject electrons, its frequency must be greater than the threshold frequency of the metal. The threshold frequency required to dislodge an electron from the potassium metal's surface is

$$\nu_o = \frac{W}{h} = \frac{3.69 \times 10^{-19} \text{ J}}{6.63 \times 10^{-34} \text{ Js}} = 5.57 \times 10^{14} \text{ Hz}$$

The frequency of radiation with a wavelength of 600 nm is

$$\nu = \frac{c}{\lambda} = \frac{3.00 \times 10^8 \text{ m/s}}{600 \times 10^{-9} \text{ m}} = 5.00 \times 10^{14} \text{ Hz}$$

Since the frequency of the light beam is less than the threshold frequency, no photoelectrons will be produced.

7.29

$$KE = h\nu - W = \frac{hc}{\lambda} - W = \frac{6.63 \times 10^{-34} \text{ Js} \times 3.00 \times 10^8 \text{ m/s}}{400 \times 10^{-9} \text{ m}} - 3.69 \times 10^{-19} \text{ J}$$

$$= 4.97 \times 10^{-19} \text{ J} - 3.69 \times 10^{-19} \text{ J} = 1.28 \times 10^{-19} \text{ J}$$

7.33   (a) $E_n = -2.179 \times 10^{-18}$ J/n^2, where n can only take on positive integer values (n = 1, 2, 3, . . .).

(b) The fact that n must be a positive integer limits the possible values of the energy. In other words, the energy is no longer continuous in the sense that it can take on any value. Any quantity that is not continuous, but is limited to certain values or is composed of distinct units, is considered to be quantized. Since it is the integral limitation on the number n that causes the discontinuity or quantization of the hydrogen energies, the number n is called or referred to as a "quantum number."

(c) Since E_n is negative, the greater the magnitude the lower the energy. Since n is in the denominator, the lower the value of n, the greater the magnitude. The lowest possible value for n is one. Therefore, the lowest allowed energy is associated with n = 1.

7.35   (a) The electron has greater (more) energy in the n = 3 level than in the n = 2 level; therefore, a photon must be absorbed when the electron makes a transition from level 2 to level 3.

(b)

$$E_{photon} = -2.179 \times 10^{-18} \text{ J}\left(\frac{1}{n_H^2} - \frac{1}{n_L^2}\right)$$

$$= -2.179 \times 10^{-18} \text{ J}\left(\frac{1}{9} - \frac{1}{4}\right) = 3.026 \times 10^{-19} \text{ J}$$

$$\lambda = \frac{hc}{E} = \frac{6.6261 \times 10^{-34} \text{ Js} \times 2.9979 \times 10^8 \text{ m/s}}{3.026 \times 10^{-19} \text{ J}} = 656.5 \text{ nm}$$

(c) The visible region of the spectrum.

7.36   As the value of n increases, the spacing between adjacent energy levels gets smaller and smaller. That means that the energy needed to advance to the next highest level continually decreases as n increases. Therefore, the energy required to go from n = 2 ——> n = 3 is greater than the energy required to go from n = 3 ——> n = 4. The greater the energy required (the larger the energy gap or spacing between levels) the higher the photon frequency must be and the shorter the wavelength. Therefore, the n = 2 ——> n = 3 transition will give the spectral absorption line of highest frequency and the n = 3 ——> n = 4 transition will give the spectral absorption line of longest wavelength.

7.37   One photon is emitted. According to Bohr, one photon of energy is given off or absorbed each time an electron moves from one energy level to another. Since the electron is going directly from the n = 4 level to the n = 1 level, only one photon is emitted.

7.39   (a) $E_n = -2.179 \times 10^{-18}$ J/n^2. As n increases without limit, n ——> ∞, E_n ——> 0. This means that the electron's energy approaches zero as it goes into higher and higher excited states.

(b) The change in energy between adjacent energy levels is (k = -2.179 x 10^{-18} J)

$$\Delta E = E_{n+1} - E_n = k\left(\frac{1}{(n+1)^2} - \frac{1}{n^2}\right) = k\left(\frac{n^2 - (n+1)^2}{(n+1)^2 \times n^2}\right)$$

$$= k\left(\frac{n^2 - n^2 + 2n + 1}{n^4 + 2n^3 + n^2}\right) = k\left(\frac{2n + 1}{n^4 + 2n^3 + n^2}\right)$$

As n ——> ∞, ΔE ——> 0 (the denominator goes to ∞ faster than the numerator). This means that the spacings between the energy levels get smaller and smaller as n increases and eventually the energy becomes continuous for all practical purposes.

7.41   The energies of the first six levels are given in Exercise 7.34. We will use these to calculate the photon energies of the first four Lyman lines. Lyman lines are caused by transitions from excited states (n = 2, 3, 4, . . .) down to the ground state (n = 1).

$n = 2 \longrightarrow n = 1$: $E_{photon} = E_2 - E_1 = -0.5448 \times 10^{-18}$ J $+ 2.179 \times 10^{-18}$ J $= 1.634 \times 10^{-18}$ J

$n = 3 \longrightarrow n = 1$: $E_{photon} = E_3 - E_1 = -0.2421 \times 10^{-18}$ J $+ 2.179 \times 10^{-18}$ J $= 1.937 \times 10^{-18}$ J

$n = 4 \longrightarrow n = 1$: $E_{photon} = E_4 - E_1 = -0.1362 \times 10^{-18}$ J $+ 2.179 \times 10^{-18}$ J $= 2.043 \times 10^{-18}$ J

$n = 5 \longrightarrow n = 1$: $E_{photon} = E_5 - E_1 = -0.08716 \times 10^{-18}$ J $+ 2.179 \times 10^{-18}$ J $= 2.092 \times 10^{-18}$ J

The wavelengths of the first four Lyman lines are:

$$n = 2 \longrightarrow n = 1: \quad \lambda = \frac{hc}{E} = \frac{6.6261 \times 10^{-34} \text{ Js} \times 2.9979 \times 10^8 \text{ m/s}}{1.634 \times 10^{-18} \text{ J}} = 121.6 \text{ nm}$$

$n = 3 \longrightarrow n = 1$: $\lambda = hc/1.937 \times 10^{-18}$ J $= 102.6$ nm

$n = 4 \longrightarrow n = 1$: $\lambda = hc/2.043 \times 10^{-18}$ J $= 97.23$ nm

$n = 5 \longrightarrow n = 1$: $\lambda = hc/2.092 \times 10^{-18}$ J $= 94.95$ nm

7.43   (a) The energy of the emitted photon is

$$E_{photon} = \frac{hc}{\lambda} = \frac{6.63 \times 10^{-34} \text{ Js} \times 3.00 \times 10^8 \text{ m/s}}{500 \times 10^{-9} \text{ m}} = 3.98 \times 10^{-19} \text{ J}$$

The final energy of the electron is $E_{initial} - E_{photon} = -7.0 \times 10^{-19}$ J -3.98×10^{-19} J $= -1.1 \times 10^{-18}$ J

(b) No. Because there is no energy level in hydrogen with an energy of -1.1×10^{-18} J (see solution to Exercise 7.34).

7.44   For He, $Z = 2$.

(a) The ground-state ($n = 1$) energy of He$^+$ is $E_1 = -(2)^2 \times 2.179 \times 10^{-18}$ J/$(1)^2 = -8.716 \times 10^{-18}$ J

(b) The energy of the $n = 2$ level of He$^+$ is $E_2 = -(2)^2 \times 2.179 \times 10^{-18}$ J/$(2)^2 = -2.179 \times 10^{-18}$ J

The photon energy needed for the transition is

$E_{photon} = E_2 - E_1 = -2.179 \times 10^{-18}$ J $+ 8.716 \times 10^{-18}$ J $= 6.537 \times 10^{-18}$ J

The wavelength of radiation that would cause the electron to jump from the ground state to the $n = 2$ level is

$$\lambda = \frac{hc}{E_{photon}} = \frac{6.6261 \times 10^{-34} \text{ Js} \times 2.9979 \times 10^8 \text{ m/s}}{6.537 \times 10^{-18} \text{ J}} = 30.39 \text{ nm}$$

7.48   The electrons. Protons have a mass approximately 1,840 times larger than that of electrons. Therefore, if protons and electrons are moving at the same speed, then from the de Broglie relationship $\lambda = h/mv$, we see that the electrons will have the longer de Broglie wavelength, since the smaller the mass the longer the wavelength.

7.50   (a) The value of Planck's constant ($h = 6.6 \times 10^{-34}$ J s), which appears in the numerator of the de Broglie equation, is an extremely small number. Therefore, the wavelengths associated with everyday life objects, which have masses very much larger than subatomic and atomic size particles, are extremely small. To observe wave phenomena, the wavelength of the wave must be of comparable size to the dimensions of the objects with which it interacts as well as to the dimensions of the spacings between the objects with which it interacts. If the wavelength is much smaller than the dimensions of the objects or the spacings between objects, then no wave phenomena are observed. Everyday life objects have such small wavelengths compared to the size of the objects and the spacings between the objects they interact with, that it is impossible to observe any wave phenomena, and this is why we are not aware of matter waves in everyday life.

(b) Subatomic particles have such small masses and, therefore, such small momenta (mv) that their wavelengths are comparable in size to the dimensions of atomic particles and the spacings between atomic particles. For example, their wavelengths are of the same dimension as the interatomic spacing in crystals. Consequently, wave phenomena should be observed for these subatomic particles in their interactions on the atomic level, and , therefore, the waves associated with these particles must be taken into consideration when dealing with subatomic particles.

7.51   The masses of the electron, proton, and neutron are 9.10953 x 10^{-31} kg, 1.67265 x 10^{-27} kg, and 1.67495 x 10^{-27} kg, respectively. The associated wavelengths are

$$\text{electron: } \lambda = \frac{h}{mv} = \frac{6.626 \times 10^{-34} \text{ Js}}{9.11 \times 10^{-31} \text{ kg} \times 50 \text{ m/s}} = 1.5 \times 10^{-5} \text{ m}$$

$$\text{proton: } \lambda = \frac{6.626 \times 10^{-34} \text{ Js}}{1.67 \times 10^{-27} \text{ kg} \times 50 \text{ m/s}} = 7.94 \times 10^{-9} \text{ m}$$

neutron: $\lambda = 7.94 \times 10^{-9}$ m

The wavelengths of the protons and neutrons are considerably smaller than those of the electrons.

7.53   The uncertainty principle states that it is impossible to make simultaneous and exact measurements of both the position and momentum of a particle. According to classical physics, to predict the precise path of a particle we have to make at least one simultaneous and exact measurement of both the position and momentum of the particle. Since the uncertainty principle tells us that such a measurement is impossible for very small particles, there is no way that we can obtain the necessary information needed to predict the precise paths of these particles and, therefore, we cannot obtain or predict precise paths for very small particles.

7.55   The measurement of the positions and momentums of everyday objects using photons affects the positions and momentums of these objects to such a small degree, since they are so massive compared to a photon's mass, that our senses and instruments cannot detect any effects at all. In other words, the degree of uncertainty introduced by these measurements is too small to be detected by our senses or the instruments with which large objects are observed.

7.56   Since the measurement of the positions and momentums of large, massive, bodies using photons has virtually no effect on the positions and momentums of these bodies, the values obtained from these measurements are accurate or valid. Hence, the distances between objects are not perceptibly changed by the measurement of those distances and the laws of classical mechanics are applicable.

7.58   (a) Bohr's quantized energy levels are retained in wave mechanics. Wave mechanics also retains the Bohr hypothesis that the absorption and emission of energy by one atom is accompanied by the transition of an electron from one energy level to another. His derived energy formula for hydrogen is also retained, since it gives the correct spectrum results and, therefore, must be correct.

(b) Bohr's model of the electron as a definite particle going around the nucleus in a precise path or orbit is abandoned. Also, any consequences directly related to this classical orbit model have been abandoned (see comment).

Comment: The Bohr orbits, since they are classical in nature, all have nonzero angular momentum values associated with them. Therefore, the Bohr model predicts that the hydrogen atom ground state has a definite angular momentum. Wave mechanics, on the other hand, predicts correctly a zero angular momentum for the hydrogen atom ground state (1s orbital).

Also, the Bohr model with its definite orbits doesn't allow the electron to get any closer than 52.9 pm to the nucleus. However, there is experimental evidence that indicates the s orbital electrons in an atom spend a fraction of their time inside the nucleus. This is explainable in wave mechanics by the fact that the s orbital electron density or electron cloud is spread out in space, including the space in and around the nucleus. Therefore, in wave mechanics there is a slight probability of finding the electron in the nucleus. These are just two interesting differences between the Bohr model and wave mechanics.

7.59   (a) Three quantum numbers are needed to specify an orbital.

(b)

quantum number	symbol
principal	n
azimuthal	l
magnetic	m_l

(c) The orbital quantum numbers are not independent. The restrictions on the quantum numbers values (or allowed values) are:
1. $n = 1, 2, 3, \ldots$, any positive integer (0 not allowed).
2. For a given value of n, l has integral values ranging from 0 to $n - 1$; $l = 0, 1, 2, \ldots, (n - 1)$.
3. For a given l value, m_l may have positive or negative integral values ranging from $-l$ to $+l$, including zero; $m_l = -l, -(l - 1), \ldots, (l - 1), +l$ or $m_l = 0, \pm 1, \pm 2, \ldots, \pm l$.

7.62   Within a given shell, all orbitals with the same l value constitute a subshell. The number of orbitals in a subshell is $2l + 1$; l is the azimuthal quantum number. Each orbital is specified by a different combination of the three orbital quantum numbers. No two orbitals have the same combination of three quantum numbers.
(a) All p orbitals have $l = 1$. Therefore, a p subshell has $2(1) + 1 = 3$ orbitals.
(b) In a subshell with $l = 2$ there would be $2(2) + 1 = 5$ orbitals.
(c) In the lowest energy shell the only allowed quantum numbers are $n = 1$, $l = 0$, and $m_l = 0$. Only one combination of the three quantum numbers exists and, therefore, there is only one orbital.
(d) The number of orbitals in the seventh shell is equal to the number of different combinations of the three orbital quantum numbers possible. In the seventh shell the allowed quantum numbers and numbers of orbitals are

```
        n = 7
        l = 0, 1, 2, 3, 4, 5, 6
l = 0:  m_l = 0                              ——> 1 orbital
l = 1:  m_l = -1, 0, 1                        ——> 3 orbitals
l = 2:  m_l = -2, -1, 0, 1, 2                 ——> 5 orbitals
l = 3:  m_l = -3, -2, -1, 0, 1, 2, 3          ——> 7 orbitals
l = 4:  m_l = -4, -3, -2, -1, 0, 1, 2, 3, 4   ——> 9 orbitals
l = 5:  m_l = -5, -4, -3, -2, -1, 0, 1, 2, 3, 4, 5 ——> 11 orbitals
l = 6:  m_l = -6, -5, ..., 5, 6               ——> 13 orbitals
                                             ————————————
                              Total = 49 orbitals
```

Answer: The seventh shell has 49 orbitals.

Comment: Thus, in general, for principle level n, there are n^2 possible orbitals in n subshells.

7.63   (a) All d orbitals have $l = 2$. The number of orbitals in a subshell is $2l + 1$; therefore, a d subshell has $2(2) + 1 = 5$ orbitals.

Answer: The 3d subshell has 5 orbitals.

(b) The number of orbitals in the fourth (n = 4) shell is equal to the number of different combinations of the three orbital quantum numbers possible. In the fourth shell the allowed quantum numbers and numbers of orbitals are

$$n = 4$$
$$l = 0, 1, 2, 3$$

$l = 0$:	$m_l = 0$	$\longrightarrow$ 1 orbital
$l = 1$:	$m_l = -1, 0, 1$	$\longrightarrow$ 3 orbitals
$l = 2$:	$m_l = -2, -1, 0, 1, 2$	$\longrightarrow$ 5 orbitals
$l = 3$:	$m_l = -3, -2, -1, 0, 1, 2, 3$	$\longrightarrow$ 7 orbitals

Total = 16 orbitals

Answer: The fourth shell has 16 orbitals.

(c) All f orbitals have $l = 3$. The number of orbitals in a subshell is $2l + 1$; therefore, an f subshell has $2(3) + 1 = 7$ orbitals.

Answer: The 4f subshell has 7 orbitals.

7.69 (a) The number of electron states in a shell is equal to $2n^2$. Therefore, for the n = 3 shell there are $2 \times (3)^2 = 18$ states.

(b) Quantum numbers of the electron states in the n = 3 shell.

Orbital Designation	n	l	m_l	m_s	Number of States
3s	3	0	0	+1/2, −1/2	2
3p	3	1	−1	+1/2, −1/2	2
3p	3	1	0	+1/2, −1/2	2
3p	3	1	+1	+1/2, −1/2	2
3d	3	2	−2	+1/2, −1/2	2
3d	3	2	−1	+1/2, −1/2	2
3d	3	2	0	+1/2, −1/2	2
3d	3	2	+1	+1/2, −1/2	2
3d	3	2	+2	+1/2, −1/2	2

7.70 The shapes of the orbitals are the surfaces or contours of equal electron density. Usually the shapes are chosen such that the probability of finding the electron residing in that orbital within the representative surface is 90% or better.

(a) The surfaces of all s orbitals are spheres. Therefore, the shape of all s orbitals is considered to be spherical.

(b) The surfaces of all p orbitals are dumbbell-shaped. Therefore, the shape of all p orbitals is considered to be like dumbbells.

(c) No. Four out of five of them have the same shape. See diagrams in text.

7.73 None of them represents the path of the electron. Because of the Heisenberg uncertainty principle it is impossible to specify a path for the electron. The best we can do is talk about or specify regions in space where there is a high probability of finding the electron. If you view the electron as being in a particle form in the atom, then the electron spends most of its time in these high-probability regions. If you view the electrons as being spread out in space as a three-dimensional electron cloud about the nucleus, then the regions of high probability are the regions in space that contain a relatively large amount or proportion of the overall or total electron cloud. (Remember, these are regions in space, not points. The small volumes around individual points may contain relatively high probabilities, while the region of space they're in contains only a small fraction of the overall electron cloud.)

7.76 1. See Fig. 7.29.
      2. (a) False. The electron can possibly be anywhere in space, though the probability of the electron being far from the nucleus is extremely small.
      (b) False. The probability of finding the electron within the balloon's boundary surface is around 90%.
      (c) False. A definite energy is associated with the orbital, not with the coordinates as in classical mechanics where only certain values of the coordinates are acceptable for a given energy value. As long as the electron remains in the orbital it will have the energy associated with that orbital, no matter where it is in space.

7.81 Absorption spectrum. Fraunhofer lines are caused by the cooler gases of the sun's outer layers absorbing light coming from the intensely hot interior of the sun. The absorptions are associated with specific transitions between the energy levels of the atoms in the gases of these outer layers. Therefore, only specific frequencies of the overall spectrum are absorbed. Whenever a specific frequency is absorbed, the light associated with that frequency isn't present any more and, therefore, a dark line appears at that frequency in the solar radiation spectrum.

7.82 The energy of one photon having a wavelength of 510 nm is

$$E_{photon} = h\nu = \frac{hc}{\lambda} = \frac{6.626 \times 10^{-34} \text{ Js} \times 2.998 \times 10^8 \text{ m/s}}{510 \times 10^{-9} \text{ m}} = 3.90 \times 10^{-19} \text{ J}$$

The number of 510-nm photons in 3.15×10^{-19} J is

3.15×10^{-17} J x 1 photon/3.90×10^{-19} J = 81 photons

7.84 (a) One mole of Br_2 molecules absorbed 193.9 kJ; therefore, one Br_2 molecule absorbed

$$\frac{193.9 \text{ kJ}}{1 \text{ mol Br}_2} \times \frac{1 \text{ mol Br}_2}{6.022 \times 10^{23} \text{ Br}_2 \text{ molecules}} = 3.22 \times 10^{-19} \text{ J/Br}_2 \text{ molecule}$$

Answer: The minimum energy of the photon is $E_{photon} = 3.22 \times 10^{-19}$ J.

(b) The maximum wavelength of the photon is

$$\lambda = \frac{hc}{E} = \frac{6.63 \times 10^{-34} \text{ Js} \times 3.00 \times 10^8 \text{ m/s}}{3.22 \times 10^{-19} \text{ J}} = 6.18 \times 10^{-7} \text{ m or 618 nm}$$

(c) From Fig. 7.3 we see that the visible region of the spectrum provides light of this wavelength.

7.86 An electron just removed from the hydrogen atom has zero energy. Therefore, the amount of energy required to remove an electron that is initially in the ground state of a hydrogen atom is the amount needed to make its energy zero. The energy of the electron in the ground state of hydrogen is -2.179×10^{-18} J. Therefore, it would take 2.179×10^{-18} J to remove or ionize the electron in the ground state of the hydrogen atom.

7.88 (a) The first Humphreys line is generated by the n = 7 —> n = 6 transition. The energy of the emitted photon accompanying this transition is

$$E_{photon} = -2.179 \times 10^{-18} \text{ J}(\frac{1}{49} - \frac{1}{36}) = 1.606 \times 10^{-20} \text{ J}$$

The wavelength of the first Humphreys line is

$$\lambda = \frac{hc}{E} = \frac{6.6261 \times 10^{-34} \text{ Js} \times 2.9979 \times 10^8 \text{ m/s}}{1.606 \times 10^{-20} \text{ J}} = 1.237 \times 10^{-5} \text{ m}$$

(b) From Fig. 7.3 we see that the first Humphreys line falls in the infrared region of the spectrum. Therefore, we should look in the infrared region of the spectrum.

7.90   Shifted to shorter wavelengths. The general energy formula for a system consisting of a nucleus and one electron is

$$E_n = -Z^2 \times 2.179 \times 10^{-18} \text{ J}/n^2$$

The general equation for the energies of the absorbed or emitted photons is therefore

$$E_{photon} = -Z^2 \times 2.179 \times 10^{-18} \text{ J} \left(\frac{1}{n_H{}^2} - \frac{1}{n_L{}^2} \right)$$

From this last equation we see that the emitted lithium ($Z = 3$) photons are 9 times more energetic than the corresponding emitted hydrogen ($Z = 1$) photons. The more energetic the photon, the shorter the wavelength. Therefore, the lines in each spectral series of Li^{2+} will be shifted to shorter wavelengths compared to the corresponding lines for hydrogen.

7.91   The radial electron density is the total amount of electron density contained within a thin spherical shell. At the nucleus the volume of the spherical shell is zero and, therefore, the radial electron density is zero, even though the electron density is at a maximum. As you go away from the nucleus, the shell volume continually increases while the electron density (ψ^2) continually decreases. At first the increasing volume factor wins out over the decreasing electron density factor and the radial electron density increases with increasing r. However, a point is reached where the decreasing electron density factor takes over and the radial electron density starts decreasing, rapidly approaching zero with increasing r after this maximum point. The maximum in the radial electron density corresponds to the most probable electron distance, i.e., the distance from the nucleus where you are most likely to find the electron.

CHAPTER 8
MANY-ELECTRON ATOMS AND
THE PERIODIC TABLE

Solutions To Practice Exercises

PE 8.1 The energy of an electron in a given orbital decreases with increasing atomic number. Within a shell the energy of an electron in an orbital increases with increasing l.
(a) The 1s electron in carbon would have a lower energy, since carbon's atomic number (Z = 6) is greater than hydrogen's (Z = 1).
(b) The 3s electron in chlorine would have a lower energy, since l = 0 for an s orbital and 1 for a p orbital.

PE 8.2 The orbital filling order for the first 36 elements is 1s 2s 2p 3s 3p 4s 3d 4p. Based on this orbital filling order:
(a) 2p will fill before 3s.   (b) 4s will fill before 3d.

PE 8.5 Lead is element 82; lead is in the sixth period, Group 4A. The preceding noble gas is zenon in the fifth period, therefore the lead configuration starts with [Xe]. Traveling from zenon to lead takes us 28 spaces across the sixth period, adding 2 electrons in the s block, 14 electrons in the f block, 10 electrons in the d block, and finally two p electrons. The configuration of lead is $[Xe]6s^24f^{14}5d^{10}6p^2$.

PE 8.6 When an atom forms a positive ion, its electrons are removed in order of decreasing principal quantum number. Within a shell electrons are removed in order of decreasing l value.
(a) The ground-state configuration of the barium atom is Ba (Z = 56): $[Xe]6s^2$. Barium will lose two 6s electrons in forming Ba^{2+}. The electron configuration of Ba^{2+} is [Xe].
(b) The configuration of the lead atom is Pb (Z = 82): $[Xe]4f^{14}5d^{10}6s^26p^2$. Lead will lose two 6p electrons in forming Pb^{2+}. The electron configuration of Pb^{2+} is $[Xe]4f^{14}5d^{10}6s^2$.

PE 8.9 (a) Ca (Z = 20): $[Ar]4s^2$. Diamagnetic – calcium has no unpaired electrons.
(b) Na (Z = 1): $[Ne]3s^1$. Paramagnetic – sodium has one unpaired electron in the 3s orbital.
(c) S (Z = 16): $[Ne]3s^23p^4$. Paramagnetic – sulfur has 2 unpaired electrons in the 3p orbitals.

PE 8.11 Monatomic positive ions (cations) are smaller than the parent atoms. Monatomic negative ions (anions) are larger than the parent atoms.
(a) Ba^{2+} is a positive ion; therefore Ba will have the larger radius.
(b) S^{2-} is a negative ion; therefore S^{2-} will have the larger radius.

PE 8.12 Ionization energies tend to decrease going down a group. Also, ionization energies tend to increase from left to right across a period.
  (a) Br lies just below Cl in Group 7A; therefore Cl should have a higher first ionization energy.
  (b) Mg (Group 2A) lies just to the right of Na (Group 1A) in the third period; therefore Mg should have a higher first ionization energy.

Solutions To Final Exercises

8.2 The energy of an electron in a given orbital decreases with increasing atomic number.
  (a) An electron in the 2p orbital of potassium would have a lower energy, since potassium's atomic number ($Z = 19$) is greater than sodium's ($Z = 11$).
  (b) The electron is more tightly bound to the atom in the 2p orbital of potassium. This is because the potassium nucleus has a greater charge and, therefore, exerts a greater attractive force. Moreover, the energy of the potassium electron is lower, so that more energy would be required to remove it.

8.4 The rule is that, regardless of filling order, electrons are removed from an atom in order of decreasing principal quantum number. Within a shell electrons are removed in order of decreasing l value.
  (a) 3d. The 4p electron in a gallium atom would be removed in ionization before the 3d electron. This means that the 3d electron is more tightly bound.
  (b) 3d. The 4s electron in a gallium atom would be removed in ionization before the 3d electron. This means that the 3d electron is more tightly bound.
  (c) 4s. The 4p electron in a gallium atom would be removed in ionization before the 4s. This means that the 4s electron is more tightly bound.

8.7 Paired electrons are two electrons that occupy the same orbital. Paired electrons have opposite (antiparallel) spins and their magnetic fields cancel. Unpaired electrons are single electrons that occupy different orbitals. In general, unpaired electrons have parallel spins and, therefore, their magnetic fields do not cancel.

8.8 The number of electron states in a shell is $2n^2$, where n is the principal quantum number of the shell. Therefore, the second shell ($n = 2$) can hold a maximum of $2 \times (2)^2 = 8$ electrons. The fourth shell ($n = 4$) can hold a maximum of $2 \times (4)^2 = 32$ electrons. The n'th shell can hold a maximum of $2n^2$ electrons.

8.9 The number of electron states is equal to twice the number of orbitals. The number of orbitals in a subshell is $2l + 1$. The number of orbitals in a shell is n^2; the number of electron states in a shell is $2n^2$.
  (a) A p subshell has $2(1) + 1 = 3$ orbitals. Therefore, it has 6 electron states. If all the states are filled the p subshell will contain 6 electrons.
  (b) A d subshell has $2(2) + 1 = 5$ orbitals. Therefore, it has 10 electron states. If all the states are filled the d subshell will contain 10 electrons.
  (c) An f subshell has $2(3) + 1 = 7$ orbitals. Therefore, it has 14 electron states. If only half the states are filled the f subshell will contain 7 electrons.
  (d) The $n = 3$ shell has $2 \times (3)^2 = 18$ electron states. If all the states are filled the $n = 3$ shell will contain 18 electrons.

8.15

N (Z = 7): ↿⇂ ↿⇂ ↿ ↿ ↿ ; three unpaired electrons.
           1s 2s   2p

Cl (Z = 17): ↿⇂ ↿⇂ ↿⇂ ↿⇂ ↿⇂ ↿⇂ ↿⇂ ↿⇂ ↿ ; one unpaired electron.
             1s 2s   2p   3s   3p

For chromium use the Table 8.1 configuration.

Cr (Z = 24): ↿⇂ ↿⇂ ↿⇂ ↿⇂ ↿⇂ ↿⇂ ↿⇂ ↿⇂ ↿⇂ ↿ ↿ ↿ ↿ ↿ ↿ ;
             1s 2s   2p   3s   3p   3d   4s

six unpaired electrons.

Zn (Z = 30): [Ar] ↿⇂ ↿⇂ ↿⇂ ↿⇂ ↿⇂ ↿⇂ ; no unpaired electrons.
                        3d   4s

As (Z = 33): [Ar] ↿⇂ ↿⇂ ↿⇂ ↿⇂ ↿⇂ ↿⇂ ↿ ↿ ↿ ; three unpaired electrons.
                        3d   4s   4p

8.17

Sc (Z = 21): ↿ — — — — ↿⇂
                  3d   4s

Ti (Z = 22): ↿ ↿ — — — ↿⇂
                 3d   4s

V (Z = 23): ↿ ↿ ↿ — — ↿⇂
                3d   4s

Cr (Z = 24): ↿ ↿ ↿ ↿ ↿ ↿
                 3d   4s

Mn (Z = 25): ↿ ↿ ↿ ↿ ↿ ↿⇂
                 3d   4s

Fe (Z = 26): ↿⇂ ↿ ↿ ↿ ↿ ↿⇂
                  3d   4s

Co (Z = 27): ↿⇂ ↿⇂ ↿ ↿ ↿ ↿⇂
                   3d   4s

Ni (Z = 28): ↿⇂ ↿⇂ ↿⇂ ↿ ↿ ↿⇂
                    3d   4s

Cu (Z = 29): ↿⇂ ↿⇂ ↿⇂ ↿⇂ ↿⇂ ↿
                     3d   4s

Zn (Z = 30): ↿⇂ ↿⇂ ↿⇂ ↿⇂ ↿⇂ ↿⇂
                     3d   4s

Note that chromium and copper are exceptions to the usual filling rule.

8.18   The ground-state configuration is the configuration that gives the atom a minimum energy. An excited-state configuration is any configuration that has a higher energy than that of the ground state.

8.19   The melting and boiling points are given below. Note that they seem to go in cycles of low and high values. The periodic nature of these fluctuations will be apparent in your plot.

Element	Melting Point ($^\circ$C)	Boiling Point
H (Z = 1)	−259	−252
He (Z = 2)	−272	−269
Li (Z = 3)	179	1317
Be (Z = 4)	1278	2970
B (Z = 5)	2300	2550
C (Z = 6)	3550	4827
N (Z = 7)	−210	−196
O (Z = 8)	−218	−183
F (Z = 9)	−220	−188
Ne (Z = 10)	−249	−246
Na (Z = 11)	98	892
Mg (Z = 12)	651	1107
Al (Z = 13)	660	2467
Si (Z = 14)	1410	2355
P (Z = 15)	44	280
S (Z = 16)	113	445
Cl (Z = 17)	−101	−35
Ar (Z = 18)	−189	−186
K (Z = 19)	64	774
Ca (Z = 20)	845	1487

8.23   (a) Representative elements: s and p blocks
(b) Transition elements: d and f blocks
(c) Inner transition elements: f block
(d) Metals: s, p, d, and f blocks
(e) Nonmetals: p block, plus H and He from the s block
(f) Rare earth elements (lanthanides): f block

8.26   (a) P (Z = 15): $[Ne]3s^23p^3$
(b) Y (Z = 39): $[Kr]4d^15s^2$
(c) Mo (Z = 42): $[Kr]4d^45s^2$
(d) Sm (Z = 62): $[Xe]4f^55d^16s^2$
(e) Hg (Z = 80): $[Xe]4f^{14}5d^{10}6s^2$

The configurations for P, Y, and Hg agree with those in Table 8.1. The configurations for Mo and Sm do not.

8.28   (a) Na (Z = 11): $[Ne]3s^1$
(b) Ca (Z = 20): $[Ar]4s^2$
(c) Ga (Z = 31): $[Ar]3d^{10}4s^24p^1$
(d) P (Z = 15): $[Ne]3s^23p^3$
(e) Te (Z = 52): $[Kr]4d^{10}5s^25p^4$
(f) Br (Z = 35): $[Ar]3d^{10}4s^24p^5$
(g) Ar (Z = 18): $[Ar]$
(h) Sn (Z = 50): $[Kr]4d^{10}5s^25p^2$

The outermost occupied electron shell is called the valence shell, and the electrons in this shell are called valence electrons. From the configurations we see that the number of valence electrons are: Na, 1; Ca, 2; Ga, 3; P, 5; Te, 6; Br, 7; Ar, 8 and Sn, 4. From Fig. 8.4 we see that in each case the number of valence electrons is equal to the group number of the group the element is in; i.e., Na - Group 1A; Ca - Group 2A; Ga - Group 3A; P - Group 5A; Te - Group 6A; Br - Group 7A; and Ar - Group 8A, and Sn - Group 4A.

8.29   (a) Halogens: ns^2np^5
(b) Alkali metals: ns^1
(c) Noble gases: ns^2np^6
(d) Alkaline earth metals: ns^2
(e) Oxygen group: ns^2np^4
(f) Group 5A: ns^2np^3

8.30   From the periodic Table:
  (a) Fe (Z = 26): $[Ar]3d^64s^2$ (d) Gd (Z = 64): $[Xe]4f^75d^16s^2$
  (b) Cu (Z = 29): $[Ar]3d^94s^2$ (e) Pt (Z = 78): $[Xe]4f^{14}5d^86s^2$
  (c) Mo (Z = 42): $[Kr]4d^45s^2$

  Cu, Mo, and Pt show irregularities.

8.32   (a) Zn (Z = 30): $[Ar]3d^{10}4s^2$. Zinc will lose two 4s electrons in forming Zn^{2+}. Zn^{2+}: $[Ar]3d^{10}$.
  (b) Co (Z = 27): $[Ar]3d^74s^2$. Cobalt will lose two 4s electrons and one 3d electron in forming Co^{3+}.
       Co^{3+}: $[Ar]3d^6$.
  (c) Al (Z = 13): $[Ne]3s^23p^1$. Aluminum will lose one 3p electron and two 3s electrons in forming
       Al^{3+}. Al^{3+}: $[Ne]$.
  (d) Ni (Z = 28): $[Ar]3d^84s^2$. Nickel will lose two 4s electrons in forming Ni^{2+}. Ni^{2+}: $[Ar]3d^8$.
  (e) V (Z = 23): $[Ar]3d^34s^2$. Vanadium will lose two 4s electrons in forming V^{2+}. V^{2+}: $[Ar]3d^3$.
  (f) F (Z = 9): $[He]2s^22p^5$. Fluorine gains one electron and, therefore, F^- has the same
       configuration as the atom with Z = 10. F^-: $[Ne]$.
  (g) S (Z = 16): $[Ne]3s^23p^4$. Sulfur gains two electrons and, therefore, S^{2-} has the same configuration
       as the atom with Z = 18. S^{2-}: $[Ar]$.
  (h) Ag (Z = 47): $[Kr]4d^{10}5s^1$. Silver will lose one 5s electron in forming Ag^+. Ag^+: $[Kr]4d^{10}$.

8.34   The number of valence electrons is equal to the number of electrons in the outermost occupied
  electron shell. Ground–state configurations can be obtained from Table 8.1.
  (a) Sr (Z = 38): $[Kr]5s^2$, two   (e) Cs (Z = 55): $[Xe]6s^1$, one
  (b) In (Z = 49): $[Kr]4d^{10}5s^25p^1$, three   (f) Si (Z = 14): $[Ne]3s^23p^2$, four
  (c) I (Z = 53): $[Kr]4d^{10}5s^25p^5$, seven   (g) Bi (Z = 83): $[Xe]4f^{14}5d^{10}6s^26p^3$, five
  (d) Se (Z = 34): $[Ar]3d^{10}4s^24p^4$, six   (h) Pb (Z = 82): $[Xe]4f^{14}6s^26p^2$, four

  Comment: For the representative elements, elements in the s and p blocks of the periodic table,
  the number of valence electrons is numerically equal to the group number of the group the
  element is in. (Helium is the only exception.) Therefore, for representative elements you can just
  consult the periodic table to determine the number of valence electrons in the atom. Check these
  answers with the answers you get from the periodic table. The results should be the same.

8.36   Paramagnetic substances have unpaired electrons. Unpaired electrons in atoms or ions gives
  the overall atom or ion a magnetic field. This magnetic field can interact with external
  magnetic fields. Therefore, paramagnetic substances are drawn into external magnetic fields
  because its constituent particles are magnetic.

  Paired electrons, two electrons in the same orbital, have opposed spins and their magnetic
  fields cancel. Atoms and ions whose electrons are all paired, i.e., atoms and ions containing no
  singly filled orbitals, have no net magnetic field. Such atoms and ions are called diamagnetic,
  and since they have no net magnetic field they cannot interact with an external magnetic field.
  Therefore, diamagnetic substances are not drawn into external magnetic fields because its
  constituent particles are not magnetic.

8.39   (a) K, Sc, Ti, V, Cr, Mn, Fe, Co, Ni, Cu, Ga, Ge, As, Se, and Br have paramagnetic atoms.
  (b) Ca, Zn, and Kr have diamagnetic atoms.

8.40   (a) N (Z = 7): $[He]2s^22p^3$. Nitrogen has three unpaired electrons in the 2p orbitals.
  (b) Cl (Z = 17): $[Ne]3s^23p^5$. Chlorine has one unpaired electron in the 3p orbitals.
  (c) Cr (Z = 24): $[Ar]3d^54s^1$. Chromium has one unpaired electron in the 4s orbital and five
       unpaired electrons in the 3d orbitals for a total of six unpaired electrons.
  (d) Zn (Z = 20): $[Ar]3d^{10}4s^2$. Zinc has no unpaired electrons.
  (e) Ag (Z = 47): $[Kr]4d^{10}5s^1$. Silver has one unpaired electron in the 5s orbital.
  (f) Ti (Z = 22): $[Ar]3d^24s^2$. Titanium has two unpaired electrons in the 3d orbitals.

8.43   The degree of paramagnetism increases with the number of unpaired electrons. The configurations of Cu, Cu^+, and Cu^{2+} are: Cu (Z = 29): $[Ar]3d^{10}4s^1$; Cu^+: $[Ar]3d^{10}$; and Cu^{2+}: $[Ar]3d^9$. Cu and Cu^{2+} both have one unpaired electron. Cu^+ has no unpaired electrons. Therefore, both Cu and Cu^{2+} should be the most paramagnetic. Cu^+ should be the least paramagnetic, since it is actually diamagnetic.

8.47   In general, atomic radii increase from top to bottom within a group. Also, in general, atomic radii decrease from left to right across a period.
(a) S (Group 6A) lies to the left of Cl (Group 7A) in the third period. S therefore has a larger atomic radius.
(b) Ba lies below Ca in Group 2A; therefore Ba has the larger atomic radius.
(c) Si (Group 4A) lies to the left of S (Group 6A) in the third period. Si therefore has a larger atomic radius.
(d) Na (Group 1A) lies to the left of Mg (Group 2A) in the third period. Na therefore has a larger atomic radius.
(e) C (Group 4A) lies to the left of N (Group 5A) in the second period; therefore C has the larger atomic radius.
(f) I lies below Br in Group 7A; therefore I has the larger atomic radius.

8.49   (a) O (Group 6A) lies to the left of F (Group 7A) in the second period. O is therefore larger than F. Mg (Group 2A, period 3) lies below and to the left of O; therefore Mg is larger than O. F is the smallest and Mg is the largest: F < O < Mg.
(b) C (Group 4A) lies to the left of F (Group 7A) in the second period. C is therefore larger than F. Si lies just below C in Group 4A; therefore Si is larger than C. F is the smallest and Si the largest: F < C < Si.
(c) K (Group 1A) lies to the left of Kr (Group 8A) in the fourth period. K is therefore larger than Kr. Rb lies just below K in Group 1A; therefore Rb is larger than K. Kr is the smallest and Rb the largest: Kr < K < Rb.

8.50   Monatomic positive ions (cations) are smaller than the parent atoms. Monatomic negative ions (anions) are larger than the parent atoms.
(a) K^+ is a positive ion; therefore K should have the larger radius.
(b) Cl^- is a negative ion; therefore Cl^- should have the larger radius.
(c) O^{2-} is a negative ion; therefore O^{2-} should have the larger radius.
(d) Fe^{3+} is more positive than Fe^{2+}; therefore Fe^{2+} should have the larger radius.
(e) P^{3-} is a negative ion; therefore P^{3-} should have the larger radius.
(f) S > O; therefore S^{2-} should have the larger radius.
(g) Both P^{3-} and S^{2-} have the configuration [Ar]. Since S^{2-} has the greater nuclear charge, Z = 16 for S^{2-} to Z = 15 for P^{3-}, P^{3-} should have the larger radius.
(h) I > Cl; therefore I^- should have the larger radius.

8.53   The electron configurations of the outer two main levels (5th and 6th shells) of the fourteen elements of the lanthanide series are the same, except for a few minor exceptions. In the lanthanide series electrons are being added to the seven 4f orbitals of the 4th shell. Therefore, the lanthanide atoms differ only in the number of underlying 4f electrons; the outer electron configurations are basically all the same. Because of this the lanthanide elements all form 3+ ions and have similar chemical properties. Furthermore, the lanthanides all have similar atomic radii. Similar sizes often leads to similar behavior. In conclusion, the lanthanides all exhibit similar behavior because they basically have the same outer electron configuration and similar sizes.

8.55   Low ionization energies. Positive ions are formed when electrons are removed from the neutral atom. This process requires the input of energy, and, in general, the lower the energy required to carry out a process the easier or more likely it is for the process to occur. Therefore, low ionization energies are more favorable for the formation of positive ions.

8.57   Ionization energies tend to decrease going down a group. Also, ionization energies tend to increase from left to right across a period. (Keep in mind that as you go across a period exceptions occur in Groups 3A and 6A.)

(a) Ca (Group 2A) lies just to the right of K (Group 1A) in the fourth period; therefore Ca should have the greater first ionization energy.

(b) F (Group 7A) lies to the right of C (Group 4A) in the second period; therefore F should have the greater first ionization energy.

(c) Se lies just below S in Group 6A; therefore S should have a higher first ionization energy.

(d) Ba lies below Mg in Group 2A; therefore Mg should have the higher first ionization energy.

(e) P (Group 5A) lies to the right of Al (Group 3A) in the third period; therefore P should have the greater first ionization energy.

(f) F (Group 7A) lies to the right of N (Group5A) in the second period; therefore F should have the greater first ionization energy.

8.59   It becomes progressively harder to remove subsequent electrons: fourth ionization energy > third ionization energy > second ionization energy > first ionization energy.

(a) Ca^{2+}, since two electrons have already been removed compared to none for Ca, i.e., third ionization energy versus first ionization energy.

(b) Fe^{3+}, since three electrons have already been removed compared to two for Fe^{2+}, i.e., fourth ionization energy versus third ionization energy.

8.60   Be ($1s^2 2s^2$) lies just to the right of Li ($1s^2 2s^1$) in period 2. Because of beryllium's greater nuclear charge, it requires more energy to remove a 2s electron from Be than from Li. Therefore, Be's first ionization energy should be greater than Li's.

After the first ionization the configurations of the ions are: Be^+ $1s^2 2s^1$ and Li^+ $1s^2$. The second ionization removes a 1s electron from Li^+ and a 2s electron from Be^+. Since a 2s electron is much further from the nucleus than a 1s electron, it requires substantially more energy to remove the 1s electron from Li^+ than the 2s electron from Be^+. Therefore, Li's second ionization energy should be substantially greater than Be's.

8.61   B ($[He]2s^2 2p^1$) and Al ($[Ne]3s^2 3p^1$) belong to Group 3A. The lone np electrons in the Group 3A atoms have a higher energy than the ns^2 electrons in the adjacent Group 2A atoms. Therefore, it is easier to remove the lone p electrons than the s electrons. Consequently, the first ionization energies of B and Al will be smaller than those of the elements immediately preceding them in the periodic table.

O ($[He]2s^2 2p^4$) and S ($[He]3s^2 3p^4$) belong to Group 6A. The paired p electrons in a Group 6A atom have slightly higher energies than the unpaired p electrons in a Group 5A atom due to repulsion between two electrons in one orbital. Therefore, it is easier to remove a paired Group 6A p electron than an unpaired Group 5A p electron. Consequently, the first ionization energies of O and S will be smaller than those of the elements immediately preceding them in the periodic table.

8.64   The second electron affinity of an atom is always positive (endothermic) because energy is required to overcome the electrostatic repulsion between the negative ion and the incoming electron.

8.71   If each electron has to have a different set of four quantum numbers, then only two electrons can have the same values of n, l, and m_l, since m_s can only take on two values $\pm 1/2$. An orbital is designated by the three quantum numbers n, l, and m_l. Since only two electrons can have the same n, l, and m_l quantum numbers, and they must have opposite spins to do so, we can conclude that orbital occupancy is limited to two electrons of opposite spins.

8.72 (a) The (n + l) values for the orbitals are: 1s, (1 + 0) = 1; 2s, (2 + 0) = 2; 2p, (2 + 1) = 3; 3s, (3 + 0) = 3; 3p, (3 + 1) = 4; 3d, (3 + 2) = 5; 4s, (4 + 0) = 4; and 4p, (4 + 1) = 5. Hence, the filling order for these orbitals based on the "n + l rule" is: 1s2s2p3s3p4s3d4p.

(b) Yes.

8.73 (a) The configurations based on the periodic table are: La (Z = 57): [Xe]5d^{1}6s^2; Ce (Z = 58): [Xe]4f^{1}5d^{1}6s^2; Pr (Z =59): [Xe]4f^{2}5d^{1}6s^2; Nd (Z = 60): [Xe]4f^{3}5d^{1}6s^2; Pm (Z = 61): [Xe]4f^{4}5d^{1}6s^2; Sm (Z = 62): [Xe]4f^{5}5d^{1}6s^2; Eu (Z = 63): [Xe]4f^{6}5d^{1}6s^2; Gd (Z = 64): [Xe]4f^{7}5d^{1}6s^2; Tb (Z = 65): [Xe]4f^{8}5d^{1}6s^2; Dy (Z = 66): [Xe]4f^{9}5d^{1}6s^2; Ho (Z = 67): [Xe]4f^{10}5d^{1}6s^2; Er (Z = 68): [Xe]4f^{11}5d^{1}6s^2; Tm (Z = 69): [Xe]4f^{12}5d^{1}6s^2; Yb (Z = 70): [Xe]4f^{13}5d^{1}6s^2; Lu (Z = 71): [Xe]4f^{14}5d^{1}6s^2; and Hf (Z = 72): [Xe]4f^{14}5d^{2}6s^2.

(b) According to the "n + l rule" the 4f should fill before the 5d, since (n + l) = 4 + 3 = 7 for 4f and (n + l) = 5 + 2 = 7 for 5d and when two orbitals have the same (n + l) value, the orbital with the lower n value fills first. The configurations based on the "n + l rule" are: La (Z = 57): [Xe]4f^{1}6s^2; Ce (Z = 58): [Xe]4f^{2}6s^2; Pr (Z = 59): [Xe]4f^{3}6s^2; Nd (Z = 60): [Xe]4f^{4}6s^2; Pm (Z = 61): [Xe]4f^{5}6s^2; Sm (Z = 62): [Xe]4f^{6}6s^2; Eu (Z = 63): [Xe]4f^{7}6s^2; Gd (Z = 64): [Xe]4f^{8}6s^2; Tb (Z = 65): [Xe]4f^{9}6s^2; Dy (Z = 66): [Xe]4f^{10}6s^2; Ho (Z = 67): [Xe]4f^{11}6s^2; Er (Z = 68): [Xe]4f^{12}6s^2; Tm (Z = 69): [Xe]4f^{13}6s^2; Yb (Z = 70): [Xe]4f^{14}6s^2; Lu (Z = 71): [Xe]4f^{14}5d^{1}6s^2; and Hf (Z = 72): [Xe]4f^{14}5d^{2}6s^2.

(c) Comparison of the configurations based on the periodic table with those in Table 8.1 shows that the configurations for Pr, Nd, Pm, Sm, Eu, Tb, Dy, Ho, Er, Tm, and Yb differ from those give in Table 8.1. Eleven configurations differ.

Comparison of the configurations based on the "n + l rule" with those in Table 8.1 shows that the configurations for La, Ce, and Gd differ from those given in Table 8.1. Three configurations differ.

(d) The "n + l rule" gives fewer wrong configurations and, therefore, gives better results for these elements.

8.74 (a) S (Z = 16): [Ne]3s^{2}3p^4 (d) Ra (Z = 88): [Rn]7s^2
(b) Sn (Z = 50): [Kr]4d^{10}5s^{2}5p^2 (e) Pu (Z = 94): [Rn]5f^{6}6d^{1}7s^2
(c) Po (Z = 84): [Xe]4f^{14}5d^{10}6s^{2}6p^4 (f) At (Z = 85): [Xe]4f^{14}5d^{10}6s^{2}6p^5

The configurations for S, Sn, Po, Ra, and At agree. The configuration for Pu is different.

8.75 (a) From Fig. 8.10 we see that the energy needed to ionize a mole of gaseous sodium atoms is 495.8 kJ/mol. The energy needed to ionize one gaseous sodium atom is

$$\frac{495.8 \times 10^3 \text{ J}}{1 \text{ mol}} \times \frac{1 \text{ mol}}{6.022 \times 10^{23} \text{ atoms}} = 8.233 \times 10^{-19} \text{ J/atom}$$

The wavelength of a photon with this energy is

$$\lambda = \frac{hc}{E} = \frac{6.6261 \times 10^{-34} \text{ Js} \times 2.9979 \times 10^8 \text{ m/s}}{8.233 \times 10^{-19} \text{ J}} = 2.413 \times 10^{-7} \text{ m or } 241.3 \text{ nm}$$

Answer: The longest wavelength of radiation that will ionize gaseous sodium atoms is 241.3 nm.

(b) From Fig. 7.3 we see that radiation with this wavelength falls in the ultraviolet region of the spectrum.

8.78   (a) O, since it is at the top of the group and, therefore, should have the smallest radius and least effective electron shielding.

   (b) Within a given group it is difficult to make predictions about the electron affinity. In Group 6A S has the most negative electron affinity. See Fig. 8.12.

   (c) O, since it is in the second period at the top of the group.

   (d) O, since it has the highest ionization energy.

   (e) Consult Fig. 8.12. O, since it has the highest electron affinity value.

   (f) Po, since it is in the sixth period at the bottom of the group and, therefore, has the lowest ionization energy and largest size.

CHAPTER S1
A SURVEY OF THE ELEMENTS 1:
GROUPS 1A, 2A, AND 8A

Solutions To Final Exercises

S1.2 (a) Water (H_2O), methane (CH_4), ethane (C_2H_6), propane (C_3H_8), and acetylene (C_2H_2).
(b) 1. The electrolysis of water.
2. The reaction of small-molecule hydrocarbons with steam at 800 to 1000°C in the presence of a catalyst (finely divided nickel).
3. The displacement of hydrogen from water by active Group 1A and Group 2A metals.
4. The displacement of hydrogen from acid solutions by active metals.
5. By the water gas reaction.
6. By the reaction of Group 1A and 2A hydrides with water.

S1.3

(a) $CH_4(g) + 2H_2O(g) \xrightarrow{\text{nickel, heat}} CO_2(g) + 4H_2(g)$

(b) $C(s) + H_2O(g) \xrightarrow{1000°C} CO(g) + H_2(g)$

(c) $2H_2O(l) \xrightarrow{\text{electrolysis}} 2H_2(g) + O_2(g)$

(d) $Zn(s) + H_2SO_4(aq) \longrightarrow ZnSO_4(aq) + H_2(g)$

S1.7 (a) Hydrogen ion, H^+, and hydride ion, H^-.
(b) H^-. H^- is larger because of electron repulsion between electrons in the same orbital.
(c) H^+. The hydrogen ion, $H^+(aq)$, can be found in aqueous solution.
(d) H^-. The hydride ion, H^-, is unstable in the presence of water and reacts instantly to form hydrogen gas and hydroxide ions.
(e) $H^- + H_2O(l) \longrightarrow H_2(g) + OH^-(aq)$

S1.12 The following compares neighboring (adjacent) Group 1A and 2A metals (elements).
(a) The alkali metals are more reactive.   (c) The alkaline earth metals are denser.
(b) The alkaline earth metals are harder.   (d) The alkali metals have lower melting points.

The atoms of the alkali metals have lower ionization energies than those of the alkaline earth metals. This accounts for their being more reactive. The atoms of the alkaline earth metals are heavier and smaller than those of the alkali metals. This accounts for their greater density. The atoms of the alkaline earth metals have a greater nuclear charge and smaller size than those of the alkali metals. Therefore, they can pack in closer and be held together more tightly. This accounts for their greater hardness. Also, because the atoms of the alkaline earth metals are packed in closer and held together more tightly, the amount of energy needed to separate their atoms is greater than that required to separate the atoms of the alkali metals. This accounts for their higher melting points. In summary, the greater hardness, density, and melting points of the Group 2A metals are physical properties caused by their smaller sizes and greater interatomic attractive forces in the solid state.

S1.13   (a) The Group 1A and Group 2A metals have relatively low ionization energies. This makes them very reactive, which means that they readily form compounds by donating their valence electrons to other atoms. Since the substances in nature are always intermingling, it is not possible for these active metals to remain in their free state for very long. Therefore, no Group 1A and Group 2A metals are found free in nature; they can only be found in their compounds.
   (b) The metals are stored under kerosene, or some other petroleum oil, in order to keep them from coming in contact with air. These metals tarnish within minutes of being exposed to air, and some spontaneously ignite when exposed to moist air.

S1.14   (a) The crust is composed of sodium carbonate. When exposed to the air, sodium unites with the oxygen and moisture in the air to form sodium hydroxide. The sodium hydroxide then reacts with the carbon dioxide present in air forming sodium carbonate.
   (b) Metallic sodium is so soft that it can easily be cut with a knife. Cutting away the tarnish crust reveals sodium's silvery-white metallic luster.

S1.16   No. A lot of energy is released in forming Group 1A and Group 2A compounds, the major proportion of which comes from the formation of the crystalline structure of the resulting ionic compounds. Therefore, a lot of energy has to be supplied in order to decompose these compounds, which means that they are not easily decomposed.

   (a) $2KCl(1) \xrightarrow{\text{electrolysis}} 2K(1) + Cl_2(g)$

   (b) $CaCl_2(1) \xrightarrow{\text{electrolysis}} Ca(s) + Cl_2(g)$

S1.21   Under ordinary conditions the beryllium and magnesium surfaces develop adherent oxide films that protect the remaining metal from further attack by air and moisture.

S1.22   (a) $2K(s) + 2H_2O(l) \longrightarrow 2KOH(aq) + H_2(g)$. The products are potassium hydroxide and hydrogen.
   (b) $CaO(s) + H_2O(l) \longrightarrow Ca(OH)_2(aq)$. The product is calcium hydroxide.
   (c) $NaH(s) + H_2O(l) \longrightarrow NaOH(aq) + H_2(g)$. The products are sodium hydroxide and hydrogen.
   (d) Nitrides form ammonia gas when decomposed by water.
   $Li_3N(s) + 3H_2O(l) \longrightarrow NH_3(g) + 3LiOH(aq)$. The products are ammonia gas and lithium hydroxide.

S1.23   (a) $Ca(s) + 2H_2O(l) \longrightarrow Ca(OH)_2(aq) + H_2(g)$. The products are calcium hydroxide and hydrogen.
   (b) $Li_2O(s) + H_2O(l) \longrightarrow 2LiOH(aq)$. The product is lithium hydroxide.
   (c) $CaH_2(s) + 2H_2O(l) \longrightarrow Ca(OH)_2(aq) + 2H_2(g)$. The products are calcium hydroxide and hydrogen.
   (d) $Mg_3N_2(s) + 6H_2O(l) \longrightarrow 2NH_3(g) + 3Mg(OH)_2(aq)$. The products are ammonia gas and magnesium hydroxide.

S1.26

(a) $2KCl(aq) + 2H_2O(l) \xrightarrow{\text{electrolysis}} 2KOH(aq) + H_2(g) + Cl_2(g)$

(b) $2NaHCO_3(s) \xrightarrow{\text{heat}} Na_2CO_3(s) + H_2O(g) + CO_2(g)$

(c) $Na_2CO_3(s) + 2HCl(aq) \longrightarrow 2NaCl(aq) + H_2O(l) + CO_2(g)$

(d) $2NaHCO_3(s) + H_2SO_4(aq) \longrightarrow Na_2SO_4(aq) + 2H_2O(l) + 2CO_2(g)$

S1.33   The noble gases remained undiscovered for so long because they are chemically inert, odorless, tasteless, liquefy only at very low temperatures, and scarce. In other words, they have no properties that affect our senses and, therefore, required the development of the appropriate and necessary scientific instruments for their discovery.

S1.34   Helium has the highest ionization energy. Because of this helium is chemically inert and acts like the Group 8A elements, which are also, with a few minor exceptions, chemically inert. On the other hand, the Group 2A elements have relatively low ionization energies and, consequently, are very chemically active. Therefore, even though He has the same outer electron configuration as the Group 2A elements, it is placed in Group 8A because its chemical properties are dissimilar to those of the Group 2A elements and similar to those of the Group 8A elements.

S1.36   (a) Helium, like hydrogen, escapes earth's gravity. The helium now present is produced underground by radioactive minerals that constantly emit alpha particles (He^{2+}) that capture electrons and become helium atoms. Earthly helium is found underground because it is produced and trapped there, and because any that escapes is lost.

(b) Radon is produced by the radioactive decay of radium, which means that only a very small amount is being produced at any given time. Radon itself is radioactive and soon decays to polonium by emitting alpha particles. Therefore, radon only has a temporary existence in transit from radium to polonium. The combination of very small production and temporary existence is why so little radon exists.

S1.37   (a) Over a period of time argon also escapes the earth's gravity. The earth's original argon supply, which consisted largely of argon–36 and argon–37, has escaped. Almost all the argon on earth now is argon–40 which is produced by the decay of radioactive potassium–40. Since the chemical atomic weight is the weighted average of the various isotopes of the element, and since all the lighter argon isotopes have been lost, the weighted average of the argon isotopes remaining turns out to be greater than the weighted average of the potassium isotopes, which includes a broader range of isotopic weights. Therefore, even though potassium ($Z = 19$) has a larger atomic number than argon ($Z = 18$), it has a smaller chemical atomic weight, since all the lighter argon isotopes have escaped.

(b) No. Since the fractional abundances of the isotopes may be different in other parts of the universe.

Since we don't know exactly how the elements were formed it is hard to make predictions of this sort. However, since the radioactive elements are the least stable elements, we can expect the greatest discrepancies to show up in these elements and the elements that are mainly products of radioactive decay.

S1.40   (1) Air contains oxygen, carbon dioxide, and water vapor, which can chemically interact with the filament and damage it. Argon and krypton are chemically inert and, therefore, will not attack the filament.

(2) The light emitted by an incandescent object is proportional to its temperature. Because Ar and Kr are heavier gases than He and N_2, they are poorer conductors of heat. Therefore, the use of Ar and Kr permits the filament to be heated to a higher temperature, and this results in a white light and a more efficient light bulb.

(3) Evaporation of the filament atoms can be retarded by collisions with gas molecules that slow down the evaporating filament atoms enough for them to reattach or return to the filament. Heavier gas molecules retard evaporation more than lighter ones. Therefore, Ar and Kr are more effective than He and N_2 in reducing the rate of evaporation of the filament. This increases the life of the light bulb.

S1.44   The heat evolved per mole of fuel combusted is its fuel value per mole.

(a) $2H_2(g) + O_2(g) \longrightarrow 2H_2O(l)$

$\Delta H° = 2 \times -285.8\ kJ - (2 \times 0\ kJ) - (1 \times 0\ kJ) = -571.6\ kJ$

fuel value of hydrogen per mole = +571.6 kJ/2 mol = +285.8 kJ/mol

(b) $CH_4(g) + 2O_2(g) \longrightarrow CO_2(g) + 2H_2O(l)$

$\Delta H° = 1 \times -393.5\ kJ + 2 \times -285.8\ kJ - (1 \times -74.8\ kJ) - (2 \times 0\ kJ) = -890.3\ kJ$

fuel value of methane per mole = +890.3 kJ/mol

(c) Water gas is composed of equimolar amounts of carbon dioxide and hydrogen. The fuel value of hydrogen per mole is known; the fuel value of carbon dioxide per mole has to be calculated.

$2CO(g) + O_2(g) \longrightarrow 2CO_2(g)$

$\Delta H° = 2 \times -393.5\ kJ - (2 \times -110.5\ kJ) = -566.0\ kJ$

fuel value of carbon monoxide per mole = +566.0 kJ/2 mol = +283.0 kJ/mol

The fuel value of water gas per mole = 0.5 mol H_2 × 285.8 kJ/mol H_2 + 0.5 mol CO × 283.0 kJ/mol CO = +284.4 kJ/mol

S1.45   The fuel values of hydrogen, methane, and water gas per gram are

H_2: $\dfrac{+285.8\ kJ}{1\ mol} \times \dfrac{1\ mol}{2.0\ g} = 142.9\ kJ/g$

CH_4: $\dfrac{+890.3\ kJ}{1\ mol} \times \dfrac{1\ mol}{16.0\ g} = 55.6\ kJ/g$

water gas: the molar mass of water gas is (28.0 g + 2.0 g)/2 = 15.0 g/mol.

$\dfrac{+284.4\ kJ}{1\ mol} \times \dfrac{1\ mol}{15.0\ g} = 19.0\ kJ/g$

Answer: Hydrogen has the highest fuel value per gram and water gas has the lowest fuel value per gram.

S1.47   (a) From the ideal gas law we have d = MP/RT. At 1.00 atm and 25°C the approximate densities are

H_2: $d = \dfrac{2.02\ g/mol \times 1.00\ atm}{0.0821\ L\ atm/mol\ K \times 298\ K} = 0.0826\ g/L$

He: $d = \dfrac{4.00\ g/mol \times 1.00\ atm}{0.0821\ L\ atm/mol\ K \times 298\ K} = 0.163\ g/L$

Ar: $d = \dfrac{39.348\ g/mol \times 1.00\ atm}{0.0821\ L\ atm/mol\ K \times 298\ K} = 1.61\ g/L$

Kr: $d = \dfrac{83.80\ g/mol \times 1.00\ atm}{0.0821\ L\ atm/mol\ K \times 298\ K} = 3.43\ g/L$

(b) Balloons filled with Ar and Kr will sink to the ground, since both gases have greater densities than air.

(c) Decrease with increasing altitude, since argon is denser and, therefore, should displace nitrogen at the lower altitudes. Consequently, the ratio of argon to nitrogen will be greatest at ground level and will steadily decrease with increasing altitude. The same holds for krypton.

S1.49 (a) The maximum wavelength the sensor will respond to is equal to the wavelength of a photon with an energy of 3.43×10^{-19} J. The maximum wavelength is

$$\lambda = \frac{hc}{E} = \frac{6.6261 \times 10^{-34} \text{ Js} \times 2.9979 \times 10^{8} \text{ m/s}}{3.43 \times 10^{-19} \text{ J}} = 579 \text{ nm}$$

(b) Yes. From Fig. 7.3 we see that the visible spectrum goes approximately from 390 nm to 750 nm. Therefore, the sensor will respond to a large portion of the visible spectrum.

S1.50 Potassium (fourth period) has considerably larger atoms than lithium (second period) and sodium (third period). As the atomic size increases, the attractive forces between the atoms in the solid metal decreases. Therefore, the potassium atoms are held together less tightly than those of lithium and sodium and, consequently, they can be more easily and rapidly removed during reaction with the water molecules, and this is why potassium has a greater reaction rate.

S1.51 $CaH_2(s) + 2H_2O(l) \longrightarrow Ca(OH)_2(aq) + 2H_2(g)$
100.0 g   mol = ?

The number of moles of H_2 produced in the decomposition is (g $CaH_2 \longrightarrow$ mol $CaH_2 \longrightarrow$ mol H_2)

$$100.0 \text{ g CaH}_2 \times \frac{1 \text{ mol CaH}_2}{42.10 \text{ g CaH}_2} \times \frac{2 \text{ mol H}_2}{1 \text{ mol CaH}_2} = 4.751 \text{ mol H}_2$$

$H_2(g) + 1/2 \, O_2(g) \longrightarrow H_2O(l)$ $\Delta H^\circ = -285.8$ kJ

The heat released by burning 4.751 moles of hydrogen is

$$4.751 \text{ mol H}_2 \times \frac{285.8 \text{ kJ}}{1 \text{ mol H}_2} = 1.358 \times 10^3 \text{ kJ}$$

The mass of water than can be heated from 25°C to 100°C by 1.358×10^3 kJ is

mass = q/specific heat x ΔT = 1.358×10^6 J/4.2 J/g°C x (100°C – 25°C) = 4.3×10^3 g.

The density of water is approximately 1.0 g/mL. Therefore, the number of liters of water that could be heated from 25°C to 100°C is

$$4.3 \times 10^3 \text{ g water} \times \frac{1 \text{ mL}}{1.0 \text{ g water}} \times \frac{1 \text{ L}}{10^3 \text{ ml}} = 4.3 \text{ L}$$

Answer: 4.3 L of water.

S1.52 $CaH_2(s) + 2H_2O(l) \longrightarrow Ca(OH)_2(aq) + 2H_2(g)$

Assume that the solution formed has a volume of 200.0 mL.

$Ca(OH)_2(aq) + 2HCl(aq) \longrightarrow CaCl_2(aq) + 2H_2O(l)$

The number of mmol of $Ca(OH)_2$ in 25.0 mL of solution is (V x M (of HCl) $\longrightarrow$ mmol HCl $\longrightarrow$ mmol of $Ca(OH)_2$)

$$29.4 \text{ mL HCl soln} \times \frac{0.200 \text{ mmol HCl}}{1 \text{ mL HCl soln}} \times \frac{1 \text{ mmol Ca(OH)}_2}{2 \text{ mmol HCl}} = 2.94 \text{ mmol Ca(OH)}_2$$

The total number of mmol of $Ca(OH)_2$ produced is 8 x 2.94 = 23.52 mmol $Ca(OH)_2$. The mass of CaH_2 originally present in the sample is (mmol $Ca(OH)_2$ —> mmol CaH_2 —> g CaH_2)

$$23.52 \text{ mmol } Ca(OH)_2 \text{ x } \frac{1 \text{ mmol } CaH_2}{1 \text{ mmol } Ca(OH)_2} \text{ x } \frac{0.0421 \text{ g } CaH_2}{1 \text{ mmol } CaH_2} = 0.990 \text{ g } CaH_2$$

The percent calcium hydride in the solid is

$$\% \; CaH_2 = \frac{\text{mass } CaH_2}{\text{mass sample}} \text{ x } 100\% = \frac{0.990 \text{ g}}{1.00 \text{ g}} \text{ x } 100\% = 99.0\%$$

S1.53   The equations for the burning of Mg in air are:

$$2Mg(s) + O_2(g) \longrightarrow 2MgO(s) \qquad\qquad 3Mg(s) + N_2(g) \longrightarrow Mg_3N_2(s)$$

x moles   x moles   3y moles   y moles

Let X and Y equal the number of moles of MgO and Mg_3N_2 formed, respectively. The molar masses of MgO and Mg_3N_2 are 40.3 g and 100.9 g, respectively. Then we have the following pair of simultaneous equations to solve

$x + 3y = 1.00, \quad x = 1.00 - 3y$ and x x 40.3 + y x 100.9 = 38.2

Substituting the value of X into the last equation we get

$$40.3(1.00 - 3y) + 100.9y = 38.2$$
$$20.0y = 2.1$$
$$y = 0.105 \text{ mol } Mg_3N_2$$
$$x = 1.00 - 0.105 = 0.895 \text{ mol MgO}$$

The fraction of the product that was MgO is

$$\text{fraction MgO} = \frac{\text{mass MgO}}{\text{mass product}} = \frac{0.895 \text{ mol MgO x } 40.3 \text{ g/mol MgO}}{38.2 \text{ g}} = 0.944$$

CHAPTER 9
THE CHEMICAL BOND

Solutions To Practice Exercises

PE 9.4   (a)   The cations Mg^{2+} and Ca^{2+} have the same charge and the anions F^- and Cl^- have the same charge. If the lattice energies differ, it will be because of size differences. In agreement with periodic trends, the sizes are $Mg^{2+} < Ca^{2+}$ and $F^- < Cl^-$. Therefore, MgF_2 should have a higher lattice energy, since smaller ions generally have higher lattice energies.

  (b)   F and O are adjacent to each other in the second period. They both form anions with the electron configuration [Ne]. Therefore, we can expect the sizes of F^- and O^{2-} to be similar. Consequently, if the lattice energies differ, it will be mainly because of charge differences. O^{2-} carries a larger charge than F^-; therefore, MgO should have a higher lattice energy.

  (c)   Al lies just to the right of Mg in the third period; therefore Al^{3+} should be smaller than Mg^{2+}. Also, Al^{3+} carries a charge of plus three while Mg^{2+} carries a charge of plus two. Consequently, AlF_3 should have a higher lattice energy.

PE 9.5   The enthalpy of sublimation is the enthalpy change accompanying the reaction

$Li(s) \longrightarrow Li(g)$ $\Delta H_{sublimation} = ?$

The following steps add up to the desired equation.

$$
\begin{array}{llll}
(1) & Li(s) + 1/2\ F_2(g) \longrightarrow LiF(s) & \Delta H_1 = -612.1\ kJ \\
(2) & LiF(s) \longrightarrow Li^+(g) + F^-(g) & \Delta H_2 = +1036\ kJ \\
(3) & Li^+(g) + e^- \longrightarrow Li(g) & \Delta H_3 = -520.3\ kJ \\
(4) & F^-(g) \longrightarrow F(g) + e^- & \Delta H_4 = +322\ kJ \\
(5) & F(g) \longrightarrow 1/2\ F_2(g) & \Delta H_5 = -78.5\ kJ \\
\end{array}
$$

The enthalpy of sublimation of lithium metal is obtained by adding the enthalpy changes of these steps.

$$
\begin{aligned}
\Delta H_{sublimation} &= \Delta H_1 + \Delta H_2 + \Delta H_3 + \Delta H_4 + \Delta H_5 \\
&= -612.1\ kJ + 1036\ kJ - 520.3\ kJ + 322\ kJ - 78.5\ kJ \\
&= +147\ kJ
\end{aligned}
$$

PE 9.12 (a) N_2O has $2(5) + 6 = 16$ valence electrons or 8 electron pairs. The resonance structures with their formal charges are

$$\overset{(-1)}{N} = \overset{(+1)}{N} = \overset{}{O} \quad \longleftrightarrow \quad :N \equiv \overset{(+1)}{N} - \overset{(-1)}{O}: \quad \longleftrightarrow \quad \overset{(-2)}{:N} - \overset{(+1)}{N} \equiv \overset{(+1)}{O}:$$

$$\text{I} \qquad\qquad\qquad \text{II} \qquad\qquad\qquad \text{III}$$

(b) Structure III is the least stable of the three structures since it has more formal charge on its atoms than structures I and II, and has positive charges on adjacent atoms as well. Therefore, structure III contributes least to the hybrid.

PE 9.16(a) $BeCl_2$ has $2 + 2(7) = 16$ valence electrons or 8 electron pairs.

$$:\!\overset{..}{\underset{..}{Cl}} - Be - \overset{..}{\underset{..}{Cl}}\!:$$

For $BeCl_2$ to follow the octet rule, Be would have to have a negative formal charge and each Cl a positive formal charge, which diminishes the importance of such a contributing structure to the hybrid. Consequently, $BeCl_2$ doesn't follow the octet rule.

(b) BCl_3 has $3 + 3(7) = 24$ valence electrons or 12 electron pairs.

$$
\begin{array}{c}
:\!\overset{..}{\underset{..}{Cl}}\!: \\
| \\
B \\
\diagup \quad \diagdown \\
:\!\overset{}{\underset{..}{Cl}} \qquad \overset{..}{\underset{..}{Cl}}\!:
\end{array}
$$

BCl_3 doesn't follow the octet rule for the same reasons that $BeCl_2$ doesn't.

(c) $SnCl_2$ has $4 + 2(7) = 18$ valence electrons or 9 electron pairs.

$$:\!\overset{..}{\underset{..}{Cl}} - \overset{..}{Sn} - \overset{..}{\underset{..}{Cl}}\!:$$

$SnCl_2$ doesn't follow the octet rule for the same reasons that $BeCl_2$ doesn't.

PE 9.17 ClO_2 has $7 + 2(6) = 19$ valence electrons or 9 electron pairs plus one odd electron.

$$:\!\overset{..}{\underset{..}{O}} - \overset{.}{\underset{..}{Cl}} - \overset{..}{\underset{..}{O}}\!:$$

To obey the octet rule, you have to have an even number of valence electrons. ClO_2 has an odd number of valence electrons and, therefore, cannot obey the octet rule.

PE 9.19 $2H_2(g) + N \equiv N(g) \longrightarrow N_2H_4(g) \qquad \Delta H° = ?$

The enthalpy change is the sum of the enthalpy changes for the following steps:

		$\Delta H°$	
1.	Breaking 2 mol of H–H bonds:	$2 \times +436 \text{ kJ} = +872$	kJ
2.	Breaking 1 mol of N≡N bonds:	$+945.3$	kJ
3.	Forming 4 mol of N–H bonds:	$4 \times -391 \text{ kJ} = -1564$	kJ
4.	Forming 1 mol of N–N bonds:	-170	kJ
		$\Delta H° = \text{Sum} = +83$	kJ

The enthalpy change is +83 kJ per mole of hydrazine.

PE 9.20 (a) For BCl_3 the electronegativity difference, $3.2 - 2.0 = 1.2$, is less than 1.7 and, therefore, each B–Cl bond is polar covalent.

(b) For RbCl the electronegativity difference, $3.2 - 0.82 = 2.38$, exceeds 1.7 and, therefore, RbCl is predominantly ionic: Rb^+Cl^-.

PE 9.21 OF_2 has $6 = 2(7) = 20$ valence electrons or 10 electron pairs. The Lewis structure for OF_2 is

$$:\!\ddot{F}\!-\!\ddot{O}\!-\!\ddot{F}\!:$$

Since both O–F bonds in OF_2 are equivalent, OF_2 can have a dipole moment only if the molecule is bent.

$$\overset{\textstyle O}{\underset{\textstyle F \qquad F}{\diagup \quad \diagdown}}$$

SO_3 has $6 + 3(6) = 24$ valence electrons or 12 electron pairs. The Lewis contributing structures to the hybrid are

expanded octet –
no formal charge

From the contributing structures we see that the three S–O bonds are equivalent. SO_3 can have a zero dipole moment only if the molecule is flat and the bonds point to the corners of an equilateral triangle.

Solutions to Final Exercises

9.10 (a) Sodium has the configuration $[He]2s^22p^63s^1$. The 3s electron is loosely held and, therefore, easily removed. The second electron would have to come from the 2p orbitals. The 2p electrons are tightly held since they are in a shell closer to the nucleus and the atom is now carrying a positive charge. Therefore, under normal conditions it requires too much energy to remove a second electron from sodium and, consequently, sodium does not normally form an Na^{2+} ion. The univalent ion, Na^+, also has a noble gas configuration, [Ne], which is quite stable.

(b) The lattice energies of the Group 2A elements are such that the lowest energies are attained with the plus two ions. The radius of Mg^+ would not be much different from the radius of the Mg atom. The radius of Mg^{2+}, on the other hand, is much smaller because the entire valence shell has been removed. The increased lattice energy in a Mg^{2+} compound more than compensates for the energy needed to remove the second electron.

(c) Cl^- has the stable noble gas configuration [Ar]. To form Cl^{2-} you would have to place an electron in a 4s orbital, i.e., in an s orbital one shell further from the nucleus. Such an electron would be loosely held, making Cl^{2-} highly reactive and unstable. Therefore, chlorine does not form a Cl^{2-} ion.

9.18   (a) Since the charges are the same any differences in lattice energies will be because of size differences. Mg (third period) lies just below Be (second period) in Group 2A. Therefore, Be^{2+} < Mg^{2+} and, consequently, $Be(NO_3)_2$ should have the higher lattice energy.

(b) The sizes of the ions involved are approximately the same and any differences in lattice energy will be because of charge differences. Ca^{2+} has a greater charge than Na^+ and, consequently, $Ca(OH)_2$ should have the higher lattice energy.

9.19   (a)

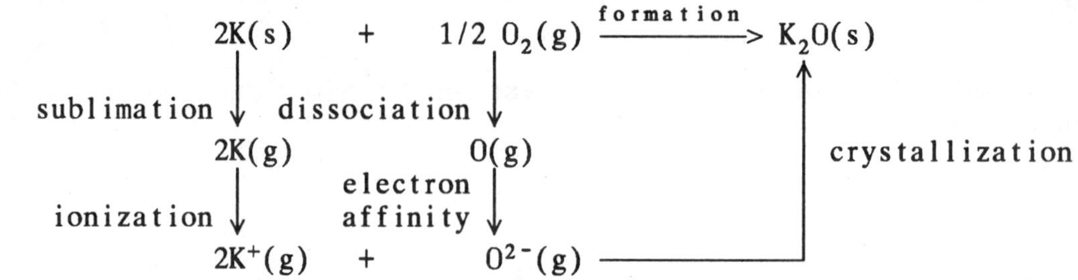

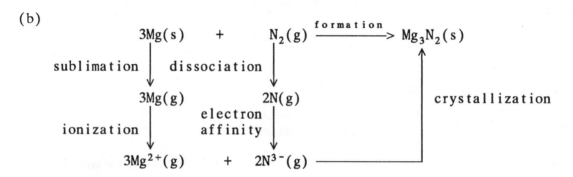

(b)

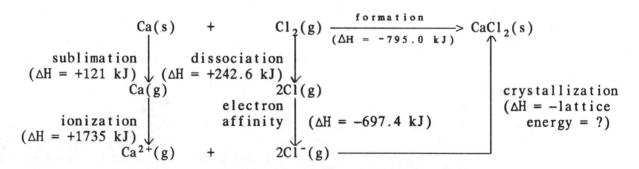

9.20   The Born-Haber Cycle for $CaCl_2$ is

The lattice energy is the enthalpy change accompanying the reaction

$CaCl_2(s) \longrightarrow Ca^{2+}(g) + 2Cl^-(g)$ lattice energy = ?

The following steps add up to the desired equation.

(1) $Ca(s)$ $\longrightarrow Ca(g)$ ΔH_1 = +121 kJ
(2) $Ca(g)$ $\longrightarrow Ca^{2+}(g) + 2e^-$ ΔH_2 = +1735 kJ
(3) $Cl_2(g)$ $\longrightarrow 2Cl(g)$ ΔH_3 = +243 kJ
(4) $2Cl(g) + 2e^- \longrightarrow 2Cl^-(g)$ ΔH_4 = −697 kJ
(5) $CaCl_2(s)$ $\longrightarrow Ca(s) + Cl_2(g)$ ΔH_5 = +795 kJ

The lattice energy is obtained by adding the enthalpy changes of these steps:

lattice energy = $\Delta H_1 + \Delta H_2 + \Delta H_3 + \Delta H_4 + \Delta H_5$
             = 121 kJ + 1735 kJ + 243 kJ − 697 kJ + 795 kJ
             = +2197 kJ

9.22   (a) N_2H_4 has 2(5) + 4(1) = 14 valence electrons or 7 electron pairs.

$$H-\overset{..}{\underset{|}{N}}-\overset{..}{\underset{|}{N}}-H$$
$$HH$$

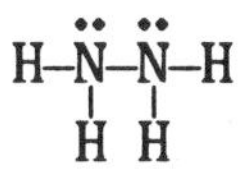

(b) H_2O_2 has 2(1) + 2(6) = 14 valence electrons or 7 electron pairs.

$$H-\overset{..}{\underset{..}{O}}-\overset{..}{\underset{..}{O}}-H$$

(c) C_2H_6 has 2(4) + 6(1) = 14 valence electrons or 7 electron pairs.

$$\overset{\displaystyle H\ \ H}{\underset{\displaystyle H\ \ H}{H-\underset{|}{\overset{|}{C}}-\underset{|}{\overset{|}{C}}-H}}$$

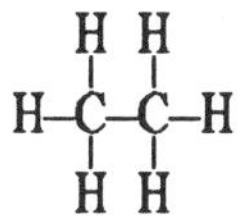

(d) C_2H_4 has 2(4) + 4(1) = 12 valence electrons or 6 electron pairs.

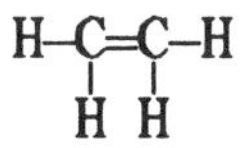

$$\underset{\displaystyle H\ \ H}{H-\underset{|}{C}=\underset{|}{C}-H}$$

(e) C_2H_2 has 2(4) + 2(1) = 10 valence electrons or 5 electron pairs.

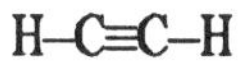

$$H-C\equiv C-H$$

(f) S_8 has 8(6) = 48 valence electrons or 24 electron pairs.

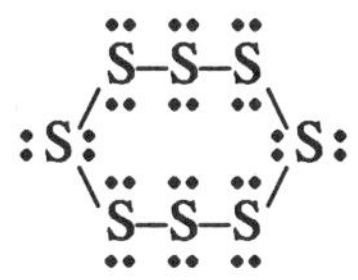

9.25   (a) O_3 has 3(6) = 18 valence electrons or 9 electron pairs.

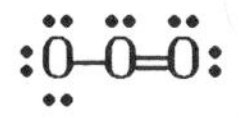

$$:\overset{..}{\underset{..}{O}}-\overset{..}{O}=\overset{..}{O}:$$

left O: formal charge = 6 − 6 − 1/2(2) = −1
middle O: formal charge = 6 − 2 − 1/2(6) = +1
right O: formal charge = 6 − 4 − 1/2(4) = 0

(b) H_2CO_3 has 2(1) + 4 + 3(6) = 24 valence electrons or 12 electron pairs.

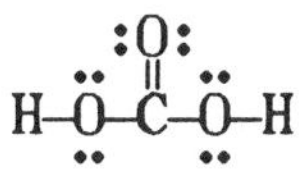

$$\overset{\displaystyle :\overset{..}{O}:}{\underset{..}{H-\overset{..}{\underset{..}{O}}-\overset{\|}{C}-\overset{..}{\underset{..}{O}}-H}}$$

H: formal charge = 1 − 0 − 1/2(2) = 0
left and right oxygen: formal charge = 6 − 4 − 1/2(4) = 0
upper oxygen: formal charge = 6 − 4 − 1/2(4) = 0
C: formal charge = 4 − 0 − 1/2(8) = 0

(c) NO_2^- has $5 + 2(6) + 1 = 18$ valence electrons or 9 electron pairs.

$$\left[:\ddot{O}-\ddot{N}=\ddot{O}: \right]^-$$

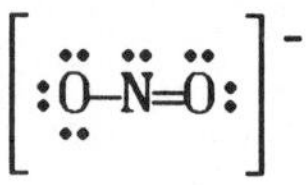

left O: formal charge = $6 - 6 - 1/2(2) = -1$
right O: formal charge = $6 - 4 - 1/2(4) = 0$

N: formal charge = $5 - 2 - 1/2(6) = 0$

9.27 (a) NO_2^- has $5 + 2(6) + 1 = 18$ valence electrons or 9 electron pairs.

$$\left[:\ddot{O}-\ddot{N}=\ddot{O} \right]^- \quad \longleftrightarrow \quad \left[\ddot{O}=\ddot{N}-\ddot{O}: \right]^-$$

(b) N_2O_4 has $2(5) + 4(6) = 34$ valence electrons or 17 electron pairs.

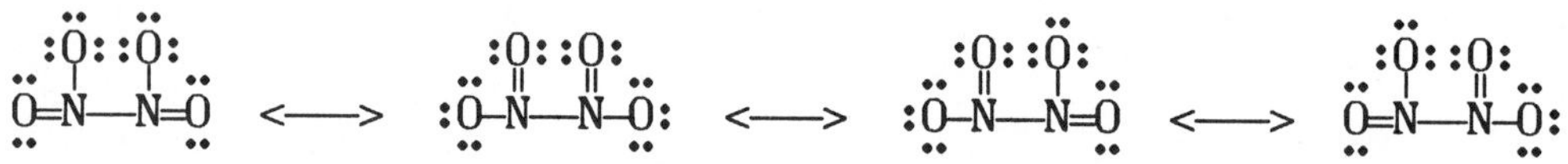

(c) HN_3 has $1 + 3(5) = 16$ valence electrons or 8 electron pairs.

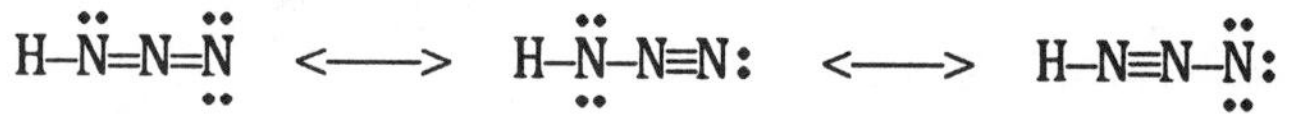

$$H-\ddot{N}=N=\ddot{N} \quad \longleftrightarrow \quad H-\ddot{N}-N\equiv N: \quad \longleftrightarrow \quad H-N\equiv N-\ddot{\ddot{N}}:$$

(d) CH_3COO^- has $3(1) + 2(4) + 2(6) + 1 = 24$ valence electrons or 12 electron pairs.

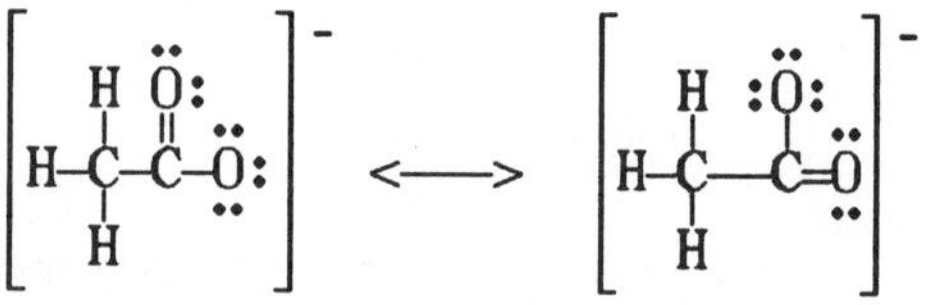

9.28 (a) Certain molecules and ions cannot be accurately depicted by a single Lewis structure. Such molecules and ions are depicted by two or more Lewis structures, which, when employed or taken together, give a better description than any single Lewis structure. The separate Lewis structures are called resonance structures or contributing structures, and the actual molecule or ion is referred to as a resonance hybrid. The actual molecule or ion, the resonance hybrid, has properties that are some combination of those of the contributing structures.

(b) Individual contributing structures do not represent the actual molecule. The properties of the individual contributing structures are different from those of the actual molecule or ion. For instance, bond length predictions based on individual contributing structures are incorrect.

9.29 (a)

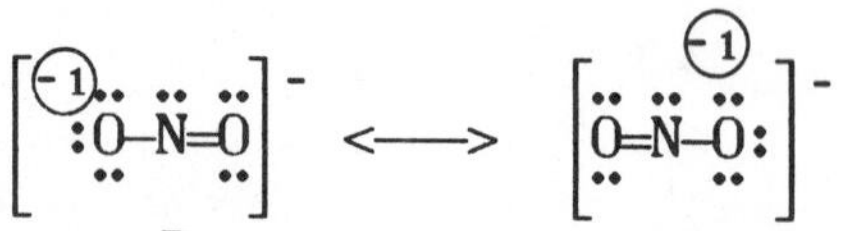

Both contribute equally.

(b)

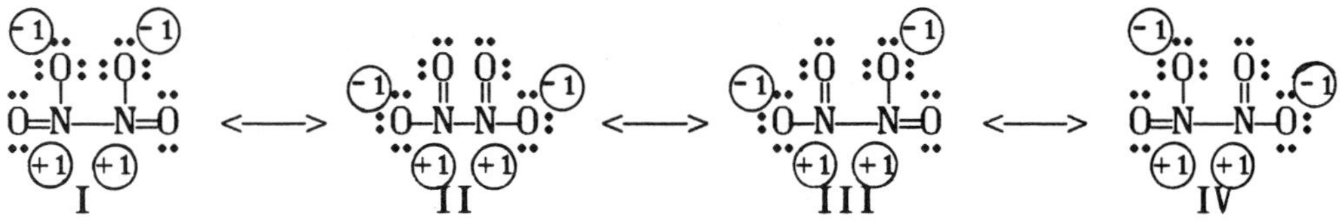

All contribute equally.

(c)

Structures I and II make greater contributions to the hybrid.

(d)

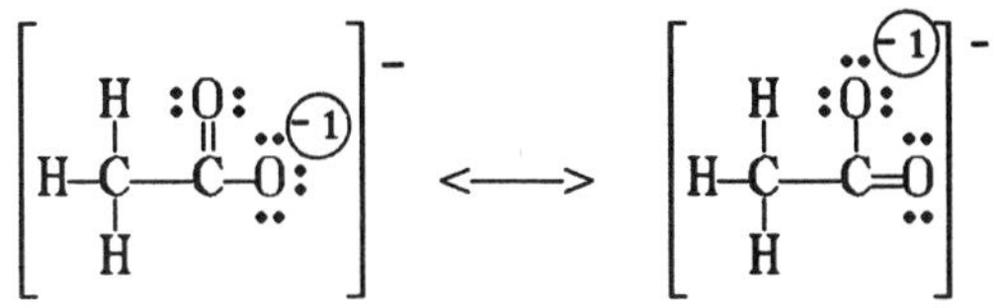

Both contribute equally.

9.33   (a) SO_2 has $6 + 2(6) = 18$ valence electrons or 9 electron pairs.

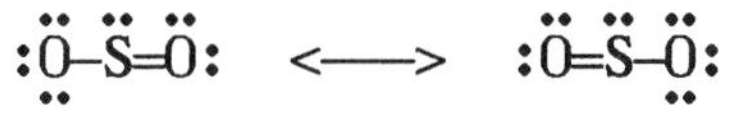

O_3 has $3(6) = 18$ valence electrons or 9 electron pairs.

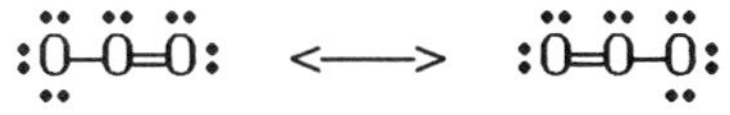

Both are triatomic molecules composed of Group 6A elements. They are both resonance hybrids and have the same number of valence electrons (18). They differ in the atom occupying the middle position.

(b)

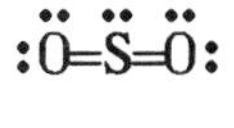

(c) No. Because oxygen has no d orbitals in its valence shell.

9.35   (a) $BeCl_2$ has $2 + 2(7) = 16$ valence electrons or 8 electron pairs.

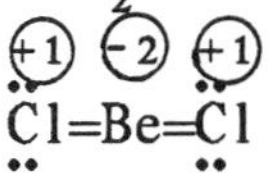

I

(b)

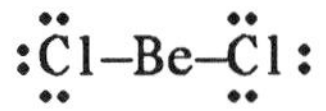

II

(c) Structure II. Structure I, which obeys the octet rule, places a positive formal charge on the Cl atoms and a negative formal charge on the Be atom. Cl has a strong electron attracting tendency and, therefore, it is unlikely that it would have a positive formal charge on it. Be, in Group 2A, has a tendency to give up electrons and, therefore, it is also unlikely that it would have a negative formal charge on it. Therefore, Structure I is unsatisfactory because of its formal charge distribution and, consequently, does not contribute as much to the resonance hybrid.

9.38   1. A free radical contains at least one unpaired electron.
        2. Free radicals are paramagnetic.
        3. Free radicals are usually colored.
        4. Most free radicals are unstable and highly reactive. Under ordinary conditions most of them have a fleeting existence.

9.40   (a) CH has $4 + 1 = 5$ valence electrons.

$$\cdot \ddot{C} - H$$

(b) C_2 has $2(4) = 8$ valence electrons.

$$\dot{C} \equiv \dot{C}$$

(c) OH has $6 + 1 = 7$ valence electrons.

$$:\dot{O} - H$$

(d) HCO has $1 + 4 + 6 = 11$ valence electrons.

$$H - \dot{C} = \ddot{O}:$$

9.42   Stronger bonds:
        (a) NH_3, since nitrogen is smaller than phosphorus.
        (b) CO, since the carbon to oxygen bond in CO is a triple bond ($:C \equiv O:$), while the carbon to

oxygen bonds in CO_2 are double bonds ($:\ddot{O} = C = \ddot{O}:$).

Shorter bonds:
(a) NH_3, since nitrogen is smaller than phosphorus.
(b) CO, since triple bonds are shorter than double bonds.

9.43   (a) Both ionic and covalent bonds are electrostatic in nature. Electrostatic attractions vary with the reciprocal of the square of the distance between the interacting charges; the smaller the distance the greater the attractive force. The small atoms can get closer to other atoms and, therefore, tend to have greater electrostatic attractions leading to stronger bonds.
        (b) The binding in covalent bonds is caused by the electrostatic attraction between the positive nuclei and the build up of negative electron density between the nuclei. The greater the negative electron density build up, the greater the electrostatic attraction, and the shorter and stronger the bond. Multiple bonds are made up of more electrons than single bonds and, therefore, build up a greater negative electron density between the nuclei. Consequently, multiple bonds have a greater electrostatic attraction, which leads to shorter and stronger bonds.

9.46   (a) C is to the left of O in the second period; therefore C is larger than O. S is in the third period; therefore S is larger than C and O. Therefore, S is the largest and O is the smallest; O < C < S. Consequently, the ranking in order of increasing bond energy is C=S < C=C < C=O.

(b) C=O < C=C < C=S

9.47   (a) Cl is above I in Group 7A; therefore Cl atoms are smaller than I atoms. In general, bonds between small atoms tend to be stronger than bonds between large atoms, therefore, the bond energy in Cl_2, with its two smaller chlorine atoms, is greater than the bond energy in I_2, with its two larger atoms.

(b) Since Cl < I, the ICl bond energy should be greater than I_2's.

9.48 $CH_4(g) + Cl_2(g) \longrightarrow CH_3Cl(g) + HCl(g)$ $\Delta H° = ?$

The enthalpy change is the sum of the enthalpy changes for the following steps:

		$\Delta H°$
(1)	Breaking 1 mol of C–H bonds:	+413 kJ
(2)	Breaking 1 mol of Cl–Cl bonds:	+242.6 kJ
(3)	Forming 1 mol of C–Cl bonds:	–330 kJ
(4)	Forming 1 mol of H–Cl bonds:	–431.8 kJ

$$\Delta H° = Sum = -106 \ kJ$$

- The enthalpy change is –106 kJ per mole of methyl chloride.

9.49 $1/2 H_2(g) + 1/2 Cl_2(g) + 1/2 O{=}O(g) \longrightarrow HOCl(g)$ $\Delta H_f° = ?$

The enthalpy of formation is the sum of the enthalpy changes for the following steps:

			$\Delta H°$
(1)	Breaking 1/2 mol of H–H bonds:	1/2 x +436 kJ =	+218 kJ
(2)	Breaking 1/2 mol of Cl–Cl bonds:	1/2 x +242.6 kJ =	+121.3 kJ
(3)	Breaking 1/2 mol of O=O bonds:	1/2 x +498.3 kJ =	+249.15 kJ
(4)	Forming 1 mol of O–H bonds:		–463 kJ
(5)	Forming 1 mol of O–Cl bonds:		–220 kJ

$$\Delta H_f° = Sum = -95 \ kJ$$

The enthalpy of formation of HOCl is -95 kJ per mole.

9.52 $1/2 H_2(g) + 1/2 Br_2(l) \longrightarrow HBr(g)$ $\Delta H° = ?$

The sum of the enthalpy changes of the following steps gives the required answer.

			$\Delta H°$
1.	$H(g) + Br(g) \longrightarrow HBr(g)$		–365.7 kJ
2.	$1/2 \ Br_2(l) \longrightarrow 1/2 \ Br_2(g)$	1/2 x +30.9 kJ =	+15.45 kJ
3.	$1/2 \ H_2(g) \longrightarrow H(g)$	1/2 x +436.0 kJ =	+218.0 kJ
4.	$1/2 \ Br_2(g) \longrightarrow Br(g)$	1/2 x +193.9 kJ =	+96.95 kJ

$$\Delta H° = Sum = -35.3 \ kJ$$

The standard enthalpy of formation of HBr is -35.3 kJ per mole.

9.54   (a) Cl is just above Br in Group 7A; therefore, Cl should be more electronegative.
       (b) P (Group 5A) lies to the left of S (Group 6A) in the third period; therefore, S should be more electronegative.
       (c) N (Group 5A) lies to the left of O (Group 6A) in the second period; therefore, O should be more electronegative.
       (d) As (Group 5A) lies to the left of Br (Group 7A) in the fourth period; therefore, Br should be more electronegative.

9.56   (a) O is to the right of N in the second period; therefore, O will be more electronegative and the bond polarity is

$$\delta+N-O\delta-.$$

       (b) Cl is just above Br in Group 7A; therefore, Cl will be more electronegative and the bond polarity is

$$\delta+Br-Cl\delta-.$$

       (c) S (Group 6A, third period) on the right side of the periodic table should be more electronegative than H (Group 1A, first period) on the left side of the periodic table. Therefore, the bond polarity is

$$\delta-S-H\delta+.$$

9.58   (a) For $BeCl_2$ the electronegativity difference, $3.2 - 1.6 = 1.6$, is less than 1.7 and, therefore, $BeCl_2$ is predominantly covalent.
       (b) For BF_3 the electronegativity difference, $4.0 - 2.0 = 2.0$, exceeds 1.7 and, therefore, BF_3 is predominantly ionic.
       (c) For KF the electronegativity difference, $4.0 - 0.82 = 3.18$, exceeds 1.7 and, therefore, KF is predominantly ionic.
       (d) For CsBr the electronegativity difference, $3.0 - 0.79 = 2.21$, exceeds 1.7 and, therefore, CsBr is predominantly ionic.
       (e) For AlF_3 the electronegativity difference, $4.0 - 1.6 = 2.4$, exceeds 1.7 and, therefore, AlF_3 is predominantly ionic.
       (f) For HBr the electronegtivity difference, $3.0 - 2.2 = 0.8$, is less than 1.7 and, therefore, HBr is predominantly covalent.

9.59   (a) HBr has $1 + 7 = 8$ valence electrons or 4 electron pairs.

$$\overset{\delta+}{H}-\overset{\overset{..}{\delta-}}{\underset{..}{Br}}:$$

       (b) H_3BO_3 has $3(1) + 3(6) = 24$ valence electrons or 12 electron pairs.

       (c)

$$\overset{\delta-}{C}-\overset{\delta+}{H} \; ; \quad \overset{\delta+}{C}-\overset{\delta-}{O} \; ; \quad \overset{\delta-}{O}-\overset{\delta+}{H}$$

9.60   (a) A bond dipole moment is the dipole moment associated with an individual bond. A molecular dipole moment is the net dipole moment associated with the whole molecule. The net dipole moment is obtained by vector addition of the individual bond dipole moments.

(b) They are identical for polar diatomic molecules and for polyatomic molecules where all but one of the bond dipole moments cancel each other out.

9.61   (a) Bent. If the molecule was linear, the two S-H bond dipole moments would cancel each other out, since they are pointed in opposite directions on the same line and have equal magnitudes. Therefore, if the molecule was linear the molecular dipole momnet would be zero and not 0.97D. Since the dipole moment is not zero the molecule must be bent.

(b)

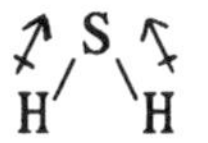

direction of individual
bond dipole moments

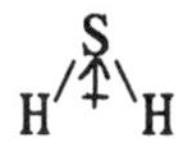

direction of net (molecular)
dipole moment

9.62   (a) CO has $4 + 6 = 10$ valence electrons or 5 electron pairs.

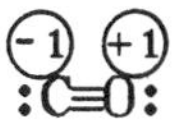

(b)

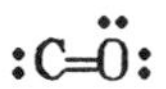

(c) Yes. The resonance structure that obeys the octet rule has a positive formal charge on the oxygen atom. The observation that the oxygen atom in the actual molecule is slightly positive is consistent with the assumption that this resonance structure contributes to the resonance hybrid.

9.63   It tells us that BF_3 must be flat with its bonds pointed to the corners of an equilateral triangle. BF_3 has $3 + 3(7) = 24$ valence electrons or 12 electron pairs. The Lewis structure is

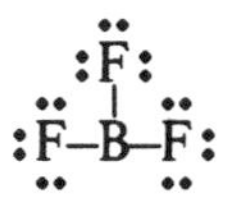

From the Lewis structure we see that all three B-F bonds are equivalent. In this situation BF_3 can have a zero dipole moment only if the molecule is flat and the bonds point to the corners of an equilateral triangle.

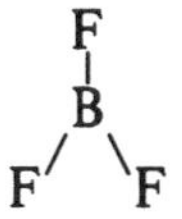

9.64 NH_3 has $5 + 3(1) = 8$ valence electrons or 4 electron pairs. The Lewis structure for NH_3 is

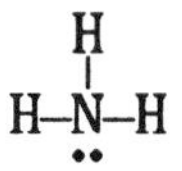

The three N–H bonds are equivalent, therefore we expect the bond angles to be equal. The 1.47 D value for the net dipole moment indicates that the individual bond dipole moments reinforce each other instead of cancelling each other. This could only happen if NH_3 is not flat, but pyramidal in shape.

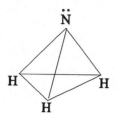

9.65   For CCl_4 to have a zero dipole moment, the individual bond dipole moments must cancel each other out. This can happen if (1) the molecule is flat and the C–Cl bonds point to the corners of a square and (2) the molecule is not flat and the C–Cl bonds point to the corners of a tetrahedron.

9.68   (a) BF_3 has $3 + 3(7) = 24$ valence electrons or 12 electron pairs.

$$\begin{array}{c} :\ddot{F}: \\ | \quad \ddot{} \\ B\text{–}F: \\ | \quad \ddot{} \\ :\ddot{F}: \end{array}$$

B: formal charge $= 3 - 0 - 3 = 0$

NH_3 has $3 + 5 = 8$ valence electrons or 4 electron pairs.

$$\begin{array}{c} H \\ | \\ H\text{–}N: \\ | \\ H \end{array}$$

N: formal charge $= 5 - 2 - 3 = 0$

F_3BNH_3 has $3(7) + 3 + 5 + 3(1) = 32$ valence electrons or 16 electron pairs.

$$\begin{array}{c} H \quad :\ddot{F}: \\ | \quad\quad | \quad \ddot{} \\ H\text{–}N\text{—}B\text{–}F: \\ | \quad\quad | \quad \ddot{} \\ H \quad :\ddot{F}: \end{array}$$

N: formal charge $= 5 - 0 - 4 = +1$
B: formal charge $= 3 - 0 - 4 = -1$

    (b) Yes. Boron's formal charge goes from 0 to –1 and nitrogen's goes from 0 to +1.

9.71   (a) NO_3^- has $5 + 3(6) + 1 = 24$ valence electrons or 12 electron pairs. The resonance structures for NO_3^- are

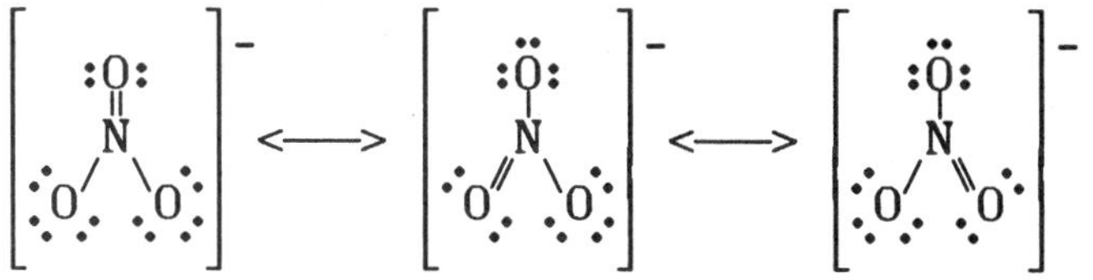

NO_2^- has $5 + 2(6) + 1 = 18$ valence electrons or 9 electron pairs. The resonance structures for NO_2^- are

NO_2^- should have the shorter N–O bonds since the double bond in NO_2^- is delocalized only over two bonds while the double bond in NO_3^- is delocalized over three bonds. Since the pi bonding electrons are spread over a greater volume or shared by more bonds in NO_3^-, the double-bond character of each of its N–O bonds should be less.

  (b) HNO_3 has $1 + 5 + 3(6) = 24$ valence electrons or 12 electron pairs. The resonance structures for HNO_3 are

The structure

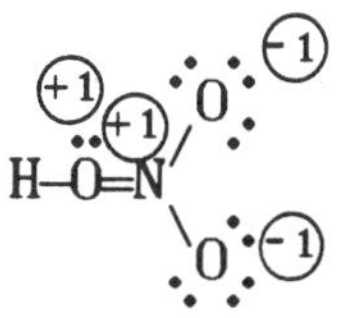

is largely discounted because of unfavorable formal charge.

Both N–O bonds should have the same length, since the double bond is delocalized equally over the two N–O bonds. The N–OH bond has less double-bond character and is therefore longer.

  (c) The two identical N–O bonds in HNO_3 should be shorter than those in NO_3^- for the same reasons given in part (a). The N–O bonds in HNO_3 have more double-bond character and, therefore, they should be shorter.

9.72 $2Se(s) + Cl_2(g) \longrightarrow Se_2Cl_2(g) \quad \Delta H_f^\circ = ?$

To solve this problem we first have to calculate the enthalpy change for the reaction

$2Se(g) + Cl_2(g) \longrightarrow Se_2Cl_2(g) \quad \Delta H^\circ = ?$

		ΔH°
(1) Breaking 1 mol of Cl–Cl bonds:		+243 kJ
(2) Forming 2 mol of Se–Cl bonds:	2 x –246 kJ =	–492 kJ
(3) Forming 1 mol of Se–Se bonds:		–175 kJ

$$\Delta H^\circ = \text{Sum} = -424 \text{ kJ}$$

The enthalpy of formation is the sum of the enthalpy changes for the following steps:

$$\Delta H^{\circ}$$

(1) $2Se(s) \longrightarrow 2Se(g)$ 2 x +203 kJ = +406 kJ
(2) $2Se(g) + Cl_2(g) \longrightarrow Se_2Cl_2(g)$ −424 kJ

$$\Delta H_f^{\circ} = Sum = -18 \ \ kJ$$

The enthalpy of formation of Se_2Cl_2 is −18 kJ per mole.

9.74   (a) O_3 has 3(6) = 18 valence electrons or 9 electron pairs. The resonance structures for ozone are

$$:\overset{..}{O}{=}\overset{..}{O}{-}\overset{..}{O}: \quad \longleftrightarrow \quad :\overset{..}{O}{-}\overset{..}{O}{=}\overset{..}{O}:$$

The formal charges on the oxygen atoms suggest that the center oxygen tends to be positive with respect to the end oxygens, and, consequently, a bond dipole moment exists.

(b) Since the resonance structures show that the two O–O bonds are equivalent, the ozone molecule cannot be linear because then it would have a zero dipole moment. Since the dipole moment is not zero, the molecule must be bent:

9.75   (a)
$$u = q \times d = 1.602 \times 10^{-19} \ C \times 128 \times 10^{-12} \ m \times \frac{1 \ D}{3.33 \times 10^{-30} \ C \ m} = 6.16 \ D$$

(b) The percent ionic character in HCl is

$$\frac{1.08 \ D}{6.16 \ D} \times 100\% = 17.5\%$$

9.76

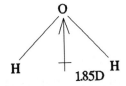

Dipole moments are vectors; they have magnitude and direction. Therefore, dipole moments can be treated mathematically like vectors are treated. In vector language, the H_2O molecular dipole moment is the resultant vector of the sum of the two individual O–H bond dipole moment vectors. This can be visualized using the parallelogram summing method.

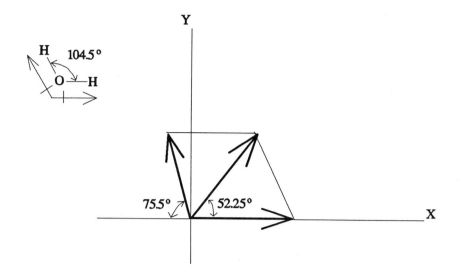

The magnitude, u_{bond}, of the bond dipole moment lying on the x axis is equal to the x component of the resultant minus the x component of the other bond dipole moment.

$u_{bond} = 1.85$ D cos $52.25° + u_{bond}$ cos $75.5°$

$u_{bond} = 1.133$ D $+ 0.250 \ u_{bond}$

$0.750 \ u_{bond} = 1.133$ D

$u_{bond} = \dfrac{1.133 \ D}{0.750} = 1.51$ D

Comment: The directions of the vectors have been reversed for mathematical simplicity. Vectors can be treated mathematically in this manner without changing the magnitude of the answer.

CHAPTER 10
CHEMICAL BONDING THEORY

Solutions To Practice Exercises

PE 10.1 (a) The Lewis structure for CO_2 is

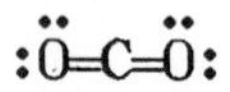

$$:\ddot{O}=C=\ddot{O}:$$

The two double bonds each contribute one pair, there are no single bonds or lone pairs; hence, there are two VSEPR pairs.

(b) The Lewis structure for NH_3 is

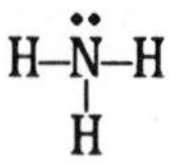

$$H-\ddot{N}-H$$
$$\underset{H}{|}$$

The three single bonds each contribute one pair, there is one lone pair, and there are no double bonds; hence, there are four VSEPR pairs.

PE 10.3 The Lewis structure for ozone (9 electron pairs) is

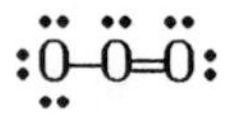

$$:\ddot{O}-\overset{\cdot\cdot}{\underset{\cdot\cdot}{O}}=\ddot{O}:$$

The central oxygen has three VSEPR pairs, which adopt a trigonal planar arrangement. The molecule is bent (V–shaped).

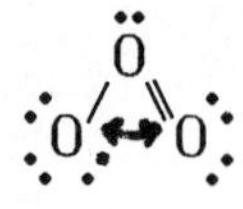

$$:\overset{\cdot}{\underset{\cdot\cdot}{O}} \longleftrightarrow \overset{\ddot{O}}{} \overset{\cdot}{\underset{\cdot\cdot}{O}}:$$

around $120°$

PE 10.8 NO_2^- has $5 + 2(6) + 1 = 18$ valence electrons or 9 electron pairs. The Lewis structure is

$$\left[:\ddot{O}-\ddot{N}=\ddot{O}: \right]^- \quad \text{(a resonance hybrid)}$$

The central N has three VSEPR pairs, which adapt a trigonal planar arrangement. Since one of the pairs is a lone pair, the molecule is bent (V-shaped). Compression caused by the lone pair should make the bond angle slightly less than $120°$.

PE 10.13

H–N–C–H with H H on top of N and C, and H below C, and lone pair on N

N and C, each with four VSEPR pairs, are sp^3 hybridized. Consequently, the bond angles (H-N-H, H-N-C, N-C-H, and H-C-H) will all be approximately $109.5°$. (Although it is likely that the H-N-H and H-N-C bond angles will be somewhat less than $109.5°$ due to the non-bonding pair on N.)

PE 10.14 (a) The ground-state configuration for H_2^+ is $(\sigma_{1s})^1$. It has one bonding electron and no anti-bonding electrons. The bond order is $(1-0)/2 = 1/2$.

(b) The ground-state configuration for H_2^- is $(\sigma_{1s})^2 (\sigma_{1s}^*)^1$. It has two bonding electrons and one antibonding electron. The bond order is $(2-1)/2 = 1/2$.

(c) The ground-state configuration for He_2 is $(\sigma_{1s})^2 (\sigma_{1s}^*)^2$. It has two bonding electrons and two antibonding electrons. The bond order is $(2-2)/2 = 0$.

PE 10.15 Be_2 has eight electrons; its molecular orbital configuration is $(\sigma_{1s})^2 (\sigma_{1s}^*)^2 (\sigma_{2s})^2 (\sigma_{2s}^*)^2$. Be_2 has four bonding electrons and four antibonding electrons. The bond order is $(4-4)/2 = 0$. Be_2 is unstable, since the bond order is zero.

PE 10.16 (a) N_2 has 14 electrons; its molecular orbital configuration is $(\sigma_{1s})^2 (\sigma_{1s}^*)^2 (\sigma_{2s})^2 (\sigma_{2s}^*)^2 (\pi_{2py})^2 (\pi_{2pz})^2 (\sigma_{2px})^2$.

(b) No. N_2 has no unpaired electrons and, therefore, is not paramagnetic.

PE 10.17 First we will determine their molecular orbital configurations and bond orders.
O_2^{2-} has 18 electrons; its molecular orbital configuration is
$(\sigma_{1s})^2(\sigma_{1s}^*)^2 (\sigma_{2s})^2 (\sigma_{2s}^*)^2 (\sigma_{2px})^2 (\pi_{2py})^2 (\pi_{2pz})^2 (\pi_{2py}^*)^2 (\pi_{2pz}^*)^2$.
O_2^{2-} has 10 bonding electrons and 8 antibonding electrons. The bond order is $(10-8)/2 = 1$.
O_2^- has 17 electrons; its molecular orbital configuration is
$(\sigma_{1s})^2 (\sigma_{1s}^*)^2 (\sigma_{2s})^2 (\sigma_{2s}^*)^2 (\sigma_{2px})^2 (\pi_{2py})^2 (\pi_{2pz})^2 (\pi_{2py}^*)^2 (\pi_{2pz}^*)^1$.
O_2^- has 10 bonding electrons and 7 antibonding electrons. The bond order is $(10-7)/2 = 3/2$.

(a) O_2^{2-} is not paramagnetic because it has no unpaired electrons. O_2^- is paramagnetic because it has an unpaired electron.

(b) O_2^- should have a higher bond energy.

(c) O_2^- should have a shorter bond length.

PE 10.18 (a) HeH^+ has 2 electrons; its molecular orbital configuration is $(\sigma_{1s})^2$.

(b) Yes. HeH^+ has two bonding electrons and no antibonding electrons. The bond order is $(2-0)/2 = 1$. Since the bond order is greater than zero, HeH^+ should be stable.

Solutions To Final Exercises

10.2

Lewis Structure	VSEPR pairs	Lone pairs	Shape	Bond Angles
(a) 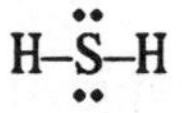 H–S–H	4	2	bent	$< 109.5°$
(b) 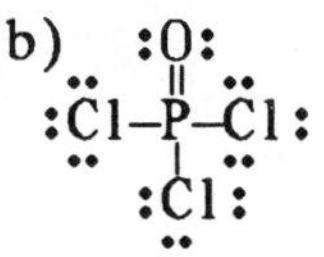 :Cl–P–Cl: (with =O above P and :Cl below)	4	0	tetrahedral	$109.5°$
(c) 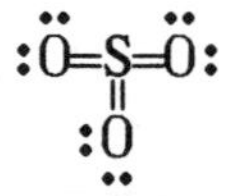 :O=S=O: (with :O below)	3	0	trigonal planar	$120°$
(d) 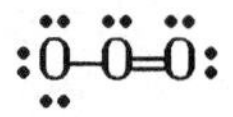 :O–O=O:	3	1	bent	$< 120°$
(e) 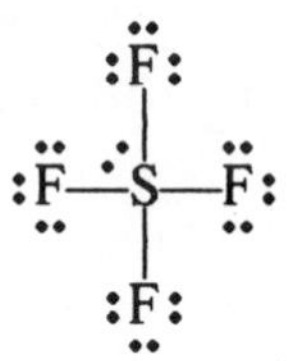 :F–S–F: (with :F above and :F below)	5	1	distorted seesaw	$120°, < 90°$
(f) 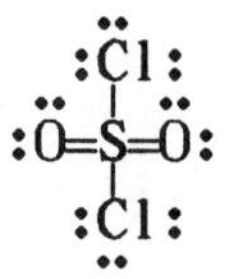 :O=S=O: (with :Cl above and :Cl below)	4	0	tetrahedral	$109.5°$
(g) 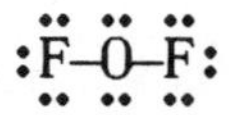 :F–O–F:	4	2	bent	$< 109.5°$
(h) 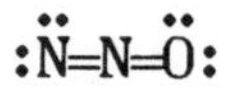 :N=N=O:	2	0	linear	$180°$
(i) 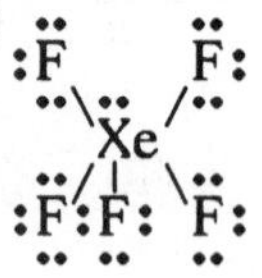 Xe with F F above and F F F below	6	1	slightly distorted square pyramid	$< 90°$
(j) 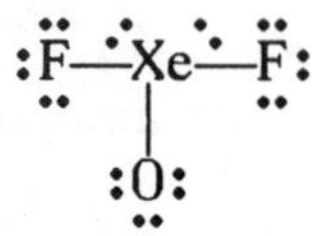 :F–Xe–F: (with :O below)	5	2	distorted T-shape	$< 90°$
(k) 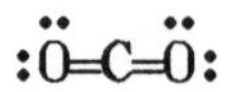 :O=C=O:	2	0	linear	$180°$

10.3

Lewis Structure	VSEPR pairs	Lone pairs	Shape	Bond Angles
(a) $\begin{bmatrix} :O: \\ \| \\ :O-P-O: \\ \| \\ :O: \end{bmatrix}^{3-}$	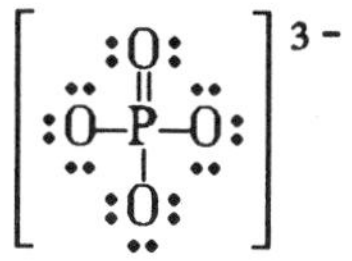 4	0	tetrahedral	109.5°
(b) $\begin{bmatrix} :O: \\ \| \\ :O-S-O: \\ \| \\ :O: \end{bmatrix}^{2-}$	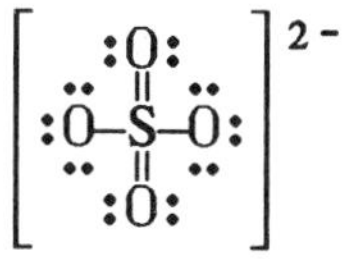 4	0	tetrahedral	109.5°
(c) $\begin{bmatrix} :O: \\ \| \\ O=Cl-O: \\ \| \\ :O: \end{bmatrix}^{-}$	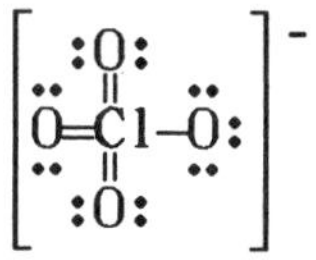 4	0	tetrahedral	109.5°
(d) $\begin{bmatrix} :O: \\ \| \\ O=Cl-O: \end{bmatrix}^{-}$	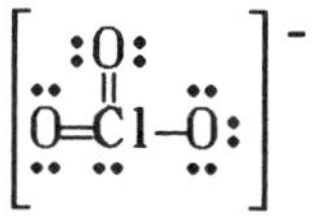 4	1	trigonal pyramidal	< 109.5°
(e) $\begin{bmatrix} O=Cl-O: \end{bmatrix}^{-}$	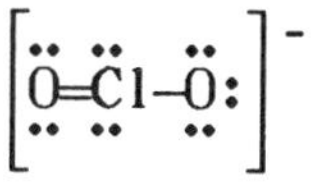 4	2	bent	< 109.5°

10.5   (a) The Lewis structure of $SnCl_2$ is

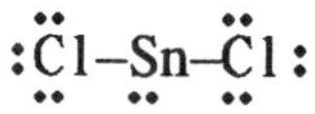

:Cl–Sn–Cl:

There are three VSEPR pairs in a trigonal planar arrangement about the central atom (two bonding and one lone pair). The shape should be bent:

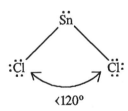

(b) The Lewis structure of $SnCl_3^-$ is

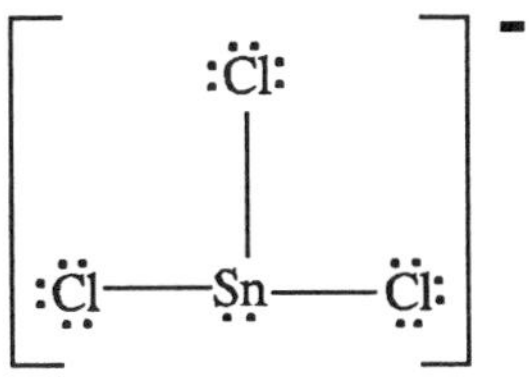

$$\begin{bmatrix} :Cl: \\ | \\ :Cl-Sn-Cl: \end{bmatrix}^{-}$$

There are four VSEPR pairs in a tetrahedral arrangement about the central atom (three bonding and one lone pair). The shape should be trigonal pyramidal.

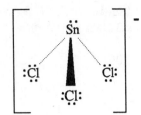

(c) The Lewis structure of PCl_3 is

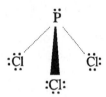

There are four VSEPR pairs in a tetrahedral arrangement about the central atom (three bonding and one lone pair). The shape should be trigonal pyramidal.

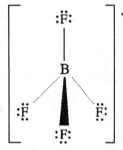

(d) The Lewis structure of BF_4^- is

There are four VSEPR pairs in a tetrahedral arrangement about the central atom (all bonding). The shape should be tetrahedral.

(e) The Lewis structure of IF_5 is

There are six VSEPR pairs in an octahedral arrangement about the central atom (five bonding and one lone pair). The shape should be a slightly distorted square pyramid.

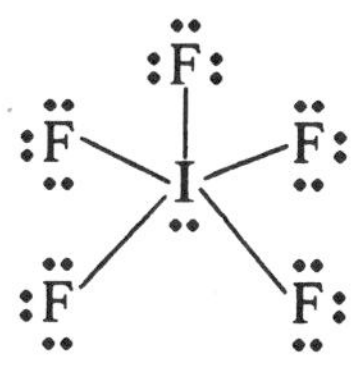

10.7   No. The Lewis structure for sulfuryl chloride that obeys the octet rule is

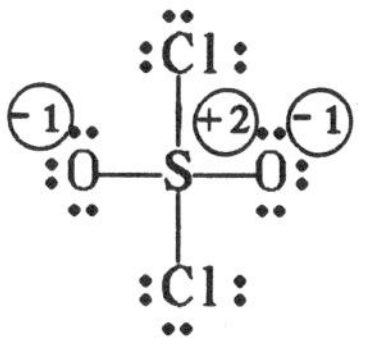

However, the S atom forms more than four covalent bonds in many of it compounds. Since the S atom has 3d orbitals available in its valence shell, the octet limit of four covalent bonds does not apply to S. Therefore, we can draw another contributing structure for sulfuryl chloride in which the oxygens have double bonds to sulfur and the formal charges are eliminated.

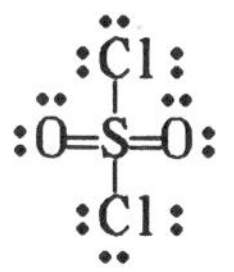

Since a multiple bond tends to expand the bond angle, the bond angles in the molecule will differ. The double-bond character of the oxygen-sulfur bonds will cause the O-S-O bond to expand, and the Cl-S-Cl to contract. Therefore, O-S-O will have the largest bond angle and Cl-S-Cl the smallest. The O-S-Cl bond angle will be in between these two.

10.14   In a free atom there is no evidence for an electron occupying anything having the properties of a hybrid orbital. However, experimentally determined bond angles and molecular shapes strongly indicate that something akin to hybrid orbitals exists in covalently bonded substances. Or, to put it another way, the experimental data are best explained in terms of hybrid orbitals.

10.18   The number of hybrid orbitals used by a central atom is equal to the number of VSEPR electron pairs around it.

(a)

Central Atom		VSEPR pairs	Type of Hybridization
(a)	S	4	sp^3
(b)	P	4	sp^3
(c)	S	3	sp^2
(d)	O	3	sp^2
(e)	S	5	sp^3d
(f)	S	4	sp^3
(g)	O	4	sp^3
(h)	N	2	sp
(i)	Xe	6	sp^3d^2
(j)	Xe	5	sp^3d
(k)	C	2	sp

(b)

Central Atom	VSEPR pairs	Type of Hybridization
(a) P	4	sp^3
(b) S	4	sp^3
(c) Cl	4	sp^3
(d) Cl	4	sp^3
(e) Cl	4	sp^3

(c)

Central Atom	VSEPR pairs	Type of Hybridization
(a) Sn	3	sp^2
(b) Sn	4	sp^3
(c) P	4	sp^3
(d) B	4	sp^3
(e) I	6	sp^3d^2

10.21 (a) S in period three has 3d orbitals available for bonding purposes in its valence shell. Therefore, the octet limit of four covalent bonds does not apply to S and S forms many compounds, like SF_6, that have more than four covalent bonds.

O in period two, on the other hand, has no available d orbitals in its valence shell. It can only form bonds with the s and p orbitals and is therefore limited to an octet or four covalent bonds. Consequently, it cannot form molecules like OF_6 that have more than four covalent bonds.

(b) Same explanation as part (a). P has 3d orbitals available for bonding purposes in its valence shell, N does not.

10.22 All single bonds are sigma bonds. A sigma bond is a shared pair of electrons whose principal density lies between the nuclei and along the line of atomic centers. Sigma bonds are symmetrical about the line of atomic centers and, therefore, offer no resistence to free rotation about the line of atomic centers.

A double bond, on the other hand, is composed of a sigma bond and a pi bond. A pi bond is a shared pair of electrons whose principal density lies above and below the line of atomic centers. A pi bond is formed by the overlap of parallel p orbitals. For rotation to occur around a double bond, the pi bond would have to be broken. Since breaking a pi bond requires considerable energy, there is no free rotation around double bonds.

10.23 (a) ethane (C_2H_6):

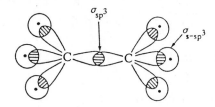

(b) ethylene (C_2H_4):

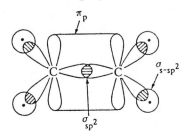

(c) acetylene (C_2H_2):

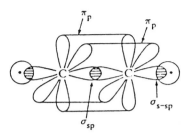

Acetylene with its triple bond will have the greatest carbon-carbon bond energy and shortest carbon-carbon bond length.

10.24 (a)

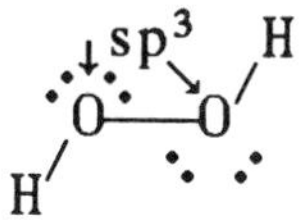

Both H-O-O angles are < 109.5°.

(b)

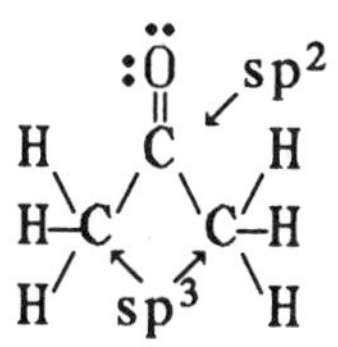

All H-C-H angles are 109.5° approximately.
The C-C-C angle is < 120°.
Both O-C-C angles are > 120°.
All C-C-H angles are 109.5° approximately.

(c)

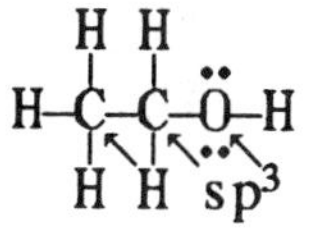

All angles are approximately 109.5°. The C–O–H angle is slightly smaller than the others.

(d)

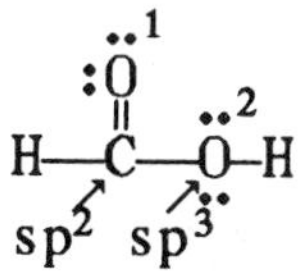

H-C-O¹ angle is > 120°, H-C-O² angle is < 120°,
O¹-C-O² angle is > 120°, C-O²-H angle is < 109.5°.

(e)

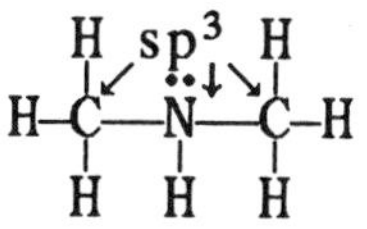

All angles are approximately 109.5°. The C-N-C and C-N-H angles are slightly smaller than the others.

(f)

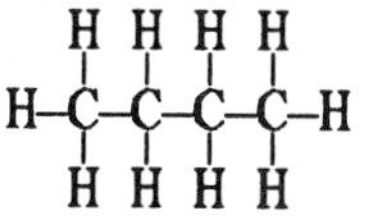

All C's are sp³, all angles are 109.5°.

(g)

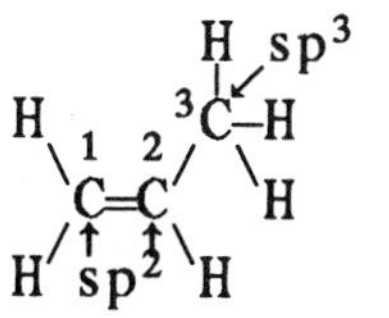

C¹: H-C¹-H angle is < 120°, both H-C¹-C² angles are > 120°.
C²: C¹-C²-C³ angle is > 120°, C¹-C²-H angle is > 120°,
     C³-C²-H angle is < 120°.
C³: All H-C³-H angles are 109.5°, all H-C³-C² angles are 109.5°.

(h)

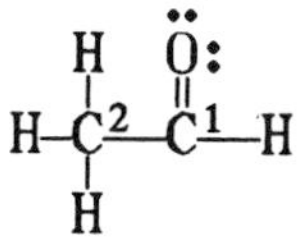

C¹: H-C¹-O angle is > 120°, O-C¹-C² angle is > 120°,
     H-C¹-C² angle is < 120°.
C²: All H-C²-H angles are 109.5°, all H-C²-C¹ angles are 109.5°.

(i)

$$sp^3$$

H–N–N–H
  | |
  H   H

All angles are $< 109.5°$.

10.28 Bonding electrons spend most of their time between the nuclei; the electrostatic attraction between the bonding electrons and the nuclei keep the molecule together. Antibonding electrons spend most of their time beyond the equilibrium distance of the nuclei; the electrostatic attraction between the antibonding electrons and the nuclei pulls the nuclei further apart, thus destabilizing the molecule.

10.29 Atomic orbitals. Hybrid orbitals are new atomic orbitals formed by mixing two or more original atomic orbitals on the same atom. Hybrid orbitals possess different directional properties than the atomic orbitals from which they are created.

10.31 1. (a) B_2 has ten electrons; its molecular orbital configuration is $(\sigma_{1s})^2 (\sigma^*_{1s})^2 (\sigma_{2s})^2 (\sigma^*_{2s})^2 (\pi_{2py})^1 (\pi_{2pz})^1$. B_2 has six bonding electrons and four antibonding electrons. The bond order is $(6 - 4)/2 = 1$.
(b) Yes. B_2 will be stable, since it has a bond order of 1.
(c) Yes. B_2 is paramagnetic, since it has two unpaired electrons.

2. (a) C_2 has 12 electrons; its molecular orbital configuration is $(\sigma_{1s})^2 (\sigma^*_{1s})^2 (\sigma_{2s})^2 (\sigma^*_{2s})^2 (\pi_{2py})^2 (\pi_{2pz})^2$. C_2 has eight bonding electrons and four antibonding electrons. The bond order is $(8 - 4)/2 = 2$.
(b) Yes. C_2 will be stable, since it has a bond order of 2.
(c) No. C_2 has no unpaired electrons and, therefore, is not paramagnetic.

3. (a) F_2 has 18 electrons; its molecular orbital configuration is $(\sigma_{1s})^2 (\sigma^*_{1s})^2 (\sigma_{2s})^2 (\sigma^*_{2s})^2 (\sigma_{2px})^2 (\pi_{2py})^2 (\pi_{2pz})^2 (\pi^*_{2py})^2 (\pi^*_{2pz})^2$. F_2 has ten bonding electrons and eight antibonding electrons. The bond order is $(10 - 8)/2 = 1$.
(b) Yes. F_2 will be stable, since it has a bond order of 1.
(c) No. F_2 has no unpaired electrons and, therefore, is not paramagnetic.

4. (a) Ne_2 has 20 electrons; its molecular orbital configuration is $(\sigma_{1s})^2 (\sigma^*_{1s})^2 (\sigma_{2s})^2 (\sigma^*_{2s})^2 (\sigma_{2px})^2 (\pi_{2py})^2 (\pi_{2pz})^2 (\pi^*_{2py})^2 (\pi^*_{2pz})^2 (\sigma^*_{2px})^2$. Ne_2 has ten bonding electrons and ten antibonding electrons. The bond order is $(10 - 10)/2 = 0$.
(b) No. Ne_2 will be unstable, since it has a bond order of zero.
(c) No. If Ne_2 existed it would not be paramagnetic, since it would have no unpaired electrons.

10.32 (a)

Molecule	Molecular Orbital Configuration	Bond Order
O_2	$(\sigma_{2s})^2 (\sigma^*_{2s})^2 (\sigma_{2px})^2 (\pi_{2py})^2 (\pi_{2pz})^2 (\pi^*_{2py})^1 (\pi^*_{2pz})^1$	2
O_2^{2-}	$(\sigma_{2s})^2 (\sigma^*_{2s})^2 (\sigma_{2px})^2 (\pi_{2py})^2 (\pi_{2pz})^2 (\pi^*_{2py})^2 (\pi^*_{2pz})^2$	1
O_2^-	$(\sigma_{2s})^2 (\sigma^*_{2s})^2 (\sigma_{2px})^2 (\pi_{2py})^2 (\pi_{2pz})^2 (\pi^*_{2py})^2 (\pi^*_{2pz})^1$	1 1/2
O_2^+	$(\sigma_{2s})^2 (\sigma^*_{2s})^2 (\sigma_{2px})^2 (\pi_{2py})^2 (\pi_{2pz})^2 (\pi^*_{2py})^1$	2 1/2

(b) O_2^+ has the highest bond order.
(c) O_2^+ with the highest bond order is a positive free radical. Therefore, O_2^+ should be highly reactive and normally have a short existence. Hence, even though O_2^+ has the highest bond order, it is not the most stable, since it is so reactive.

10.34 (a) 1. F_2^+ has 17 electrons; its molecular orbital configuration is
$(\sigma_{1s})^2 (\sigma^*_{1s})^2 (\sigma_{2s})^2 (\sigma^*_{2s})^2 (\sigma_{2px})^2 (\pi_{2py})^2 (\pi_{2pz})^2 (\pi^*_{2py})^2 (\pi^*_{2pz})^1$.

2. Ne_2^+ has 19 electrons; its molecular orbital configuration is
$(\sigma_{1s})^2 (\sigma^*_{1s})^2 (\sigma_{2s})^2 (\sigma^*_{2s})^2 (\sigma_{2px})^2 (\pi_{2py})^2 (\pi_{2pz})^2 (\pi^*_{2py})^2 (\pi^*_{2pz})^2 (\sigma^*_{2px})^1$.

(b) 1. F_2^+ has ten bonding electrons and seven antibonding electrons. Since there are more bonding electrons than antibonding electrons, F_2^+ will be stable.
2. Ne_2^+ has ten bonding electrons and nine antibonding electrons. Since there are more bonding electrons than antibonding electrons, Ne_2^+ will be stable.
(c) 1. F_2^+ is paramagnetic, since it has an unpaired electron.
2. Ne_2^+ is paramagnetic, since it has an unpaired electron.
(d) The bond order of F_2^+ is $(10 - 7)/2 = 1\ 1/2$. The bond order of Ne_2^+ is $(10 - 9)/2 = 1/2$. Ne_2^+ should have the longer bond length. F_2^+ should have the greater bond energy.

10.41   (a) O_3 with $3(6) = 18$ valence electrons has the contributing Lewis structures

The central oxygen atom has three VSEPR electron pairs and, therefore, uses sp^2 hybrid orbitals to form the σ bonding skeleton or framework. The remaining 2p orbital not used in the sp^2 hybrid set is perpendicular to the molecular plane of the molecule and overlaps with similarly situated 2p orbitals on the other oxygen atoms forming delocalized pi molecular orbitals. (Four of the valence electrons are in the sigma bonds, ten more are lone pairs in nonbonding orbitals, and four are in the pi molecular orbitals.)
(b) The CO_3^{2-} ion with $4 + 3(6) + 2 = 24$ valence electrons is triangular planar, and each O-C-O bond angle is $120°$ (see solution to PE 9.11 for Lewis structures). The central C atom uses sp^2 hybrid orbitals to form the σ bonding skeleton or framework. The remaining carbon 2p orbital is perpendicular to the plane of the ion and overlaps with similarly situated 2p orbitals on each of the oxygen atoms forming delocalized pi molecular orbitals. (Six of the valence electrons are in the sigma bonds, 12 more are lone pairs in nonbonding orbitals, and six are in the pi molecular orbitals.)

10.42   (a) 1. SO_2 with $6 + 2(6) = 18$ valence electrons is V-shaped, and the O-S-O bond angle is around $120°$. The central S atom uses sp^2 hybrid orbitals to form the sigma bonding skeleton. The remaining sulfur 3p orbital is perpendicular to the molecular plane and overlaps with similarly situated 2p orbitals on the oxygen atoms forming delocalized pi molecular orbitals.
2. The Lewis structure is

The sigma-bonded skeleton and the lone pairs of electrons on S and each O account for 14 of the 18 valence electrons. Therefore, the remaining 4 electrons must be in the delocalized pi system.
3.

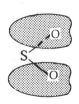

(b) 1. SO_3 with $6 + 3(6) = 24$ valence electrons is trigonal planar, and the O–S–O bond angles are 120°. The central S atom uses sp^2 hybrid orbitals to form the sigma bonding skeleton. The remaining sulfur 3p orbital is perpendicualr to the molecular plane and overlaps with similarly situated 2p orbitals on the oxygen atoms forming delocalized pi molecular orbitals.

2. The Lewis structure is

The sigma-bonded skeleton and the lone pairs of electrons on each O account for 18 of the 24 valence electrons. Therefore, the remaining 6 electrons must be in the delocalized pi system.

3.

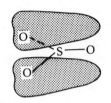

(c) 1. NO_2^- with $5 + 2(6) + 1 = 18$ valence electrons is V-shaped, and the O–N–O bond angle is around 120°. The central N atom uses sp^2 hybrid orbitals to form the sigma-bonding skeleton. The remaining nitrogen 2p orbital is perpendicular to the plane of the ion and overlaps with similarly situated 2p orbitals on the oxygen atoms forming delocalized pi molecular orbitals.

2. The Lewis contributing structures are

$$\left[\begin{array}{c} \ddot{N} \\ :\ddot{O} \quad \ddot{O}: \end{array}\right]^- \longleftrightarrow \left[\begin{array}{c} \ddot{N} \\ :\ddot{O} \quad \ddot{O}: \end{array}\right]^-$$

The sigma-bonded skeleton and the lone pairs of electrons on N and each O account for 14 of the 18 valence electrons. Therefore, the remaining 4 electrons must be in the delocalized pi system.

3.

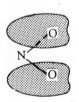

10.44   (a) Since the nitrogen and central carbon (bonded to oxygen) atoms are sp² hybridized, they both have 2p orbitals perpendicular to the plane of the peptide linkage. These two p orbitals and a similarly situated 2p orbital on oxygen overlap forming delocalized pi molecular orbitals. There is no rotation around the central C–N bond, since rotation would destroy the delocalized pi molecular orbital structure. This may be represented by the resonance structures

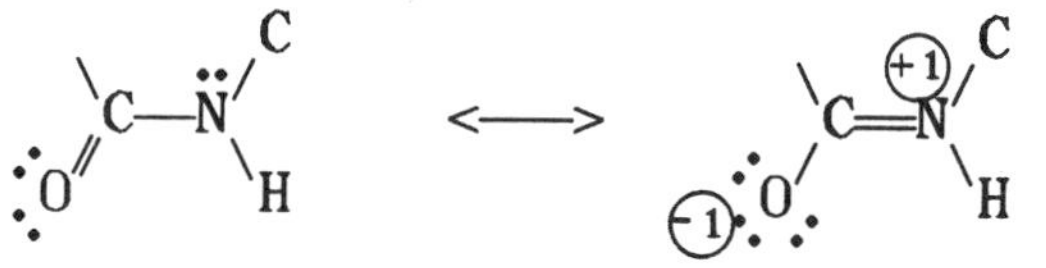

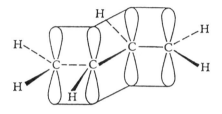

   (b) Since both central C (bonded to O) and central N are sp² hybridized, all bond angles should be around 120°.

10.45   (a) All four of 1,3–butadiene's carbon atoms are sp² hybridized.

   (b) Four.
   (c) 1,3–butadiene has 6(1) + 4(4) = 22 valence electrons. The sigma-bonded skeleton accounts for 18 of the 22 valence electrons. Therefore, the remaining 4 electrons must be in the delocalized pi system. Since there are four pi molecular orbitals in the delocalized pi system and each pi orbital can only hold 2 electrons, the two lowest energy pi orbitals must be doubly occupied. The two higher energy ones are empty.

10.46   (a)

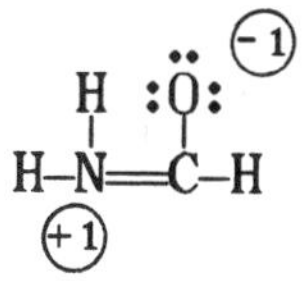

   (b) The original Lewis structure

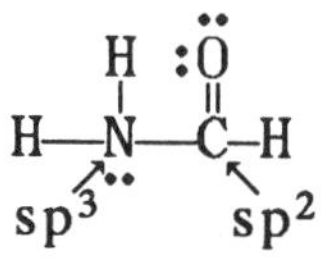

   predicts that N is sp³ hybridized with bond angles of approximately 109.5°, and C is sp² hybridized with bond angles of approximately 120°.

   The second Lewis structure

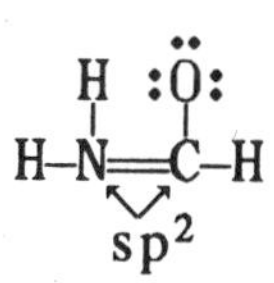

   predicts that both N and C are sp² hybridized with bond angles of approximately 120°.

The observed bond angles of 119° for H–N–H and 123.6° for N–C–O indicates that N and C are basically sp² hybridized. Therefore, the second resonance structure contributes most to the hybrid.

10.48   (a) H_2. The orbital occupancy diagram for H_2 is

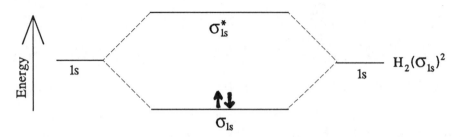

From the diagram we see that in the ground state both of the H_2 electrons are lower in energy than the ground-state hydrogen atom electron. Therefore, H_2 should have a greater first ionization energy, since it would require more energy to remove one of its ground state electrons.

(b)   O. The orbital occupancy diagram for O_2 is given in the text (Fig. 10.25). Referring to Fig. 10.25 we see that in the ground state O_2 has two electrons that are higher in energy than any of those in the ground state of the oxygen atom (O). Therefore, O should have the greater first ionization energy.

10.49   (a) S_8 has $8(6) = 48$ valence electrons or 24 electron pairs.

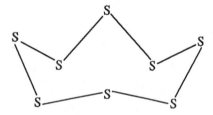

(b)   Since the S atoms are sp³ hybridized, S_8 cannot be planar. The S–S–S tetrahedral bond angles requires that S_8 take on the shape of a puckered ring having a crownlike structure.

CHAPTER 11
OXIDATION-REDUCTION REACTIONS

Solutions To Practice Exercises

PE 11.5   In each compound $x_H = +1$ (Rule 5) and $x_O = -2$ (Rule 4).

$HBrO_3$: $x_H + x_{Br} + 3x_O = 0$

            $+1 + x_{Br} + 3(-2) = 0$

              and $x_{Br} = +5$

HBr: $x_{Br} = -1$

$HBrO_4$: $x_H + x_{Br} + 4x_O = 0$

            $+1 + x_{Br} + 4(-2) = 0$

              and $x_{Br} = +7$

$HBrO_2$: $x_H + x_{Br} + 2x_O = 0$

            $+1 + x_{Br} + 2(-2) = 0$

              and $x_{Br} = +3$

The order of increasing oxidation number of bromine is

$HBr < HBrO_2 < HBrO_3 < HBrO_4$

PE 11.7 $2FeCl_3(aq) + 3H_2S(aq) \longrightarrow 2FeS(s) + S(s) + 6HCl(aq)$

Fe goes from +3 in $FeCl_3$ on the reactant side to +2 in FeS on the product side. Therefore, $FeCl_3$ is reduced. S goes from −2 in H_2S on the reactant side to −2 in FeS and 0 in S on the product side. Therefore, some H_2S is oxidized.

PE 11.8 $IO_3^-(aq) \longrightarrow I_2(s)$ (unbalanced)

Balance I: $2IO_3^-(aq) \longrightarrow I_2(s)$

Balance O: $2IO_3^-(aq) \longrightarrow I_2(s) + 6H_2O(l)$

Balance H: $2IO_3^-(aq) + 12H^+(aq) \longrightarrow I_2(s) + 6H_2O(l)$

Balance charge by adding ten electrons to the more positive side:

$2IO_3^-(aq) + 12H^+(aq) + 10e^- \longrightarrow I_2(s) + 6H_2O(l)$ (balanced)

PE 11.9 1. $Ag(s) + H^+(aq) + NO_3^-(aq) \longrightarrow Ag^+(aq) + NO(g)$

2. $Ag(s) \longrightarrow Ag^+(aq)$ (oxidation)
$NO_3^-(aq) \longrightarrow NO(g)$ (reduction)

3. $Ag(s) \longrightarrow Ag^+(aq) + e^-$ (balanced oxidation)
$NO_3^-(aq) + 4H^+(aq) + 3e^- \longrightarrow NO(g) + 2H_2O(l)$ (balanced reduction)

4. $3Ag(s) \longrightarrow 3Ag^+(aq) + 3e^-$
$NO_3^-(aq) + 4H^+(aq) + 3e^- \longrightarrow NO(g) + 2H_2O(l)$

5. $3Ag(s) + 4H^+(aq) + NO_3^-(aq) \longrightarrow 3Ag^+(aq) + NO(g) + 2H_2O(l)$

6. $3Ag(s) + 4HNO_3(aq) \longrightarrow 3AgNO_3(aq) + NO(g) + 2H_2O(l)$

PE 11.11 1. $CrO_4^{2-}(aq) + I^-(aq) \longrightarrow Cr^{3+}(aq) + IO_3^-(aq)$

2. $I^-(aq) \longrightarrow IO_3^-(aq)$ (oxidation)
$CrO_4^{2-}(aq) \longrightarrow Cr^{3+}(aq)$ (reduction)

3. $I^-(aq) + 6OH^-(aq) \longrightarrow IO_3^-(aq) + 3H_2O(l) + 6e^-$ (balanced oxidation)
$CrO_4^{2-}(aq) + 4H_2O(l) + 3e^- \longrightarrow Cr^{3+}(aq) + 8OH^-(aq)$ (balanced reduction)

4. $I^-(aq) + 6OH^-(aq) \longrightarrow IO_3^-(aq) + 3H_2O(l) + 6e^-$
$2CrO_4^{2-}(aq) + 8H_2O(l) + 6e^- \longrightarrow 2Cr^{3+}(aq) + 16OH^-(aq)$

5. $2CrO_4^{2-}(aq) + I^-(aq) + 5H_2O(l) \longrightarrow 2Cr^{3+}(aq) + IO_3^-(aq) + 10OH^-(aq)$

PE 11.12 1. $MnO_4^{2-}(aq) \longrightarrow MnO_4^-(aq) + MnO_2(s)$

2. $MnO_4^{2-}(aq) \longrightarrow MnO_4^-(aq)$ (oxidation)
$MnO_4^{2-}(aq) \longrightarrow MnO_2(s)$ (reduction)

3. $MnO_4^{2-}(aq) \longrightarrow MnO_4^-(aq) + e^-$ (balanced oxidation)
$MnO_4^{2-}(aq) + 4H^+(aq) + 2e^- \longrightarrow MnO_2(s) + 2H_2O(l)$ (balanced reduction)

4. $2MnO_4^{2-}(aq) \longrightarrow 2MnO_4^-(aq) + 2e^-$
$MnO_4^{2-}(aq) + 4H^+(aq) + 2e^- \longrightarrow MnO_2(s) + 2H_2O(l)$

5. $3MnO_4^{2-}(aq) + 4H^+(aq) \longrightarrow 2MnO_4^-(aq) + MnO_2(s) + 2H_2O(l)$

PE 11.14 The balanced net ionic equation is

$5Fe^{2+}(aq) + MnO_4^-(aq) + 8H^+(aq) \longrightarrow 5Fe^{3+}(aq) + Mn^{2+}(aq) + 4H_2O(l)$

(a) For every mole of MnO_4^- that reacts, 5 mol of Fe^{2+} reacts. Therefore, the mole ratio of MnO_4^- to Fe^{2+} is 1:5.

(b) The problem is solved in the usual way: V x M (of $KMnO_4$) $\longrightarrow$ mol $KMnO_4$ $\longrightarrow$ mol $FeSO_4$.

$$0.1000 \text{ L } KMnO_4 \text{ soln} \times \frac{0.02118 \text{ mol } KMnO_4}{1 \text{ L } KMnO_4 \text{ soln}} \times \frac{5 \text{ mol } FeSO_4}{1 \text{ mol } KMnO_4} = 0.01059 \text{ mol } FeSO_4$$

Solutions to Final Exercises

11.1 (a) $Mg(s) + 2HCl(aq) \longrightarrow MgCl_2(aq) + H_2(g)$
1. $Mg(s) \longrightarrow Mg^{2+}(aq) + 2e^-$ (oxidation); $2H^+(aq) + 2e^- \longrightarrow H_2(g)$ (reduction)
2. $Mg(s) + 2H^+(aq) \longrightarrow Mg^{2+}(aq) + H_2(g)$ (net ionic)

(b) $Al(s) + 3AgNO_3(aq) \longrightarrow Al(NO_3)_3(aq) + 3Ag(s)$
   1. $Al(s) \longrightarrow Al^{3+}(aq) + 3e^-$ (oxidation); $Ag^+(aq) + e^- \longrightarrow Ag(s)$ (reduction)
   2. $Al(s) + 3Ag^+(aq) \longrightarrow Al^{3+}(aq) + 3Ag(s)$ (net ionic)
(c) $Pb(s) + CuSO_4(aq) \longrightarrow PbSO_4(aq) + Cu(s)$
   1. $Pb(s) \longrightarrow Pb^{2+}(aq) + 2e^-$ (oxidation); $Cu^{2+}(aq) + 2e^- \longrightarrow Cu(s)$ (reduction)
   2. $Pb(s) + Cu^{2+}(aq) \longrightarrow Pb^{2+}(aq) + Cu(s)$ (net ionic)
(d) $2Na(s) + 2H_2O(l) \longrightarrow 2NaOH(aq) + H_2(g)$
   1. $Na(s) \longrightarrow Na^+(aq) + e^-$ (oxidation); $2H_2O(l) + 2e^- \longrightarrow 2OH^-(aq) + H_2(g)$ (reduction)
   2. $2Na(s) + 2H_2O(l) \longrightarrow 2Na^+(aq) + 2OH^-(aq) + H_2(g)$ (net ionic)
(e) $Cl_2(g) + 2KBr(aq) \longrightarrow Br_2(l) + 2KCl(aq)$
   1. $2Br^-(aq) \longrightarrow Br_2(l) + 2e^-$ (oxidation); $Cl_2(g) + 2e^- \longrightarrow 2Cl^-(aq)$ (reduction)
   2. $Cl_2(g) + 2Br^-(aq) \longrightarrow Br_2(l) + 2Cl^-(aq)$ (net ionic)

11.2 (a) 1. $H^+(aq)$ is the oxidizing agent; $Mg(s)$ is the reducing agent.
      2. $Mg(s)$ is oxidized and $H^+(aq)$ is reduced.
   (b) 1. $Ag^+(aq)$ is the oxidizing agent; $Al(s)$ is the reducing agent.
      2. $Al(s)$ is oxidized and $Ag^+(aq)$ is reduced.
   (c) 1. $Cu^{2+}(aq)$ is the oxidizing agent; $Pb(s)$ is the reducing agent.
      2. $Pb(s)$ is oxidized and $Cu^{2+}(aq)$ is reduced.
   (d) 1. $H_2O(l)$ is the oxidizing agent; $Na(s)$ is the reducing agent.
      2. $Na(s)$ is oxidized and $H_2O(l)$ is reduced.
   (e) 1. $Cl_2(g)$ is the oxidizing agent; $Br^-(aq)$ is the reducing agent.
      2. $Br^-(aq)$ is oxidized and $Cl_2(g)$ is reduced.

11.4 (a) The maximum oxidation number of a main group element is equal to its group number.
      Arsenic in Group 5A has a maximum oxidation number of +5 and selenium in Group 6A has a
      maximum oxidation number of +6.
   (b) The most negative oxidation state for a nonmetal from groups 4A through 7A is the group
      number minus eight. Therefore, arsenic's lowest oxidation state is $5 - 8 = -3$ and selenium's
      lowest oxidation state is $6 - 8 = -2$.

11.8 (a) H-O-O-H. $x_H = +1$ (Rule 5) and $x_O = -1$ (Rule 7).
   (b) BaO_2. $x_{Ba} = +2$ (Rule 6) and $x_O = -1$ (Rule 7).
   (c) O_2^-. $x_O = -1/2$ (Rule 7).
   (d) OF_2. $x_F = -1$ (Rule 3) and $x_O = +2$ (Rule 7).
   (e) O_2F_2. $x_F = -1$ (Rule 3) and $x_O = +1$ (Rule 7).

11.9 (a) No. $x_N = +5$ in N_2O_5 on the reactant side and +5 in HNO_3 on the product side.
   (b) Yes. $x_N = +4$ in NO_2 on the reactant side and +5 in HNO_3 and +2 in NO on the product side.
      NO_2 is both the oxidizing and reducing agent, i.e., some of it gets oxidized and some of it gets
      reduced.
   (c) Yes. $x_S = +4$ in SO_2 on the reactant side and +6 in SO_3 on the product side. O_2 is the oxidizing
      agent and SO_2 the reducing agent.
   (d) No. Oxygen is zero in both O_3 and O_2.
   (e) Yes. $x_N = -3$ in NH_3 on the reactant side and +2 in NO on the product side. O_2 is the oxidizng
      agent and NH_3 is the reducing agent.
   (f) Yes. $x_C = -2$ in CH_3OH on the reactant side and zero in CH_2O on the product side. CH_3OH is
      both the oxidizing and reducing agent.
   (g) No. $x_{Cr} = +6$ in $K_2Cr_2O_7$ on the reactant side and +6 in $PbCrO_4$ on the product side.
   (h) Yes. $x_S = -2$ in K_2S on the reactant side and zero in S on the product side. $K_2Cr_2O_7$ is the
      oxidizing agent and K_2S is the reducing agent.

11.11   The balanced half-reaction equations and net ionic equations are:
(a) $P_4(s) + 16H_2O(l) \longrightarrow 4H_3PO_4(aq) + 20H^+(aq) + 20e^-$ (oxidation)
$NO_3^-(aq) + 4H^+(aq) + 3e^- \longrightarrow NO(g) + 2H_2O(l)$ (reduction)
$3P_4(s) + 20H^+(aq) + 20NO_3^-(aq) + 8H_2O(l) \longrightarrow 12H_3PO_4(aq) + 20NO(g)$
(b) $Sn^{2+}(aq) + 6Cl^-(aq) \longrightarrow SnCl_6^{2-}(aq) + 2e^-$ (oxidation)
$H_2O_2(aq) + 2H^+(aq) + 2e^- \longrightarrow 2H_2O(l)$ (reduction)
$Sn^{2+}(aq) + H_2O_2(aq) + 2H^+(aq) + 6Cl^-(aq) \longrightarrow SnCl_6^{2-}(aq) + 2H_2O(l)$
(c) $HAsO_2(aq) + 2H_2O(l) \longrightarrow H_3AsO_4(aq) + 2H^+(aq) + 2e^-$ (oxidation)
$H_2O_2(aq) + 2H^+(aq) + 2e^- \longrightarrow 2H_2O(l)$ (reduction)
$HAsO_2(aq) + H_2O_2(aq) \longrightarrow H_3AsO_4(aq)$
(d) $CH_3OH(aq) \longrightarrow CH_2O(aq) + 2H^+(aq) + 2e^-$ (oxidation)
$Cr_2O_7^{2-}(aq) + 14H^+(aq) + 6e^- \longrightarrow 2Cr^{3+}(aq) + 7H_2O(l)$ (reduction)
$Cr_2O_7^{2-}(aq) + 8H^+(aq) + 3CH_3OH(aq) \longrightarrow 2Cr^{3+}(aq) + 3CH_2O(aq) + 7H_2O(l)$
(e) $H_2S(aq) \longrightarrow S(s) + 2H^+(aq) + 2e^-$ (oxidation)
$SO_4^{2-}(aq) + 8H^+(aq) + 6e^- \longrightarrow S(s) + 4H_2O(l)$ (reduction)
$SO_4^{2-}(aq) + 2H^+(aq) + 3H_2S(aq) \longrightarrow 4S(s) + 4H_2O(l)$
(f) $Fe(s) \longrightarrow Fe^{2+}(aq) + 2e^-$ (oxidation)
$NO_3^-(aq) + 10H^+(aq) + 8e^- \longrightarrow NH_4^+(aq) + 3H_2O(l)$ (reduction)
$4Fe(s) + 10H^+(aq) + NO_3^-(aq) \longrightarrow 4Fe^{2+}(aq) + NH_4^+(aq) + 3H_2O(l)$
(g) $Ag(s) \longrightarrow Ag^+(aq) + e^-$ (oxidation)
$NO_3^-(aq) + 4H^+(aq) + 3e^- \longrightarrow NO(g) + 2H_2O(l)$ (reduction)
$3Ag(s) + 4H^+(aq) + NO_3^-(aq) \longrightarrow 3Ag^+(aq) + NO(g) + 2H_2O(l)$
(h) $Ru(s) + 6Cl^-(aq) \longrightarrow RuCl_6^{3-}(aq) + 3e^-$ (oxidation)
$NO_3^-(aq) + 2H^+(aq) + e^- \longrightarrow NO_2(g) + H_2O(l)$ (reduction)
$Ru(s) + 6H^+(aq) + 3NO_3^-(aq) + 6Cl^-(aq) \longrightarrow RuCl_6^{3-}(aq) + 3NO_2(g) + 3H_2O(l)$
(i) $Ta(s) + 5F^-(aq) + H_2O(l) \longrightarrow H_2TaOF_5(aq) + 5e^-$ (oxidation)
$NO_3^-(aq) + 4H^+(aq) + 3e^- \longrightarrow NO(g) + 2H_2O(l)$ (reduction)
$3Ta(s) + 20H^+(aq) + 15F^-(aq) + 5NO_3^-(aq) \longrightarrow 3H_2TaOF_5(aq) + 5NO(g) + 7H_2O(l)$

11.13   The balanced half-reaction equations and net ionic equations are:
(a) $C_2O_4^{2-}(aq) + 4OH^-(aq) \longrightarrow 2CO_3^{2-}(aq) + 2H_2O(l) + 2e^-$ (oxidation)
$MnO_4^-(aq) + 2H_2O(l) + 3e^- \longrightarrow MnO_2(s) + 4OH^-(aq)$ (reduction)
$2MnO_4^-(aq) + 3C_2O_4^{2-}(aq) + 4OH^-(aq) \longrightarrow 2MnO_2(s) + 6CO_3^{2-}(aq) + 2H_2O(l)$
(b) $Sn(OH)_3^-(aq) + 3OH^-(aq) \longrightarrow Sn(OH)_6^{2-}(aq) + 2e^-$ (oxidation)
$Bi(OH)_3(s) + 3e^- \longrightarrow Bi(s) + 3OH^-(aq)$ (reduction)
$2Bi(OH)_3(s) + 3Sn(OH)_3^-(aq) + 3OH^-(aq) \longrightarrow 2Bi(s) + 3Sn(OH)_6^{2-}(aq)$
(c) $SO_3^{2-}(aq) + 2OH^-(aq) \longrightarrow SO_4^{2-}(aq) + H_2O(l) + 2e^-$ (oxidation)
$MnO_4^-(aq) + 2H_2O(l) + 3e^- \longrightarrow MnO_2(s) + 4OH^-(aq)$ (reduction)
$2MnO_4^-(aq) + 3SO_3^{2-}(aq) + H_2O(l) \longrightarrow 2MnO_2(s) + 3SO_4^{2-}(aq) + 2OH^-(aq)$
(d) $S_2O_4^{2-}(aq) + 4OH^-(aq) \longrightarrow 2SO_3^{2-}(aq) + 2H_2O(l) + 2e^-$ (oxidation)
$Cu(NH_3)_4^{2+}(aq) + 2e^- \longrightarrow Cu(s) + 4NH_3(aq)$ (reduction)
$Cu(NH_3)_4^{2+}(aq) + S_2O_4^{2-}(aq) + 4OH^-(aq) \longrightarrow Cu(s) + 2SO_3^{2-}(aq) + 4NH_3(aq) + 2H_2O(l)$

11.15   The balanced half-reaction equations and net ionic equations are:
(a) $NO_2(g) + H_2O(l) \longrightarrow NO_3^-(aq) + 2H^+(aq) + e^-$ (oxidation)
$NO_2(g) + 2H^+(aq) + 2e^- \longrightarrow NO(g) + H_2O(l)$ (reduction)
$3NO_2(g) + H_2O(l) \longrightarrow 2NO_3^-(aq) + NO(g) + 2H^+(aq)$
(b) $ClO_2(g) + 2OH^-(aq) \longrightarrow ClO_3^-(aq) + H_2O(l) + e^-$ (oxidation)
$ClO_2(g) + e^- \longrightarrow ClO_2^-(aq)$ (reduction)
$2ClO_2(g) + 2OH^-(aq) \longrightarrow ClO_2^-(aq) + ClO_3^-(aq) + H_2O(l)$

(c) $Se(s) + 6OH^-(aq) \longrightarrow SeO_3^{2-}(aq) + 3H_2O(l) + 4e^-$ (oxidation)

$Se(s) + 2e^- \longrightarrow Se^{2-}(aq)$ (reduction)

$3Se(s) + 6OH^-(aq) \longrightarrow 2Se^{2-}(aq) + SeO_3^{2-}(aq) + 3H_2O(l)$

(d) $P_4(s) + 8OH^-(aq) \longrightarrow 4H_2PO_2^-(aq) + 4e^-$ (oxidation)

$P_4(s) + 12H_2O(l) + 12e^- \longrightarrow 4PH_3(g) + 12OH^-(aq)$ (reduction)

$P_4(s) + 3H_2O(l) + 3OH^-(aq) \longrightarrow PH_3(g) + 3H_2PO_2^-(aq)$

11.17 The balanced equations are (the oxidation number changes are given in parentheses):

(a)

$$(+1) \times 4$$
$$4Mn(OH)_2(s) + O_2(g) + 2H_2O(l) \longrightarrow 4Mn(OH)_3(s)$$
$$(-2) \times 2$$

(b)

$$(+1) \times 3$$
$$3Ti^{3+}(aq) + RuCl_5^{2-}(aq) + 6OH^-(aq) \longrightarrow Ru(s) + 3TiO^{2+}(aq) + 5Cl^-(aq) + 3H_2O(l)$$
$$(-3) \times 1$$

(c)

$$(+2) \times 2$$
$$2H_2S(g) + SO_2(g) \longrightarrow 3S(s) + 2H_2O(g)$$
$$(-4) \times 1$$

(d)

$$(+1) \times 6$$
$$6FeSO_4(aq) + K_2Cr_2O_7(aq) + 8H_2SO_4(aq) \longrightarrow 3Fe_2(SO_4)_3(aq) + Cr_2(SO_4)_3(aq)$$
$$(-3) \times 2$$
$$+ 2KHSO_4(aq) + 7H_2O(l)$$

(e)

$$(+2) \times 2$$
$$N_2H_4(aq) + 2Cu(OH)_2(s) \longrightarrow 2Cu(s) + N_2(g) + 4H_2O(l)$$
$$(-2) \times 2$$

(f)

$$(+1) \times 2$$
$$2Cr(OH)_2(s) \longrightarrow Cr_2O_3(s) + H_2O(g) + H_2(g)$$
$$(-1) \times 2$$

(g)

$$(+2) \times 2$$
$$4HNO_3(g) \longrightarrow 4NO_2(g) + O_2(g) + 2H_2O(g)$$
$$(-1) \times 4$$

11.18 The balanced equation is

$$3Cu(s) + 8HNO_3(aq) \longrightarrow 3Cu(NO_3)_2(aq) + 2NO(g) + 4H_2O(l)$$

The steps in solving the problem are: $0.500 \text{ mol } HNO_3 \longrightarrow \text{mol Cu} \longrightarrow \text{g Cu}$.

$$0.500 \text{ mol } HNO_3 \times \frac{3 \text{ mol Cu}}{8 \text{ mol } HNO_3} \times \frac{63.54 \text{ g Cu}}{1 \text{ mol Cu}} = 11.9 \text{ g Cu}$$

11.20 The balanced net ionic equation is

$$8KI(s) + SO_4^{2-}(aq) + 10H^+(aq) \longrightarrow 4I_2(s) + H_2S(g) + 4H_2O(l) + 8K^+(aq)$$

The steps in the calculation are: $\text{g } H_2SO_4 \longrightarrow \text{mol } H_2SO_4 \longrightarrow \text{mol } H^+ \longrightarrow \text{mol KI} \longrightarrow$ g KI.

$$3.0 \text{ g } H_2SO_4 \times \frac{1 \text{ mol } H_2SO_4}{98.08 \text{ g } H_2SO_4} \times \frac{2 \text{ mol } H^+}{1 \text{ mol } H_2SO_4} \times \frac{8 \text{ mol KI}}{10 \text{ mol } H^+} \times \frac{166.00 \text{ g KI}}{1 \text{ mol KI}} = 8.1 \text{ g KI}$$

Comment: Be careful, net ionic equations can sometimes be misleading. For instance, the relationship between KI and SO_4^{2-} in the net ionic equation cannot be used because SO_4^{2-} also participates as a spectator ion, as can readily be seen from the balanced molecular equation.

$$8KI(s) + 5H_2SO_4(aq) \longrightarrow 4I_2(s) + H_2S(g) + 4H_2O(l) + 4K_2SO_4(aq)$$

Using the relationship 8 mol KI/1 mol SO_4^{2-} (or 8 mol KI/1 mol H_2SO_4) from the net ionic equation, instead of the actual relationship 8 mol KI/5 mol SO_4^{2-} (or 8 mol KI/5 mol H_2SO_4) as seen in the balanced molecular equation, would lead to the wrong result. By the way, the balanced molecular equation could also be used to solve this problem if you prefer.

11.22 The balanced net ionic equation is $I_2(s) + 2S_2O_3^{2-}(aq) \longrightarrow 2I^-(aq) + S_4O_6^{2-}(aq)$

The calculation proceeds as follows:

$$\text{g } I_2 \longrightarrow \text{mol } I_2 \longrightarrow \text{mol } Na_2S_2O_3 \longrightarrow \text{mL } Na_2S_2O_3 \text{ soln.}$$

$$7.50 \text{ g } I_2 \times \frac{1 \text{ mol } I_2}{253.81 \text{ g } I_2} \times \frac{2 \text{ mol } Na_2S_2O_3}{1 \text{ mol } I_2} = 0.0591 \text{ mol } Na_2S_2O_3$$

The number of milliliters of 0.100 M $Na_2S_2O_3$ needed is

$$0.0591 \text{ mol } Na_2S_2O_3 \times \frac{1 \text{ L}}{0.100 \text{ mol } Na_2S_2O_3} = 0.591 \text{ L or } 591 \text{ mL}$$

11.24 The balanced net ionic equation is

$$Cr_2O_7^{2-}(aq) + 3Sn^{2+}(aq) + 14H^+(aq) + 18Cl^-(aq) \longrightarrow 2Cr^{3+}(aq) + 3SnCl_6^{2-}(aq) + 7H_2O(l)$$

The steps in the calculation are: $\text{g } SnCl_2 \longrightarrow \text{mol } SnCl_2 \longrightarrow \text{mol } K_2Cr_2O_7 \longrightarrow \text{mL of}$ $K_2Cr_2O_7$ soln.

$$3.50 \text{ g } SnCl_2 \times \frac{1 \text{ mol } SnCl_2}{189.62 \text{ g } SnCl_2} \times \frac{1 \text{ mol } K_2Cr_2O_7}{3 \text{ mol } SnCl_2} = 6.15 \times 10^{-3} \text{ mol } K_2Cr_2O_7$$

The number of milliliters of 0.250 M $K_2Cr_2O_7$ needed is

$$6.15 \times 10^{-3} \text{ mol } K_2Cr_2O_7 \times \frac{1 \text{ L}}{0.250 \text{ mol } K_2Cr_2O_7} = 2.46 \times 10^{-2} \text{ L or } 24.6 \text{ mL}$$

11.26   The balanced equation is $2Ce^{4+}(aq) + H_2O_2(aq) \longrightarrow 2Ce^{3+}(aq) + O_2(g) + 2H^+(aq)$

The steps in the calculation are: $V \times M$ (Ce^{4+} soln) $\longrightarrow$ mol Ce^{4+} $\longrightarrow$ mol H_2O_2 $\longrightarrow$ molarity H_2O_2.

$$0.0400 \text{ L } Ce^{4+} \text{ soln} \times \frac{0.500 \text{ mol } Ce^{4+}}{1 \text{ L } Ce^{4+} \text{ soln}} \times \frac{1 \text{ mol } H_2O_2}{2 \text{ mol } Ce^{4+}} = 0.0100 \text{ mol } H_2O_2$$

The molarity of the H_2O_2 solution is $\dfrac{0.0100 \text{ mol } H_2O_2}{0.0100 \text{ L soln}} = 1.00 \text{ M } H_2O_2$

11.29   (a) The oxidation number of S would be +8 if none of the oxygens were bonded to each other. Since S is +6, Caro's acid must contain peroxide oxygen.

(b) One. Each oxygen in a peroxide bond has an oxidation number of –1. Therefore, for S to be +6 there could only be one O–O bond in H_2SO_5.

11.31   The balanced equation is $2MnO_4^-(aq) + 3SO_3^{2-}(aq) + H_2O(l) \longrightarrow 2MnO_2(s) + 3SO_4^{2-}(aq) + 2OH^-(aq)$

The steps in the calculation are: $V \times M$ ($KMnO_4$) $\longrightarrow$ mol $KMnO_4$ $\longrightarrow$ mol Na_2SO_3 $\longrightarrow$ g Na_2SO_3.

$$0.0500 \text{ L } KMnO_4 \text{ soln} \times \frac{0.0500 \text{ mol } KMnO_4}{1 \text{ L } KMnO_4 \text{ soln}} \times \frac{3 \text{ mol } Na_2SO_3}{2 \text{ mol } KMnO_4} \times \frac{126.04 \text{ g } Na_2SO_3}{1 \text{ mol } Na_2SO_3}$$

$$= 0.473 \text{ g } Na_2SO_3$$

11.33   The balanced equation is $4Fe^{2+}(aq) + O_2(g) + 4H^+(aq) \longrightarrow 4Fe^{3+}(aq) + 2H_2O(l)$

The steps in the calculation are: g $FeCl_2$ $\longrightarrow$ mol $FeCl_2$ $\longrightarrow$ mol O_2 $\longrightarrow$ volume O_2 at STP.

$$5.0 \text{ g } FeCl_2 \times \frac{1 \text{ mol } FeCl_2}{126.75 \text{ g } FeCl_2} \times \frac{1 \text{ mol } O_2}{4 \text{ mol } FeCl_2} = 9.86 \times 10^{-3} \text{ mol } O_2$$

One mole of gas occupies approximately 22.4 L at STP. The volume of O_2, measured in milliliters at STP, is

$$9.86 \times 10^{-3} \text{ mol } O_2 \times \frac{22.4 \text{ L}}{1 \text{ mol } O_2} = 0.22 \text{ L or } 2.2 \times 10^2 \text{ mL}$$

11.35   (a) $I_2(s) + 2S_2O_3^{2-}(aq) \longrightarrow 2I^-(aq) + S_4O_6^{2-}(aq)$

(b) The steps in the calculation are: $V \times M$ ($Na_2S_2O_3$) $\longrightarrow$ mol $Na_2S_2O_3$ $\longrightarrow$ mol I_2 $\longrightarrow$ g I_2.

$$0.0500 \text{ L } Na_2S_2O_3 \text{ soln} \times \frac{0.362 \text{ mol } Na_2S_2O_3}{1 \text{ L } Na_2S_2O_3 \text{ soln}} \times \frac{1 \text{ mol } I_2}{2 \text{ mol } Na_2S_2O_3} \times \frac{253.81 \text{ g } I_2}{1 \text{ mol } I_2}$$

$$= 2.30 \text{ g } I_2$$

CHAPTER S2
A SURVEY OF THE ELEMENTS 2: OXYGEN, NITROGEN, AND THE HALOGENS

Solutions To Practice Exercises

PE S2.4   Linear. The Lewis contributing structures for N_2O (eight electron pairs) are

$$:\overset{..}{N}=N=\overset{..}{O}: \longleftrightarrow :N\equiv N-\overset{..}{\underset{..}{O}}:$$

The central nitrogen has two VSEPR pairs (both bonding), which adopt a linear arrangement. The molecule is linear.

PE S2.5   Bent. The Lewis structure for the nitrite ion (nine electron pairs) is

$$[\ :\overset{..}{\underset{..}{O}}-\overset{..}{N}=\overset{..}{O}:\ ]^-$$

The central nitrogen has three VSEPR pairs (two bonding and one lone), which adopt a trigonal planar arrangement. The molecule is bent.

PE S2.8

(1) $HNO_3(aq) \xrightarrow{h\nu} NO_2(g) + O_2(g)$

(2) and (3) $2H_2O(l) \longrightarrow O_2(g) + 4H^+(aq) + 4e^-$ (balanced oxidation)

$HNO_3(aq) + H^+(aq) + e^- \longrightarrow NO_2(g) + H_2O(l)$ (balanced reduction)

(4) $2H_2O(l) \longrightarrow O_2(g) + 4H^+(aq) + 4e^-$

$\quad 4HNO_3(aq) + 4H^+(aq) + 4e^- \longrightarrow 4NO_2(g) + 4H_2O(l)$

(5) $4HNO_3(aq) \xrightarrow{h\nu} 4NO_2(g) + O_2(g) + 2H_2O(l)$

PE S2.9 (a) Carbon reduces concentrated HNO_3 to NO_2.

$C(s) + 2H_2O(l) \longrightarrow CO_2(g) + 4H^+(aq) + 4e^-$ (oxidation)

$NO_3^-(aq) + 2H^+(aq) + e^- \longrightarrow NO_2(g) + H_2O(l)$ (reduction)

(b) Copper, a less active metal, reduces nitric acid to NO or NO_2, depending on the acid concentration. With 6 M HNO_3 the principal reduction product is NO.

$$Cu(s) \longrightarrow Cu^{2+}(aq) + 2e^- \quad \text{(oxidation)}$$

$$NO_3^-(aq) + 4H^+(aq) + 3e^- \longrightarrow NO(g) + 2H_2O(l) \quad \text{(reduction)}$$

PE S2.11

(a) Lewis Structure	VSEPR pairs	Lone pairs	Shape
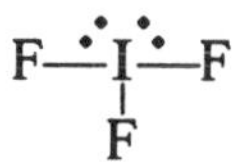 F—I—F (with F below)	5	2	distorted T-shape
(b) Br with F's	 6	1	distorted square pyramid

PE S2.15

(a) Lewis Structure	VSEPR pairs	Lone pairs	Shape
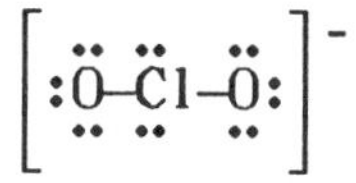 $[:\ddot{O}—\ddot{C}l—\ddot{O}:]^-$	4	2	bent
(b) $[:\ddot{O}—\ddot{C}l—\ddot{O}:$ with $:\ddot{O}:]^-$	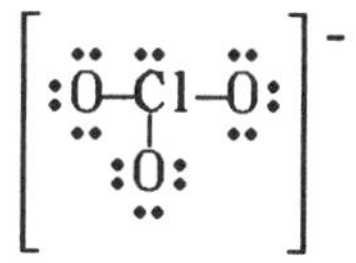 4	1	trigonal pyramid
(c) $[:\ddot{O}—Cl—\ddot{O}:$ with O above and below$]^-$	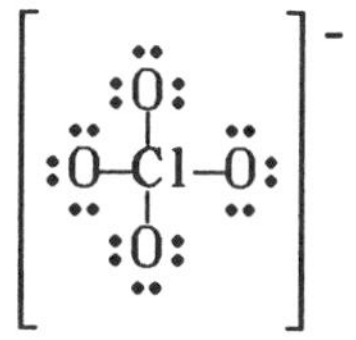 4	0	tetrahedral

Solutions To Final Exercises

S2.6
(a) $2Mg(s) + O_2(g) \longrightarrow MgO(s)$
(b) $4Al(s) + 3O_2(g) \longrightarrow 3Al_2O_3(s)$
(c) $C(s) + O_2(g) \longrightarrow CO_2(g)$
(d) $CH_4(g) + 2O_2(g) \longrightarrow CO_2(g) + 2H_2O(g)$
(e) $2CO(g) + O_2(g) \longrightarrow 2CO_2(g)$
(f) $C_2H_5OH(l) + 3O_2(g) \longrightarrow 2CO_2(g) + 3H_2O(g)$

S2.7
(a) O_2 has 16 electrons and its molecular orbital configuration is
$(\sigma_{1s})^2(\sigma^*_{1s})^2(\sigma_{2s})^2(\sigma^*_{2s})^2(\sigma_{2px})^2(\pi_{2py})^2(\pi_{2pz})^2(\pi^*_{2py})^1(\pi^*_{2pz})^1$.

(b) 1. The configuration shows that oxygen should be a paramagnetic diradical, and it is.
2. The configuration shows that O_2 has a bond order of 2, which roughly corresponds to a double bond in valence bond theory terminology. In actual fact, O_2 has a bond length and bond energy that is consistent with a double bond between the oxygen atoms.
3. The configurations shows that O_2 is a diradical and since radicals are usually reactive we would expect O_2 to be reactive. In actual fact, O_2 is the most reactive element in Group 6A.

S2.9 (a) Two or more forms of the same element that can exist in the same physical state.
       (b) Since O_2, diatomic molecules, and O_3, triatomic molecules, are both gases and different forms of the same element, oxygen, they are by definition allotropes.
       (c) Yes. They are both solids and different forms of the element carbon.
       (d) No. Allotropes must have the same physical state.

S2.15 (a) $SO_2(g) + H_2O(l) \longrightarrow H_2SO_3(aq)$ (unstable diprotic acid)
        (b) $SO_3(g) + H_2O(l) \longrightarrow H_2SO_4(aq)$
        (c) $CO_2(g) + H_2O(l) \longrightarrow H_2CO_3(aq)$ (unstable diprotic acid)
        (d) $N_2O_5(s) + H_2O(l) \longrightarrow 2HNO_3(aq)$
        (e) $P_4O_{10}(s) + 6H_2O(l) \longrightarrow 4H_3PO_4(aq)$

S2.18 (a) $CaO(s) + 2HCl(aq) \longrightarrow CaCl_2(aq) + H_2O(l)$
             $CaO(s) + H_2SO_4(aq) \longrightarrow CaSO_4(aq) + H_2O(l)$
        (b) $Li_2O(s) + 2HCl(aq) \longrightarrow 2LiCl(aq) + H_2O(l)$
             $Li_2O(s) + H_2SO_4(aq) \longrightarrow Li_2SO_4(aq) + H_2O(l)$
        (c) $Fe_2O_3(s) + 6HCl(aq) \longrightarrow 2FeCl_3(aq) + 3H_2O(l)$
             $Fe_2O_3(s) + 3H_2SO_4(aq) \longrightarrow Fe_2(SO_4)_3(aq) + 3H_2O(l)$

S2.22 (a) The oxygen atoms in hydrogen peroxide are held together by a single bond, while the oxygen atoms in molecular oxygen are held together by a double bond. Therefore, it requires less energy to disrupt the peroxide bond than the oxygen bond and, consequently, hydrogen peroxide should be a stronger oxidizing agent than oxygen.
        (b) See Peroxides and Superoxides in Section S2.1 in the text.

S2.24 (a) See Table S2.3 in the text.
        (b) Both O_2^{2-} and O_2^- have more antibonding electrons than O_2. Therefore, the bond holding the oxygen atoms together in O_2^{2-} and O_2^- is weaker than that in O_2 and, consequently, they are more reactive.

S2.26 (a) $PbS(s) + 4H_2O_2(aq) \longrightarrow PbSO_4(s) + 4H_2O(l)$
        (b) $2Na_2O_2(s) + 2H_2O(l) \longrightarrow 4NaOH(aq) + O_2(g)$
        (c) $2Na_2O_2(s) + 2CO_2(g) \longrightarrow 2Na_2CO_3(s) + O_2(g)$
        (d) $4KO_2(s) + 2CO_2(g) \longrightarrow 2K_2CO_3(s) + 3O_2(g)$
        (e)
             $$2BaO_2(s) \xrightarrow{\Delta} 2BaO(s) + O_2(g)$$
        (f)
             $$BaO_2(s) + H_2SO_4(aq) \xrightarrow{\text{cold, dilute}} BaSO_4(s) + H_2O_2(aq)$$
        (g) $2Fe(OH)_2(s) + H_2O_2(aq) \longrightarrow 2Fe(OH)_3(aq)$

S2.29 (a) N_2 has 14 electrons and its molecular orbital configuration is
             $(\sigma_{1s})^2(\sigma_{1s}^*)^2(\sigma_{2s})^2(\sigma_{2s}^*)^2(\pi_{2py})^2(\pi_{2pz})^2(\sigma_{2px})^2$.
        (b) The two N atoms are bound together by a strong and stable triple bond, which would have to be broken in order for N_2 to react. A substantial amount of energy is required to break such a triple bond, energy that is not usually available under normal conditions. Consequently, the N_2 molecule is unreactive.

S2.32   The electric discharge breaks the bonds of the N_2 molecules. The resulting atoms are reactive, since they have incomplete octets.

S2.38 (a) $+1{:}N_2O$; $+2{:}NO$; $+3{:}N_2O_3$; $+4{:}NO_2$ and N_2O_4; $+5{:}N_2O_5$
        (b) $+3{:}HNO_2$; $+5{:}HNO_3$
        (c) $+3{:}NO_2^-$; $+5{:}NO_3^-$

S2.39

	Lewis Structure	VSEPR pairs	Lone pairs	Shape
(1)	:N̈=Ö:			linear
(2)	:N̈=N=Ö:	2	0	linear
(3)	:Ö–N̈–Ö:	3	1	bent
(4)	N–N–Ö: (with =O O: below)	3(each N)	1 0	bent(O–N–N part) planar(N–NO$_2$ portion)
(5)	:Ö–N–N–Ö: (with O O below)	3(each N)	0	planar(each N trigonal planar)

Note: Four Lewis contributing structures can be drawn for the nitrogen dioxide (NO$_2$) molecule, two of which place three VSEPR electron pairs on the central N atom.

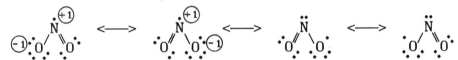

S2.41 NO and NO$_2$. NO and NO$_2$ each have an unpaired electron. Therefore, they are both paramagnetic and will be attracted into a magnetic field. The electrons in N$_2$O and N$_2$O$_4$ are all paired. Therefore, they are diamagnetic and will not be attracted into a magnetic field.

S2.42 Some of the possible reactions are:

(a)
$$NH_4NO_3(s) \xrightarrow{\Delta} N_2O(g) + 2H_2O(g)$$
(b)
$$N_2(g) + O_2(g) \xrightarrow[\text{electric discharge}]{\Delta \text{ or}} 2NO(g)$$

(Also reactions in which HNO$_3$ or HNO$_2$ is reduced)

(c) $2NO(g) + O_2(g) \longrightarrow 2NO_2(g)$ (Also reactions in which HNO$_3$ is reduced)

(d) $2NO_2(g) \rightleftharpoons N_2O_4(g)$

S2.47 (a) Since zinc is a moderately active metal, the principal reduction product with 6 M nitric acid is ammonium ion.

$Zn(s) \longrightarrow Zn^{2+}(aq) + 2e^-$ (oxidation)

$NO_3^-(aq) + 10H^+(aq) + 8e^- \longrightarrow NH_4^+(aq) + 3H_2O(l)$ (reduction)

(b) Since copper is a less active metal, the principal reduction product with 12 M nitric acid is NO$_2$.

$Cu(s) \longrightarrow Cu^{2+}(aq) + 2e^-$ (oxidation)

$NO_3^-(aq) + 2H^+(aq) + e^- \longrightarrow NO_2(g) + H_2O(l)$ (reduction)

S2.50 (a) $Au(s) + 4Cl^-(aq) \longrightarrow AuCl_4^-(aq) + 3e^-$ (oxidation)
$NO_3^-(aq) + 4H^+(aq) + 3e^- \longrightarrow NO(g) + 2H_2O(l)$ (reduction)

(b) $Pt(s) + 6Cl^-(aq) \longrightarrow PtCl_6^{2-}(aq) + 6e^-$ (oxidation)
$NO_3^-(aq) + 4H^+(aq) + 3e^- \longrightarrow NO(g) + 2H_2O(l)$ (reduction)

S2.51

(a) $\left[:C\equiv N:\right]^-$; (b) $\left[H-\overset{\cdot\cdot}{\underset{\cdot\cdot}{N}}-H\right]^-$; (c) $H-\overset{|}{\underset{H}{N}}-\overset{|}{\underset{H}{N}}-H$;

(d) $H-\overset{\cdot\cdot}{\underset{|}{N}}-\overset{\cdot\cdot}{\underset{\cdot\cdot}{O}}-H$; (e) $H-C\equiv N:$
$\overset{}{\underset{H}{}}$

S2.53 (a) $Na_2CO_3(s) + 2HNO_3(aq) \longrightarrow 2NaNO_3(aq) + CO_2(g) + H_2O(l)$
(b) $Mg(OH)_2(s) + 2HNO_3(aq) \longrightarrow Mg(NO_3)_2(aq) + 2H_2O(l)$
(c) $N_2O_5(s) + H_2O(l) \longrightarrow 2HNO_3(aq)$
(d) $Li_3N(s) + 3H_2O(l) \longrightarrow NH_3(g) + 3LiOH(aq)$
(e) $NaCN(s) + HCl(aq) \longrightarrow NaCl(aq) + HCN(g)$
(f) $2NH_3(l) + OCl^-(aq) \longrightarrow N_2H_4(aq) + Cl^-(aq) + H_2O(l)$
(g) $N_2H_4(l) + 2H_2O_2(l) \longrightarrow N_2(g) + 4H_2O(g)$
(h) $N_2H_2(CH_3)_2(l) + 4O_2(l) \longrightarrow N_2(g) + 2CO_2(g) + 4H_2O(g)$
(i) See solution to PE S2.8

S2.57 (a) The physical properties of the halogens are compared in Table S2.11 of the text.
(b) A group trend is a consistent pattern of variation in some property from top to bottom in a group. Group trends can generally be explained on the basis of atomic and molecular structure. The halogen elements are all diatomic molecules. In general, the melting points and boiling points of nonpolar molecules depend on the strength of the London dispersion forces (see Chapter 12, Section 12.3) between the molecules, which generally increase as the number of electrons per molecule increases. Therefore, we would expect the melting points and boiling points of the halogens to increase as we proceed down the group, which they do. Likewise, we would expect the physical state of the halogens to change from gas ⟶ liquid ⟶ solid with the increasing London dispersion forces as we proceed down the group, which also happens. Furthermore, we would imagine that the colors of the elements should get darker as we proceed down the group, since each succeeding element has more electrons, which are spread over a wider range of energy levels, and which can therefore absorb more of the visible light frequencies. The more of the visible light frequencies absorbed by a substance, the darker the substance will appear, and this is also what happens.

S2.58 (a) Fluorine
(b) Iodine
The smaller the atom the greater its ability to attract an electron, since the positively charged nucleus of a small atom can get closer to an electron than that of a larger atom. Therefore, the first member of the halogen group should have the strongest attraction for an electron and the last member the least. Consequently, fluorine should be the strongest oxidizing agent and iodine the weakest. Also, electronegativity decreases going down the group.

S2.62 (a) $Cl^-(aq) + MnO_4^-(aq) \longrightarrow Cl_2(g) + Mn^{2+}(aq)$

$2Cl^-(aq) \longrightarrow Cl_2(g) + 2e^-$ (oxidation)

$MnO_4^-(aq) + 8H^+(aq) + 5e^- \longrightarrow Mn^{2+}(aq) + 4H_2O(l)$ (reduction)

(b) $I^-(aq) + MnO_2(s) \longrightarrow I_2(s) + Mn^{2+}(aq)$

$2I^-(aq) \longrightarrow I_2(s) + 2e^-$ (oxidation)

$MnO_2(s) + 4H^+(aq) + 2e^- \longrightarrow Mn^{2+}(aq) + 2H_2O(l)$ (reduction)

S2.68   (a) $CaF_2(s) + H_2SO_4(18\ M) \longrightarrow CaSO_4(s) + 2HF(g)$
       (b) $NaCl(s) + H_2SO_4(18\ M) \longrightarrow NaHSO_4(s) + HCl(g)$
       (c) $NaBr(s) + H_3PO_4(15\ M) \longrightarrow HBr(g) + NaH_2PO_4(aq)$
       (d) $NaI(s) + H_3PO_4(15\ M) \longrightarrow HI(g) + NaH_2PO_4(aq)$

S2.70   (a) $Mg(s) + 2HF(g) \longrightarrow MgF_2(s) + H_2(g)$
       (b) $HF(aq) \rightleftharpoons H^+(aq) + F^-(aq)$
       (c) $SiO_2(s) + 4HF(g\text{ or }aq) \longrightarrow SiF_4(g) + 2H_2O(g)$

S2.74

Lewis Structure	VSEPR pairs	Lone pairs	Shape
(a) H–Ö–Cl–Ö: with :Ö: below Cl	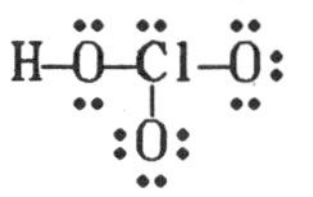 4	1	trigonal pyramid
(b) [:Ö–I–Ö:]⁻	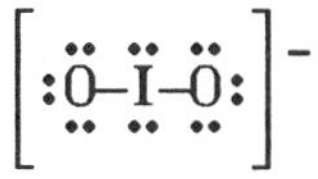 4	2	bent
(c) H–Ö–Ï:	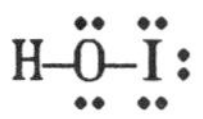 4	2	bent
(d) [:Ï–Ï–Ï:]⁻	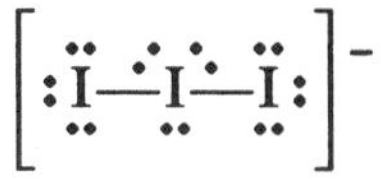 5	3	linear
(e) :Ö–Cl–Ö:	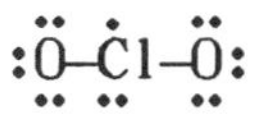 4	2	bent

S2.77   (a)

$$2NaCl(aq) + 2H_2O(l) \xrightarrow{\text{electrolysis}} 2NaOH(aq) + Cl_2(g) + H_2(g)$$

The products NaOH and Cl_2 are not allowed to mix.

(b)

$$NaCl(aq) + H_2O(l) \xrightarrow[\text{cold}]{\text{electrolysis}} NaOCl(aq) + H_2(g)$$

The products of the electrolysis are allowed to mix.

(c)

$$KCl(aq) + 3H_2O(l) \xrightarrow[\text{hot; conc}]{\text{electrolysis}} KClO_3(aq) + 3H_2(g)$$

During electrolysis the solution is stirred so that the products will mix.

(d)

$$KCl(aq) + 4H_2O(l) \xrightarrow[\text{hot; conc}]{\text{electrolysis}} KClO_4(aq) + 4H_2(g)$$

During electrolysis the solution is stirred so that the products will mix and the electrolysis is prolonged in order to allow the chlorate ion to be oxidized to the perchlorate ion.

S2.78   (a) Fluorine cannot attack fluorspar, CaF_2, because the calcium is already in its maximum oxidation state of +2. Therefore, there is nothing for the fluorine to oxidize.

(b) The fluorine initially attacks or reacts with the specially formulated steel producing a thin adherent coating of metal fluoride. This adherent metal fluoride coating, safe from fluorine attack since it is fully oxidized, protects the remaining unoxidized metal from further attack by not allowing the fluorine to come in contact with it.

S2.80   1. $BrO_3^-(aq) + XeF_2(s) \longrightarrow BrO_4^-(aq) + Xe(g) + HF(aq)$

2. and 3. $BrO_3^-(aq) + H_2O(l) \longrightarrow BrO_4^-(aq) + 2H^+(aq) + 2e^-$ (balanced oxidation)
$XeF_2(s) + 2e^- \longrightarrow Xe(g) + 2F^-(aq)$ (balanced reduction)

5. $BrO_3^-(aq) + XeF_2(s) + H_2O(l) \longrightarrow BrO_4^-(aq) + Xe(g) + 2HF(aq)$

S2.81   (a) A bromine concentration of 4000 ppm by mass means that there is 4000 g of Br_2 in one million (1.00×10^6) grams of brine. The volume of brine that will yield 1.00 kg of bromine is

$$1.00 \times 10^3 \text{ g } Br_2 \text{ x } \frac{1.00 \times 10^6 \text{ g brine}}{4000 \text{ g } Br_2} \text{ x } \frac{1.00 \text{ mL brine}}{1.1 \text{ g brine}}$$

$$= 227 \times 10^3 \text{ mL or } 2.3 \times 10^2 \text{ L brine}$$

(b) The equation for the reaction is $Cl_2(g) + 2Br^-(aq) \longrightarrow Br_2(l) + 2Cl^-(aq)$

The steps in the calculation are: g $Br_2 \longrightarrow$ mol $Br_2 \longrightarrow$ mol $Cl_2 \longrightarrow$ volume Cl_2.

$$1.00 \times 10^3 \text{ g } Br_2 \text{ x } \frac{1 \text{ mol } Br_2}{159.81 \text{ g } Br_2} \text{ x } \frac{1 \text{ mol } Cl_2}{1 \text{ mol } Br_2} = 6.26 \text{ mol } Cl_2$$

The volume of Cl_2 measured at STP needed to produce 1.00 kg Br_2 is

$$6.26 \text{ mol } Cl_2 \text{ x } \frac{22.4 \text{ L } Cl_2}{1 \text{ mol } Cl_2} = 140 \text{ L } Cl_2$$

S2.82

$$2NaCl(aq) + 2H_2O(l) \xrightarrow{\text{electrolysis}} 2NaOH(aq) + Cl_2(g) + H_2(g)$$

To obtain an actual yield of 1.00 kg Cl_2, there would have to be a theoretical yield of

$$\text{theoretical yield} = \frac{\text{actual yield x 100\%}}{\text{percent yield}} = \frac{1.00 \text{ kg } Cl_2 \text{ x 100\%}}{80\%} = 1.25 \text{ kg } Cl_2$$

The volume of NaCl solution required to produce 1.00 kg Cl_2 can now be calculated from this theoretical Cl_2 mass value of 1.25 kg Cl_2. The steps in the calculation are:
1.25 kg $Cl_2 \longrightarrow$ mol $Cl_2 \longrightarrow$ mol NaCl $\longrightarrow$ g NaCl $\longrightarrow$ vol. NaCl soln.

$$1.25 \times 10^3 \text{ g } Cl_2 \text{ x } \frac{1 \text{ mol } Cl_2}{70.9 \text{ g } Cl_2} \text{ x } \frac{2 \text{ mol NaCl}}{1 \text{ mol } Cl_2} \text{ x } \frac{58.44 \text{ g NaCl}}{1 \text{ mol NaCl}} = 2061 \text{ g NaCl}$$

The volume of 25% NaCl solution required is

$$2061 \text{ g NaCl x } \frac{100 \text{ g NaCl soln}}{25 \text{ g NaCl}} \text{ x } \frac{1 \text{ mL soln}}{1.2 \text{ g soln}}$$

$$= 6870 \text{ mL or } 6.9 \text{ L NaCl soln (to two significant figures)}$$

S2.83 A fluoride ion concentration of 1 ppm by mass means that there is 1 g of F^- in one million (1.0 $\times 10^6$) grams of water.

$$\frac{100 \text{ gal water}}{1 \text{ day} \times 1 \text{ person}} \times 1.5 \times 10^6 \text{ persons} \times \frac{3.785 \text{ L}}{1 \text{ gal}} \times \frac{10^3 \text{ mL}}{1 \text{ L}} \times \frac{1 \text{ g water}}{1 \text{ mL water}}$$

$$\times \frac{1 \text{ g } F^-}{1.0 \times 10^6 \text{ g water}} \times \frac{41.99 \text{ g NaF}}{19.00 \text{ g } F^-} = 1 \times 10^6 \text{ g/day or } 1 \times 10^3 \text{ kg NaF/day}$$

S2.85

$$\text{molarity} = \frac{\text{moles of solute}}{\text{liters of solution}}$$

(a)

$$\text{molarity} = \frac{9.5 \times 10^2 \text{ g soln}}{1 \text{ L soln}} \times \frac{25 \text{ g NH}_3}{100 \text{ g soln}} \times \frac{1 \text{ mol NH}_3}{17.03 \text{ g NH}_3}$$

$$= 14 \text{ mol NH}_3/\text{L} = 14 \text{ M NH}_3$$

(b)

$$\text{molarity} = \frac{1.0 \times 10^3 \text{ g soln}}{1 \text{ L soln}} \times \frac{3.0 \text{ g H}_2\text{O}_2}{100 \text{ g soln}} \times \frac{1 \text{ mol H}_2\text{O}_2}{34.0 \text{ g H}_2\text{O}_2}$$

$$= 0.88 \text{ mol H}_2\text{O}_2/\text{L} = 0.88 \text{ M H}_2\text{O}_2$$

(c)

$$\text{molarity} = \frac{1.0 \times 10^3 \text{ g soln}}{1 \text{ L soln}} \times \frac{0.90 \text{ g NaCl}}{100 \text{ g soln}} \times \frac{1 \text{ mol NaCl}}{58.44 \text{ g NaCl}}$$

$$= 0.15 \text{ mol NaCl/L} = 0.15 \text{ M NaCl}$$

S2.86 $3\text{O}_2(g) \longrightarrow 2\text{O}_3(g)$

$2\text{I}^-(aq) + \text{O}_3(g) + \text{H}_2\text{O}(l) \longrightarrow 2\text{OH}^-(aq) + \text{I}_2(aq) + \text{O}_2(g)$

4.15 L of dry air at 25°C and 1.00 atm contains (carry an extra significant figure)

$$n = \frac{PV}{RT} = \frac{1.00 \text{ atm} \times 4.15 \text{ L}}{0.0821 \text{ L atm/mol K} \times 298 \text{ K}} = 0.1696 \text{ mol}$$

The number of moles of O_2 is

$$0.1696 \text{ mol air} \times \frac{20.9 \text{ mol O}_2}{100 \text{ mol air}} = 0.03545 \text{ mol O}_2$$

If all the O_2 were converted to O_3 we would have

$$0.03545 \text{ mol O}_2 \times \frac{2 \text{ mol O}_3}{3 \text{ mol O}_2} \times \frac{48.0 \text{ g O}_3}{1 \text{ mol O}_3} = 1.134 \text{g O}_3$$

The actual amount of O_3 produced can be calculated from the amount of I_2 formed. The steps in the calculation are: g $\text{I}_2 \longrightarrow$ mol $\text{I}_2 \longrightarrow$ mol $\text{O}_3 \longrightarrow$ g O_3.

$$0.0751 \text{ g I}_2 \times \frac{1 \text{ mol I}_2}{253.81 \text{ g I}_2} \times \frac{1 \text{ mol O}_3}{1 \text{ mol I}_2} \times \frac{48.0 \text{ g O}_3}{1 \text{ mol O}_3} = 0.01420 \text{ g O}_3$$

The percent yield is

$$\text{percent yield} = \frac{0.01420 \text{ g}}{1.134 \text{ g}} \times 100\% = 1.25\%$$

S2.87 (a) $2H_2O_2(aq) \longrightarrow 2H_2O(l) + O_2(g)$

The steps in the calculation are: $g\ H_2O_2 \longrightarrow mol\ H_2O_2 \longrightarrow mol\ O_2 \longrightarrow volume\ O_2.$

$$1.00 \times 10^3\ mL\ soln \times \frac{1.00\ g\ soln}{1\ mL\ soln} \times \frac{6\ g\ H_2O_2}{100\ g\ soln} \times \frac{1\ mol\ H_2O_2}{34.0\ g\ H_2O_2} \times \frac{1\ mol\ O_2}{2\ mol\ H_2O_2}$$

$$= 0.88\ mol\ O_2$$

The volume of O_2 produced at 25°C and 1.00 atm is

$$V = \frac{nRT}{P} = \frac{0.88\ mol \times 0.0821\ L\ atm/mol\ K \times 298\ K}{1.00\ atm}$$

$$= 21.5\ L\ or\ 2 \times 10\ L\ \text{(to one significant figure)}$$

(b) "20 volume H_2O_2" means that 20 mL of O_2 is produced from 1 mL of peroxide solution or 20 L of O_2 from 1 L of peroxide solution. One liter of a 6% peroxide solution produces 2×10 L of O_2 to one significant figure. Therefore, the older designation is fairly accurate.

S2.90 (a)

$$2NH_4NO_3(s) \longrightarrow \quad N_2(g) \quad + \quad 4H_2O(g) \quad + \quad O_2(g)$$
$\Delta H_f°:\quad 2 \times -365.6\ kJ \qquad 1 \times 0\ kJ \quad\ 4 \times -241.8\ kJ \qquad 1 \times 0\ kJ$

$$\Delta H° = 1 \times 0\ kJ + 4 \times -241.8\ kJ + 1 \times 0\ kJ - (2 \times -365.6\ kJ) = -236.0\ kJ$$

(b) The equation shows that 3 mol of gas are produced for every 1 mol of NH_4NO_3 exploded. The steps in the calculation are :
$g\ NH_4NO_3 \longrightarrow mol\ NH_4NO_3 \longrightarrow mol\ gas \longrightarrow volume\ gas.$

$$1.00 \times 10^3\ g\ NH_4NO_3 \times \frac{1\ mol\ NH_4NO_3}{80.04\ g\ NH_4NO_3} \times \frac{3\ mol\ gas}{1\ mol\ NH_4NO_3} = 37.5\ mol\ gas$$

The volume of gas produced, measured at 800°C and 1.00 atm, is

$$V = \frac{nRT}{P} = \frac{37.5\ mol \times 0.0821\ L\ atm/mol\ K \times 1073\ K}{1.00\ atm} = 3.30 \times 10^3\ L$$

S2.91

$$2NH_4ClO_4(s) \longrightarrow \quad N_2(g) \quad + \quad Cl_2(g) \quad + \quad 2O_2(g) \quad + \quad 4H_2O(g)$$
$\Delta H_f°:\ 2 \times -295.3\ kJ \qquad 1 \times 0\ kJ \quad\ 1 \times 0\ kJ \qquad 2 \times 0\ kJ \quad\ 4 \times -241.8\ kJ$

$$\Delta H° = 1 \times 0\ kJ + 1 \times 0\ kJ + 2 \times 0\ kJ + 4 \times -241.8\ kJ - (2 \times -295.3\ kJ) = -376.6\ kJ$$

The heat released when 1.5 million pounds of ammonium perchlorate decomposes is

$$1.5 \times 10^6\ lbs \times \frac{453.6\ g}{1\ lb} \times \frac{1\ mol\ NH_4ClO_4}{117.49\ g\ NH_4ClO_4} \times \frac{376.6\ kJ}{2\ mol\ NH_4ClO_4} = 1.1 \times 10^9\ kJ$$

S2.93 (a) Laughing gas; N_2O, nitrous oxide.
(b) Tincture of iodine; alcohol solution of iodine.
(c) Aqua regia, a mixture of one part concentrated nitric acid to three parts concentrated hydrochloric acid.
(d) Saltpeter; KNO_3, potassium nitrate.
(e) Chile saltpeter; $NaNO_3$, sodium nitrate.
(f) Fluorspar; CaF_2, calcium fluoride.
(g) Teflon; polytetrafluoroethylene, a fluorocarbon polymer.
(h) Freon-12, CCl_2F_2, dichlorodifluoromethane.
(i) Bleaching powder; $Ca(OCl)_2$, calcium hypochlorite.

CHAPTER 12
LIQUIDS, SOLIDS, AND INTERMOLECULAR FORCES

Solutions To Practice Exercises

PE 12.2   First we must find the value of the constant B for ethanol. We know that the vapor pressure P of ethanol is 1.00 atm at $78.5^\circ C = 351.7$ K. R = 8.314 J/mol K and the heat of vaporization is +38.6 kJ/mol.

$$B = \ln P + \Delta H^\circ_{vap}/RT = \ln 1.00 \; atm + \frac{38.6 \times 10^3 \; J/mol}{8.314 \; J/mol \; K \times 351.7 \; K} = 13.20$$

Now we can use the value of B to find the vapor pressure P that corresponds to T = 298 K.

$$\ln P = \frac{-38.6 \times 10^3 \; J/mol}{8.314 \; J/mol \; K \times 298 \; K} + 13.20 = -15.58 + 13.20 = -2.38$$

$$P = 0.0926 \; atm \times \frac{760 \; torr}{1 \; atm} = 70.4 \; torr$$

Answer: The pressure has to be reduced from 760 torr to 70.4 torr.

PE 12.4 (a) Liquid to solid to vapor. Decreasing the pressure with no change in temperature is equivalent to moving vertically downward in the phase diagram. At 1.1 atm and $0^\circ C$, water is liquid. The phase diagram (Fig. 12.10) shows that the liquid turns to solid and then to vapor as the pressure decreases at $0^\circ C$.

(b) Liquid to vapor. Heating under a constant pressure of 1.1 atm is represented by moving from left to right along a horizontal line at 1.1 atm in the phase diagram (Fig 12.10). The phase diagram shows that the liquid water warms until it reaches the vaporization curve; further heating vaporizes the liquid.

PE 12.6 (a) No. The pressure must be at least 5.2 atm for liquid CO_2 to exist.

(b) Yes. Liquid H_2O is stable above 0.0060 atm for certain temperatures within this temperature range.

PE 12.8 (a) I_2. I_2 has more electrons and is larger than Br_2.

(b) SiH_4. C is in the second period and Si is in the third; hence, SiH_4 is larger and has more electrons than CH_4.

(c) CH_3CH_3. CH_3CH_3 is larger than CH_4.

PE 12.9 (a) No. The size of P prevents the formation of a strong hydrogen bond.

145

(b) No. The C–H bonds are not strongly polar.

(c) Yes. The N–H bonds are strongly polar and the hydrogen atom in the N–H bond will be attracted to a nitrogen atom in a nearby CH_3NH_2 molecule and will form a strong hydrogen bond.

PE 12.10   A body-centered cubic lattice contains one-eighth of each corner atom and the entire center atom:

```
8 corner atoms  x  1/8 = 1 atom
1 center atom   x   1  = 1 atom
                  Sum = 2 atoms per cell
```

PE 12.12   We can calculate the molar mass from the number of atoms per unit cell, the mass of the unit cell, and Avogadro's number. Our steps will be (1) find the number of atoms in the unit cell, (2) find the mass of this number of atoms from the unit cell length and density data, (3) use this number of atoms and mass to find the mass of 6.022×10^{23} atoms, and (4) use the calculated molar mass to identify the element.

Step 1: The unit cell is a face-centered cube and therefore contains four atoms (Table 12.8).

Step 2: The volume of any cubic cell is equal to its edge cubed.

$$V = (edge)^3 = (404 \times 10^{-10}\ cm)^3 = 6.59 \times 10^{-23}\ cm^3$$

The density of the unit cell is the same as the density of the metal. The mass m of the unit cell is the product of its volume V and density d.

$$m = V \times d = 6.59 \times 10^{-23}\ cm^3 \times 2.70\ g/cm^3 = 1.78 \times 10^{-22}\ g$$

Step 3: The molar mass is equal to the mass of 6.022×10^{23} atoms. The mass of a single atom is equal to the unit cell mass divided by the number of atoms per unit cell. Hence, the molar mass is

$$\frac{1.78 \times 10^{-22}\ g}{4\ atoms} \times \frac{6.022 \times 10^{23}\ atoms}{1\ mol} = 26.8\ g/mol$$

Step 4: The table of atomic weights shows that the element closest to this molar mass is aluminum.

PE 12.13 (a) Table 12.8 shows that each unit cell in a body-centered cubic lattice contains the equivalent of two atoms. Hence, the percent of occupied space is

$$\%\ occupied\ space = \frac{volume\ of\ two\ atoms}{unit\ cell\ volume} \times 100\%$$

volume of two atoms = $2 \times 4\pi r^3/3$

body-centered unit cell volume = $(edge)^3 = (4r/\sqrt{3})^3 = 64r^3/3\sqrt{3}$

Substituting these volumes into the percent expression gives

$$\%\ occupied\ space = \frac{2 \times 4\pi r^3/3}{64r^3/3\sqrt{3}} \times 100\% = \frac{\sqrt{3}\pi}{8} \times 100\% = 68.02\%$$

(b) Table 12.8 shows that each unit cell in a face-centered cubic lattice contains the equivalent of four atoms. Hence, the percent of occupied space is

$$\%\ occupied\ space = \frac{volume\ of\ four\ atoms}{unit\ cell\ volume} \times 100\%$$

volume of four atoms = $4 \times 4\pi r^3/3$

face-centered unit cell volume = $(2\sqrt{2}r)^3 = 16\sqrt{2}r^3$

Substituting these volumes into the percent expression gives

$$\text{\% occupied space} = \frac{4 \times 4\pi r^3/3}{16\sqrt{2}r^3} \times 100\% = \frac{\pi}{3\sqrt{2}} \times 100\% = 74.05\%$$

PE 12.14 (a) For chloride ions:

$$8 \text{ corner } Cl^- \times 1/8 = 1 \ Cl^-$$
$$6 \text{ face } Cl^- \times \underline{1/2 = 3 \ Cl^-}$$
$$\text{Sum} = 4 \ Cl^- \text{ per cell}$$

(b) For sodium ions:

$$12 \text{ edge } Na^+ \times 1/4 = 3 \ Na^+$$
$$1 \text{ center } Na^+ \times \underline{\ 1 \ \ = 1 \ Na^+}$$
$$\text{Sum} = 4 \ Na^+ \text{ per cell}$$

Solutions to Final Exercises

12.3 (a) Molecular substances are held together in the liquid and solid state by intermolecular forces of attraction. The strength of these forces is highly dependent on the distance between the interacting molecules. High pressures force the molecules closer together, thus increasing the strength of the intermolecular forces and favoring the formation of the liquid and solid states.

(b) Low temperatures slow down the molecular speeds. At these lower speeds the intermolecular attractive forces are strong enough to form groups or clusters of molecules, thus leading to the formation of the liquid and solid states.

12.7 Less. The pressure on the top of Mt. Everest is lower than that at sea level. The boiling point of a liquid is the temperature at which its vapor pressure equals the pressure on the liquid. Since the pressure is less, the boiling point will be lower. Remember that the vapor pressure of a liquid increases with increasing temperature.

12.9 The melting point of a substance is the temperature at which the solid and liquid states are in equilibrium. If the vapor pressure of the solid didn't equal the vapor pressure of the liquid at the melting point, then the solid would change over to the liquid or vice versa, since material would continuously evaporate from the higher vapor pressure state and condense into the lower vapor pressure state, so that the two states would not be in equilibrium. In other words, the vapor pressures must be equal in order for the solid and liquid to be in equilibrium.

12.10

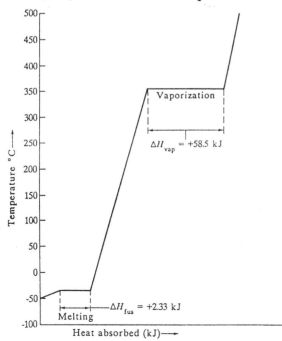

Heating curve for one mole of mercury, not drawn to scale.

12.13   Steam contains 40.67 kJ/mol (= ΔH_{vap}) more energy at 100°C than water at 100°C. Therefore, a given mass of steam at 100°C can transfer more heat energy to your skin as it condenses and cools than an equivalent mass of water at 100°C, and consequently, causes a more severe burn.

12.14   Ethyl chloride is a very volatile substance and when sprayed on tissue immediately starts evaporating. The evaporating ethyl chloride rapidly cools down the tissue by drawing heat from it. Below a certain temperature the chemical processes that conduct nerve impulses to the brain cannot function. The ethyl chloride anesthetizes the tissue by cooling it down below this temperature.

12.17   (a) In going from ice at 0°C to steam at 100°C, we have to (1) melt the ice at 0°C, (2) bring the liquid water at 0°C up to 100°C, and (3) vaporize the liquid at 100°C. The amount of kilojoules required to carry out each step is:

Step 1:   1 mol x $\dfrac{6.01\ kJ}{1\ mol}$ = 6.01 kJ

Step 2:   q = mass x specific heat x ΔT

= 18.02 g x 4.18 J/g°C x (100°C – 0°C) = 7530 J or 7.53 kJ

Step 3:   1 mol x $\dfrac{40.67\ kJ}{1\ mol}$ = 40.67 kJ

The total kilojoules required is the sum of the three steps:

6.01 kJ + 7.53 kJ + 40.67 kJ = 54.21 kJ

(b)
54.21 kJ x $\dfrac{1\ kcal}{4.184\ kJ}$ = 12.96 kcal

12.19   The value of B is 13.1 (see Example 12.2 in textbook). Substituting P = 0.28 atm, B = 13.1, and ΔH°_{vap} = +40.7 kJ/mol into Equation 12.2 gives

ln 0.28 = $\dfrac{-40.7\ x\ 10^3\ J/mol}{8.314\ J/mol\ K\ x\ T}$ + 13.1

Solving for T gives T = 341 K = 68°C

12.22   Greater. The upward fusion curve slants very slightly to the right. Therefore, a vertical line drawn in the direction of increasing pressure from any point on the fusion curve takes liquid hydrogen into solid hydrogen. This means that solid hydrogen is more compact than liquid hydrogen, so the density of solid hydrogen must be greater than that of liquid hydrogen.

12.23   If the air above the open vessel has a water vapor partial pressure below the vapor pressure of water at 25°C, then liquid water will evaporate in an attempt to bring the water vapor partial pressure up to the vapor pressure value. However, since the vessel is open, the partial pressure can never equal the vapor pressure because the water vapor continuously diffuses away. Consequently, the liquid water continues to evaporate gradually until it is all vapor.

12.25   Liquid helium I. Increasing pressure tends to decrease the volume of a substance. Since increasing pressure changes liquid helium II into liquid helium I, liquid helium I must be more compact and, consequently, must have a greater density.

12.26 (a) A triple point is a point on a phase diagram showing the temperature and pressure at which three states can coexist in equilibrium. There are three such points on the sulfur phase diagram. At one point, solid rhombic, solid monoclinic, and vapor are in equilibrium. At another point, solid monoclinic, liquid sulfur, and vapor are in equilibrium; and at a third point, solid rhombic, solid monoclinic, and liquid sulfur are in equilibrium.

          Note: Each distinct solid or liquid is a separate state.

  (b) The process can be represented by moving from left to right along a line drawn at 1 atm. The rhombic sulfur will warm until its temperature reaches a point on the rhombic-monoclinic transition curve. At this point, the solid rhombic sulfur changes over to solid monoclinic sulfur. After the rhombic sulfur changes, continued heating will warm the monoclinic sulfur until its temperature reaches a point on the monoclinic fusion curve. After the monoclinic sulfur melts, continued heating will raise the temperature of the liquid to 160°C.

12.29   Increase. Since solid benzene is more dense than liquid benzene, a vertical line drawn in the direction of increasing pressure from any point on the fusion curve should take liquid benzene into solid benzene. This would mean that the fusion curve slants upward to the right and, consequently, the melting point increases with increasing pressure.

12.31 (a) Yes, if the temperature is at or below the critical temperature. In fact, it will be either liquefied of solidified, depending on the temperature. Below the critical temperature each vertical line (increasing P at constant T) crosses either a vapor/liquid boundary or a vapor/solid boundary.

  (b) Yes. Sufficient cooling will liquefy any vapor. In fact, it will be condensed to liquid or solid, depending on the pressure; i.e., depending on which horizontal line is traveled from right to left.

12.35 (a) Both I_2 and CCl_4 are nonpolar molecules. Therefore, only London dispersion forces exist.

  (b) Al^{3+} is an ion and H_2O is a polar molecule containing a highly electronegative atom, oxygen. Therefore, there exists an electrostatic attraction, called an ion-dipole attraction, between the ion and the polar water molecule. London dispersion forces also exist.

  (c) Both CH_3Br and CH_3Cl are polar molecules. Therefore, both dipole-dipole forces and London dispersion forces exist.

  (d) Both CH_3OH and CH_3NH_2 have very polar bonds involving the hydrogen atom. Therefore, both hydrogen bonding and London dispersion forces exist.

12.37   Large massive molecules are much more easily polarized than small molecules. Therefore, large massive molecules have much stronger London dispersion forces than small molecules. These stronger intermolecular forces between the large massive molecules means that more energy is required to separate them so that they can enter the vapor state. Consequently, large massive molecules are less volatile.

12.38 C_2H_5OH. $CH_3CH_2CH_3$ is a nonpolar substance and, therefore, only London dispersion forces exist between the $CH_3CH_2CH_3$ molecules. On the other hand, C_2H_5OH can participate in hydrogen bonding, since it has a very polar bond involving the hydrogen atom. The hydrogen bond is the strongest intermolecular attractive force; much stronger than London dispersion forces. Therefore, C_2H_5OH should have the higher heat of vaporization.

12.40 CH_2O. CO_2 is a nonpolar molecule while CH_2O is polar; therefore there will be greater intermolecular attractions between the CH_2O molecules.

12.42 (a) Yes.   (b) No.

        H–F---H–F

(c) Yes.

$$H_3C-\overset{\overset{\displaystyle H}{|}}{\underset{\underset{\displaystyle H}{|}}{C}}-O-H---O-\overset{\overset{\displaystyle H}{|}}{\underset{\underset{\displaystyle H}{|}}{C}}-CH_3$$

(d) No.

(e) Yes.

$$H_3C-C\overset{O---H-O}{\underset{O-H---O}{\diagdown}}C-CH_3$$

(f) No.

12.45 (a) Liquids contain small groups of molecules with orderly arrangements, but these orderly domains are continuously breaking apart and reforming so that disorder prevails over the liquid as a whole.

   (b) The intermolecular forces in liquids are strong enough to cause the formation of small groups of molecules with orderly arrangements. This is short-range order since these groups do not get very large.

   (c) The intermolecular forces are not strong enough to stop the faster moving liquid molecules from disrupting the orderly domains. Therefore, long-range disorder is caused by thermal motion.

12.51 (a) Mothballs–molecular solid. Mothballs are volatile, low melting, and poor conductors of heat and electricity.

   (b) Sand–network covalent solid. Sand is very hard and brittle. It has a very high melting point and very low volatility. It is also a poor conductor of electricity.

   (c) Ice–molecular solid. Ice is low melting with a low heat of fusion. It is also a poor conductor of heat and electricity.

   (d) Table salt–ionic solid. Table salt is hard and brittle. It has a high melting point and low volatility. Salt only conducts electricity in the molten state.

   (e) Toaster filament–metallic solid. A toaster filament is a good conductor of heat and electricity.

12.54 (a) Sugar–crystalline. Sugar has a definite melting point and shape.

   (b) Rubber–amorphous. Rubber doesn't have a definite melting point and can take on any shape.

   (c) Polyethylene–amorphous. Polyethylene doesn't have a definite melting point and can take on any shape.

   (d) Aluminum–crystalline. Aluminum has a definite melting point and shape.

   (e) Tar–amorphous. Tar doesn't have a definite melting point and can take on any shape.

   (f) Potassium sulfate–crystalline. K_2SO_4 has a definite melting point and shape.

   (g) Diamond–crystalline. Diamond has a definite melting point and shape.

12.56 Local conditions in the solution or melt (fluid motion, varying solute concentrations, confining boundaries, etc.) could favor the horizontal growth of the crystal over vertical growth. The unit cells could still be cubic, but the crystal would contain more unit cells side by side horizontally than on top of each other vertically.

12.61 (a) Equation 12.4 applies to face-centered unit cells.

$$r = \frac{edge}{2\sqrt{2}} = \frac{407.86 \ pm}{2\sqrt{2}} = 144.20 \ pm$$

   (b) The density of gold is the same as the density of the unit cell. A face-centered unit cell contains four atoms. The volume of the unit cell is

$$V = (edge)^3 = (407.86 \times 10^{-10} \ cm)^3 = 6.7847 \times 10^{-23} \ cm^3$$

The density of gold is

$$d = \frac{m}{V} = \frac{4 \ Au \ atoms \times 196.9665 \ u/Au \ atom \times 1.661 \times 10^{-24} \ g/u}{6.7847 \times 10^{-23} \ cm^3} = 19.29 \ g/cm^3$$

12.64 (a) The volume of the unit cell is $V = (edge)^3 = (495.05 \times 10^{-10} \ cm)^3 = 1.2132 \times 10^{-22} \ cm^3$.

The mass of the unit cell is m = V x d = 1.2132 x 10^{-22} cm^3 x 11.3 g/cm^3 = 1.37 x 10^{-21} g.

One mole of lead, 207.19 g, contains 6.022 x 10^{23} atoms. The number of atoms in 1.37 x 10^{-21} g is

$$1.37 \times 10^{-21} \text{ g} \times \frac{6.022 \times 10^{23} \text{ atoms}}{207.19 \text{ g}} = 3.98 = 4 \text{ atoms}$$

Four atoms per unit cell corresponds to a face-centered cubic lattice (Table 12.8).
(b) Equation 12.4 applies to face-centered unit cells.

$$r = \frac{edge}{2\sqrt{2}} = \frac{495.05 \text{ pm}}{2\sqrt{2}} = 175.03 \text{ pm}$$

12.67   (a) Refer to Fig. 12.38 in the textbook.
(b) The number of zinc atoms in the unit cell can either be calculated using the entire hexagonal arrangement and dividing by three or it can be calculated using a single unit cell. Using the entire hexagonal arrangement and dividing by three gives

```
2 face atoms (centers of hexagon) x 1/2   = 1 atom
12 corner atoms x 1/6                      = 2 atoms
3 inside atoms x 1                         = 3 atoms
                                     Sum  = 6 atoms
```

Therefore, the unit cell contains 6 atoms/3 = 2 zinc atoms.
(c) Each zinc atom is in contact with 12 other zinc atoms. Therefore, the coordination number is 12.

12.73   No. The wavelength of the radiation must be comparable to the distance between the scattering centers in order for there to be a diffraction effect. A wavelength of 500 nm is considerably larger than the distances between the particles in crystalline solids and, therefore, will not produce a diffraction pattern.

12.76   (a) The first-order scattering angle is

$$\sin \theta = \lambda/2d = \frac{0.154 \text{ nm}}{2 \times 0.335 \text{ nm}} = 0.230$$

$\theta = 13.3°$

The second-order scattering angle is

$$\sin \theta = \frac{2\lambda}{2d} = \frac{0.154 \text{ nm}}{0.335 \text{ nm}} = 0.460$$

$\theta = 27.4°$

(b) The first-order scattering angle is

$$\sin \theta = \frac{\lambda}{2d} = \frac{0.225 \text{ nm}}{2 \times 0.335 \text{ nm}} = 0.336$$

$\theta = 19.6°$

The second-order scattering angle is

$$\sin \theta = \frac{2\lambda}{2d} = \frac{0.225 \text{ nm}}{0.335 \text{ nm}} = 0.672$$

$\theta = 42.2°$

12.77   (a) The molecules leaving the liquid state are the ones that have a higher kinetic energy than the average. Therefore, as they escape, the average kinetic energy of the remaining molecules drops as well as the temperature of the remaining liquid, since the temperature depends on the average kinetic energy.

(b) As the water on the skin evaporates, the remaining water drops in temperature. Body heat then flows to the cooler water and any excess body heat is removed in the process.

(c) The tree's respiration process produces O_2 and H_2O. The H_2O is removed by evaporation from the leaves and this cools down the tree.

12.83 (a) The volume of the unit cell is $V = (edge)^3 = (356.7 \times 10^{-10}$ cm$)^3 = 4.5385 \times 10^{-23}$ cm^3.

The mass of the unit cell is m$= V \times d = 4.5385 \times 10^{-23}$ cm$^3 \times 3.513$ g/cm$^3 = 1.5944 \times 10^{-22}$ g.

The number of carbon atoms in the unit cell is

$$1.5944 \times 10^{-22} \text{ g C} \times \frac{1 \text{ u}}{1.661 \times 10^{-24} \text{ g}} \times \frac{1 \text{ C atom}}{12.011 \text{ u C}} = 7.99 \text{ or } 8 \text{ C atoms}$$

(b) In drawing the unit cell keep in mind that:
1. Each corner atom contributes only one eighth of an atom to the unit cell and there must be eight of them, since it is a cubic unit cell. The total contribution of the corner atoms is one atom.
2. Each face atom contributes one-half of an atom to the unit cell. There are six face atoms in the unit cell. The total contribution of the face atoms is three atoms.
3. An internal atom contributes one whole atom to the unit cell. There are four of them.
4. Each atom is bonded to four other atoms by covalent bonds.

We can draw this unit cell by bonding each internal atom to one corner atom and three face atoms. Alternating corners are thus bonded within one cell:

(c) No.

12.84 The hexagonal close-packed lattice unit cell contains two atoms. The volume of the unit cell is equal to the area of the upper face times the height. The area of the upper face is

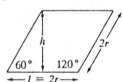

$$A = l \times h = 2r \times 2r\sin 60° = 2\sqrt{3} \, r^2$$

The height is equal to twice the altitude of the pictured equilateral trigonal pyramid.

Referring to the figures, we see that the altitude can be computed by first finding the value of y and then using it to compute a using the Pythagorean theorem.

$$y = \frac{r}{\cos 30°} = \frac{2r}{\sqrt{3}}$$

$$(2r)^2 = \left(\frac{2r}{\sqrt{3}}\right)^2 + a^2$$

$$4r^2 - \frac{4r^2}{3} = \frac{8r^2}{3} = a^2$$

$$a = \frac{\sqrt{8}}{\sqrt{3}} \, r$$

and height $= 2a = \frac{2\sqrt{8}}{\sqrt{3}} \, r$

The volume of the unit cell is therefore

$$V_{unit\ cell} = A \times height = 2\sqrt{3}r^2 \times \frac{2\sqrt{8}}{\sqrt{3}} \, r = 4\sqrt{8}r^3$$

The volume of two atoms is $V_{atoms} = 2 \times 4\pi r^3/3$

The percent occupied space is

$$\%\ occupied\ space = \frac{V_{atoms}}{V_{unit\ cell}} \times 100\% = \frac{8\pi r^3/3}{8\sqrt{2}\ r^3} \times 100\% = \frac{\pi}{3\sqrt{2}} \times 100\% = 74.05\%$$

The hexagonal close-packed lattice and the face-centered cubic lattice have the same amount of occupied space (see PE 12.13).

12.85   The density of NaCl is the same as the unit cell density. Each unit cell contains the equivalent of four chlorine atoms and four sodium atoms. The unit cell is a cube; therefore, its volume is equal to the cube of its edge. From Fig. 12.40 we see that the edge length is equal to twice the distance between the centers of the Na^+ and Cl^- ions, or edge $= 2 \times 282$ pm $= 564$ pm. The volume of the unit cell is

$$V = (edge)^3 = (564 \times 10^{-10}\ cm)^3 = 1.794 \times 10^{-22}\ cm^3$$

The density of NaCl is

$$d = \frac{m}{V} = \frac{(4\ Na\ atoms \times 22.99\ u/Na\ atom + 4\ Cl\ atoms \times 35.453\ u/Cl\ atom) \times 1.661 \times 10^{-24}\ g/u}{1.794 \times 10^{-22}\ cm^3}$$

$$= 2.16\ g/cm^3$$

The calculated density is slightly lower than the observed density.

12.86   The density of the unit cell is the same as the density of CaO. The volume of the unit cell is

$$V = (edge)^3 = (480 \times 10^{-10}\ cm)^3 = 1.106 \times 10^{-22}\ cm^3$$

The mass of the unit cell is

mass unit cell $= V \times d = 1.106 \times 10^{-22}\ cm^3 \times 3.35\ g/cm^3 = 3.705 \times 10^{-22}\ g$

The mass of one CaO formula unit is

mass CaO formula unit $= (40.08\ u + 15.9994\ u) \times 1.661 \times 10^{-24}\ g/u = 9.314 \times 10^{-23}\ g$

The number of CaO formula units in the unit cell is

$$\frac{3.705 \times 10^{-22}\ g/unit\ cell}{9.314 \times 10^{-23}\ g/CaO\ formula\ unit} = 3.98 = 4\ CaO\ formula\ units/unit\ cell$$

This number of formula units in a unit cell indicates that the Ca^+ ions form a face-centered cubic lattice and the O^{2-} ions form a face-centered cubic lattice. The complete lattice is a superposition of the two separate lattices. The unit cell is a face-centered cube like that of NaCl, which is depicted in Fig. 12.40.

CHAPTER 13
SOLUTIONS

Solutions To Practice Exercises

PE 13.3 At 25°C the vapor pressure of pure water is 23.8 torr. The vapor pressure lowering is

$$\text{VPL} = P^{\circ}_{\text{solvent}} - P_{\text{solution}} = 23.8 \text{ torr} - 22.0 \text{ torr} = 1.8 \text{ torr}$$

The mole fraction of sucrose is

$$X_{\text{sucrose}} = \frac{\text{VPL}}{P^{\circ}_{\text{water}}} = \frac{1.8 \text{ torr}}{23.8 \text{ torr}} = 0.076$$

PE 13.4 The molar mass of ethanol is 46.07 g. The number of moles of ethanol is

$$n_{\text{ethanol}} = 6.00 \text{ g} \times \frac{1 \text{ mol}}{46.07 \text{ g}} = 0.130 \text{ mol}$$

This number of moles is dissolved in 75.0 g = 0.0750 kg of water. The molality is

$$\text{molality} = \frac{\text{number of moles of ethanol}}{\text{number of kilograms of water}} = \frac{0.130 \text{ mol}}{0.0750 \text{ kg}} = 1.73 \text{ mol/kg or } 1.73 \text{ m}$$

PE 13.5 The molar mass of biphenyl is 154.21 g. The number of moles of biphenyl is

$$n_{\text{biphenyl}} = 1.25 \text{ g} \times \frac{1 \text{ mol}}{154.21 \text{ g}} = 8.11 \times 10^{-3} \text{ mol}$$

The molality of the solution is

$$m_{\text{biphenyl}} = \frac{\text{number of moles of biphenyl}}{\text{number of kilograms of water}} = \frac{8.11 \times 10^{-3} \text{ mol}}{50.0 \times 10^{-3} \text{ kg}} = 0.162 \text{ mol/kg}$$

K_b for benzene is

$$K_b = \frac{\text{BPE}}{m_{\text{biphenyl}}} = \frac{0.411°C}{0.162 \text{ mol/kg}} = 2.54°C \text{ kg/mol}$$

PE 13.6   The normal freezing point and K_f of benzene are $5.5°C$ and $4.90°C$ kg/mol, respectively (see Table 13.2). The freezing point depression is

$$FPD = T°_f - T_f = 5.5°C - 3.41°C = 2.1°C$$

The molality is

$$m_{benzene} = \frac{FPD}{K_f} = \frac{2.1°C}{4.90°C \ kg/mol} = 0.43 \ mol/kg$$

PE 13.8   Step 1. $BPE = 0.376°C$

Step 2.

$$m = \frac{BPE}{K_b} = \frac{0.376°C}{3.63°C \ kg/mol} = 0.104 \ mol/kg$$

Step 3. The number of moles of cholesterol in 25.0 g = 0.0250 kg of solvent is

$$n_{cholesterol} = 0.0250 \ kg \ solvent \ x \ \frac{0.104 \ mol}{1 \ kg \ solvent} = 2.60 \ x \ 10^{-3} \ mol$$

Step 4. $2.60 \ x \ 10^{-3}$ mol of cholesterol corresponds to 1.00 g. The molar mass of cholesterol is $1.00 \ g/2.60 \ x \ 10^{-3}$ mol = 385 g/mol.

PE 13.9   Step 1. The osmotic pressure of the solution is 12.0 torr x 1 atm/760 torr = $1.58 \ x \ 10^{-2}$ atm. Steps 2. and 3. The number of moles of protein in 1 mL of solution is obtained by substituting $\pi = 1.58 \ x \ 10^{-2}$ atm, $V_{solution} = 1.00 \ x \ 10^{-3}$ L, R = 0.0821 L atm/mol K, and the temperature $25°C = 298$ K into Equation 13.12a:

$$n_{protein} = \frac{\pi V_{soln}}{RT} = \frac{1.58 \ x \ 10^{-2} \ atm \ x \ 1.00 \ x \ 10^{-3} \ L}{0.0821 \ L \ atm/mol \ K \ x \ 298 \ K} = 6.46 \ x \ 10^{-7} \ mol$$

Step 4. The mass of $6.46 \ x \ 10^{-7}$ mol is 28.8 mg. The molar mass is 28.8 x 10^{-3} g/6.46 x 10^{-7} mol = $4.46 \ x \ 10^4$ g/mol.

PE 13.12   The i factor for 1.00 m H_2SO_4 is

$$i = \frac{4.04°C}{1.86°C} = 2.17$$

If we assume no dissociation, the calculated BPE for a 1.00 m aqueous solution would be $0.512°C$. The observed BPE is therefore

observed BPE = i x calculated BPE assuming no dissociation = 2.17 x $0.512°C = 1.11°C$

The boiling point of the solution will be $100.00°C + 1.11°C = 101.11°C.$

Solutions to Final Exercises

13.1   (a) The molar mass of H_2SO_4 is 98.1 g. The molarity is

$$molarity = \frac{1.07 \ g \ soln}{1 \ mL} \ x \ \frac{10.0 \ g \ H_2SO_4}{100.0 \ g \ soln} \ x \ \frac{1000 \ mL}{1 \ L} \ x \ \frac{1 \ mol \ H_2SO_4}{98.1 \ g \ H_2SO_4}$$

$$= 1.09 \ mol \ H_2SO_4/L \ or \ 1.09 \ M \ H_2SO_4$$

(b)

$$X_{H_2SO_4} = \frac{n_{H_2SO_4}}{n_{H_2SO_4} + n_{H_2O}}$$

The number of moles of H_2SO_4 and H_2O in 100.0 g of solution are

$$n_{H_2SO_4} = 10.0 \text{ g } H_2SO_4 \times \frac{1 \text{ mol } H_2SO_4}{98.1 \text{ g } H_2SO_4} = 0.102 \text{ mol } H_2SO_4$$

$$n_{H_2O} = 90.0 \text{ g } H_2O \times \frac{1 \text{ mol } H_2O}{18.0 \text{ g } H_2O} = 5.00 \text{ mol } H_2O$$

The mole fraction of sulfuric acid in the solution is

$$X_{H_2SO_4} = \frac{0.102 \text{ mol}}{0.102 \text{ mol} + 5.00 \text{ mol}} = 0.0200$$

13.8   It is the heat of solution at the saturation point and not the overall heat of solution that determines if a substance is more or less soluble with increasing temperature. Increased temperature makes for increased solubility when the solution process at the saturation point is endothermic; decreased solubility when the solution process is exothermic. For NaOH the process of dissolving at the saturation point is endothermic and, therefore, the solubility of NaOH increases with increasing temperature.

13.12   The solubility of a sparingly soluble gas, CO_2 in this case, is directly proportional to the pressure of the gas above the solution. Carbonated soda beverages are bottled under CO_2 pressures of up to 4 atm. When the cap is removed, the partial pressure of CO_2 above the soda water becomes very small, since the CO_2 vapor diffuses away. The CO_2 in the solution exceeds the saturation concentration for the lower CO_2 pressure, and the excess gas bubbles out.

13.13   The partial pressure of O_2 decreases from 1.00 atm to 0.21 x 1.00 atm = 0.21 atm. Henry's law states that the solubility will decrease by the same factor as the partial pressure. Hence, the new solubility will be

$$2.2 \text{ mmol/L} \times \frac{0.21 \text{ atm}}{1.00 \text{ atm}} = 0.46 \text{ mmol/L}$$

The partial pressure of N_2 decreases from 1.00 atm to 0.79 x 1.00 atm = 0.79 atm. The solubility will decrease by the same factor as the partial pressure, and the new solubility will be

$$1.03 \text{ mmol/L} \times \frac{0.79 \text{ atm}}{1.00 \text{ atm}} = 0.81 \text{ mmol/L}$$

13.15   More soluble. Sea water contains numerous dissolved salts and the solubility of a sparingly soluble ionic compound in water is increased by the presence of other salts that do not have an ion in common with the compound. This effect is called "salting-in."

13.17   An ideal solution is an imaginary solution in which the component molecules experience forces identical to those they would experience in the pure state. Aqueous solutions are not ideal because water forms hydration layers around the solute molecules and the hydrogen bonding between the water molecules is disrupted.

13.19   (a) Negative deviation. Negative deviations from Raoult's law are caused by stronger interactions, which release energy when they come into play.
        (b) Positive deviation. Positive deviations from Raoult's law are caused by the replacement of stronger interactions by weaker interactions. The disruption of the stronger interactions is endothermic.

13.21   (a) To solve this problem we first have to calculate the mole fractions of CCl_4 and $CHCl_3$ in the solution. The molar masses of CCl_4 and $CHCl_3$ are 153.8 g and 119.4 g, respectively. The numbers of moles of CCl_4 and $CHCl_3$ are

$$n_{CCl_4} = 70.0 \text{ g} \times \frac{1 \text{ mol}}{153.8 \text{ g}} = 0.455 \text{ mol}$$

$$n_{CHCl_3} = 30.0 \text{ g} \times \frac{1 \text{ mol}}{119.4 \text{ g}} = 0.251 \text{ mol}$$

The mole fractions of CCl_4 and $CHCl_3$ are

$$X_{CCl_4} = \frac{n_{CCl_4}}{n_{CCl_4} + n_{CHCl_3}} = \frac{0.455 \text{ mol}}{0.455 \text{ mol} + 0.251 \text{ mol}} = 0.644$$

$$X_{CHCl_3} = 1 - X_{CCl_4} = 1 - 0.644 = 0.356$$

The partial pressures of CCl_4 and $CHCl_3$ are

$$P_{CCl_4} = X_{CCl_4} P^{\circ}_{CCl_4} = 0.644 \times 143 \text{ torr} = 92.1 \text{ torr}$$

$$P_{CHCl_3} = X_{CHCl_3} P^{\circ}_{CHCl_3} = 0.356 \times 199 \text{ torr} = 70.8 \text{ torr}$$

(b) The total pressure is obtained by adding the two partial pressures:

$$P_{total} = P_{CCl_4} + P_{CHCl_3} = 92.1 \text{ torr} + 70.8 \text{ torr} = 162.9 \text{ torr}$$

13.26   The molar mass of $C_6H_4Cl_2$ is 147.0 g. The number of moles of $C_6H_4Cl_2$ is

$$n_{dichlorobenzene} = 0.615 \text{ g} \times \frac{1 \text{ mol}}{147.0 \text{ g}} = 4.18 \times 10^{-3} \text{ mol}$$

This number of moles is dissolved in 21.8 g = 0.0218 kg of benzene. The molality is

$$molality = \frac{\text{number of moles of dichlorobenzene}}{\text{number of kilograms of benzene}} = \frac{4.18 \times 10^{-3} \text{ mol}}{2.18 \times 10^{-2} \text{ kg}}$$

$$= 0.192 \text{ mol/kg or } 0.192 \text{ m}$$

13.28   A 100.00-g solution contains 36.00 g of $AlCl_3$ and 64.00 g of H_2O. The number of moles of $AlCl_3$ in 100.00 g of solution is

$$36.00 \text{ g} \times \frac{1 \text{ mol}}{133.34 \text{ g}} = 0.2700 \text{ mol}$$

The molality is

$$molality = \frac{0.2700 \text{ mol}}{0.06400 \text{ kg}} = 4.219 \text{ m}$$

13.29   The molarity depends on the volume of the solution. Since the volume expands and contracts with temperature, the molarity will also vary with temperature or be temperature dependent. Molality, on the other hand, depends only on the masses of solute and solvent and not on volume measurements. Consequently, the molality is temperature independent, since the mass of a substance is temperature independent.

13.33 (a) The number of moles of CCl_4 is

$$3.00 \text{ g} \times \frac{1 \text{ mol}}{153.82 \text{ g}} = 0.0195 \text{ mol}$$

The molality of the solution is

$$\text{molality} = \frac{0.0195 \text{ mol}}{0.190 \text{ kg}} = 0.103 \text{ m}$$

The freezing point depression and freezing point of the solution are

$$\text{FPD} = K_f m = \frac{4.90^\circ \text{C kg}}{1 \text{ mol}} \times \frac{0.103 \text{ mol}}{1 \text{ kg}} = 0.505^\circ \text{C}$$

$$T_f = T^\circ_f - \text{FPD} = 5.5^\circ \text{C} - 0.505^\circ \text{C} = 5.0^\circ \text{C}$$

(b) The freezing point depression and freezing point of the solution are

$$\text{FPD} = K_f m = \frac{1.86^\circ \text{C kg}}{1 \text{ mol}} \times \frac{1.51 \text{ mol}}{1 \text{ kg}} = 2.81^\circ \text{C}$$

$$T_f = T^\circ_f - \text{FPD} = 0.00^\circ \text{C} - 2.81^\circ \text{C} = -2.81^\circ \text{C}$$

(c) The number of moles of naphthalene is

$$1.00 \text{ g} \times \frac{1 \text{ mol}}{128.17 \text{ g}} = 7.80 \times 10^{-3} \text{ mol}$$

The molality of the solution is

$$\text{molality} = \frac{7.80 \times 10^{-3} \text{ mol}}{0.0250 \text{ kg}} = 0.312 \text{ m}$$

The freezing point depression and freezing point of the solution are

$$\text{FPD} = K_f m = \frac{31.8^\circ \text{C kg}}{1 \text{ mol}} \times \frac{0.312 \text{ mol}}{1 \text{ kg}} = 9.92^\circ \text{C}$$

$$T_f = T^\circ_f - \text{FPD} = -23.0^\circ \text{C} - 9.92^\circ \text{C} = -32.9^\circ \text{C}$$

(d) The molality of the solution is

$$\text{molality} = \frac{0.0025 \text{ mol}}{0.200 \text{ kg}} = 0.012 \text{ m}$$

The freezing point depression and freezing point of the solution is

$$\text{FPD} = K_f m = \frac{1.86^\circ \text{C kg}}{1 \text{ mol}} \times \frac{0.012 \text{ mol}}{1 \text{ kg}} = 0.022^\circ \text{C}$$

$$T_f = T^\circ_f - \text{FPD} = 0.00^\circ \text{C} - 0.022^\circ \text{C} = -0.02^\circ \text{C}$$

13.35 -25°F is equivalent to -32°C. One liter of water has a mass of approximately 1 kg.
(a) To prevent freezing at -32°C, the freezing point depression would have to be

$$\text{FPD} = T^\circ_f - T_f = 0.00^\circ \text{C} - (-32^\circ \text{C}) = 32^\circ \text{C}$$

The molality of the solution would have to be

$$m = \frac{\text{FPD}}{K_f} = \frac{32^\circ \text{C}}{1.86^\circ \text{C kg/mol}} = 17 \text{ mol/kg}$$

The grams of ethylene glycol needed for 1 L would be

17 mol x 62 g/mol = 1054 g or 1.1 x 10^3 g to two significant figures

(b)

$$BPE = K_b m = \frac{0.512°C \text{ kg}}{1 \text{ mol}} \times \frac{17 \text{ mol}}{1 \text{ kg}} = 8.7°C$$

$$T_b = T°_b + BPE = 100.00°C + 8.7°C = 108.7°C$$

(c) No. The FPD and BPE equations are not valid for such high concentrations of solute. For such solutions the actual freezing and boiling points must be obtained experimentally.

13.37   (a) The vapor pressure of the solution can be obtained from Raoult's law. The moles and mole fraction of water in the solution are

$$n_{water} = 100 \text{ g} \times \frac{1 \text{ mol}}{18.0 \text{ g}} = 5.56 \text{ mol}$$

$$X_{water} = \frac{5.56 \text{ mol}}{5.56 \text{ mol} + 0.10 \text{ mol}} = 0.982$$

The vapor pressure is

$$P_{solution} = P_{water} = X_{water} P°_{water} = 0.982 \times 23.8 \text{ torr} = 23.4 \text{ torr}$$

(b) The molality of the solution is

$$molality = \frac{0.10 \text{ mol}}{0.100 \text{ kg}} = 1.0 \text{ mol/kg}$$

The boiling point elevation and boiling point of the solution are

$$BPE = K_b m = \frac{0.512°C \text{ kg}}{1 \text{ mol}} \times \frac{1.0 \text{ mol}}{1 \text{ kg}} = 0.51°C$$

$$T_b = T°_b + BPE = 100.00°C + 0.51°C = 100.51°C$$

(c) The freezing point depression and freezing point of the solution are

$$FPD = K_f m = \frac{1.86°C \text{ kg}}{1 \text{ mol}} \times \frac{1.0 \text{ mol}}{1 \text{ kg}} = 1.9°C$$

$$T_f = T°_f - FPD = 0.0°C - 1.9°C = -1.9°C$$

13.41   According to Raoult's law the vapor pressure of the solvent above the concentrated solution is less than that above the pure solvent. When the partial pressure of the solvent in the closed system exceeds the concentrated solution's vapor pressure, solvent molecules will start to condense into the concentrated solution. As the solvent vapor condenses into the concentrated solution, more pure solvent will evaporate to replace that which has condensed. This will continue until the pure solvent is completely evaporated, since a solution, no matter how dilute, always has a vapor pressure lower than that of the pure solvent.

13.42   (a) The number of moles of naphthalene is

$$5.00 \text{ g} \times \frac{1 \text{ mol}}{128.17 \text{ g}} = 0.0390 \text{ mol}$$

The molality is

$$molality = \frac{0.0390 \text{ mol}}{0.100 \text{ kg}} = 0.390 \text{ m}$$

The freezing point depression is

$$FPD = T^{\circ}_f - T_f = 6.5^{\circ}C - (-1.4^{\circ}C) = 7.9^{\circ}C$$

The freezing point depression constant of cyclohexane is

$$K_f = \frac{FPD}{m} = \frac{7.9^{\circ}C}{0.390 \text{ mol/kg}} = 20^{\circ}C \text{ kg/mol}$$

(b) Step 1. $FPD = T^{\circ}_f - T_f = 6.5^{\circ}C - 3.4^{\circ}C = 3.1^{\circ}C$

Step 2.
$$m = \frac{FPD}{K_f} = \frac{3.1^{\circ}C}{20^{\circ}C \text{ kg/mol}} = 0.155 \text{ mol/kg} \quad \text{(carry an extra significant figure)}$$

Step 3.
$$n_{compound} = \frac{0.155 \text{ mol}}{1 \text{ kg solvent}} \times 0.100 \text{ kg solvent} = 0.0155 \text{ mol}$$

Step 4. 0.0155 mol corresponds to 2.00 g. The molar mass is 2.00 g/0.0155 mol = 129 g/mol or 1.3×10^2 g/mol to two significant figures.

13.43   Step 1. VPL = 6.35 torr
Step 2.

$$X_{compound} = \frac{VPL}{P^{\circ}_{benzene}} = \frac{6.35 \text{ torr}}{74.7 \text{ torr}} = 0.0850$$

Step 3. The number of moles of benzene is

$$250 \text{ g} \times \frac{1 \text{ mol}}{78.11 \text{ g}} = 3.20 \text{ mol}$$

The number of moles of compound is obtained as follows:

$$X_{compound} = \frac{n_{compound}}{n_{compound} + n_{benzene}}$$

Rearranging and solving for $n_{compound}$ gives

$$n_{compound} = \frac{X_{compound} \, n_{benzene}}{(1 - X_{compound})} = \frac{0.0850 \times 3.20 \text{ mol}}{(1 - 0.0850)} = 0.297 \text{ mol}$$

Step 4. The molar mass of the compound is

$$M_{compound} = \frac{25.0 \text{ g}}{0.297 \text{ mol}} = 84.2 \text{ g/mol}$$

13.51   (a) Complete ionization of H_2SO_4 would proceed as follows

$$H_2SO_4(aq) \longrightarrow 2H^+(aq) + SO_4^{2-}(aq)$$

Therefore, a 2.69 m H_2SO_4 solution will be 3 x 2.69 m = 8.07 m in ions. The freezing point depression and freezing point of the solution are

$$FPD = K_f m = \frac{1.86^{\circ}C \text{ kg}}{1 \text{ mol}} \times \frac{8.07 \text{ mol}}{1 \text{ kg}} = 15.0^{\circ}C$$

$$T_f = T^{\circ}_f - FPD = 0.00^{\circ}C - 15.0^{\circ}C = -15.0^{\circ}C$$

The boiling point elevation and boiling point of the solution are

$$BPE = K_b m = \frac{0.512°C \ kg}{1 \ mol} \ x \ \frac{8.07 \ mol}{1 \ kg} = 4.13°C$$

$$T_b = T°_b + BPE = 100.00°C + 4.13°C = 104.13°C$$

(b) $AlCl_3$ dissociates according to the equation

$$AlCl_3(aq) \longrightarrow Al^{3+}(aq) + 3Cl^-(aq)$$

Therefore, a 4.219 m $AlCl_3$ solution will be 4 x 4.219 m = 16.88 m in ions. The freezing point depression and freezing point of the solution are

$$FPD = K_f m = \frac{1.86°C \ kg}{1 \ mol} \ x \ \frac{16.88 \ mol}{1 \ kg} = 31.4°C$$

$$T_f = T°_f - FPD = 0.00°C - 31.4°C = -31.4°C$$

The boiling point elevation and boiling point of the solution are

$$BPE = K_b m = \frac{0.512°C \ kg}{1 \ mol} \ x \ \frac{16.88 \ mol}{1 \ kg} = 8.64°C$$

$$T_b = T°_b + BPE = 100.00°C + 8.64°C = 108.64°C$$

13.54 (a)

$$m = \frac{FPD}{K_f} = \frac{2.00°C}{1.86°C \ kg/mol} = 1.08 \ mol/kg$$

(b) The boiling point elevation and boiling point of the sample is

$$BPE = K_b m = \frac{0.512°C \ kg}{1 \ mol} \ x \ \frac{1.08 \ mol}{1 \ kg} = 0.553°C$$

$$T_b = T°_b + BPE = 100.000°C + 0.553°C = 100.553°C$$

13.55   The i factor calculated from one colligative effect can be used to calculate other colligative effects at the same concentration. If we assume no dissociation, the calculated freezing point depression for a 1.00 m aqueous solution would be 1.86°C. Therefore, the i factor for the solution is

$$i = \frac{observed \ colligative \ effect}{calculated \ effect \ assuming \ no \ dissociation} = \frac{5.21°C}{1.86°C} = 2.80$$

If we assume no dissociation, the calculated boiling point elevation for a 1.00 m aqueous solution would be 0.512°C. The observed boiling point elevation is therefore

observed BPE = i x calculated BPE assuming no dissociation = 2.80 x 0.512°C = 1.43°C

The boiling point of the solution will be 100.00°C + 1.43°C = 101.43°C.

13.59 (a) If we assume no dissociation, the calculated freezing point depression for a 0.100 m aqueous solution would be 0.186°C. Therefore, the observed FPD is

observed FPD = i x calculated FPD assuming no dissociation = 1.87 x 0.186°C = 0.348°C

The freezing point of the solution will be 0.00°C - 0.348°C = -0.348°C.

(b) If we assume no dissociation, the calculated boiling point elevation for a 0.100 m aqueous solution would be $0.0512°C$. Therefore, the observed BPE is

observed BPE = i x calculated BPE assuming no dissociation = 1.87 x $0.0512°C$ = $0.0957°C$

The boiling point of the solution will be $100.00°C + 0.0957°C = 100.10°C$.

(c) To estimate the osmotic pressure of the solution we must first calculate its molarity. The molar mass of NaCl is 58.44 g. Therefore, there is 0.100 mol of NaCl in 1000.00 g + 5.84 g = 1005.84 g of solution. The volume of 1005.84 g of solution is 1005.84 g x 1 mL/1.00 g = 1.01 x 10^3 mL or 1.01 L. The molarity is therefore 0.100 mol/1.01 L = 0.0990 mol/L to three significant figures. If we assume no dissociation, the calculated osmotic pressure of a 0.0990 M solution at $25°C$ is

$$\pi = MRT = \frac{0.0990 \text{ mol}}{1 \text{ L}} \times \frac{0.0821 \text{ L atm}}{\text{mol K}} \times 298 \text{ K} = 2.42 \text{ atm}$$

Therefore, the observed osmotic pressure is

observed osmotic pressure = i x calculated osmotic pressure assuming no dissociation
= 1.87 x 2.42 atm = 4.53 atm.

13.72 (a)

$$50.0 \text{ g KNO}_3 \times \frac{100 \text{ g H}_2\text{O}}{247 \text{ g KNO}_3} \times \frac{1 \text{ mL H}_2\text{O}}{1 \text{ g H}_2\text{O}} = 20.2 \text{ mL H}_2\text{O}$$

(b) The maximum amount of KNO_3 that 20.2 mL H_2O can dissolve at $0°C$ is

$$\frac{13.3 \text{ g KNO}_3}{100 \text{ g H}_2\text{O}} \times \frac{1 \text{ g H}_2\text{O}}{1 \text{ mL H}_2\text{O}} \times 20.2 \text{ mL H}_2\text{O} = 2.69 \text{ g KNO}_3$$

The amount of KNO_3 that will recrystallize is 50.0 g – 2.69 g = 47.3 g.

13.74 (a) $P_{benzene} = X_{benzene} P°_{benzene}$ = 0.451 x 1108 torr = 500 torr

$X_{toluene}$ = 1 – 0.451 = 0.549

$P_{toluene} = X_{toluene} P°_{toluene}$ = 0.549 x 474 torr = 260 torr

Alternately, $P_{toluene}$ could be calculated from the fact that the solution boils at $94.8°C$ and, therefore, must have a total vapor pressure of 760 torr; i.e.,

$P_{toluene} = P_T - P_{benzene}$ = 760 torr – 500 torr = 260 torr

Hence, the composition of the vapor is

$$X_{benzene} = \frac{P_{benzene}}{P_T} = \frac{500 \text{ torr}}{760 \text{ torr}} = 0.658$$

$X_{toluene}$ = 1 – 0.658 = 0.342

(b) The condensed liquid has the same mole fractions as the vapor. Therefore, the partial pressures of benzene and toluene above such a solution at $94.8°C$ are

$P_{benzene}$ = 0.658 x 1108 torr = 729 torr

$P_{toluene}$ = 0.342 x 474 torr = 162 torr

The total vapor pressure of the condensed liquid at $94.8°C$ is therefore

$P_T = P_{benzene} + P_{toluene}$ = 729 torr + 162 torr = 891 torr

13.76   The osmotic pressure of the protein solution is

$$\pi = MRT = \frac{0.010 \text{ mol}}{1 \text{ L}} \times \frac{0.0821 \text{ L atm}}{\text{mol K}} \times 298 \text{ K} = 0.24 \text{ atm}$$

The maximum height is the height of a column of protein solution that exerts a pressure of 0.24 atm. The osmotic pressure of 0.24 atm can be converted into millimeters of mercury.

$$0.24 \text{ atm} \times \frac{760 \text{ torr}}{1 \text{ atm}} \times \frac{1 \text{ mm Hg}}{1 \text{ torr}} = 182 \text{ mm or } 18 \text{ cm Hg to two significant figures}$$

Therefore, a Hg column 18 cm in height provides a pressure of 0.24 atm. Since the density of Hg is 13.6 times greater than the density of the solution, it takes a column of solution 13.6 x 18 cm = 2.4×10^2 cm in height to provide a pressure of 0.24 atm.

13.77   (a) Water will transfer from the beaker with the higher vapor pressure solution (less concentrated solution) to the beaker with the lower vapor pressure solution (more concentrated solution) until the vapor pressures of both solutions are identical. The numbers of moles of sucrose and vitamin C are

$$2.00 \text{ g sucrose} \times \frac{1 \text{ mol sucrose}}{342.2 \text{ g sucrose}} = 5.84 \times 10^{-3} \text{ mol sucrose}$$

$$2.00 \text{ g vitamin C} \times \frac{1 \text{ mol vitamin C}}{176.1 \text{ g vitamin C}} = 1.14 \times 10^{-2} \text{ mol vitamin C}$$

Since the vitamin C solution is more concentrated at the start, the sucrose solution will become more concentrated and the vitamin C solution will become more dilute.

(b) At equilibrium the mole fractions of water in both beakers are equal and the mole fraction of sucrose equals the mole fraction of vitamin C. The number of moles of water initially in each beaker is

$$30.0 \text{ g H}_2\text{O} \times \frac{1 \text{ mol H}_2\text{O}}{18.0 \text{ g H}_2\text{O}} = 16.7 \text{ mol H}_2\text{O}$$

Let x equal the number of moles of H_2O transferred from one beaker to another. Then, at equilibrium

$$X_{\text{sucrose}} = \frac{n_{\text{sucrose}}}{n_{\text{sucrose}} + n_{H_2O}} = \frac{5.84 \times 10^{-3} \text{ mol}}{5.84 \times 10^{-3} \text{ mol} + 1.67 \text{ mol} - x \text{ mol}}$$

$$X_{\text{vitamin C}} = \frac{n_{\text{vitamin C}}}{n_{\text{vitamin C}} + n_{H_2O}} = \frac{1.14 \times 10^{-2} \text{ mol}}{1.14 \times 10^{-2} \text{ mol} + 1.67 \text{ mol} + x \text{ mol}}$$

Equating the sucrose and Vitamin C mole fractions gives us

$5.84 \times 10^{-3} \times (1.6814 + x) = 1.14 \times 10^{-2} \times (1.67584 - x)$

$0.01724x = 0.0092852$

$x = 0.539 \text{ mol}$

Therefore, at equilibrium the mole fraction of each solute will be

$$X_{\text{vitamin C}} = X_{\text{sucrose}} = \frac{1.14 \times 10^{-2} \text{ mol}}{1.14 \times 10^{-2} \text{ mol} + 1.67 \text{ mol} + 0.539 \text{ mol}} = 5.13 \times 10^{-3}$$

13.78 (a) Step 1. FPD = $T^\circ_f - T_f = 5.5^\circ C - 4.27^\circ C = 1.23^\circ C$ (carry an extra significant figure)

Step 2.

$$m = \frac{FPD}{K_f} = \frac{1.23^\circ C}{4.90^\circ C \text{ kg/mol}} = 0.251 \text{ mol/kg}$$

Step 3.

$$n_{hormone} = \frac{0.251 \text{ mol}}{1 \text{ kg}} \times 5.00 \times 10^{-3} \text{ kg} = 1.26 \times 10^{-3} \text{ mol}$$

Step 4.

$$M = \frac{0.363 \text{ g}}{0.00126 \text{ mol}} = 288 \text{ g/mol or } 2.9 \times 10^2 \text{ g/mol to two significant figures}$$

(b) The numbers of moles of C, H, and O in the molar mass are

C: 2.9×10^2 g hormone $\times \dfrac{79.12 \text{ g C}}{100 \text{ g hormone}} \times \dfrac{1 \text{ mol C atoms}}{12.01 \text{ g C}} = 19$ mol C atoms

H: 2.9×10^2 g hormone $\times \dfrac{9.79 \text{ g H}}{100 \text{ g hormone}} \times \dfrac{1 \text{ mol H atoms}}{1.01 \text{ g H}} = 28$ mol H atoms

O: 2.9×10^2 g hormone $\times \dfrac{11.09 \text{ g O}}{100 \text{ g hormone}} \times \dfrac{1 \text{ mol O atoms}}{16.00 \text{ g O}} = 2$ mol O atoms

The molecular formula for testosterone is therefore $C_{19}H_{28}O_2$. The precise molar mass of testosterone is $(19 \times 12.011) + (28 \times 1.00794) + (2 \times 15.9994) = 288.43$ g/mol.

13.79 (a) Assuming no ionization, the FPD and freezing point of the solution would be

$$FPD = K_f m = \frac{1.86^\circ C \text{ kg}}{1 \text{ mol}} \times \frac{0.0100 \text{ mol}}{1 \text{ kg}} = 0.0186^\circ C$$

$$T_f = T^\circ_f - FPD = 0.000^\circ C - 0.0186^\circ C = -0.0186^\circ C$$

(b) Let α equal the fraction of the acetic acid molecules that are ionized. The total molality of the solution is

$$m = \frac{FPD}{K_f} = \frac{0.0195^\circ C}{1.86^\circ C \text{ kg/mol}} = 0.0105 \text{ mol/kg}$$

The molalities present in the solution are:

$$CH_3COOH(aq) \rightleftharpoons H^+(aq) + CH_3COO^-(aq)$$

	CH_3COOH	H^+	CH_3COO^-
Initial molality	0.0100	0	0
Change	-0.0100α	+0.0100α	+0.0100α
Molality after ionization	0.0100(1 − α)	0.0100α	0.0100α

The total molality of the solution is the sum of the molalities of each solute species present. Therefore,

$$m = m_{CH_3COOH} + m_{H^+} + m_{CH_3COO^-} = 0.0100(1 - \alpha) + 0.0100\alpha + 0.0100\alpha = 0.0100(1 + \alpha)$$

Since, m = 0.0105,

$$0.0100(1 + \alpha) = 0.0105$$

$$\alpha = \frac{0.0105}{0.0100} - 1 = 0.05 \text{ or } 5\%$$

CHAPTER 14
CHEMICAL KINETICS

Solutions To Practice Exercises

PE 14.1 The difference in the temperatures $35°C - 5°C = 30°C$ is equivalent to three temperature rises of ten degrees each. The growth rate of the colony doubles for each ten degree rise in temperature. Therefore, the growth rate at $35°C$ should be $2 \times 2 \times 2 = 8$ times faster than that at $5°C$.

PE 14.4 Draw the tangent line to the $[NO_2]$ versus time curve at $t = 40$ s. The actual values for $\Delta[NO_2]$ and Δt depend on which right triangle is employed, i.e., on the length chosen for the tangent segment. One right triangle gives $\Delta[NO_2] = 0.006$ mol/L $- 0.00925$ mol/L $= -0.003$ mol/L and $\Delta t = 58.75$ s $- 30$ s $= 29$ s. The slope of the tangent line is

$$slope = \frac{\Delta[NO_2]}{\Delta t} = \frac{-0.003 \text{ mol/L}}{29 \text{ s}} = -1 \times 10^{-4} \text{ mol/L s}$$

Because concentration is decreasing with time, the instantaneous reaction rate is the negative of the slope, or 1×10^{-4} mol/L s.

PE 14.5 Assume the rate law has the form

rate $= k[I^-]^m [S_2O_8^{2-}]^n$

We have to determine the values of m and n; m can be determined from runs 1 and 3, since the initial $[S_2O_8^{2-}]$ is the same in both runs.

$$\frac{rate\ 3}{rate\ 1} = \frac{8.6 \times 10^{-4} \text{ mol/L s}}{2.6 \times 10^{-4} \text{ mol/L s}} = \frac{\cancel{k}(0.50)^m\cancel{(0.45)^n}}{\cancel{k}(0.15)^m\cancel{(0.45)^n}} = \left[\frac{0.50}{0.15}\right]^m$$

or $3.3 = (3.3)^m$ and $m = 1$

In a like manner, n can be determined from runs 1 and 2, since the initial $[I^-]$ is the same in both runs.

$$\frac{rate\ 1}{rate\ 2} = \frac{2.6 \times 10^{-4} \text{ mol/L s}}{1.4 \times 10^{-4} \text{ mol/L s}} = \frac{\cancel{k(0.15)^m}(0.45)^n}{\cancel{k(0.15)^m}(0.25)^n} = \left[\frac{0.45}{0.25}\right]^n$$

or $1.9 = (1.8)^n$ and $n = 1$

Substituting $m = 1$ and $n = 1$ into the rate law gives

rate = $k [I^-] [S_2O_8^{2-}]$

PE 14.9 $\ln([N_2O_5]/[N_2O_5]_0) = -kt$

$\ln \dfrac{0.385 \text{ mol/L}}{0.400 \text{ mol/L}} = -k \times 1.0 \text{ min}$

Rearranging and solving for k gives

$-k \times 1.0 \text{ min} = \ln(0.385/0.400) = \ln 0.962 = -3.874 \times 10^{-2}$ and $k = 0.03874/1.0 \text{ min} = 0.039 \text{ min}^{-1}$

PE 14.10 The fraction of N_2O_5 remaining can be obtained by substituting
$A = N_2O_5$, $k = 0.038 \text{ min}^{-1}$, and $t = 45$ min in Equation 14.3.

$\dfrac{[N_2O_5]}{[N_2O_5]_0} = e^{-kt} = e^{-0.038 \text{ min}^{-1} \times 45 \text{ min}} = e^{-1.71} = 0.18$

PE 14.11 The rate constant, k, can be obtained by substituting $[\text{sucrose}]/[\text{sucrose}]_0 = 2/3$ and $t = 139$ min into Equation 14.4.

$\ln ([\text{sucrose}]/[\text{sucrose}]_0) = -kt$

$\ln (2/3) = -k \times 139 \text{ min}$

$-0.4055 = -k \times 139 \text{ min}$ (keep 1 extra significant figure)

and $k = 0.4055/139 \text{ min} = 2.92 \times 10^{-3} \text{ min}^{-1}$

PE 14.14 The NO_2 concentration can be obtained by substituting $A = NO_2$, $k = 10.1$ L/mol s, $t = 30.0$ s, and $[NO_2]_0 = 0.0300$ mol/L into Equation 14.8.

$\dfrac{1}{[NO_2]} = kt + \dfrac{1}{[NO_2]_0}$

$\dfrac{1}{[NO_2]} = 10.1 \text{ L/mol s} \times 30.0 \text{ s} + \dfrac{1}{0.0300 \text{ mol/L}}$

$\dfrac{1}{[NO_2]} = 303 \text{ L/mol} + 33.3 \text{ L/mol} = 336 \text{ L/mol}$

and $[NO_2] = 2.98 \times 10^{-3}$ mol/L

PE 14.18 A slow first step starting with $NO_2(g) + F_2(g) \longrightarrow$ products
would account for the observed rate law. Likely products might be NO_2F and F.

Step 1: $NO_2(g) + F_2(g) \longrightarrow NO_2F(g) + F(g)$ (slow)

A second step to complete the mechanism brings in the second NO_2 molecule and eliminates the intermediate F.

Step 2: $NO_2(g) + F(g) \longrightarrow NO_2F(g)$ (fast)

PE 14.19 The rate of Step 3, the rate-determining step, is

rate = $k_3[NO_3][NO]$

This rate law has the intermediate NO_3 in it. To eliminate the intermediate NO_3 and have a rate law only in terms of the initial reactants and final products, we employ the steady-state approximation.

rate of NO_3 formation = rate of Step 1 = $k_1[NO][O_2]$

rate of NO_3 consumption = rate of Step 2 = $k_2[NO_3]$

Equating these rates gives $k_1[NO][O_2] = k_2[NO_3]$

Rearranging gives the steady-state concentration of NO_3:

$$[NO_3] = \frac{k_1}{k_2} [NO][O_2]$$

The rate law for the slow step can now be rewritten as follows:

$$\text{rate} = k_3[NO_3][NO] = k_3 \frac{k_1}{k_2} [NO][O_2][NO] = \frac{k_3 k_1}{k_2} [NO]^2[O_2] = k[NO]^2[O_2]$$

PE 14.21 Substituting $E_a = 18.7 \times 10^3$ J/mol, $k_1 = 0.0400$ s^{-1}, $T_1 = 273$ K, $T_2 = 298$ K, and $R = 8.314$ J/mol K into Equation 14.15 gives

$$\ln \frac{0.0400}{k_2} = \frac{18.7 \times 10^3 \text{ J/mol}}{8.314 \text{ J/mol K}} \left[\frac{1}{298 \text{ K}} - \frac{1}{273 \text{ K}} \right]$$

$\ln 0.0400 - \ln k_2 = -0.691$

$\ln k_2 = -2.528$

and $k_2 = e^{-2.528} = 0.0798$ s^{-1}

PE 14.22 The frequency of bimolecular collisions is proportional to the concentration of each of the colliding molecules. Therefore, tripling the concentration of A will triple the collision frequency, while halving the concentration of B will cut the collision frequency in half. Consequently, the collision frequency will increase by a factor of $3/2 = 1.5$.

PE 14.23 To solve the problem, first calculate the fraction of collisions with energies greater than or equal to 10.0 kJ/mol at 25°C and 35°C.

At 25°C: Substituting E_a, R, and T = 298 K in Equation 14.17 gives

$f_a = e^{-(10,000 \text{ J/mol})/(8.314 \text{ J/mol K}) (298 \text{ K})} = e^{-4.04} = 1.76 \times 10^{-2}$

At 35°C: Substituting E_a, R and T= 308 K into Equation 14.17 gives $f_a = e^{-3.91} = 2.00 \times 10^{-2}$

The reaction rate will increase by a factor of $2.00 \times 10^{-2}/1.76 \times 10^{-2} = 1.14$.

Solutions to Final Exercises

14.6 Four. The difference in the temperatures $15.5°C - 35.5°C = -20.2°C$ is equivalent to two temperature drops of ten degrees each. The animal's oxygen consumption doubles for each ten degree rise in temperature. Therefore, the animal's oxygen consumption at 15.5°C should be 2 x 2 = 4 times slower or less than that at 35.5°C.

14.10

$$\frac{-\Delta[O_2]}{\Delta t} = \frac{-1}{2} \frac{\Delta[CO]}{\Delta t} \quad \text{and} \quad \frac{\Delta[CO_2]}{\Delta t} = \frac{-\Delta[CO]}{\Delta t}$$

14.12　(a)　Substituting P = 1.00 atm, V = 0.0100 L, T = 300 K, and R = 0.0821 L atm/mol K in the ideal gas equation and solving for n will give the number of moles of O_2 produced in a second's time.

$$n = \frac{PV}{RT} = \frac{1.00 \text{ atm} \times 0.0100 \text{ L}}{0.0821 \text{ L atm/ mol K} \times 300 \text{ K}} = 4.06 \times 10^{-4} \text{ mol}$$

Hence, the rate in terms of moles of oxygen produced per second is 4.06×10^{-4} mol/s.

(b)　From the reaction equation we see that

$$\frac{-\Delta n_{H_2O_2}}{\Delta t} = \frac{2\Delta n_{O_2}}{\Delta t} = 2 \times 4.06 \times 10^{-4} \text{ mol/s} = 8.12 \times 10^{-4} \text{ mol/s}$$

The volume of the solution in 0.0250 L. Therefore, the change in molarity of H_2O_2 per second is

$$\frac{-\Delta[H_2O_2]}{\Delta t} = \frac{8.12 \times 10^{-4} \text{ mol/s}}{0.0250 \text{ L}} = 3.25 \times 10^{-2} \text{ mol/L s}$$

14.14　(a)　The average reaction rate is only defined between two points on the concentration versus time curve and is the negative of the slope of the straight line connecting the points. The instantaneous reaction rate is only defined at a particular point on the concentration versus time curve and is the negative of the slope of the tangent line to the curve at that point.

(b)　These rates are seldom equal to each other because for most reactions the reaction rates are not constant; i.e., the reaction rates usually change during the course of a reaction.

(c)　The instantaneous and average reaction rates will be equal whenever the reaction rate is constant during the course of a reaction.

14.17　(a)　The graph shows the tangent line to the [sucrose] versus time curve at t = 0 min. A right triangle has been drawn with part of the tangent line as the hypotenuse. The legs of the triangle are Δ[sucrose] = 0.230 mol/L – 0.480 mol/L = –0.250 mol/L and Δt = 170 min – 50 min = 120 min. The slope of the tangent line is

$$\text{slope} = \frac{\Delta[\text{sucrose}]}{\Delta t} = \frac{-0.250 \text{ mol/L}}{120 \text{ min}} = -2.1 \times 10^{-3} \text{ mol/L min}$$

The initial reaction rate is the negative of the slope, or 2.1×10^{-3} mol/L min.

(b)　The graph shows the tangent line to the [sucrose] versus time curve at t = 440 min. A right triangle has been drawn with part of the tangent line as the hypotenuse. The legs of the triangle are Δ[sucrose] = 0.070 mol/L – 0.210 mol/L = –0.140 mol/L and Δt = 600 min – 290 min = 310 min. The slope of the tangent line is

$$\text{slope} = \frac{\Delta[\text{sucrose}]}{\Delta t} = = \frac{-0.140 \text{ mol/L}}{319 \text{ min}} = -4.5 \times 10^{-4} \text{ mol/L min}$$

The rate at 440 min is the negative of the slope, or 4.5×10^{-4} mol/L min.

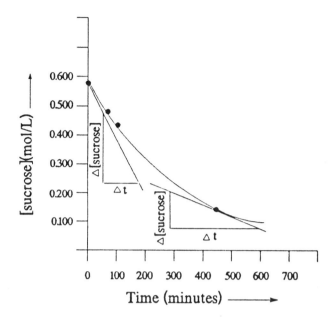

14.18   The average reaction rate over a time interval is equal to the change in concentration divided by the change in time. For the hydrolysis of sucrose, the average rate between 0 and 100 minutes is

$$\text{average rate } \frac{-\Delta[\text{sucrose}]}{\Delta t} = \frac{-(0.427 \text{ mol/L} - 0.584 \text{ mol/L})}{100 \text{ min}}$$

$$= \frac{-(-0.157 \text{ mol/L})}{100 \text{ min}} = 1.57 \times 10^{-3} \text{ mol/L min}$$

14.19   (a) The graph shows the tangent line to the $[(CH_3)_3CBr]$ versus time curve at t = 0 h. A right triangle has been drawn with part of the tangent line as the hypotenuse. The legs of the triangle are $\Delta[(CH_3)_3CBr]$ = 0.1039 mol/L − 0.0520 mol/L = −0.0519 mol/L and Δt = 10.0 h − 0.0 h = 10.0 h. The slope of the tangent line is

$$\text{slope} = \frac{\Delta[(CH_3)_3CBr]}{\Delta t} = \frac{-0.0519 \text{ mol/L}}{10.0 \text{ h}} = -5.19 \times 10^{-3} \text{ mol/L h}$$

The initial reaction rate is the negative of the slope, or 5.19×10^3 mol/L h.

(b) The graph shows the tangent line to the $[(CH_3)_3CBr]$ versus time curve at t = 14.0 h. A right triangle has been drawn with part of the tangent line as the hypotenuse. The legs of the triangle are $\Delta[(CH_3)_3CBr]$ = 0.0560 mol/L − 0.0280 mol/L = −0.0280 mol/L and Δt = 22.0 h − 12.0 h = 10.0 h. The slope of the tangent line is

$$\text{slope} = \frac{\Delta[(CH_3)_3CBr]}{\Delta t} = \frac{-0.0280 \text{ mol/L}}{10.0 \text{ h}} = -2.80 \times 10^{-3} \text{ mol/L h}$$

The rate at 14.0 h is the negative of the slope, or 2.80×10^{-3} mol/L h.

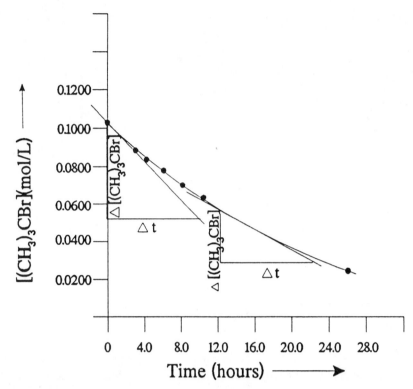

14.23   (a) From runs (1) and (2), increasing [A] threefold while keeping [B] constant increases the rate by 0.108/0.012 or ninefold. Since $9 = 3^2$, the rate is proportional to $[A]^2$. From runs (1) and (3), cutting [B] in half while keeping [A] constant also cuts the rate in half. The rate is proportional to [B]. Therefore, rate = $k[A]^2[B]$. The reaction is third order.
        (b) Using data from the first run gives

0.012 mol/L s = k(0.10 mol/L)^2 (0.60 mol/L) and k = 2.0 L^2/mol^2 s
        (c) Rate = 2.0 L^2/mol^2 s x (0.010 mol/L)^2 (0.010 mol/L) = 2.0 x 10^{-6} mol/L s

14.24   (a) In the first two runs, the rate changed by the same factor as [NH$_4$$^+$], when [HNO$_2$] was constant. In the last two runs, the rate changed by the same factor as [HNO$_2$], when [NH$_4$$^+$] was constant. Therefore,

rate = k[NH$_4$$^+$][HNO$_2$]
        (b) Using data from the third run gives 335.0 x 10^{-8} mol/L s = k(0.196 mol/L) (0.0488 mol/L)

Hence, k = 3.50 x 10^{-4} L/mol s

Note: A better value for k would be the average over the four runs, which is 3.56 x 10^{-4} L/mol s.
        (c)
$$\frac{\Delta[N_2]}{\Delta t} = 3.50 \times 10^{-4} \text{ L/mol s} \times 0.040 \text{ mol/L} \times 0.040 \text{ mol/L} = 5.6 \times 10^{-7} \text{ mol/L s}$$

14.26   (a) For a first-order reaction, a plot of the logarithm of the concentration versus time should yield a straight line.

t(hours)	0	3.15	4.10	6.20	8.20	10.0	26.0
ln[(CH$_3$)$_3$CBr]	-2.2643	-2.4124	-2.4546	-2.5562	-2.6578	-2.7504	-3.6119

The graph shows that this is essentially the case.

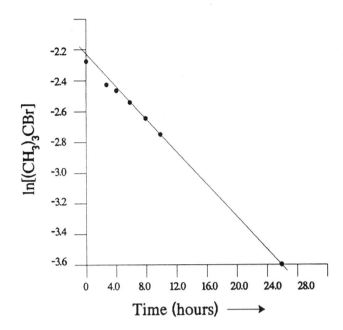

(b) Since m = –k, (see Equation 14.5) the rate constant for this first-order reaction can be obtained from the slope of the graph of $\ln[(CH_3)_3CBr]$ versus time. It can also be obtained using Equation 14.4 and any two concentration values (data obtainable from Exercise 14.19).

From graph: Using the points (t = 6.20 h, $\ln[(CH_3)_3CBr]$ = –2.5562) and (t = 10.0 h, $\ln[(CH_3)_3CBr]$ = –2.7504) we get for the slope

$$slope = \frac{\Delta \ln[(CH_3)_3CBr]}{\Delta t} = \frac{-0.1942}{3.8 \ h} = -0.051 \ h^{-1}$$

Hence, the rate constant is $0.051 \ h^{-1}$.

Using Equation 14.4: Using the time interval t = 6.20 h to t = 10.0 h and substituting the values into Equation 14.4 gives

$$\ln \frac{[(CH_3)_3CBr]}{[(CH_3)_3CBr]_0} = -kt; \quad \ln \frac{0.0639 \ mol/L}{0.0776 \ mol/L} = -k \times 3.8 \ h$$

and k = 0.1942/3.8 h = $0.051 \ h^{-1}$

(c) If 80% of the $(CH_3)_3CBr$ is hydrolized, then 20% remains: the fraction remaining is $[(CH_3)_3CBr]/[(CH_3)_3CBr]_0$ = 0.20. This fraction and k = $0.051 \ h^{-1}$ are substituted in Equation 14.4.

$\ln ([(CH_3)_3CBr]/[(CH_3)_3CBr]_0) = -kt$

$\ln 0.20 = -0.051 \ h^{-1} \times t$ and t = 1.61/0.051 h^{-1} = 32 h

14.27   (a) Substitute moles of N_2O_5 for [A] in Equation 14.3

$$n_{N_2O_5}/(n_{N_2O_5})_0 = e^{-kt}$$

The time $t = 1.0$ h $= 3600$ s, $k = 4.98 \times 10^{-4}$ s^{-1}, and the original number of moles of N_2O_5 is $(n_{N_2O_5})_0 = 1.0$ mol. Hence,

$$\frac{n_{N_2O_5}}{1.0 \text{ mol}} = e^{-4.98 \times 10^{-4} \text{ s}^{-1} \times 3.6 \times 10^{-3} \text{ s}} = e^{-1.8} = 0.17$$

and $n_{N_2O_5} = 0.17 \times 1.0$ mol $= 0.17$ mol

(b) From the reaction equation we see that for every mole of N_2O_5 gas that decomposes, 2.5 mol of gas is produced. Therefore, after 1 h there is 0.17 mol + 0.83 mol x 2.5 = 2.2 mol. Hence, the pressure should increase by a factor of 2.2, or total gas pressure = 0.50 atm x 2.2 = 1.1 atm.

14.33 First the rate constant k must be calculated.

$$k = \frac{\ln 2}{t_{1/2}} = \frac{0.693}{32.0 \text{ min}} = 0.0217 \text{ min}^{-1}$$

The time required can be obtained by substituting $[A]/[A]_0 = 0.0160$ M/0.256 M and $k = 0.0217$ min^{-1} into Equation 14.4.

$$\ln \frac{0.0160 \text{ mol/L}}{0.256 \text{ mol/L}} = -0.0217 \text{ min}^{-1} \times t \text{ and } t = 2.773/0.217 \text{ min}^{-1} = 128 \text{ min}$$

14.36 (a) First the rate constant k of the reaction must be calculated.

$$k = \frac{1}{t_{1/2}[A]_0} = \frac{1}{32.0 \text{ min } \times 0.256 \text{ mol/L}} = 0.122 \text{ L/mol min}$$

The time can be obtained by substituting $[A]_0 = 0.256$ mol/L, $[A] = 0.016$ mol/L, and $k = 0.122$ L/mol min into Equation 14.8.

$$\frac{1}{0.016 \text{ mol/L}} = 0.122 \text{ L/mol min } \times t + \frac{1}{0.256 \text{ mol/L}}$$

$$\text{and } t = \frac{59 \text{ L/mol}}{0.122 \text{ L/mol min}} = 480 \text{ min}$$

(b) Comparing the answers we see that the time required for the second–order reaction to reach the 0.0160 M concentration is considerably longer that that required by the first–order reaction. This is because the half-life of a second–order reaction increases as the concentration decreases, while that of a first–order reaction remains the same.

14.37 (a) For a second–order reaction, a graph of 1/[A] versus t will be a straight line whose slope is k. Therefore, a plot of 1/[A] versus t can be used to show if a reaction is second order. The numbers needed are

t(minutes)	0	45.0	72.0	107.0	230.0
[NH$_4$CNO]	0.1000	0.0808	0.0716	0.0638	0.0463
1/[NH$_4$CNO]	10.00	12.38	14.0	15.7	21.6

A plot of these numbers (not shown) gives a straight line and shows that the reaction is second order. (Convince yourself of this by making the actual plot.)

(b) The slope = k can be calculated using any two points in the above data. Using t = 0 min and t = 45.0 min we get

$$k = \text{slope} = \frac{\Delta 1/[NH_4CNO]}{\Delta t} = \frac{12.38 \text{ L/mol} - 10.00 \text{ L/mol}}{45.0 \text{ min}} = 0.0529 \text{ L/mol min}$$

A somewhat more accurate value for the slope = k can be obtained from the graph.

(c) The time required can be obtained by substituting $[A]_0 = 0.1000$ mol/L, $[A] = 0.0750$ mol/L, and $k = 0.0529$ L/mol min into Equation 14.8.

$$\frac{1}{0.0750 \text{ mol/L}} = 0.0529 \text{ L/mol min} \times t + \frac{1}{0.1000 \text{ mol/L}}$$

0.0529 L/mol min $\times$ t $= 3.33$ L/mol and t $= 62.9$ min

14.38 (a) The numbers needed are

t(seconds)	0	60.0	120.0	180.0	240.0	300.0
M of each reactant	0.01000	0.00917	0.00840	0.00775	0.00724	0.00675
1/M of each reactant	100	109	119	129	138	148

The rate constant is equal to the slope of the graph of 1/M versus t. A decent quick approximation can be obtained by using the initial and final points in the above data. Using t = 0 s and t = 300.0 s we get

$$k = \text{slope} = \frac{\Delta(1/M)}{\Delta t} = \frac{148 \text{ L/mol} - 100 \text{ L/mol}}{300.0 \text{ s}} = 0.160 \text{ L/mol s}$$

(b)

$$t_{1/2} = \frac{1}{k[A]_0} = \frac{1}{0.160 \text{ L/mol s} \times 0.01000 \text{ mol/L}} = 625 \text{ s}$$

(c) If 75% of the ethyl acetate has reacted, then the concentration of ethyl acetate remaining will be 0.01000 mol/L $\times$ 0.25 = 0.0025 mol/L. The time required can be obtained by substituting $[A] = 0.0025$ mol/L, $[A]_0 = 0.01000$ mol/L, and $k = 0.160$ L/mol s into Equation 14.8.

$$\frac{1}{0.0025 \text{ mol/L}} = 0.160 \text{ L/mol s} \times t + \frac{1}{0.01000 \text{ mol/L}}$$

0.160 L/mol s $\times$ t $= 3.0 \times 10^{-2}$ L/mol and t $= 1.9 \times 10^3$ s

Comment: The general form of the second-order rate law

rate = $k[A][B]$

reduces to the simpler form

rate = $k[A]^2$ or $k[B]^2$

for the special case where the initial concentrations of A and B are identical and A and B also disappear at the same rate. Consequently, the mathematical equations derived for the simpler second-order rate law also apply for this special case, and can be used to solve this problem, since this problem meets all the special case criteria.

14.46 The rate law for the reaction is determined by the slow third step.

rate = $k_3 [H_2] [I]^2$

The intermediate I can be removed from the rate law by employing the steady-state approximation.

rate of I formation = rate of I consumption

$k_1[I_2] = k_2[I]^2$

The steady-state concentration of atomic iodine is therefore $[I] = \sqrt{\dfrac{k_1}{k_2}} [I_2]^{1/2}$

Substituting this expression for [I] into the rate law gives

$$\text{rate} = \frac{k_3 k_1}{k_2} [H_2][I_2] = k[H_2][I_2]$$

where $k = k_3 k_1 / k_2$.

14.55   (a)

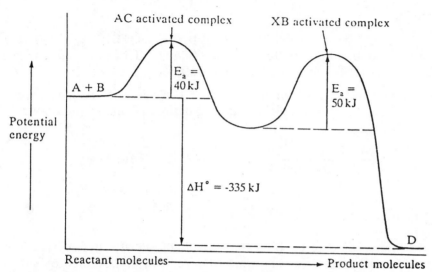

(b) The second step, since it has a greater activation energy.
(c) $\Delta H^° = \Delta H^°$ Step 1 + $\Delta H^°$ Step 2 = –20 kJ – 315 kJ = –335 kJ.
(d) None. The $\Delta H^°$ for the reaction is the same for both the catalyzed and uncatalyzed reactions, but this is calculated from the given information.

14.58 $k_1 = Ae^{-E_a/RT_1}$ and $k_2 = Ae^{-E_a/RT_2}$

Dividing k_1 by k_2 gives

$$\frac{k_1}{k_2} = \frac{e^{-E_a/RT_1}}{e^{-E_a/RT_2}}$$

Taking the logarithm of both sides gives

$$\ln \frac{k_1}{k_2} = \frac{-E_a}{RT_1} + \frac{E_a}{RT_2} = \frac{E_a}{R}\left[\frac{1}{T_2} - \frac{1}{T_1}\right] \quad \text{(Equation 14.15)}$$

14.59   (a) If the rate constant doubles, then the fraction $k_1/k_2 = 1/2$. Substituting this fraction and $T_1 = 298$ K, $T_2 = 308$ K, and R = 8.314 J/mol K into Equation 14.15 gives

$$\ln(1/2) = \frac{E_a}{8.314 \text{ J/mol K}}\left[\frac{1}{308 \text{ K}} - \frac{1}{298 \text{ K}}\right]$$

and $E_a = 52900$ J/mol = 52.9 kJ/mol

(b) If the rate constant triples, then the fraction $k_1/k_2 = 1/3$. Substituting this fraction and $T_1 = 298$ K, $T_2 = 308$ K, and R = 8.314 J/mol K into Equation 14.15 gives

$$\ln(1/3) = \frac{E_a}{8.314 \ J/mol \ K} \left[\frac{1}{308 \ K} - \frac{1}{298 \ K} \right]$$

and $E_a = 83,800$ J/mol = 83.8 kJ/mol.

14.60   If a reaction follows the Arrhenius equation, then a graph of ln k versus 1/T should yield a straight line whose slope $m = -E_a/R$ and intercept $b = \ln A$. To prepare the graph we must first calculate ln k and $1/T(K^{-1})$. The resulting numbers are given below.

k(L/mol s)	ln k	T(K)	$1/T(K^{-1})$
1.6×10^{-20}	-45.58	298	3.36×10^{-3}
1.3×10^{-19}	-43.49	308	3.25×10^{-3}
8.7×10^{-19}	-41.59	318	3.14×10^{-3}
5.4×10^{-18}	-39.76	328	3.05×10^{-3}
3.0×10^{-17}	-38.05	338	2.96×10^{-3}

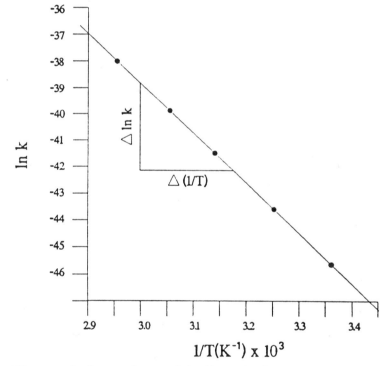

The graph shows the straight line obtained by plotting ln k versus 1/T. A right triangle has been drawn with part of the straight line as the hypotenuse. The legs of the triangle are $\Delta \ln k = -42.20 - (-38.80) = -3.40$ and $\Delta(1/T) = 3.18 \times 10^{-3} \ K^{-1} - 3.00 \times 10^{-3} \ K^{-1} = 0.18 \times 10^{-3} \ K^{-1}$. The slope of the line is

$$slope = \frac{\Delta \ln k}{\Delta(1/T)} = \frac{-3.40}{0.18 \times 10^{-3} \ K^{-1}} = -19 \times 10^3 \ K$$

The activation energy for the reaction can be obtained from the slope.

$$E_a = -mR = 19 \times 10^3 \ K \times 8.314 \ J/mol \ K = 160 \times 10^3 \ J/mol \ or \ 160 \ kJ/mol$$

A can now be obtained by substituting the given data and E_a into the Arrhenius equation. Substituting $k = 1.6 \times 10^{-20}$ L/mol s, $T = 298$ K, and $E_a = 160,000$ J/mol into Equation 14.13 gives

1.6×10^{-20} L/mol s = $Ae^{-(160,000 \text{ J/mol})/(8.314 \text{ J/mol K}) (298 \text{ K})}$

and A = 1.78×10^8 L/mol s or 1.8×10^8 L/mol s to two significant figures.

14.61   (a)   Let k_1 and T_1 be 0.105 L/mol s and 759 K; let k_2 and T_2 be 0.343 L/mol s and 791 K. Substituting these values and R = 8.314 J/mol K into Equation 14.15 gives

$$\ln \frac{0.105}{0.343} = \frac{E_a}{8.314 \text{ J/mol K}} \left[\frac{1}{791 \text{ K}} - \frac{1}{759 \text{ K}} \right]$$

Solving gives E_a = 185,000 J/mol = 185 kJ/mol.

(b)   Substituting E_a = 185,000 J/mol, k_1 = 0.343 L/mol s, T_1 = 791 K, T_2 = 840 K, and R = 8.314 J/mol K into Equation 14.15 gives

$$\ln \frac{0.343}{k_2} = \frac{185,000 \text{ J/mol}}{8.314 \text{ J/mol K}} \left[\frac{1}{840 \text{ K}} - \frac{1}{791 \text{ K}} \right]$$

$\ln 0.343 - \ln k_2 = -1.64$

$\ln k_2 = 0.57$ and $k_2 = e^{+0.57} = 1.77$ L/mol s

14.63   The rate constant for the reaction at $40°C = 313$ K is

$$k = \frac{\ln 2}{t_{1/2}} = \frac{0.693}{6.0 \text{ h}} = 0.12 \text{ h}^{-1}$$

The rate constant at $25°C = 298$ K can be obtained by substituting $k_1 = 0.12$ h⁻¹, $T_1 = 313$ K, $T_2 = 298$ K, $E_a = 75,300$ J/mol, and R = 8.314 J/mol K into Equation 14.15.

$$\ln \frac{0.12}{k_2} = \frac{75,300 \text{ J/mol}}{8.314 \text{ J/mol K}} \left[\frac{1}{298 \text{ K}} - \frac{1}{313 \text{ K}} \right]$$

$\ln 0.12 - \ln k_2 = 1.46$ and $k_2 = 0.028$ h⁻¹

Using k_2 we can calculate the value of the half-life at $25°C$.

$$t_{1/2} = \frac{\ln 2}{k} = \frac{0.693}{0.028 \text{ h}^{-1}} = 25 \text{ h}$$

Answer: It would take 25 h for a solution of H_2O_2 to lose half of its strength at $25°C$.

14.66   (a)   The collision frequencies are proportional to the square roots of these temperatures.

$$\frac{\text{collision frequency at 373 K}}{\text{collision frequency at 273 K}} = \sqrt{\frac{373 \text{ K}}{273 \text{ K}}} = 1.17$$

The collision frequency will increase by a factor of 1.17.

(b) $$\frac{e^{-(85,000 \text{ J/mol})/(8.314 \text{ J/mol K})(373 \text{ K})}}{e^{-(85,000 \text{ J/mol})/(8.314 \text{ J/mol K})(273 \text{ K})}} = 2.29 \times 10^4$$

$e^{-E_a/RT}$ increases by a factor of 2.29×10^4.

(c) The reaction rate will increase by a factor of $1.17 \times 2.29 \times 10^4 = 2.68 \times 10^4$.

14.70   Nitrogen dioxide, NO_2, is a free radical with a bent or V-shape. A reactive collision should put the nitrogen atom of one NO_2 molecule in a position to capture an oxygen from one end of another NO_2 molecule.

14.73   (a) The activation energy for the reverse catalyzed reaction can be obtained by substituting $\Delta H° = +46$ kJ and E_a (forward) = 165 kJ into Equation 14.12:

+ 46 kJ = 165 kJ – E_a (reverse) and E_a (reverse) = 165 kJ – 46 kJ = 119 kJ

(b) The activation energy for the reverse uncatalyzed reaction can be obtained by substituting $\Delta H° = +46$ kJ and E_a (forward) = 335 kJ into Equation 14.12:

+46 kJ = 335 kJ – E_a (reverse) and E_a (reverse) = 335 kJ – 46 kJ = 289 kJ

14.76   By Dalton's law, the total pressure is $P_T = P_{CO_2} + P_{CH_4} = C(n_{CO_2} + n_{CH_4})$

where $C = RT/V$ = constant, since T and V are constant. From the reaction equation, we see that for every x moles of glucose that decomposes, $3x$ moles of CO_2 are formed and $3x$ moles of CH_4 are formed. Letting n_0 stand for the initial number of moles of glucose, this can be expressed mathematically as follows:

$n_{glucose} = n_0 - x;\ x = n_0 - n_{glucose}$

$n_{CO_2} = 3x = 3n_0 - 3n_{glucose}$ and $n_{CH_4} = 3x = 3n_0 - 3n_{glucose}$

Substituting the expressions for n_{CO_2} and n_{CH_4} into the total pressure expression gives

$P_T = C(3n_0 - 3n_{glucose} + 3n_0 - 3n_{glucose}) = 6Cn_0 - 6Cn_{glucose}$

The change in the total pressure can be obtained in the usual manner and is

$\Delta P_T = -6C\Delta n_{glucose}$

since $6Cn_0$ is a constant and, therefore, doesn't change with time. This expression relates the change in pressure to the change in the number of moles of glucose.

14.78   (a) $kt_{1/2} = \ln 2 = 0.693$

$k = \dfrac{0.693}{3.823 \text{ days}} = 0.181 \text{ days}^{-1}$

(b) Substituting A = radon–222, k = 0.181 days^{-1}, and t = 7 days into Equation 14.3 gives

$\dfrac{[\text{radon-222}]}{[\text{radon-222}]_0} = e^{-0.181 \text{ days}^{-1} \times 7 \text{ days}} = 0.282$

14.79   To solve the problem, we first have to obtain the rate constant for the reaction at 600°C.

$$k = \frac{0.693}{t_{1/2}} = \frac{0.693}{81 \text{ s}} = 8.6 \times 10^{-3} \text{ s}^{-1}$$

The time can be obtained by substituting [acetone] = 0.45 atm, [acetone]$_0$ = 0.51 atm, and k = 8.6 x 10^{-3} s^{-1} into Equation 14.4.

$$\ln \frac{0.45}{0.51} = -8.6 \times 10^{-3} \text{ s}^{-1} \times t \text{ and } t = 15 \text{ s}$$

14.82   The rate law for this elementary step is

rate = k[H$^+$][OH$^-$]

This rate law is an example of one having the general form

rate = k[A][B]

For the special case in which A and B have the same initial concentrations and also react at the same rate, because they have identical coefficients in the reaction equation, this rate law reduces to the same form as Equation 14.7:

rate = k[A][B] = k[A]^2 or k[B]^2

and can be mathematically treated in the same manner. In other words, the same integrated rate law, Equation 14.8, also applies in this special case. Since the problem specifies that the initial concentrations are identical and since the reaction equation shows that they both are consumed at the same rate, Equation 14.8 can be used to calculate the time. Substituting [A] = 10^{-7} mol/L, [A]$_0$ = 1.0 mol/L, and k = 1.3 x 10^{11} L/mol into Equation 14.8 gives

$$\frac{1}{10^{-7} \text{ mol/L}} = 1.3 \times 10^{11} \text{ L/mol s} \times t + \frac{1}{1.0 \text{ mol/L}}$$

1.3 x 10^{11} L/mol s x t = 1.0 x 10^7 L/mol and t = 7.7 x 10^{-5} s

14.84   The rate constants for the first-order decomposition at 25°C and 50°C are

25°C: k = 0.693/20.0 s = 3.46 x 10^{-2} s^{-1}

50°C: k = 0.693/1.0 s = 0.69 s^{-1}

The activation energy can be obtained by substituting k$_1$ = 3.46 x 10^{-2} s^{-1}, T$_1$ = 298 K, k$_2$ = 0.69 s^{-1}, T$_2$ = 323 K, and R = 8.314 J/mol K into Equation 14.15.

$$\ln \frac{3.46 \times 10^{-2}}{0.69} = \frac{E_a}{8.314 \text{ J/mol K}} \left[\frac{1}{323 \text{ K}} - \frac{1}{298 \text{ K}} \right]$$

and E$_a$ = 95,800 J/mol or 95.8 kJ/mol

The preexponential factor A can be obtained by substituting k = 3.46 x 10^{-2} s^{-1}, T = 298 K, E$_a$ = 95,800 J/mol, and R = 8.314 J/mol K into Equation 14.13.

$$A = \frac{k}{e^{-E_a/RT}} = \frac{3.46 \times 10^{-2} \text{ s}^{-1}}{e^{-(95,800 \text{ J/mol})/(8.314 \text{ J/mol K})(298 \text{ K})}} = 2.15 \times 10^{15} \text{ s}^{-1}$$

14.86   If one collision per mole of collisions has enough energy to dissociate a Cl_2 molecule, then the fraction of reactive collisions is $f_a = 1/6.022 \times 10^{23} = 1.661 \times 10^{-24}$. The temperature required for this to happen can be obtained by substituting $f_a = 1.661 \times 10^{-24}$, $E_a = 243,000$ J/mol, and $R = 8.314$ J/mol K into Equation 14.17.

$$1.661 \times 10^{-24} = e^{-(243,000 \text{ J/mol})/(8.314 \text{ J/mol K}) \times T}$$

$$\ln 1.661 \times 10^{-24} = \frac{-243,000 \text{ J/mol}}{(8.314 \text{ J/mol K}) \times T} \text{ and } T = 534 \text{ K}$$

14.88   (a) Assuming that the preexponential factor A does not change, the factor by which the rate constant, and, hence, the rate, decreases when switching from catalase to I^- is

$$\frac{k_2}{k_1} = \frac{e^{-(56,500 \text{ J/mol})/(8.314 \text{ J/mol K})(298 \text{ K})}}{e^{-(8,400 \text{ J/mol})/(8.314 \text{ J/mol K})(298 \text{ K})}} = 3.70 \times 10^{-9}$$

Therefore, it should take the I^- catalyzed reaction $1/3.70 \times 10^{-9} = 2.70 \times 10^8$ times longer to evolve 1.00 L of oxygen, or 2.70×10^9 s.

(b) Assuming that the preexponential factor A does not change, the factor by which the rate constant, and, hence, the rate, decreases when switching from catalase to an uncatalyzed reaction is

$$\frac{k_2}{k_1} = \frac{e^{-(75,300 \text{ J/mol})/(8.314 \text{ J/mol K})(298 \text{ K})}}{e^{-(8,400 \text{ J/mol})/(8.314 \text{ J/mol K})(298 \text{ K})}} = 1.88 \times 10^{-12}$$

Therefore, it should take the uncatalyzed reaction $1/1.88 \times 10^{-12} = 5.32 \times 10^{11}$ times longer to evolve 1.00 L of oxygen, or 5.32×10^{12} s.

CHAPTER 15
CHEMICAL EQUILIBRIUM

Solutions To Practice Exercises

PE 15.3   Concentration Summary:

Equation:	$H_2O(g)$	$+ CO(g)$	$\rightleftharpoons H_2(g)$	$+ CO_2(g)$
Initial concentrations, mol/L	1.00	1.00	0	0
Concentration changes, mol/L	-0.58	-0.58	+0.58	+0.58
Equilibrium concentrations, mol/L	0.422	0.422	0.58	0.58

$$K_c = (Q_c)_{eq} = \frac{[H_2]_{eq} \, [CO_2]_{eq}}{[H_2O]_{eq} \, [CO]_{eq}} = \frac{(0.58)(0.58)}{(0.422)(0.422)} = 1.9$$

PE 15.4

$$Q_c = \frac{[ICl]^2}{[I_2][Cl_2]} = \frac{(0.0025)^2}{(0.10)(0.10)} = 6.2 \times 10^{-4}$$

Since $Q_c < K_c$, the reaction will move in the forward direction.

PE 15.5   There is no Br to begin with, so the reaction can move only in the forward direction.

Concentration Summary:

Equation:	$Br_2(g)$	$\rightleftharpoons 2Br(g)$
Initial concentrations, mol/L	1.00	0
Concentration changes, mol/L	$-x$	$+2x$
Equilibrium concentrations, mol/L	$1.00 - x$	$2x$

The K_c expression is $K_c = [Br]^2/[Br_2]$

Substituting the equilibrium concentrations and $K_c = 2.64 \times 10^{-4}$ into the above expression gives

$$2.64 \times 10^{-4} = \frac{(2x)^2}{1.00 - x}$$

$4x^2 + 2.64 \times 10^{-4}x - 2.64 \times 10^{-4} = 0$

and $x = 8.09 \times 10^{-3}$ mol/L

The equilibrium concentration of Br is therefore $[Br] = 2x = 2 \times 0.00809$ mol/L $= 0.0162$ mol/L.

PE 15.6   Since only CO_2 is present to begin with, the reaction must proceed in the forward direction. The initial CO_2 concentration is 0.100 mol/2.00 L = 0.0500 mol/L.

Concentration Summary:

Equation:	$2CO_2(g)$	$\rightleftharpoons$	$2CO(g)$	$+$	$O_2(g)$
Initial concentrations, mol/L	0.0500		0		0
Concentration changes, mol/L	$-2x$		$+2x$		$+x$
Equilibrium concentrations, mol/L	$0.0500 - 2x$		$2x$		x

The K_c expression is $K_c = [CO]^2[O_2]/[CO_2]^2$

Substituting the equilibrium concentrations and $K_c = 4.50 \times 10^{-23}$ into the above expression gives

$$4.50 \times 10^{-23} = \frac{(2x)^2(x)}{(0.0500 - 2x)^2}$$

Since K_c is so small we can simplify the calculation by assuming that $0.0500 - 2x$ is approximately equal to 0.0500. Replacing $0.0500 - 2x$ with 0.0500 in the above equation gives

$$4.50 \times 10^{-23} = \frac{(2x)^2(x)}{(0.0500)^2} = \frac{4x^3}{(0.0500)^2}$$

and $x = [O_2] = 3.04 \times 10^{-9}$ mol/L.

PE 15.8 Q_c is initially zero, so the reaction can only move in the forward direction.

Concentration Summary:

Equation:	$NH_3(aq)$	$+$	$H_2O(l)$	$\rightleftharpoons$	$NH_4^+(aq)$	$+$	$OH^-(aq)$
Initial concentrations, mol/L	0.10				0		0
Concentration changes, mol/L	$-x$				$+x$		$+x$
Equilibrium concentrations, mol/L	$-0.10 - x$				x		x

Substituting the equilibrium concentrations and $K_c = 1.77 \times 10^{-5}$ into the K_c expression gives $K_c = [NH_4^+][OH^-]/[NH_3]$

$$1.77 \times 10^{-5} = \frac{(x)(x)}{(0.10 - x)}$$

$x^2 + 1.77 \times 10^{-5}x - 1.77 \times 10^{-6} = 0$ and $x = [OH^-] = 0.0013$ mol/L

PE 15.9 (a) The initial pressure of NOCl is 1.000 atm. The initial pressures of NO and Cl_2 are zero. Since Q_c is initially zero, the reaction moves in the forward direction.

Pressure Summary:

Equation:	$2NOCl(g)$	$\rightleftharpoons$	$2NO(g)$	$+$	$Cl_2(g)$
Initial pressures, atm	1.000		0		0
Pressure changes, atm	$-2x$		$+2x$		$+x$
Equilibrium pressures, atm	$1.000 - 2x$		$2x$		x

The total pressure at equilibrium, 1.135 atm, is the sum of the partial pressures. Therefore, 1.135 atm = $P_{NOCl} + P_{NO} + P_{Cl_2}$ = $1.000 - 2x + 2x + x = 1.000 + x$ and $x = 0.135$ atm

The equilibrium pressures are

$P_{NOCl} = 1.000 - 2x = 1.000$ atm $- 0.270$ atm $= 0.730$ atm

$P_{NO} = 2x = 0.270$ atm

$P_{Cl_2} = x = 0.135$ atm

    (b) Substituting the equilibrium pressures into the K_p expression gives

$$K_p = \frac{P^2_{NO} \, P_{Cl_2}}{P^2_{NOCl}} = \frac{(0.270)^2(0.135)}{(0.730)^2} = 1.85 \times 10^{-2}$$

PE 15.10   The reaction moves in the forward direction.

Pressure Summary:

Equation:	$C_2H_2(g)$	$+$	$3H_2(g)$	$\rightleftharpoons$	$2CH_4(g)$
Initial pressures, atm	1.00		1.00		0
Pressure changes, atm	$-x$		$-3x$		$+2x$
Equilibrium pressures, atm	$1.00 - x$		$1.00 - 3x$		$2x$

Substituting $K_p = 2.41 \times 10^{-4}$ and the equilibrium pressures into the K_p expression gives

$$K_p = P^2_{CH_4}/P_{C_2H_2} \, P^3_{H_2}$$

$$2.41 \times 10^{-4} = \frac{(2x)^2}{(1.00 - x)(1.00 - 3x)^3}$$

K_p is small, and we can assume that $2x$ and $3x$ will be small relative to 1.00. Substituting 1.00 for $(1.00 - 2x)$ and $(1.00 - 3x)$ gives

$$2.41 \times 10^{-4} = \frac{(2x)^2}{(1.00)(1.00)^3} = 4x^2$$

and $x = 0.00776$ atm. The approximation is justified because $3x = 3 \times 0.00776$ atm $= 0.0233$ atm is less than 5% of 1.00 atm. The partial pressure of methane is $P_{CH_4} = 2x = 2 \times 0.00776$ atm $= 1.55 \times 10^{-2}$ atm.

PE 15.12 (a)   The equation in (a) is obtained by multiplying the original equation by 1/2, so its K_p is the square root of the original equilibrium constant:

$$K_p = (7.6 \times 10^{-16})^{1/2} = 2.8 \times 10^{-8}$$

    (b) The equation in (b) is obtained by reversing the original equation and multiplying it by 1/2, so its K_p is the square root of the reciprocal of the original equilibrium constant:

$$K_p = (1/7.6 \times 10^{-16})^{1/2} = 3.6 \times 10^7$$

PE 15.13   The first equation is the third equation plus the reverse of the second equation. Hence

$$K_p = \frac{1}{K_{p_2}} \times K_{p_3} = \frac{6.90 \times 10^{-19}}{4.27 \times 10^{-31}} = 1.62 \times 10^{12}$$

PE 15.15   The reaction moves in the reverse direction.

Pressure Summary:

Equation:	$C(graphite)$	$+$	$S_2(g)$	$\rightleftharpoons$	$CS_2(g)$
Initial pressures, atm			0		1.00
Pressure changes, atm			$+x$		$-x$
Equilibrium pressures, atm			x		$1.00 - x$

Substituting the equilibrium pressures and $K_p = 5.60$ into the equilibrium constant expression gives

$$K_p = P_{CS_2}/P_{S_2}$$

$$5.60 = \frac{1.00 - x}{x} \quad \text{and} \quad x = 0.152 \text{ atm}$$

The equilibrium pressures are $P_{S_2} = x = 0.152$ atm

$P_{CS_2} = 1.00 - x = 1.00$ atm $- 0.152$ atm $= 0.85$ atm

PE 15.17   Proportion of NO_2 will increase. Two moles of NO_2 occupy a greater volume than 1 mol of N_2O_4. Greater volume favors a larger proportion of NO_2 in the equilibrium mixture.

PE 15.18 (a) The forward reaction is exothermic. Increasing the temperature will cause the reaction to move in the reverse direction, thus the amounts of H_2 and F_2 increase and the amount of HF decreases.

(b) The partial pressures of H_2 and O_2 will increase; the partial pressure of HF will decrease. Hence, K_p will decrease.

Solutions To Final Exercises

15.4   (a)

$$Q_c = \frac{[CH_3OH]}{[CO][H_2]^2} \qquad\qquad K_c = \frac{[CH_3OH]_{eq}}{[CO]_{eq}[H_2]^2_{eq}}$$

(b) The Q_c expression is valid for all concentrations of the reactants and products; its value is variable. The K_c expression is only valid for the equilibrium concentrations of the reactants and products; its value is fixed at a given temperature.

15.5   (a) If $Q_c > K_c$, then the reaction will move in the reverse direction.
(b) If $Q_c < K_c$, then the reaction will move in the forward direction.

15.7 O_2. Since the equilibrium constant is so small, the equilibrium mixture will contain mostly reactant and very little product. (A very small value of K means the reaction lies predominantly to the left or reactant side).

15.8   (a) Since only PCl_5 is present to begin with, the reaction must proceed in the forward direction.

Concentration Summary:

Equation:	$PCl_5(g) \rightleftharpoons PCl_3(g) + Cl_2(g)$		
Initial concentrations, mol/L	0.100	0	0
Concentration changes, mol/L	$-x$	$+x$	$+x$
Equilibrium concentrations, mol/L	$0.100 - x$	x	x

The equilibrium concentrations are

$[Cl_2] = x = 0.47$ mol/10.0 L $= 0.047$ mol/L

$[PCl_3] = x = 0.047$ mol/L

$[PCl_5] = 0.100 - x = 0.100$ mol/L $- 0.047$ mol/L $= 0.053$ mol/L

(b) The K_c expression is $K_c = [PCl_3][Cl_2]/[PCl_5]$

Substituting the above concentrations into the K_c expression gives

$$K_c = \frac{(0.047)(0.047)}{(0.053)} = 0.042$$

(c) The fraction of PCl_5 dissociated is

$$\frac{0.047}{0.100} = 0.47$$

15.10 (a) To determine whether the reaction will move in the forward or reverse direction, we have to calculate Q_c and compare it with K_c. The Q_c expression is

$$Q_c = [PCl_3][Cl_2]/[PCl_5]$$

Substituting the initial concentrations into the Q_c expression gives

$$Q_c = \frac{(0.100)(0.100)}{(0.100)} = 0.100$$

Since Q_c (= 0.100) > K_c (= 0.042), the reaction will move in the reverse direction.

(b)

Concentration Summary:

Equation:	$PCl_5(g)$	$\rightleftharpoons$ $PCl_3(g)$	+ $Cl_2(g)$
Initial concentrations, mol/L	0.100	0.100	0.100
Concentration changes, mol/L	$+x$	$-x$	$-x$
Equilibrium concentrations, mol/L	$0.100 + x$	$0.100 - x$	$0.100 - x$

The K_c expression is $K_c = [PCl_3][Cl_2]/[PCl_5]$

Substituting the equilibrium concentrations and $K_c = 0.042$ into the above expression gives

$$0.042 = \frac{(0.100 - x)(0.100 - x)}{(0.100 + x)}$$

$x^2 - 0.242x + 0.0058 = 0$ and $x = 0.027$ mol/L

The solution was obtained by using the negative sign before the square root. The positive sign would have given a value for x greater than 0.100. The equilibrium concentrations are

$[PCl_5] = 0.100 + x = 0.100$ mol/L + 0.027 mol/L = 0.127 mol/L

$[PCl_3] = 0.100 - x = 0.100$ mol/L - 0.027 mol/L = 0.073 mol/L

$[Cl_2] = 0.100 - x = 0.073$ mol/L

15.12 (a) The Q_c expression is $Q_c = [H^+][CH_3COO^-]/[CH_3COOH]$

Substituting the initial concentrations into the Q_c expression gives

$$Q_c = \frac{(1.0 \times 10^{-7})(0.50)}{(0.50)} = 1.0 \times 10^{-7}$$

Since $Q_c < K_c$, the reaction will move in the forward direction.

(b)

Concentration Summary:

Equation:	$CH_3COOH(aq)$	$\rightleftharpoons$ $H^+(aq)$	+ $CH_3COO^-(aq)$
Initial concentrations, mol/L	0.50	1.0×10^{-7}	0.50
Concentration changes, mol/L	$-x$	$+x$	$+x$
Equilibrium concentrations, mol/L	$0.50 - x$	$1.0 \times 10^{-7} + x$	$0.50 + x$

Substituting the equilibrium concentrations and $K_c = 1.76 \times 10^{-5}$ into the K_c expression gives
$K_c = [H^+][CH_3COO^-]/[CH_3COOH]$

$$1.76 \times 10^{-5} = \frac{(1.0 \times 10^{-7} + x)(0.50 + x)}{(0.50 - x)}$$

Since K_c is small we will assume that both $0.50 - x$ and $0.50 + x$ are approximately equal to 0.50. Making these replacements in the above equation gives

$$1.76 \times 10^{-5} = \frac{(1.0 \times 10^{-7} + x)(0.50)}{(0.50)} = 1.0 \times 10^{-7} + x$$

and $x = 1.75 \times 10^{-5}$ mol/L

The equilibrium concentrations are

$[CH_3COOH] = 0.50 - x = 0.50$ mol/L $- 1.75 \times 10^{-5}$ mol/L $= 0.50$ mol/L

$[H^+] = 1.0 \times 10^{-7} + x = 1.0 \times 10^{-7}$ mol/L $+ 1.75 \times 10^{-5}$ mol/L $= 1.76 \times 10^{-5}$ mol/L

$[CH_3COO^-] = 0.50 + x = 0.50$ mol/L $+ 1.75 \times 10^{-5}$ mol/L $= 0.50$ mol/L

15.14 The reactions moves in the forward direction. Forty percent of the initial CO_2 concentration is $(0.0037)(0.40) = 0.0015$ mol/L.

Concentration Summary:

Equation:	$2CO_2(g)$	$\rightleftharpoons$ $2CO(g)$	$+ O_2(g)$
Initial concentrations, mol/L	0.0037	0	0
Concentration changes, mol/L	−0.0015	+0.0015	+0.00075
Equilibrium concentrations, mol/L	0.0022	0.0015	0.00075

Substituting the equilibrium concentrations into the K_c expression gives

$$K_c = \frac{[CO]^2[O_2]}{[CO_2]^2} = \frac{(0.0015)^2(0.00075)}{(0.0022)^2} = 3.5 \times 10^{-4}$$

15.17 The reaction moves in the forward direction.

Concentration Summary:

Equation:	$CH_3NH_2(aq)$	$+ H_2O(1)$ $\rightleftharpoons$	$CH_3NH_3^+(aq)$	$+ OH^-(aq)$
Initial concentrations, mol/L	0.250		0	0
Concentration changes, mol/L	−x		+x	+x
Equilibrium concentrations, mol/L	0.250 − x		x	x

Substituting the equilibrium concentrations and $K_c = 2.70 \times 10^{-11}$ into the K_c expression gives
$K_c = [CH_3NH_3^+][OH^-]/[CH_3NH_2]$

$$2.70 \times 10^{-11} = \frac{(x)(x)}{(0.250 - x)}$$

Since K_c is small we will assume that $0.250 - x$ is approximately equal to 0.250. Replacing $0.250 - x$ by 0.250 in the above equation gives

$$2.70 \times 10^{-11} = \frac{x^2}{0.250} \text{ and } x = 2.60 \times 10^{-6} \text{ mol/L}$$

The equilibrium concentration of $CH_3NH_3^+$ is $[CH_3NH_3^+] = x = 2.60 \times 10^{-6}$ mol/L.

15.22   Increases. A larger K_p means that the reaction goes further to the right as the temperature increases and, therefore, more Cl_2 molecules are dissociated at the higher temperature.

15.23   (a)

$$P_{PCl_5} = [PCl_5]RT = \frac{0.053 \text{ mol}}{1 \text{ L}} \times \frac{0.0821 \text{ L atm}}{\text{mol K}} \times 523 \text{ K} = 2.3 \text{ atm}$$

$$P_{PCl_3} = [PCl_3]RT = \frac{0.047 \text{ mol}}{1 \text{ L}} \times \frac{0.0821 \text{ L atm}}{\text{mol K}} \times 523 \text{ K} = 2.0 \text{ atm}$$

$$P_{Cl_2} = P_{PCl_3} = 2.0 \text{ atm}$$

(b) Substituting the equilibrium pressures into the K_p expression gives

$$K_p = \frac{P_{PCl_3} P_{Cl_2}}{P_{PCl_5}} = \frac{(2.0)(2.0)}{(2.3)} = 1.7$$

15.25   The total pressure will always be 1.00 atm, since the reaction equation shows that for every 2 mol of gaseous reactant consumed, 2 mol of gaseous products are produced; i.e., the total number of moles of gas never changes and, consequently, the total pressure never changes.

15.27   The reaction moves in the forward direction.

Pressure Summary:

Equation:	$N_2O_4(g) \rightleftharpoons 2NO_2(g)$	
Initial pressures, atm	0.500	0
Pressure changes, atm	$-x$	$+2x$
Equilibrium pressures, atm	$0.500 - x$	$2x$

Substituting $K_p = 0.113$ and the equilibrium pressures into the K_p expression gives

$$K_p = P^2_{NO_2}/P_{N_2O_4}$$

$$0.113 = \frac{(2x)^2}{0.500 - x}$$

$4x^2 + 0.113x - 0.0565 = 0$ and $x = 0.106$ atm

The partial pressures at equilibrium are

$$P_{NO_2} = 2x = 2 \times 0.106 \text{ atm} = 0.212 \text{ atm}$$

$$P_{N_2O_4} = 0.500 - x = 0.500 \text{ atm} - 0.106 \text{ atm} = 0.394 \text{ atm}$$

15.29   The reaction moves in the forward direction.

Pressure Summary:

Equation:	$Br_2(g) \rightleftharpoons 2Br(g)$	
Initial pressures, atm	2.00	0
Pressure changes, atm	$-x$	$+2x$
Equilibrium pressures, atm	$2.00 - x$	$2x$

Substituting $K_p = 0.255$ and the equilibrium pressures into the K_p expression gives

$$K_p = P^2_{Br}/P_{Br_2}$$

$$0.255 = \frac{(2x)^2}{2.00 - x}$$

$4x^2 + 0.255x - 0.510 = 0$ and $x = 0.327$ atm

The partial pressures at equilibrium are

$P_{Br_2} = 2.00 - x = 2.00$ atm $- 0.327$ atm $= 1.67$ atm

$P_{Br} = 2x = 2 \times 0.327$ atm $= 0.654$ atm

(b) $\dfrac{0.327}{2.00} = 0.164$

15.30 The reaction moves in the forward direction.

Pressure Summary:

Equation:	$N_2(g)$	$+ 3H_2(g)$	$\rightleftharpoons$	$2NH_3(g)$
Initial pressures, atm	2.5	7.5		0
Pressure changes, atm	$-x$	$-3x$		$+2x$
Equilibrium pressures, atm	$2.5 - x$	$7.5 - 3x$		$2x$

The total pressure at equilibrium is

$P_{total} = P_{N_2} + P_{H_2} + P_{NH_3} = 2.5 - x + 7.5 - 3x + 2x = 10.0 - 2x$

By Dalton's law $P_{NH_3} = X_{NH_3} P_{total}$

$2x = 0.0385 \times (10.0 - 2x)$ and $x = 0.185$ atm

The equilibrium partial pressures are (carry an extra significant figure)

$P_{N_2} = 2.5 - x = 2.5$ atm $- 0.185$ atm $= 2.32$ atm

$P_{H_2} = 7.5 - 3x = 7.5$ atm $- 3 \times 0.185$ atm $= 6.94$ atm

$P_{NH_3} = 2x = 2 \times 0.185$ atm $= 0.370$ atm

Substituting the equilibrium partial pressures into the K_p expression gives

$K_p = P^2_{NH_3}/P_{N_2}P^3_{H_2}$

$K_p = \dfrac{(0.370)^2}{(2.32)(6.94)^3} = 1.8 \times 10^{-4}$

15.32 $\Delta n = 1 - 3/2 = -1/2$

$K_p = K_c(RT)^{\Delta n} = K_c/(RT)^{1/2}$

$K_p = \dfrac{2.5 \times 10^{15}}{(0.0821 \times 773)^{1/2}} = 3.1 \times 10^{14}$

15.34 (a) The equation in (a) is obtained by reversing the original equation, so its K_p is the reciprocal of the original equilibrium constant:

$K_p = \dfrac{1}{5.2 \times 10^{-7}} = 1.9 \times 10^6$

(b) The equation in (b) is obtained by reversing the original equation and multiplying it by 1/2, so its K_p is the square root of the reciprocal of the original equilibrium constant:

$K_p = \left[\dfrac{1}{5.2 \times 10^{-7}}\right]^{1/2} = 1.4 \times 10^3$

15.37 The desired equation can be obtained by adding the following equations:

$HBr(g) \rightleftharpoons 1/2H_2(g) + 1/2Br_2(g)$ $\quad K_p = (1/6.7 \times 10^4)^{1/2}$

$1/2H_2(g) \rightleftharpoons H(g)$ $\quad K_p = (2.96 \times 10^{-11})^{1/2}$

$1/2Br_2(g) \rightleftharpoons Br(g)$ $\quad K_p = (3.03 \times 10^{-2})^{1/2}$

Therefore, its K_p is equal to the product of these three equilibrium constants:

$$K_p = \frac{(2.96 \times 10^{-11})^{1/2}(3.03 \times 10^{-2})^{1/2}}{(6.7 \times 10^4)^{1/2}} = 3.7 \times 10^{-9}$$

15.43 The final equation is the sum of two times the reverse of the first equation and two times the second equation. Hence,

$$K_p = \frac{1}{K^2_{P_1}} \times K^2_{P_2} = \frac{(1.25 \times 10^{69})^2}{(1.13 \times 10^{24})^2} = 1.22 \times 10^{90}$$

15.44 The reaction moves in the forward direction.

Pressure Summary:

Equation:	$NH_2COONH_4(s) \rightleftharpoons$	$2NH_3(g)$	$+ CO_2(g)$
Initial pressures, atm		0	0
Pressure changes, atm		$+2x$	$+x$
Equilibrium pressures, atm		$2x$	x

Substituting $K_p = 2.87 \times 10^5$ and the equilibrium pressures into the K_p expression gives

$K_p = P^2_{NH_3}P_{CO_2}$

$2.87 \times 10^5 = (2x)^2x$ and $x = 41.6$ atm

The equilibrium pressures are

$P_{CO_2} = x = 41.6$ atm

$P_{NH_3} = 2x = 2 \times 41.6$ atm $= 83.2$ atm

The total pressure is $P_{total} = P_{NH_3} + P_{CO_2} = 41.6$ atm $+ 83.2$ atm $= 124.8$ atm

15.46 The total pressure coming from the reaction is: $P_{total} = P_{NH_3} + P_{H_2S}$

0.66 atm $= x + x = 2x$ and $x = 0.33$ atm

Substituting the equilibrium partial pressures into the K_p expression gives

$K_p = P_{NH_3} P_{H_2S} = (0.33)(0.33) = 0.11$

15.47 The reaction moves in the forward direction.

Pressure Summary:

Equation:	$NH_4HS(s) \rightleftharpoons$	$NH_3(g)$	$+ H_2S(g)$
Initial pressures, atm		0	0.750
Pressure changes, atm		$+x$	$+x$
Equilibrium pressures, atm		x	$0.750 + x$

Substituting $K_p = 0.11$ (from Exercise 15.46) and the equilibrium partial pressures into the K_p expression gives

$K_p = P_{NH_3} P_{H_2S}$

$0.11 = (x)(0.750 + x)$

$x^2 + 0.750x - 0.11 = 0$ and $x = 0.13$ atm

The equilibrium pressures are

$P_{NH_3} = x = 0.13$ atm

$P_{H_2S} = 0.750 + x = 0.750$ atm $+ 0.13$ atm $= 0.88$ atm

The total pressure is $P_{total} = P_{NH_3} + P_{CO_2} = 0.13$ atm $+ 0.88$ atm $= 1.01$ atm

(b) mol% $NH_3 = X_{NH_3}$ x 100% = (P_{NH_3}/P_{total}) x 100%

$$= \frac{0.13 \text{ atm}}{1.01 \text{ atm}} \times 100\% = 13\%$$

15.50 (a) The color will increase; more intense. From the K_c values, we see that the reaction is driven to the right by increasing temperature. Therefore, there will be a greater proportion of NO_2 in the equilibrium mixture at higher temperatures.

(b) The color will increase; more intense. Higher N_2O_4 concentrations move the reaction to the right.

(c) The color will increase; more intense. Higher NO_2 partial pressures move the reaction to the left. However, the partial pressure of NO_2 after the increase will always be greater than what it was initially, since only some of the additional NO_2 introduced will be consumed in the reverse reaction.

(d) The color will remain the same; no change. Helium is a nonparticipating substance. Helium does not appear in the reaction quotient and, therefore, does not affect the equilibrium.

15.51 Endothermic. When heated, the reaction will move in the direction that absorbs heat. Since the equilibrium constant increases with increasing temperature, the reaction moves in the forward direction when heated and, therefore, the forward reaction must be endothermic.

15.52 (a) Adding NaOH drives the reaction to the right and, therefore, should make the color less orange and more yellow.

(b) Adding HCl drives the reaction to the left by reducing the OH⁻ concentration and, therefore, should make the color more orange and less yellow.

15.55 (a) Increase. Compression moves the reaction in the forward direction, since there are 3 mol of gas on the left side of the equation and only 2 mol of gas on the right side of the equation. Therefore, compression should increase the equilibrium yield of SO_3.

(b) Decrease. Increasing the temperature moves the reaction in the reverse direction, since the forward reaction is exothermic. Therefore, increasing temperature should decrease the equilibrium yield of SO_3.

15.58 Substituting $K_1 = 6.9$ x 10^{-5}, $T_1 = 298$ K, $T_2 = 373$ K, $\Delta H° = -92.2$ kJ/mol, and R = 8.314 x 10^{-3} kJ/mol K into Equation 15.4 gives

$$\ln \frac{K_2}{6.9 \times 10^{-5}} = \frac{+92.2 \text{ kJ/mol}}{8.314 \times 10^{-3} \text{ kJ/mol K}} \left[\frac{1}{373 \text{ K}} - \frac{1}{298 \text{ K}} \right]$$

Solving gives $K_2 = 3.9$ x 10^{-8}

15.60 First we have to calculate $\Delta H°$ for the reaction. Substituting $K_1 = 4540$, $T_1 = 936$ K, $K_2 = 1580$, $T_2 = 1125$ K, and R = 8.314 x 10^{-3} kJ/mol K into Equation 15.4 gives

$$\ln \frac{1580}{4540} = \frac{-\Delta H°}{8.314 \times 10^{-3} \text{ kJ/mol K}} \left[\frac{1}{1125 \text{ K}} - \frac{1}{936 \text{ K}} \right]$$

Solving gives $\Delta H^\circ = -48.9$ kJ/mol. The value of K_p at 1025 K can now be obtained by substituting $K_1 = 4540$ K, $T_1 = 936$ K, $T_2 = 1025$ K, $\Delta H^\circ = -48.9$ kJ/mol, and $R = 8.314 \times 10^{-3}$ kJ/mol into Equation 15.4.

$$\ln \frac{K_2}{4540} = \frac{+48.9 \text{ kJ/mol}}{8.314 \times 10^{-3} \text{ kJ/mol K}} \left[\frac{1}{1025 \text{ K}} - \frac{1}{936 \text{ K}} \right]$$

Solving gives $K_2 = 2631$.

15.63   The reaction moves in the reverse direction.

Pressure Summary:

Equation:	$2NO(g)$	$+$	$Br_2(g)$	$\rightleftharpoons$	$2NOBr(g)$
Initial pressures, atm	0		0.282		0.150
Pressure changes, atm	$+x$		0		$-x$
Equilibrium pressures, atm	x		0.282		$0.150 - x$

Substituting $K_p = 113$ and the equilibrium pressures into the K_p expression gives

$$K_p = P^2_{NOBr} / P^2_{NO} \, P_{Br_2}$$

$$113 = \frac{(0.150 - x)^2}{(x)^2 (0.282)}$$

$30.9x^2 + 0.300x - 0.0225 = 0$ and $x = 0.0226$ atm

The equilibrium pressures of NO and NOBr are

$P_{NO} = x = 0.0226$ atm

$P_{NOBr} = 0.150 - x = 0.150$ atm $- 0.0226$ atm $= 0.127$ atm

15.67   (a) Increase. Increasing the temperature moves the reaction in the forward direction, since the forward reaction is endothermic. Therefore, increasing temperature should lead to an increase in the fraction of $COCl_2$ dissociated.

(b) Decrease. Compression moves the reaction in the reverse direction, since there are 2 mol of gas on the right side of the equation and only 1 mol of gas on the left side of the equation. Therefore, compression should lead to a decrease in the fraction of $COCl_2$ dissociated.

(c) Decrease. Higher Cl_2 partial pressures move the reaction to the left. Therefore, increasing partial pressure of Cl_2 should lead to a decrease in the fraction of $COCl_2$ dissociated.

CHAPTER 16
ACIDS AND BASES

Solutions To Practice Exercises

PE 16.4 $HC_2O_4^-(aq) + HS^-(aq) \longrightarrow C_2O_4^{2-}(aq) + H_2S(g)$

$HC_2O_4^-$ gives up a proton and is an acid; its conjugate base is $C_2O_4^{2-}$. HS^- accepts a proton and is a base; its conjugate acid is H_2S.

PE 16.6 (a) $2H_2S(l) \rightleftharpoons H_3S^+ + HS^-$

The strongest base that can exist in liquid hydrogen sulfide is HS^-.

(b) $2CH_3NH_2(l) \rightleftharpoons CH_3NH_3^+ + CH_3NH^-$

The strongest acid that can exist in liquid methylamine is $CH_3NH_3^+$.

PE 16.11 $Ca(OH)_2$ is an ionic compound; 1.0×10^{-3} mol of $Ca(OH)_2$ furnishes $2 \times 1.0 \times 10^{-3}$ mol $= 2.0 \times 10^{-3}$ mol of $OH^-(aq)$. The hydroxide ion furnished by the water is negligible compared to that furnished by the $Ca(OH)_2$, so $[OH^-] = 2.0 \times 10^{-3}$ M. The $H^+(aq)$ ions come only from the water. Their concentration is

$$[H^+] = \frac{K_w}{[OH^-]} = \frac{1.00 \times 10^{-14}}{2.0 \times 10^{-3}} = 5.0 \times 10^{-12} \text{ M}$$

PE 16.15   In a neutral solution $[OH^-] = 1.0 \times 10^{-7}$ M. Hence,

$pOH = -\log[OH^-] = -\log(1.0 \times 10^{-7}) = -(-7.00) = 7.00$

PE 16.16 $pH = 4.3 = -\log[H^+]$

$\log[H^+] = -4.3$

and $[H^+] = $ antilog$(-4.3) = 10^{-4.3} = 5 \times 10^{-5}$ M

The answer has one significant figure because its logarithm, -4.3, has one digit after the decimal place.

PE 16.17   For the pH 8.0 solution we have

$$pOH = 14.00 - pH = 14.00 - 8.0 = 6.0$$

$$\log[OH^-] = -pOH = -6.0$$

and $[OH^-] = $ antilog$(-6.0) = 10^{-6.0} = 1 \times 10^{-6}$ M

The pH 10.0 solution has an $[OH^-]$ of 1×10^{-4} M (see Example 16.8). Therefore, the pH 8.0 solution has an $OH^-(aq)$ concentration 100 times smaller than that of the pH 10.0 solution.

PE 16.19 (a) $CHCl_2COOH$. $CHCl_2COOH$ has two electronegative chlorine atoms drawing electron density away from the COOH group, while $CH_2ClCOOH$ only has one.
   (b) OI^-. Since chlorine is more electronegative than iodine, HOCl is a stronger acid than HOI and, consequently, OCl^- is a weaker base than OI^-.

PE 16.22

From the reaction written in terms of Lewis structures we see that $AlCl_3$ is the Lewis acid and Cl^- is the Lewis base.

Solutions to Final Exercises

16.5   (a) Using $H_3O^+(aq)$ instead of $H^+(aq)$ emphasizes the fact that the ionization of acids in water is actually a Brönsted-Lowry proton transfer reaction with water acting as the Brönsted base.
   (b) 1. The hydronium ion (H_3O^+) in solution is further hydrated and, therefore, $H_3O^+(aq)$ doesn't represent the actual situation.
   2. Since the $[H_2O]$ is constant, the H_2O concentration is omitted from equilibrium constant expressions and, therefore, the use of H_2O is not really necessary when writing the acid ionization reaction equations. In other words, $H^+(aq)$ has the advantage of simplicity over $H_3O^+(aq)$ in situations where the role of H_2O doesn't have to be emphasized or can be ignored.

16.8   Both OH^- and NH_3 are generally thought of as bases because their tendency or ability to accept a proton is considerably greater than their tendency to part with or donate a proton. From Table 16.2 we see that both OH^- and NH_3 are classified as very weak acids, while OH^- is classified as a strong base and NH_3 a weak base. In other words, since they most often act as bases, they are generally thought of as bases. Also, both OH^- and NH_3 are <u>basic toward water</u>, and since life exists in an aqueous medium we naturally see them as bases.

16.12   (a) NH_3 and NH_4^+; HCO_3^- and CO_3^{2-} (d) H^- and H_2; H_2O and OH^-
   (b) CH_3NH_2 and $CH_3NH_3^+$; HCl and Cl^- (e) $Zn(H_2O)_4^{2+}$ and $Zn(H_2O)_3(OH)^+$; H_2O and H_3O^+
   (c) H_3O^+ and H_2O; OH^- and H_2O

16.15   (a) If the conjugate base isn't weak, then it will hold on to the protons strongly and the acid wouldn't be a strong acid.
   (b) If the conjugate acid isn't weak, then it will part with the protons easily and the base wouldn't be a strong base.

16.19   1. In a reaction between HBr and HI, the weaker acid will act as a base and accept protons from the stronger acid. Therefore, an examination of the products of this reaction will determine which is the stronger acid.

2. Strong acids can also be differentiated by the use of a solvent that is not easily protonated. For example, determining how extensively HBr and HI are ionized in liquid acetic acid should show which one is the stronger acid.

16.23 (a) $H_2SO_4(aq) + H_2O(l) \longrightarrow H_3O^+(aq) + HSO_4^-(aq)$
$HSO_4^-(aq) + H_2O(l) \rightleftharpoons H_3O^+(aq) + SO_4^{2-}(aq)$
(b) $H_2SO_3(aq) + H_2O(l) \rightleftharpoons H_3O^+(aq) + HSO_3^-(aq)$
$HSO_3^-(aq) + H_2O(l) \rightleftharpoons H_3O^+(aq) + SO_3^{2-}(aq)$
(c) $H_2S(aq) + H_2O(l) \rightleftharpoons H_3O^+(aq) + HS^-(aq)$
$HS^-(aq) + H_2O(l) \rightleftharpoons H_3O^+(aq) + S^{2-}(aq)$
(d) $H_2CO_3(aq) + H_2O(l) \rightleftharpoons H_3O^+(aq) + HCO_3^-(aq)$
$HCO_3^-(aq) + H_2O(l) \rightleftharpoons H_3O^+(aq) + CO_3^{2-}(aq)$
(e) $H_3AsO_4(aq) + H_2O(l) \rightleftharpoons H_3O^+(aq) + H_2AsO_4^-(aq)$
$H_2AsO_4^-(aq) + H_2O(l) \rightleftharpoons H_3O^+(aq) + HAsO_4^{2-}(aq)$
$HAsO_4^{2-}(aq) + H_2O(l) \rightleftharpoons H_3O^+(aq) + AsO_4^{3-}(aq)$

16.24 (a) $HCOOH(aq) + H_2O(l) \rightleftharpoons H_3O^+(aq) + HCOO^-(aq)$
(b) $CH_3CH_2COOH(aq) + H_2O(l) \rightleftharpoons H_3O^+(aq) + CH_3CH_2COO^-(aq)$
(c) $H_2C_2O_4(aq) + H_2O(l) \rightleftharpoons H_3O^+(aq) + HC_2O_4^-(aq)$
$HC_2O_4^-(aq) + H_2O(l) \rightleftharpoons H_3O^+(aq) + C_2O_4^{2-}(aq)$
(d) $H_2C_4H_4O_6(aq) + H_2O(l) \rightleftharpoons H_3O^+(aq) + HC_4H_4O_6^-(aq)$
$HC_4H_4O_6^-(aq) + H_2O(l) \rightleftharpoons H_3O^+(aq) + C_4H_4O_6^{2-}(aq)$

16.25 (a) $NH_4^+(aq) + H_2O(l) \rightleftharpoons H_3O^+(aq) + NH_3(aq)$
(b) $O^{2-} + H_2O(l) \longrightarrow 2OH^-(aq)$
(c) $CN^-(aq) + H_2O(l) \rightleftharpoons HCN(aq) + OH^-(aq)$
(d) $NH_2^-(aq) + H_2O(l) \longrightarrow NH_3(aq) + OH^-(aq)$
(e) $Cd(H_2O)_4^{2+}(aq) + H_2O(l) \rightleftharpoons H_3O^+(aq) + Cd(H_2O)_3(OH)^+(aq)$
(f) $H_2PO_4^-(aq) + H_2O(l) \rightleftharpoons H_3O^+(aq) + HPO_4^{2-}(aq)$
and $H_2PO_4^-(aq) + H_2O(l) \rightleftharpoons H_3PO_4(aq) + OH^-(aq)$
(g) $HS^-(aq) + H_2O(l) \rightleftharpoons H_3O^+(aq) + S^{2-}(aq)$
and $HS^-(aq) + H_2O(l) \rightleftharpoons H_2S(aq) + OH^-(aq)$

16.27 (a) $Zn(s) + 2HCl(aq) \longrightarrow H_2(g) + Zn^{2+}(aq) + 2Cl^-(aq)$
(b) $Zn(H_2O)_2(OH)_2(s) + 2HNO_3(aq) \longrightarrow Zn(H_2O)_4^{2+}(aq) + 2NO_3^-(aq)$
or $Zn(OH)_2(s) + 2HNO_3(aq) \longrightarrow Zn(NO_3)_2(aq) + 2H_2O(l)$
(c) $2HClO_4(aq) + Ba(OH)_2(aq) \longrightarrow Ba(ClO_4)_2(aq) + 2H_2O(l)$
(d) $NaOH(aq) + H_2C_2O_4(aq) \longrightarrow NaHC_2O_4(aq) + H_2O(l)$
(e) $2NaOH(aq) + H_2C_2O_4(aq) \longrightarrow Na_2C_2O_4(aq) + 2H_2O(l)$
(f) $NaHCO_3(s) + HCl(aq) \longrightarrow NaCl(aq) + CO_2(g) + H_2O(l)$
(g) $CaCO_3(s) + H_2SO_4(aq) \longrightarrow CaSO_4(aq) + CO_2(g) + H_2O(l)$

16.28 The carbonate ion, CO_3^{2-}, is a moderately strong base, since it is the conjugate base of the weak acid HCO_3^-. Since vinegar is a dilute solution of acetic acid, the carbonate ion will react with the vinegar to form carbonic acid, which subsequently decomposes into carbon dioxide and water. Consequently, the vinegar solution will dissolve the coral and, therefore, cannot be used to clean it.

16.30   The ΔH° for the reaction
$$HNO_2(aq) + H_2O(l) \longrightarrow H_3O^+(aq) + NO_2^-(aq) \quad \Delta H^\circ = ?$$

is the sum of the enthalpy changes for the following steps:
$$HNO_2(aq) + OH^-(aq) \longrightarrow NO_2^-(aq) + H_2O(l) \quad \Delta H^\circ = -41.2 \text{ kJ}$$
$$2H_2O(l) \longrightarrow H_3O^+(aq) + OH^-(aq) \qquad\qquad \Delta H^\circ = +55.8 \text{ kJ}$$
Therefore, $\Delta H^\circ = -41.2 \text{ kJ} + 55.8 \text{ kJ} = +14.6 \text{ kJ}$

16.33   All these acids are strong acids and, therefore, ionize completely.

(a)
$$[H^+] = 1.25 \text{ M}; \quad [OH^-] = \frac{K_w}{[H^+]} = \frac{1.00 \times 10^{-14}}{1.25} = 8.00 \times 10^{-15} \text{ M}$$

(b)
$$[H^+] = 3.4 \text{ M}; \quad [OH^-] = \frac{K_w}{[H^+]} = \frac{1.00 \times 10^{-14}}{3.4} = 2.9 \times 10^{-15} \text{ M}$$

(c)
$$[H^+] = 0.0500 \text{ M}; \quad [OH^-] = \frac{K_w}{[H^+]} = \frac{1.00 \times 10^{-14}}{0.0500} = 2.00 \times 10^{-13} \text{ M}$$

16.34   These bases are ionic compounds.

(a)
$$[OH^-] = 2 \times 10^{-3} \text{ M}; \quad [H^+] = \frac{K_w}{[OH^-]} = \frac{1.00 \times 10^{-14}}{2 \times 10^{-3}} = 5 \times 10^{-12} \text{ M}$$

(b) $[OH^-] = 2 \times 1.33 \times 10^{-2} = 2.66 \times 10^{-2} \text{ M}$

$$[H^+] = \frac{K_w}{[OH^-]} = \frac{1.00 \times 10^{-14}}{2.66 \times 10^{-2}} = 3.76 \times 10^{-13} \text{ M}$$

(c) $[OH^-] = 0.050 + 2 \times 0.010 = 0.070 \text{ M}$

$$[H^+] = \frac{K_w}{[OH^-]} = \frac{1.00 \times 10^{-14}}{0.070} = 1.4 \times 10^{-13} \text{ M}$$

16.37   These bases are ionic compounds.
(a) $pOH = -\log[OH^-] = -\log 0.025 = 1.60$
(b) $[OH^-] = 2 \times 0.025 = 0.050 \text{ M}$
   $pOH = -\log[OH^-] = -\log 0.050 = 1.30$
(c)
$$[NaOH] = \frac{0.0100 \text{ mol}}{0.250 \text{ L}} = 0.0400 \text{ M}$$

$$[Ba(OH)_2] = \frac{0.0016 \text{ mol}}{0.250 \text{ L}} = 0.0064 \text{ M}$$

$[OH^-] = 0.0400 + 2 \times 0.0064 = 0.0528 \text{ M}$
$pOH = -\log[OH^-] = -\log 0.0528 = 1.277$

Comment: In general, the volume change accompanying the dissolving of small amounts of solids is slight and can usually be ignored.

16.40   Trichloracetic acid is the stronger acid. The strength of an acid depends on how readily it is willing to part with its protons. Since the trichloracetic acid solution has a lower pH, it is more willing to give up its protons and, therefore, must be the stronger acid of the two. Remember, the lower the pH, the greater the hydrogen ion concentration.

16.41   Ammonia is the stronger base. The strength of a base depends on how readily it is willing to accept protons. Since the ammonia solution has a higher pH, it is more willing to accept protons and, therefore, must be the stronger base of the two. Remember, the higher the pH, the greater the hydroxide ion concentration; and the greater the hydroxide ion concentration, the more basic the solution.

16.42   (a) Exercise 16.40:

0.10 M HF: $\log[H^+] = -2.23$ and $[H^+] = \text{antilog}(-2.23) = 10^{-2.23} = 5.9 \times 10^{-3}$ M

$$[OH^-] = \frac{K_w}{[H^+]} = \frac{1.00 \times 10^{-14}}{5.9 \times 10^{-3}} = 1.7 \times 10^{-12} \text{ M}$$

0.10 M trichloracetic acid: $\log[H^+] = -1.13$ and $[H^+] = \text{antilog}(-1.13) = 10^{-1.13} = 7.4 \times 10^{-2}$ M

$$[OH^-] = \frac{K_w}{[H^+]} = \frac{1.00 \times 10^{-14}}{7.4 \times 10^{-2}} = 1.4 \times 10^{-13} \text{ M}$$

(b) Exercise 16.41:

0.050 M aniline: $\log[H^+] = -8.64$ and $[H^+] = \text{antilog}(-8.64) = 10^{-8.64} = 2.3 \times 10^{-9}$ M

$$[OH^-] = \frac{K_w}{[H^+]} = \frac{1.00 \times 10^{-14}}{2.3 \times 10^{-9}} = 4.3 \times 10^{-6} \text{ M}$$

0.050 M NH_3: $\log[H^+] = -10.85$ and $[H^+] = \text{antilog}(-10.85) = 10^{-10.85} = 1.4 \times 10^{-11}$ M

$$[OH^-] = \frac{K_w}{[H^+]} = \frac{1.00 \times 10^{-14}}{1.4 \times 10^{-11}} = 7.1 \times 10^{-4} \text{ M}$$

16.43   (a) Acidic. Solutions with pH values below 7.0 are acidic.
       (b) $\log[H^+] = -5.6$

and $[H^+] = \text{antilog}(-5.6) = 10^{-5.6} = 3 \times 10^{-6}$ M

16.51   (a) The charge on Br^- is more delocalized than that on Cl^-, since bromine is larger than chlorine. Therefore, Br^- is a weaker base than Cl^- and, consequently, HBr is a stronger acid than HCl.
       (b) Cl is more electronegative than Br. Because Cl is more electronegative, the H–O bond in $HClO_3$ is more polar than that in $HBrO_3$ and, consequently, $HClO_3$ is a stronger acid than $HBrO_3$.
       (c) HNO_3 has an additional electronegative atom attached to the central nitrogen atom. This additional electronegative atom increases the O–H bond polarity and makes for a larger oxo anion, which is less effective in attracting protons because its charge is delocalized over a greater volume. Therefore, the additional electronegative atom makes HNO_3 a stronger acid than HNO_2.
       (d) Aluminum with its 3+ positive charge is better able to attract the electron clouds of the bonded water molecules than zinc with only its 2+ positive charge. Consequently, the O–H bond polarity is greater in $Al(H_2O)_6^{3+}$ than in $Zn(H_2O)_4^{2+}$, and $Al(H_2O)_6^{3+}$ is a stronger acid than $Zn(H_2O)_4^{2+}$.

16.52   (a) O is more electronegative than N. Therefore, the O–H bond in water is more polar than the N–H bond in ammonia, and that makes water a stronger acid or better proton donor than ammonia.
       (b) I is more electronegative than Te. Because I is more electronegative, the H–O bond in H_5IO_6 is more polar than that in H_6TeO_6 and, consequently, H_5IO_6 is a stronger acid than H_6TeO_6.
       (c) Since As is above Sb in Group 5A, it is more electronegative than Sb. Because As is more electronegative, the H–O bond in $As(OH)_3$ is more polar than that in $Sb(OH)_3$ and, consequently, $As(OH)_3$ is a stronger acid than $Sb(OH)_3$.

(d) The charge on S^{2-} is more delocalized than that on O^{2-}, since sulfur is larger than oxygen. Therefore, S^{2-} is a weaker base than O^{2-} and, consequently, HS^- is a stronger acid than OH^-.

16.53 (a) HI. I^- is a weaker base than Br^-, because iodine is larger than bromine.
(b) H_3PO_4. P is more electronegative than As.
(c) H_2S. HS^- is a larger anion than HO^-.
(d) HCl. Cl is more electronegative than S and HS^- is an anion, while HCl is neutral.
(e) $Cr(H_2O)_6^{3+}$. Chromium in $Cr(H_2O)_6^{3+}$ has a 3+ charge, while in $Cr(H_2O)_6^{2+}$ it only has a 2+ charge.
(f) $HClO_4$. $HClO_4$ has an additional electronegative oxygen atom.
(g) $CH_3CH_2ClCOOH$. Cl is more electronegative than Br.

16.54 (a) O^{2-}. Oxygen is smaller than sulfur.
(b) Cl^-. Chlorine is smaller than bromine.
(c) ClO_2^-. ClO_3^- is a larger anion than ClO_2^-; its charge is more delocalized, so it is a weaker base. Also, $HClO_3$ has a more polar O–H bond and is a stronger acid.
(d) NH_3. The electronegative oxygen atom in NH_2OH draws away electron density from the nitrogen atom so it is less able to attract protons.
(e) SeO_3^{2-}. S is more electronegative than Se and, therefore, HSO_3^- is a stronger acid than $HSeO_3^-$. Consequently, the conjugate base of $HSeO_3^-$, SeO_3^{2-}, should be a stronger base than SO_3^{2-}, the conjugate base of HSO_3^-.
(f) CO_3^{2-}. CO_3^{2-} is more negative than HCO_3^-.
(g) $H_2SbO_4^-$. P is more electronegative than Sb and, therefore, H_3PO_4 is a stronger acid than H_3SbO_4. Consequently, the conjugate base of H_3SbO_4, $H_2SbO_4^-$, should be a stronger base than the conjugate base of H_3PO_4, $H_2PO_4^-$.

16.56 (a) A Lewis acid is called an electrophile, because it seeks out and accepts electron pairs.
(b) The corresponding term for a Lewis base is a nucleophile, because it is seeking out a positive nucleus (or site) or an electron-deficient species (or site). The term literally means "nucleus-lover."

16.60 (a)

Lewis acid   Lewis base

(b)

Lewis base   Lewis acid

(c)

new covalent bonds

Ag^+ +   2 $:NH_3$ ⟶ $[H_3N\!:\!Ag\!:\!NH_3]^+$

Lewis acid   Lewis base

(d)

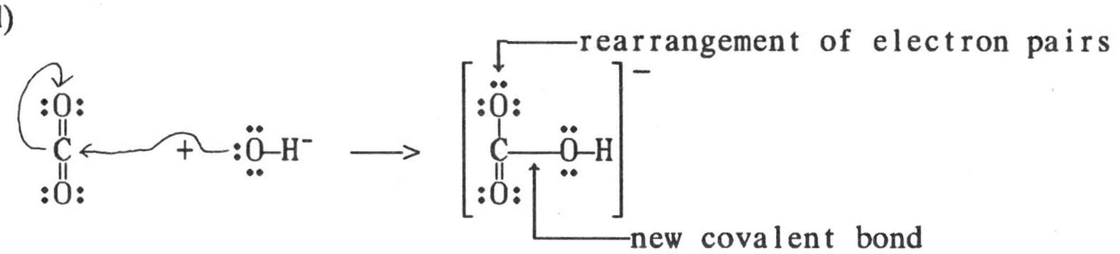

Lewis acid   Lewis base

16.61 (a) $CH_3NH_2(aq) + H_2O(l) \rightleftharpoons CH_3NH_3^+(aq) + OH^-(aq)$
$HCl(aq) + H_2O(l) \longrightarrow H_3O^+(aq) + Cl^-(aq)$

Arrhenius neutralization:

$H_3O^+(aq) + Cl^-(aq) + CH_3NH_3^+(aq) + OH^-(aq) \longrightarrow 2H_2O(l) + CH_3NH_3Cl(aq)$
or $H_3O^+(aq) + OH^-(aq) \longrightarrow 2H_2O(l)$

In the Arrhenius system, neutralization is interpreted as the combination of hydrogen and hydroxide ions to form water.

(b) $HCl(aq) + H_2O(l) \longrightarrow H_3O^+(aq) + Cl^-(aq)$
   acid_1 base_2 acid_2 base_1

Brönsted-Lowry neutralization:

$CH_3NH_2(aq) + H_3O^+(aq) \longrightarrow CH_3NH_3^+(aq) + H_2O(l)$
base_1 acid_2 acid_1 base_2

In the Brönsted-Lowry system, a neutralization or acid-base reaction is interpreted as a proton transfer; the acid is the proton donor and the base is the proton acceptor. For the reaction of weak bases with strong acids in aqueous solution, the weak base accepts protons directly from $H_3O^+(aq)$

(c)

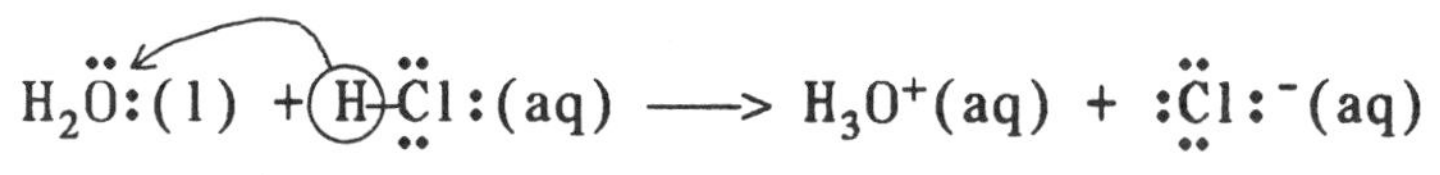

$H_2O:(l) + H-Cl:(aq) \longrightarrow H_3O^+(aq) + :Cl:^-(aq)$

Lewis neutralization:

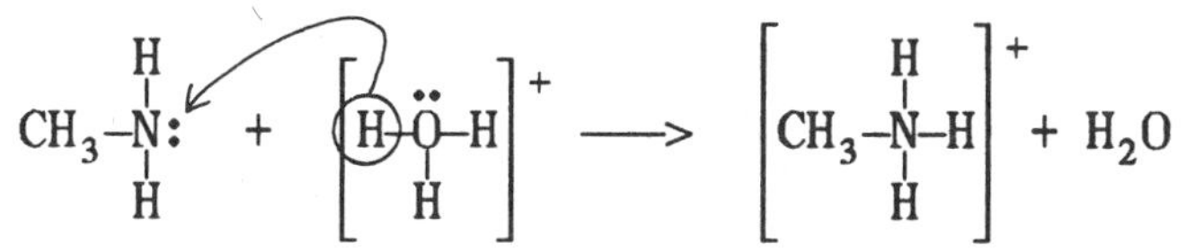

Lewis base   Lewis acid

In the Lewis system, a neutralization or acid-base reaction is interpreted as the formation of a covalent bond, with the base donating the electron pair that is shared between the acid and base.

(d) The Brönsted-Lowry and Lewis interpretations seem simpler, because they don't require the reaction between the weak base and water.

16.62 (a) $CO_2(g) + 2H_2O(l) \rightleftharpoons H_3O^+(aq) + HCO_3^-(aq)$
$NaOH(aq) \longrightarrow Na^+(aq) + OH^-(aq)$

Arrhenius neutralization:

$H_3O^+(aq) + HCO_3^-(aq) + Na^+(aq) + OH^-(aq) \longrightarrow 2H_2O(l) + NaHCO_3(aq)$
or $H_3O^+(aq) + OH^-(aq) \longrightarrow 2H_2O(l)$

In the Arrenhius system, neutralization is interpreted as the combination of hydrogen and hydroxide ions to form water.

(b) $CO_2(g) + H_2O(l) \rightleftharpoons H_2CO_3(aq)$
$NaOH(aq) \longrightarrow Na^+(aq) + OH^-(aq)$

Brönsted–Lowry neutralization:

$H_2CO_3(aq) + OH^-(aq) \longrightarrow HCO_3^-(aq) + H_2O(l)$
acid$_1$ base$_2$ base$_1$ acid$_1$

In the Brönsted–Lowry system, a neutralization or acid-base reaction is interpreted as a proton transfer; the acid is the proton donor and the base is the proton acceptor. For the reaction of hydroxide bases with weak acids in aqueous solution, the weak acid gives protons directly to $OH^-(aq)$.

(c) $NaOH(aq) \longrightarrow Na^+(aq) + OH^-(aq)$

Lewis neutralization:

Lewis acid   Lewis base

In the Lewis system, a neutralization or acid-base reaction is interpreted as the formation of a covalent bond, with the base donating the electron pair that is shared between the acid and base.

(d) The Lewis system seems simplest, because it doesn't require the reaction between CO_2 and water.

16.63   No. The exact number of water molecules associated with the proton or H^+ ion is not known. In fact, it is possible that several types of hydrated ions exist simultaneously in aqueous solution.

16.64 (a) Water is an amphiprotic solvent. Amphiprotic solvents have the property that the strongest acid that can exist in solution is the conjugate acid of the solvent, and the strongest base that can exist in solution is the conjugate base of the solvent. Therefore, in water an acid is considered strong if it is stronger than $H_3O^+(aq)$, and weak if it is weaker than $H_3O^+(aq)$. Also, in water a base is considered strong if it is stronger than $OH^-(aq)$, and weak if it is weaker than $OH^-(aq)$.

(b) Since ammonia is an amphiprotic solvent, the strongest acid that can exist in solution is NH_4^+, and the strongest base that can exist in solution is NH_2^-. Therefore, the weak acids above NH_4^+, $H_2PO_4^-$ to HSO_4^-, would be considered strong on such a planet.

16.65 (a) $3CaO(s) + 2H_3PO_4(aq) \longrightarrow Ca_3(PO_4)_2(s) + 3H_2O(l)$
(b) $12NaOH(aq) + P_4O_{10}(s) \longrightarrow 4Na_3PO_4(aq) + 6H_2O(l)$
(c) $CaO(s) + SO_2(g) \longrightarrow CaSO_3(s)$
(d) $MgO(s) + 2HNO_3(aq) \longrightarrow Mg(NO_3)_2(aq) + H_2O(l)$
(e) $Ba(OH)_2(aq) + SO_2(aq) \longrightarrow BaSO_3(aq) + H_2O(l)$
(f) $Cr_2O_3(s) + 3H_2SO_4(aq) \longrightarrow Cr_2(SO_4)_3(aq) + 3H_2O(l)$
(g) $2KOH(aq) + CO_2(aq) \longrightarrow K_2CO_3(aq) + H_2O(l)$

16.66   The initial $[H^+]$ of the gastric juice sample is $[H^+]$ = antilog(–1.1) = $10^{-1.1}$ = 0.08 M

The final $[H^+]$ of the gastric juice sample is $[H^+]$ = antilog(–1.9) = $10^{-1.9}$ = 0.01 M

The number of moles of H^+(aq) that has to be neutralized is

moles H^+(aq) neutralized = initial number of H^+(aq) moles – final number of H^+(aq) moles

$$= 0.100 \text{ L} \times \frac{0.08 \text{ mol } H^+(aq)}{1 \text{ L}} - 0.100 \text{ L} \times \frac{0.01 \text{ mol } H^+(aq)}{1 \text{ L}} = 0.007 \text{ mol } H^+(aq)$$

Since each mole of $Mg(OH)_2$ supplies 2 mol of hydroxide ion, we need 0.0035 mol of $Mg(OH)_2$. The number of grams of $Mg(OH)_2$ needed is

$$0.0035 \text{ mol } Mg(OH)_2 \times \frac{58.32 \text{ g } Mg(OH)_2}{1 \text{ mol } Mg(OH)_2} = 0.20 \text{ g } Mg(OH)_2$$

Comment: In general, there are only slight volume changes when solids are dissolved and usually these volume changes can be ignored.

16.68 H^+(aq) + OH^-(aq) ⟶ H_2O(l)

$$\frac{0.027 \text{ L NaOH}}{0.100 \text{ L "stomach acid"}} \times \frac{0.1 \text{ mol NaOH}}{1 \text{ L NaOH}} \times \frac{1 \text{ mol } H^+(aq)}{1 \text{ mol NaOH}} = \frac{0.03 \text{ mol } H^+(aq)}{1 \text{ L "stomach acid"}}$$

16.70 OH^-(aq) + H^+(aq) ⟶ H_2O(l)

The number of grams of NaOH neutralized is calculated as follows: V x M (of HCl) ⟶ mol HCl ⟶ mol NaOH ⟶ g NaOH.

$$0.0600 \text{ L HCl} \times \frac{0.500 \text{ mol HCl}}{1 \text{ L HCl}} \times \frac{1 \text{ mol NaOH}}{1 \text{ mol HCl}} \times \frac{40.0 \text{ g NaOH}}{1 \text{ mol NaOH}} = 1.20 \text{ g NaOH}$$

The percentage of NaOH in the sample is

$$\% \text{ NaOH} = \frac{\text{mass NaOH}}{\text{mass sample}} \times 100\% = \frac{1.20 \text{ g}}{2.00 \text{ g}} \times 100\% = 60.0\%$$

16.71 $Al(OH)_3$(s) + 3HCl(aq) ⟶ $AlCl_3$(aq) + $3H_2O$(l)
(a) The number of grams of $Al(OH)_3$ neutralized is calculated as follows:
V x M (of HCl) ⟶ mol HCl ⟶ mol $Al(OH)_3$ ⟶ g $Al(OH)_3$.

$$0.100 \text{ L HCl} \times \frac{0.150 \text{ mol HCl}}{1 \text{ L HCl}} \times \frac{1 \text{ mol } Al(OH)_3}{3 \text{ mol HCl}} \times \frac{78.0 \text{ g } Al(OH)_3}{1 \text{ mol } Al(OH)_3} = 0.390 \text{ g } Al(OH)_3$$

(b) The percentage of $Al(OH)_3$ in the tablet is

$$\% \text{ } Al(OH)_3 = \frac{\text{mass } Al(OH)_3}{\text{mass tablet}} \times 100\% = \frac{0.390 \text{ g}}{0.800 \text{ g}} \times 100\% = 48.8\%$$

CHAPTER 17
ACID-BASE EQUILIBRIA IN AQUEOUS SOLUTION

Solutions To Practice Exercises

PE 17.2 $[H^+]$ = antilog(-2.23) = $10^{-2.23}$ = 5.9×10^{-3} M

Concentration Summary;

Equation:	$HCOOH(aq) \rightleftharpoons H^+(aq) + HCOO^-(aq)$		
Initial concentrations, mol/L	0.200	0	0
Concentration changes, mol/L	-5.9×10^{-3}	$+5.9 \times 10^{-3}$	$+5.9 \times 10^{-3}$
Equilibrium concentrations, mol/L	0.194	5.9×10^{-3}	5.9×10^{-3}

Substituting the equilibrium concentrations in the K_a expression gives

$$K_a = \frac{[H^+][HCOO^-]}{[HCOOH]} = \frac{(5.9 \times 10^{-3})^2}{0.194} = 1.8 \times 10^{-4}$$

PE 17.3   Concentration Summary:

Equation:	$HCN(aq) \rightleftharpoons H^+(aq) + CN^-(aq)$		
Initial concentrations, mol/L	0.050	0	0
Concentration changes, mol/L	$-x$	$+x$	$+x$
Equilibrium concentrations, mol/L	$0.050 - x$	x	x
Approximate concentrations, mol/L	0.050	x	x

Substituting the approximate concentrations and $K_a = 4.93 \times 10^{-10}$ (Table 17.1) into the K_a expression gives

$$K_a = [H^+][CN^-]/[HCN]$$

$$4.93 \times 10^{-10} = \frac{x^2}{0.050} \text{ and } x = [H^+] = [CN^-] = 5.0 \times 10^{-6} \text{ M}$$

PE 17.4 (a) 0.100 M acetic acid:

Concentration Summary:

Equation:	$CH_3COOH(aq) \rightleftharpoons H^+(aq) + CH_3COO^-(aq)$		
Initial concentrations, mol/L	0.100	0	0
Concentration changes, mol/L	$-x$	$+x$	$+x$
Equilibrium concentrations, mol/L	$0.100 - x$	x	x
Approximate concentrations, mol/L	0.100	x	x

1. With approximation: Substituting the approximate concentrations and $K_a = 1.76 \times 10^{-5}$ (Table 17.1) into the K_a expression gives

$K_a = [H^+][CH_3COO^-]/[CH_3COOH]$

$1.76 \times 10^{-5} = \dfrac{x^2}{0.100}$ and $x = [H^+] = 1.33 \times 10^{-3}$ M

2. Without approximation: Substituting the equilibrium concentrations and $K_a = 1.76 \times 10^{-5}$ into the K_a expression gives

$1.76 \times 10^{-5} = \dfrac{x^2}{0.100 - x}$

$x^2 + 1.76 \times 10^{-5}x - 1.76 \times 10^{-6} = 0$ and $x = [H^+] = 1.32 \times 10^{-3}$ M

(b) 1.00×10^{-4} M acetic acid (replace 0.100 with 1.00×10^{-4} in the above concentration summary):

1. With approximation: Substituting the approximate concentrations and $K_a = 1.76 \times 10^{-5}$ into the K_a expression gives

$1.76 \times 10^{-5} = \dfrac{x^2}{1.00 \times 10^{-4}}$ and $x = [H^+] = 4.20 \times 10^{-5}$ M

2. Without approximation: Substituting the equilibrium concentrations and K_a value into the K_a expression gives

$1.76 \times 10^{-5} = \dfrac{x^2}{1.00 \times 10^{-4} - x}$

$x^2 + 1.76 \times 10^{-5}x - 1.76 \times 10^{-9} = 0$ and $x = [H^+] = 3.41 \times 10^{-5}$ M

PE 17.6   Concentration Summary:

Equation:	$C_6H_5NH_2(aq) + H_2O(l) \rightleftharpoons C_6H_5NH_3^+(aq) + OH^-(aq)$		
Initial concentrations, mol/L	0.15	0	0
Concentration changes, mol/L	$-x$	$+x$	$+x$
Equilibrium concentrations, mol/L	$0.15 - x$	x	x
Approximate concentrations, mol/L	0.15	x	x

Substituting the approximate concentrations and $K_b = 4.3 \times 10^{-10}$ (Table 17.2) into the K_b expression gives

$K_b = [C_6H_5NH_3^+][OH^-]/[C_6H_5NH_2]$

$4.3 \times 10^{-10} = \dfrac{x^2}{0.15}$ and $x = [OH^-] = 8.0 \times 10^{-6}$ M

The pOH of the solution is pOH $= -\log[OH^-] = -\log(8.0 \times 10^{-6}) = 5.10$

The pH is pH $= 14.00 - \text{pOH} = 14.00 - 5.10 = 8.90$

PE 17.8 Concentration Summary:

Equation:	$NH_3(aq) + H_2O(1) \rightleftharpoons$	$NH_4^+(aq)$	$+ OH^-(aq)$
Initial concentrations, mol/L	0.200	0	0
Concentration changes, mol/L	$-x$	$+x$	$+x$
Equilibrium concentrations, mol/L	$0.200 - x$	x	x
Approximate concentrations, mol/L	0.200	x	x

Substituting the approximate concentrations and $K_b = 1.77 \times 10^{-5}$ (Table 17.2) into the K_b expression gives

$$K_b = [NH_4^+][OH^-]/[NH_3]$$

$$1.77 \times 10^{-5} = \frac{x^2}{0.200} \text{ and } x = [NH_4^+] = [OH^-] = 1.88 \times 10^{-3} \text{ M}$$

The number of moles of NH_3 ionized per liter is equal to the hydroxide ion concentration. The percent ionization is

$$\% \text{ ionization} = 100\% \times \frac{\text{moles of } NH_3 \text{ ionized per liter}}{\text{initial moles of } NH_3 \text{ per liter}}$$

$$= 100\% \times \frac{1.88 \times 10^{-3} \text{ M}}{0.200 \text{ M}} = 0.940\%$$

PE 17.9 $NH_3(aq) + H_2O(1) \rightleftharpoons NH_4^+(aq) + OH^-(aq)$

(a) Decreases. In addition to decreasing all concentrations, dilution also drives the reaction to the right.

(b) No change. The K_b value depends only on temperature as long as the solution is dilute.

(c) Increases. Dilution drives the reaction to the right, therefore the total number of moles of OH^- increases.

(d) Increases. Dilution drives the reaction to the right, therefore the fraction of molecules ionized increases.

PE 17.11 (a) The $[H^+]$ can be calculated from the first step alone.

Concentration Summary:

Equation:	$H_2C_3H_2O_4(aq) \rightleftharpoons$	$H^+(aq)$	$+ HC_3H_2O_4^-(aq)$
Initial concentrations, mol/L	0.80	0	0
Concentration changes, mol/L	$-x$	$+x$	$+x$
Equilibrium concentrations, mol/L	$0.80 - x$	x	x
Approximate concentrations, mol/L	0.80	x	x

Substituting the approximate concentrations and $K_{a_1} = 1.49 \times 10^{-3}$ (Table 17.1) into the K_{a_1} expression gives

$$K_{a_1} = [H^+][HC_3H_2O_4^-]/[H_2C_3H_2O_4]$$

$$1.49 \times 10^{-3} = \frac{x^2}{0.80} \text{ and } x = [H^+] = 0.035 \text{ M}$$

The approximation is valid, since x is less than 5% of 0.80. The pH is

$$pH = -\log[H^+] = -\log(0.035) = 1.46$$

(b) The concentration of the doubly charged anion is approximately equal to K_{a_2}. Therefore,

$$[C_3H_2O_4^{2-}] = K_{a_2} = 2.0 \times 10^{-6} \text{ M}$$

PE 17.14 (a) Basic. The solution contains $Na^+(aq)$ and $PO_4^{3-}(aq)$. The hydrated sodium ion does not react with water and has no effect on the pH of the solution. The phosphate ion is the anion of the weak acid HPO_4^{2-} and is therefore basic with respect to water. The solution will be basic.

(b) Acidic. The solution contains $Cu^{2+}(aq)$ and $NO_3^-(aq)$. The hydrated copper(II) ion is acidic with respect to water. The nitrate ion is the anion of a strong acid and will not react with water. The solution will be acidic.

(c) Neutral. The solution contains $Li^+(aq)$ and $NO_3^-(aq)$. The hydrated lithium ion is monovalent and will not react with water. The nitrate ion is the anion of a strong acid and will not react with water. The solution will be neutral.

(d) Slightly acidic. The solution contains $(CH_3)_3NH^+(aq)$ and $F^-(aq)$. K_a for the $(CH_3)_3NH^+$ ion is

$$K_a = \frac{K_w}{K_b} = \frac{1.00 \times 10^{-14}}{6.3 \times 10^{-5}} = 1.6 \times 10^{-10}$$

K_b for the fluoride ion is

$$K_b = \frac{K_w}{K_a} = \frac{1.00 \times 10^{-14}}{3.53 \times 10^{-4}} = 2.83 \times 10^{-11}$$

K_a for $(CH_3)_3NH^+$ is slightly greater than K_b for F^-; hence, the acid strength of $(CH_3)_3NH^+$ is slightly greater than the base strength of F^-. The solution should be slightly acidic.

PE 17.15 Barium acetate provides the ions $Ba^{2+}(aq)$ and $CH_3COO^-(aq)$. The barium ion does not react with water and does not affect the pH of the solution. The acetate ion is basic and will form hydroxide ions. The concentration summary will be based on this reaction.

Concentration Summary:

Equation:	$CH_3COO^-(aq) + H_2O(l) \rightleftharpoons CH_3COOH(aq) + OH^-(aq)$		
Initial concentrations, mol/L	0.400	0	0
Concentration changes, mol/L	$-x$	$+x$	$+x$
Equilibrium concentrations, mol/L	$0.400 - x$	x	x
Approximate concentrations, mol/L	0.400	x	x

Substituting the approximate concentrations and $K_b = 5.68 \times 10^{-10}$ (Example 17.5) into the K_b expression gives

$$K_b = [CH_3COOH][OH^-]/[CH_3COO^-]$$

$$5.68 \times 10^{-10} = \frac{x^2}{0.400}$$

$$x = [OH^-] = 1.51 \times 10^{-5}\ M$$

$$pOH = -\log[OH^-] = -\log(1.51 \times 10^{-5}) = 4.821 \text{ and } pH = 14.00 - pOH = 14.00 - 4.821 = 9.18$$

PE 17.16 Basic. The reactions of HCO_3^- with water are

1. $HCO_3^-(aq) \rightleftharpoons H^+(aq) + CO_3^{2-}(aq)$ $K_{a_2} = 5.61 \times 10^{-11}$
2. $HCO_3^-(aq) + H_2O(l) \rightleftharpoons H_2CO_3(aq) + OH^-(aq)$

K_b for the second reaction is

$$K_b = \frac{K_w}{K_{a_1}} = \frac{1.00 \times 10^{-14}}{4.30 \times 10^{-7}} = 2.33 \times 10^{-8}$$

K_b is greater than K_{a_2}, showing that HCO_3^- is a stronger base than acid. A solution containing HCO_3^- ions will therefore be basic.

PE 17.18   Concentration Summary:

Equation: $CH_3NH_2(aq) + H_2O(l) \rightleftharpoons CH_3NH_3^+(aq) + OH^-(aq)$
Initial concentrations, mol/L   0.200   0.200   0
Concentration changes, mol/L $-x$ $+x$ $+x$
Equilibrium concentrations, mol/L $0.200 - x$ $0.200 + x$ x
Approximate concentrations, mol/L   0.200   0.200 x

Substituting the approximate concentrations and $K_b = 3.70 \times 10^{-4}$ (Table 17.2) into the K_b expression gives

$K_b = [CH_3NH_3^+][OH^-]/[CH_3NH_2]$

$3.70 \times 10^{-4} = \dfrac{(0.200)(x)}{0.200}$ and $x = [OH^-] = 3.70 \times 10^{-4}$ M

PE 17.19   Concentration Summary:

Equation: $HC_3H_2O_4^-(aq) \rightleftharpoons H^+(aq) + C_3H_2O_4^{2-}(aq)$
Initial concentrations, mol/L   0.10   0   0.10
Concentration changes, mol/L $-x$ $+x$ $+x$
Equilibrium concentrations, mol/L $0.10 - x$ x $0.10 + x$
Approximate concentrations, mol/L   0.10 x 0.10

Substituting the approximate concentrations and $K_a = 2.03 \times 10^{-6}$ into the K_a expression gives

$K_a = [H^+][C_3H_2O_4^{2-}]/[HC_3H_2O_4^-]$

$2.03 \times 10^{-6} = \dfrac{(x)(0.10)}{0.10}$

$x = 2.03 \times 10^{-6}$ M = $[H^+]$ and pH = $-\log[H^+] = -\log(2.03 \times 10^{-6}) = 5.69$

PE 17.21   NaOH, a strong base, will repress the ionization of NH_3. Therefore, virtually all of the hydroxide ions in the mixture will come from the NaOH. The $[OH^-]$ concentration is

$[OH^-] = 0.010$ mol/0.250 L = 0.040 M

pOH = $-\log[OH^-] = -\log 0.040 = 1.40$ and pH = $14.00 - $ pOH = $14.00 - 1.40 = 12.60$

PE 17.22   HCOOH is the acid and $HCOO^-$ is the base. Equation 17.4 becomes

$pH = pK_a + \log \dfrac{[HCOO^-]}{[HCOOH]}$

$\log \dfrac{[HCOO^-]}{[HCOOH]} = pH - pK_a = 3.95 + \log(1.9 \times 10^{-4}) = 0.23$

and $\dfrac{[HCOO^-]}{[HCOOH]} = $ antilog$(0.23) = 10^{+0.23} = 1.7$

PE 17.23   Since NaOH is a strong base, it will react completely with the acid component of the buffer; 1.00×10^{-3} mol NaOH will convert 1.00×10^{-3} mol C_6H_5COOH to 1.00×10^{-3} mol $C_6H_5COO^-$

$C_6H_5COOH(aq) + OH^-(aq) \longrightarrow C_6H_5COO^-(aq) + H_2O(l)$

The new quantities are:

$C_6H_5COO^-$: 0.0100 mol + 0.00100 mol = 0.0110 mol

C_6H_5COOH: 0.0100 mol $-$ 0.00100 mol = 0.0090 mol

The final pH is calculated from Equation 17.4:

$$pH = pK_a + \log \frac{[C_6H_5COO^-]}{[C_6H_5COOH]} = 4.190 + \log \frac{0.0110}{0.0090} = 4.28$$

Note: The mole ratio, which is the same as the concentration ratio, was used in this calculation.

PE 17.25 The pK_a for the formic acid–sodium formate buffer is 3.72 (Table 17.1).

$$pH = pK_a + \log \frac{[HCOO^-]}{[HCOOH]}$$

$$3.52 = 3.72 + \log \frac{[HCOO^-]}{[HCOOH]}$$

$$\log \frac{[HCOO^-]}{[HCOOH]} = 3.52 - 3.72 = -0.20; \text{ and } \frac{[HCOO^-]}{[HCOOH]} = \text{antilog}(-0.20) = 10^{-0.20} = 0.63$$

The concentration of HCOOH is 0.10 M. Hence, the concentration of HCOO$^-$ must be

$[HCOO^-] = 0.63 \times [HCOOH] = 0.63 \times 0.10 \text{ M} = 0.063 \text{ M}$

The number of moles of sodium formate that must be added to 500 mL of the solution is

$$0.500 \text{ L} \times \frac{0.063 \text{ mol}}{1 \text{ L}} = 0.032 \text{ mol}$$

PE 17.26 The pH of this solution at equivalence will be less than 7 because $C_6H_5NH_3^+$ is a weak acid

$C_6H_5NH_3^+(aq) \rightleftharpoons H^+(aq) + C_6H_5NH_2(aq)$

The number of moles of aniline at the beginning of the titration is

$$0.0350 \text{ L} \times \frac{0.0500 \text{ mol}}{1 \text{ L}} = 0.00175 \text{ mol}$$

From the neutralization equation

$C_6H_5NH_2(aq) + HCl(aq) \rightleftharpoons C_6H_5NH_3Cl(aq)$

we see that 0.00175 mol of aniline will react with 0.00175 mol of hydrochloric acid to form 0.00175 mol of $C_6H_5NH_3^+$. The volume of 0.0500 M HCl required to reach equivalence is

$$0.00175 \text{ mol HCl} \times \frac{1 \text{ L}}{0.0500 \text{ mol HCl}} = 0.0350 \text{ L} = 35.0 \text{ mL}$$

The total volume of the solution at the equivalence point is

35.0 mL + 35.0 mL = 70.0 mL = 0.0700 L

The molarity of $C_6H_5NH_3^+$ at equivalence is initially

$\dfrac{0.00175 \text{ mol}}{0.0700 \text{ L}} = 0.0250 \text{ M}$; but some of this ionizes to form hydrogen ions.

Concentration Summary:

Equation:	$C_6H_5NH_3^+(aq)$	$\rightleftharpoons$	$H^+(aq)$	$+$	$C_6H_5NH_2(aq)$
Initial concentrations, mol/L	0.0250		0		0
Concentration changes, mol/L	$-x$		$+x$		$+x$
Equilibrium concentrations, mol/L	$0.0250 - x$		x		x
Approximate concentrations, mol/L	0.0250		x		x

Substituting $K_a = K_w/K_b = 1.00 \times 10^{-14}/4.3 \times 10^{-10} = 2.3 \times 10^{-5}$ and the approximate concentrations into the K_a expression gives

$$K_a = [H^+][C_6H_5NH_2]/[C_6H_5NH_3^+]$$

$$2.3 \times 10^{-5} = \frac{x^2}{0.0250}$$

$x = [H^+] = 7.6 \times 10^{-4}$ M and pH $= -\log[H^+] = -\log(7.6 \times 10^{-4}) = 3.12$

PE 17.27   initial moles of HCl = 0.02500 L $\times$ 0.1000 mol/L = 2.500×10^{-3} mol

moles of HCl neutralized = moles of NaOH added = 0.02400 L $\times$ 0.1000 mol/L = 2.400×10^{-3} mol

moles of HCl remaining = $2.500 \times 10^{-3} - 2.400 \times 10^{-3} = 0.100 \times 10^{-3}$ mol

concentration of HCl = moles of HCl remaining/final solution volume

$\quad = 0.100 \times 10^{-3}$ mol/(0.02500 L + 0.02400 L)

$\quad = 2.04 \times 10^{-3}$ M and pH $= -\log[H^+] = -\log(2.04 \times 10^{-3}) = 2.69$

PE 17.28   At points between the initial point and the equivalence point the pH can be calculated using Equation 17.4.

initial moles of acetic acid = 0.02500 L $\times$ 0.1000 mol/L = 2.500×10^{-3} mol

moles of acetic acid neutralized = moles of NaOH added = 0.02000 L $\times$ 0.1000 mol/L = 2.000×10^{-3} mol

moles of acetic acid remaining = $2.500 \times 10^{-3} - 2.000 \times 10^{-3} = 0.500 \times 10^{-3}$ mol

The number of moles of acetic ion formed is 2.00×10^{-3} mol, and the buffer ratio is

$$\frac{[CH_3COO^-]}{[CH_3COOH]} = \frac{2.00 \times 10^{-3} \text{ mol}}{0.500 \times 10^{-3} \text{ mol}} = 4.00$$

Substituting $pK_a = 4.754$ and 4.00 for the buffer ratio into Equation 17.4 gives

$$pH = pK_a + \log \frac{[CH_3COO^-]}{[CH_3COOH]} = 4.754 + \log 4.00 = 5.356$$

Solutions To Final Exercises

17.3   Stronger. The lower pK_b value at 50°C means that the ammonia ionization reaction is driven further to the right as the temperature goes up.

17.5   Concentration Summary:

Equation:	HCOOH(aq) $\rightleftharpoons$	H$^+$(aq) +	HCOO$^-$(aq)
Initial concentrations, mol/L	0.0800	0	0
Concentration changes, mol/L	$-x$	$+x$	$+x$
Equilibrium concentrations, mol/L	0.0800 $- x$	x	x
Approximate concentrations, mol/L	0.0800	x	x

Substituting the approximate concentrations and K_a = 1.9 x 10^{-4} (Table 17.1) into the K_a expression gives

K_a = [H$^+$][HCOO$^-$]/[HCOOH]

$1.9 \times 10^{-4} = \dfrac{x^2}{0.0800}$ and x = [H$^+$] = 3.9 x 10^{-3} M

The approximation is acceptable, since x is less than 5% of 0.0800. The pH is

pH = $-$log[H$^+$] = $-$log(3.9 x 10^{-3}) = 2.41

17.7   (a) Concentration Summary:

Equation:	HC$_3$H$_5$O$_3$(aq) $\rightleftharpoons$	H$^+$(aq) +	C$_3$H$_5$O$_3$$^-$(aq)
Initial Concentrations, mol/L	0.180	0	0
Concentration changes, mol/L	$-x$	$+x$	$+x$
Equilibrium concentrations, mol/L	0.180 $- x$	x	x
Approximate concentrations, mol/L	0.180	x	x

Substituting the approximate concentrations and K_a = 1.37 x 10^{-4} (Table 17.1) into the K_a expression gives

K_a = [H$^+$][C$_3$H$_5$O$_3$$^-$]/[HC$_3H_5O_3$]

$1.37 \times 10^{-4} = \dfrac{x^2}{0.180}$ and x = [H$^+$] = 4.97 x 10^{-3} M

The approximation is acceptable, since x is less than 5% of 0.180. The pH is

pH = $-$log[H$^+$] = $-$log(4.97 x 10^{-3}) = 2.304

(b) Exchanging 0.0180 for 0.180 in the above concentration summary and substituting the approximate concentrations and K_a value into the K_a expression gives

$1.37 \times 10^{-4} = \dfrac{x^2}{0.0180}$ and x = [H$^+$] = 1.57 x 10^{-3}

The approximation is unacceptable or not valid, since x is more than 5% of 0.0180. The correct value of x is obtained by substituting the equilibrium concentrations and K_a value into the K_a expression and using the quadratic formula.

$1.37 \times 10^{-4} = \dfrac{x^2}{0.0180 - x}$

$x^2 + 1.37 \times 10^{-4}x - 2.47 \times 10^{-6} = 0$

x = [H$^+$] = 1.50 x 10^{-3} M and pH = $-$log[H$^+$] = $-$log(1.50 x 10^{-3}) = 2.824

17.8   (a) [H$^+$] = antilog($-$4.0) = 10$^{-4.0}$ = 1 x 10^{-4} M

$[OH^-] = \dfrac{K_w}{[H^+]} = \dfrac{1.00 \times 10^{-14}}{1 \times 10^{-4}} = 1 \times 10^{-10}$ M

(b) The [H^+] from the self-ionization of water is repressed by the presence of the weak acid and, therefore, is usually several orders of magnitude smaller than that obtained from the ionization of the weak acid.

17.11 (a) $K_a = 2.8 \times 10^{-8}$ for HOCl (Table 17.1)

$$K_b = \frac{K_w}{K_a} = \frac{1.00 \times 10^{-14}}{2.8 \times 10^{-8}} = 3.6 \times 10^{-7}$$

(b) $K_a = 6.46 \times 10^{-5}$ for C_6H_5COOH (Table 17.1)

$$K_b = \frac{K_w}{K_a} = \frac{1.00 \times 10^{-14}}{6.46 \times 10^{-5}} = 1.55 \times 10^{-10}$$

(c) $K_a = 4.93 \times 10^{-10}$ for HCN (Table 17.1)

$$K_b = \frac{K_w}{K_a} = \frac{1.00 \times 10^{-14}}{4.93 \times 10^{-10}} = 2.03 \times 10^{-5}$$

(d) $K_a = 1.4 \times 10^{-5}$ for $Al(H_2O)_6^{3+}$ (Table 17.1)

$$K_b = \frac{K_w}{K_a} = \frac{1.00 \times 10^{-14}}{1.4 \times 10^{-5}} = 7.1 \times 10^{-10}$$

17.12 Use of a concentration summary similar to the one in Exercise 17.5 for the acids and the one in Practice Exercise 17.8 for the bases, and substituting the approximate concentrations and K_a and K_b values from Tables 17.1 and 17.2 into the K_a and K_b expressions gives

(a) $K_a = [H^+][C_3H_5O_3^-]/[HC_3H_5O_3]$

$$1.37 \times 10^{-4} = \frac{x^2}{0.10} \text{ and } x = [H^+] = 3.7 \times 10^{-3} \text{ M}$$

The number of moles of $HC_3H_5O_3$ ionized per liter is equal to x, so the percent ionization is

$$\% \text{ ionization} = 100\% \times \frac{3.7 \times 10^{-3} \text{ M}}{0.10 \text{ M}} = 3.7\%$$

(b) $K_a = [H^+][F^-]/[HF]$

$$3.53 \times 10^{-4} = \frac{x^2}{0.15} \text{ and } x = [H^+] = 7.3 \times 10^{-3} \text{ M}$$

The number of moles of HF ionized per liter is equal to x, so the percent ionization is

$$\% \text{ ionization} = 100\% \times \frac{7.3 \times 10^{-3} \text{ M}}{0.15 \text{ M}} = 4.9 \%$$

(c) $K_b = [CH_3NH_3^+][OH^-]/[CH_3NH_2]$

$$3.70 \times 10^{-4} = \frac{x^2}{0.25} \text{ and } x = [OH^-] = 9.6 \times 10^{-3} \text{ M}$$

The number of moles of CH_3NH_2 ionized per liter is equal to x, so the percent ionization is

$$\% \text{ ionization} = 100\% \times \frac{9.6 \times 10^{-3} \text{ M}}{0.25 \text{ M}} = 3.8\%$$

(d) $K_b = [C_6H_5NH_3^+][OH^-]/[C_6H_5NH_2]$

$4.3 \times 10^{-10} = \dfrac{x^2}{0.050}$ and $x = [OH^-] = 4.6 \times 10^{-6}$ M

The number of moles of $C_6H_5NH_2$ ionized per liter is equal to x, so the percent ionization is

% ionization $= 100\% \times \dfrac{4.6 \times 10^{-6} \text{ M}}{0.050 \text{ M}} = 0.0092\%$

17.14 (a) moles of formic acid ionized per liter

$= \dfrac{\% \text{ ionization}}{100\%} \times$ initial moles of formic acid per liter

$= \dfrac{34\%}{100\%} \times 0.0010$ M $= 0.00034$ M

The hydrogen ion concentration is equal to the number of moles of formic acid ionized per liter, or $[H^+] = 0.00034$ M. The pH is

pH $= -\log[H^+] = -\log(0.00034) = 3.47$

(b) The equilibrium concentrations are

$[H^+] = [HCOO^-] = 0.00034$ M

$[HCOOH] = 0.0010 - 0.00034 = 0.0007$ M

Substituting these equilibrium concentrations into the K_a expression gives

$K_a = [H^+][HCOO^-]/[HCOOH] = \dfrac{(0.00034)^2}{(0.0007)} = 2 \times 10^{-4}$ to one significant figure

17.16 $CH_3COOH(aq) \rightleftharpoons H^+(aq) + CH_3COO^-(aq)$
(a) Decreases. Dilution decreases all the concentrations and also drives the reaction to the right.
(b) Decreases. Even though the overall number of moles of CH_3COO^- increases, the $[CH_3COO^-]$ must decrease in order to satisfy the K_a expression.
(c) Increases. Even though the overall number of moles of H^+ increases, the $[H^+]$ must decrease to satisfy the K_a expression.
(d) Increases. Since the $[H^+]$ decreases, the $[OH^-]$ must increase to satisfy the K_w expression.
(e) Remains the same. In dilute solution the K_a value depends only on the temperature.
(f) Increases. Dilution drives the reaction to the right. Therefore, the fraction of molecules ionized increases.

17.18 The $[H^+]$ and $[HSO_3^-]$ can be calculated from the first step alone. Since K_{a_1} is large, the exact solution will be used.

Concentration Summary:

Equation:	$H_2SO_3(aq)$	$\rightleftharpoons$	$H^+(aq)$	$+$	$HSO_3^-(aq)$
Initial concentrations, mol/L	0.150		0		0
Concentration changes, mol/L	$-x$		$+x$		$+x$
Equilibrium concentrations, mol/L	$0.150 - x$		x		x

Substituting the equilibrium concentrations and $K_{a_1} = 1.71 \times 10^{-2}$ (Table 17.1) into the K_{a_1} expression and using the quadratic formula gives

$$K_{a_1} = [H^+][HSO_3^-]/[H_2SO_3]$$

$$1.71 \times 10^{-2} = \frac{x^2}{0.150 - x}$$

$x^2 + 1.71 \times 10^{-2}x - 0.2565 \times 10^{-2} = 0$ and $x = [H^+] = [HSO_3^-] = 0.0428$ M

The concentration of SO_3^{2-} is approximately equal to K_{a_2}. Therefore,

$$[SO_3^{2-}] = K_{a_2} = 6.0 \times 10^{-8} \text{ M}$$

17.20   (a)   The $[H_2PO_4^-]$ can be calculated from the first step alone. Since K_{a_1} is large, the exact solution will be used.

Concentration Summary:

Equation:	$H_3PO_4(aq)$	$\rightleftharpoons$	$H^+(aq)$	+	$H_2PO_4^-(aq)$
Initial concentrations, mol/L	0.20		0		0
Concentration changes, mol/L	$-x$		$+x$		$+x$
Equilibrium concentrations, mol/L	$0.20 - x$		x		x

Substituting the equilibrium concentrations and $K_{a_1} = 7.52 \times 10^{-3}$ (Table 17.1) into the K_{a_1} expression and using the quadratic formula gives

$$K_{a_1} = [H^+][H_2PO_4^-]/[H_3PO_4]$$

$$7.52 \times 10^{-3} = \frac{x^2}{0.20 - x}$$

$x^2 + 7.52 \times 10^{-3}x - 1.504 \times 10^{-3} = 0$ and $x = [H_2PO_4^-] = 0.035$ M

The concentration of HPO_4^{2-} is approximately equal to K_{a_2}. Therefore,

$$[HPO_4^{2-}] = K_{a_2} = 6.2 \times 10^{-8} \text{ M}$$

(b)   Using the same concentration summary employed in (a) gives

$$7.52 \times 10^{-3} = \frac{x^2}{0.020 - x}$$

$$x^2 + 7.52 \times 10^{-3}x - 1.504 \times 10^{-4} = 0$$

and $x = [H_2PO_4^-] = 0.0091$ M

The concentration of HPO_4^{2-} is approximately equal to K_{a_2}. Therefore,

$$[HPO_4^{2-}] = K_{a_2} = 6.2 \times 10^{-8} \text{ M}$$

17.22   1. The anions of strong acids, excluding the amphiprotic anions like HSO_4^-. These anions are weaker bases than water. Examples are: ClO_4^-, Cl^-, NO_3^-, I^-, Br^-, and ClO_3^-.
2. Monovalent metal cations and divalent alkaline earth metal cations other than beryllium. These hydrated cations are weaker acids than water. Examples are: Li^+, Na^+, K^+, Mg^{2+}, Ca^{2+}, and Ba^{2+}.

17.23   The anions of weak acids. These anions are the conjugate bases of weak acids and are stronger bases than water. Examples are: CH_3COO^-, CN^-, S^{2-}, CO_3^{2-}, F^-, and NO_2^-.

$$S^{2-}(aq) + H_2O(l) \rightleftharpoons HS^-(aq) + OH^-(aq)$$
$$F^-(aq) + H_2O(l) \rightleftharpoons HF(aq) + OH^-(aq)$$
$$NO_2^-(aq) + H_2O(l) \rightleftharpoons HNO_2(aq) + OH^-(aq)$$

Note: Some amphiprotic anions are basic and some are acidic. HS^-, HPO_4^{2-}, and HCO_3^-, for example, are basic.

17.24 1. Small, highly charged metal cations. These hydrated cations are stronger acids than water. Examples are: Al^{3+}, Be^{2+}, Cu^{2+}, Fe^{3+}, Cr^{3+}, and Zn^{2+}.

$$Zn(H_2O)_4^{2+}(aq) + H_2O(l) \rightleftharpoons Zn(H_2O)_3(OH)^+(aq) + H_3O^+(aq)$$
$$Be(H_2O)_4^{2+}(aq) + H_2O(l) \rightleftharpoons Be(H_2O)_3(OH)^+(aq) + H_3O^+(aq)$$
$$Cr(H_2O)_6^{3+}(aq) + H_2O(l) \rightleftharpoons Cr(H_2O)_5(OH)^{2+}(aq) + H_3O^+(aq)$$

2. Ammonium ion (NH_4^+) and protonated amines. These cations are stronger acids than water. Examples are: NH_4^+, $CH_3NH_3^+$, and $C_6H_5NH_3^+$.

$$NH_4^+(aq) + H_2O(l) \rightleftharpoons NH_3(aq) + H_3O^+(aq)$$
$$CH_3NH_3^+(aq) + H_2O(l) \rightleftharpoons CH_3NH_2(aq) + H_3O^+(aq)$$
$$C_6H_5NH_3^+(aq) + H_2O(l) \rightleftharpoons C_6H_5NH_2(aq) + H_3O^+(aq)$$

Note: Some amphiprotic anions may be acidic; examples are $H_2PO_4^-$, HSO_4^-, and $HC_2O_4^-$.

17.27 $$CN^-(aq) + H_2O(l) \rightleftharpoons HCN(aq) + OH^-(aq)$$

$$K_b = [HCN][OH^-]/[CN^-]$$

$$K_b = \frac{K_w}{K_a} = \frac{1.00 \times 10^{-14}}{4.93 \times 10^{-10}} = 2.03 \times 10^{-5}$$

$$F^-(aq) + H_2O(l) \rightleftharpoons HF(aq) + OH^-(aq)$$

$$K_b = [HF][OH^-]/[F^-]$$

$$K_b = \frac{K_w}{K_a} = \frac{1.00 \times 10^{-14}}{3.53 \times 10^{-4}} = 2.83 \times 10^{-11}$$

Since the K_b for CN^- is considerably greater than the K_b for F^-, the KCN solution should be more basic than the KF solution.

17.29 $$Al(H_2O)_6^{3+}(aq) + H_2O(l) \rightleftharpoons Al(H_2O)_5(OH)^{2+}(aq) + H_3O^+(aq)$$

$$K_a = \frac{[Al(H_2O)_5(OH)^{2+}][H_3O^+]}{[Al(H_2O)_6^{3+}]} = 1.4 \times 10^{-5}$$

$$Fe(H_2O)_6^{3+}(aq) + H_2O(l) \rightleftharpoons Fe(H_2O)_5(OH)^{2+}(aq) + H_3O^+(aq)$$

$$K_a = \frac{[Fe(H_2O)_5(OH)^{2+}][H_3O^+]}{[Fe(H_2O)_6^{3+}]} = 7.9 \times 10^{-3}$$

Since the K_a for $Fe(H_2O)_6^{3+}$ is greater than the K_a for $Al(H_2O)_6^{3+}$, the $FeCl_3$ solution should be more acidic than the $AlCl_3$ solution.

17.31 (a) The K_a for benzoic acid is 6.46×10^{-5} (Table 17.1).

$$K_b = \frac{K_w}{K_a} = \frac{1.00 \times 10^{-14}}{6.46 \times 10^{-5}} = 1.55 \times 10^{-10}$$

(b) Calcium benzoate ($Ca(C_6H_5COO)_2$) provides the ions $Ca^{2+}(aq)$ and $C_6H_5COO^-(aq)$. The calcium ion does not react with water and does not affect the pH of the solution. The benzoate ion is basic and will form hydroxide ions. The concentration summary will be based on this reaction.

Concentration Summary:

Equation:	$C_6H_5COO^-(aq)$ + $H_2O(1)$ $\rightleftharpoons$ $C_6H_5COOH(aq)$ + $OH^-(aq)$		
Initial concentrations, mol/L	0.100	0	0
Concentration changes, mol/L	$-x$	$+x$	$+x$
Equilibrium concentrations, mol/L	$0.100 - x$	x	x
Approximate concentrations, mol/L	0.100	x	x

Substituting the approximate concentrations and $K_b = 1.55 \times 10^{-10}$ into the K_b expression gives

$$K_b = [C_6H_5COOH][OH^-]/[C_6H_5COO^-]$$

$$1.55 \times 10^{-10} = \frac{x^2}{0.100}$$

$$x = [OH^-] = 3.94 \times 10^{-6} \text{ M}$$

$$pOH = -\log[OH^-] = -\log(3.94 \times 10^{-6}) = 5.405 \text{ and } pH = 14.00 - pOH = 14.00 - 5.405 = 8.60$$

17.33   Potassium cyanide provides the ions $K^+(aq)$ and $CN^-(aq)$. The potassium ion does not react with water and does not affect the pH of the solution. The cyanide ion is basic and will form hydroxide ions. The concentration summary will be based on this reaction.

Concentration Summary:

Equation:	$CN^-(aq)$ + $H_2O(1)$ $\rightleftharpoons$ $HCN(aq)$ + $OH^-(aq)$		
Initial concentrations, mol/L	0.075	0	0
Concentration changes, mol/L	$-x$	$+x$	$+x$
Equilibrium concentrations, mol/L	$0.075 - x$	x	x
Approximate concentrations, mol/L	0.075	x	x

Substituting the approximate concentrations and $K_b = 2.03 \times 10^{-5}$ (Exercise 17.27) into the K_b expression gives

$$K_b = [HCN][OH^-]/[CN^-]$$

$$2.03 \times 10^{-5} = \frac{x^2}{0.075}$$

$$x = [OH^-] = 1.2 \times 10^{-3} \text{ M}$$

$$pOH = -\log[OH^-] = -\log(1.2 \times 10^{-3}) = 2.92 \text{ and } pH = 14.00 - pOH = 14.00 - 2.92 = 11.08$$

17.35   Only the first hydrolysis step is important in determining the pH of this solution.

Concentration Summary:

Equation:	$PO_4^{3-}(aq)$ + $H_2O(1)$ $\rightleftharpoons$ $HPO_4^{2-}(aq)$ + $OH^-(aq)$		
Initial concentrations, mol/L	0.50	0	0
Concentration changes, mol/L	$-x$	$+x$	$+x$
Equilibrium concentrations, mol/L	$0.50 - x$	x	x

K_b for the reaction is

$$K_b = \frac{K_w}{K_{a_3}} = \frac{1.00 \times 10^{-14}}{4.5 \times 10^{-13}} = 2.2 \times 10^{-2}$$

Since the K_b value is not small, we must perform an exact solution. Substituting the equilibrium concentrations and K_b value into the K_b expression and using the quadratic formula gives

$$K_b = \frac{[HPO_4{}^{2-}][OH^-]}{[PO_4{}^{3-}]}$$

$$2.2 \times 10^{-2} = \frac{x^2}{0.50 - x}$$

$$x^2 + 2.2 \times 10^{-2}x - 1.1 \times 10^{-2} = 0$$

$$x = [OH^-] = 9.4 \times 10^{-2} \text{ M}$$

$$pOH = -\log[OH^-] = -\log(9.4 \times 10^{-2}) = 1.03 \text{ and } pH = 14.00 - pOH = 14.00 - 1.03 = 12.97$$

17.36 Sodium acetate provides the ions $Na^+(aq)$ and $CH_3COO^-(aq)$. The sodium ion does not react with water and does not affect the pH of the solution. The acetate ion is basic and will form hydroxide ions. The concentration summary will be based on this reaction. The $[OH^-]$ of the solution is

$$pOH = 14.00 - pH = 14.00 - 9.00 = 5.00$$

$$[OH^-] = \text{antilog}(-5.00) = 10^{-5.00} = 1.0 \times 10^{-5} \text{ M}$$

Concentration Summary:

Equation:	$CH_3COO^-(aq)$	$+ H_2O(l) \rightleftharpoons$	$CH_3COOH(aq)$	$+ OH^-(aq)$
Initial concentrations, mol/L	x		0	0
Concentration changes, mol/L	-1.0×10^{-5}		$+1.0 \times 10^{-5}$	$+1.0 \times 10^{-5}$
Equilibrium concentrations, mol/L	$x - 1.0 \times 10^{-5}$		1.0×10^{-5}	1.0×10^{-5}
Approximate concentrations, mol/L	x		1.0×10^{-5}	1.0×10^{-5}

Substituting the approximate concentrations and $K_b = 5.68 \times 10^{-10}$ (Example 17.5) in the K_b expression gives

$$K_b = [CH_3COOH][OH^-]/[CH_3COO^-]$$

$$5.68 \times 10^{-10} = \frac{(1.0 \times 10^{-5})^2}{x} \text{ and } x = [CH_3COO^-] = 0.18 \text{ M to two significant figures}$$

Answer: 0.18 mol of sodium acetate should be dissolved in 1 L of water.

17.38 The sodium formate concentration is

$$\frac{10.0 \text{ g HCOONa}}{1.00 \text{ L}} \times \frac{1 \text{ mol HCOONa}}{68.0 \text{ g HCOONa}} = \frac{0.147 \text{ mol HCOONa}}{1.00 \text{ L}} = 0.147 \text{ M HCOONa}$$

Concentration Summary:

Equation:	$HCOOH(aq) \rightleftharpoons$	$HCOO^-(aq)$	$+ H^+(aq)$
Initial concentrations, mol/L	0.0800	0.147	0
Concentration changes, mol/L	$-x$	$+x$	$+x$
Equilibrium concentrations, mol/L	$0.0800 - x$	$0.147 + x$	x
Approximate concentrations, mol/L	0.0800	0.147	x

Substituting the approximate concentrations and $K_a = 4.93 \times 10^{-4}$ (Table 17.1) into the K_a expression gives

$$K_a = [HCOO^-][H^+]/[HCOOH]$$

$$4.93 \times 10^{-4} = \frac{(0.147)(x)}{0.0800}$$

$x = [H^+] = 2.68 \times 10^{-4}$ M and pH $= -\log[H^+] = -\log(2.68 \times 10^{-4}) = 3.57$

The pH without the 10.0 g of HCOONa is 2.41. The added HCOONa represses the ionization of HCOOH, lowering the $[H^+]$ and, consequently, increasing the pH of the solution.

17.40   The solution contains CO_3^{2-}, which is basic:

$$CO_3^{2-}(aq) + H_2O(l) \rightleftharpoons HCO_3^-(aq) + OH^-(aq)$$

$$\frac{[HCO_3^-][OH^-]}{[CO_3^{2-}]} = K_b = \frac{K_w}{K_{a_2}} = \frac{1.00 \times 10^{-14}}{5.61 \times 10^{-11}} = 1.78 \times 10^{-4}$$

The solution also contains amphoteric HCO_3^-:

$$HCO_3^-(aq) + H_2O(l) \rightleftharpoons H_2CO_3(aq) + OH^-(aq)$$

$$\frac{[H_2CO_3][OH^-]}{[HCO_3^-]} = K_b = \frac{K_w}{K_{a_1}} = \frac{1.00 \times 10^{-14}}{4.30 \times 10^{-7}} = 2.33 \times 10^{-8}$$

$$HCO_3^-(aq) \rightleftharpoons H^+(aq) + CO_3^{2-}(aq)$$

$$\frac{[H^+][CO_3^{2-}]}{[HCO_3^-]} = K_{a_2} = 5.61 \times 10^{-11}$$

Since the K_b constant for CO_3^{2-} is considerably greater than the HCO_3^- K_b and HCO_3^- K_{a_2} values, we can confine our attention to the first hydrolysis step of CO_3^{2-}.

Concentration Summary:

Equation:	$CO_3^{2-}(aq)$	$+ H_2O(l) \rightleftharpoons$	$HCO_3^-(aq)$	$+ OH^-(aq)$
Initial concentrations, mol/L	0.050		0.050	0
Concentration changes, mol/L	$-x$		$+x$	$+x$
Equilibrium concentrations, mol/L	$0.050 - x$		$0.050 + x$	x
Approximate concentrations, mol/L	0.050		0.050	x

Substituting the approximate concentrations and $K_b = 1.78 \times 10^{-4}$ into the K_b expression gives

$$1.78 \times 10^{-4} = \frac{(0.050)(x)}{(0.050)}$$

$x = 1.78 \times 10^{-4}$ M $= [OH^-]$

pOH $= -\log[OH^-] = -\log(1.78 \times 10^{-4}) = 3.75$ and pH $= 14.00 - pOH = 14.00 - 3.75 = 10.25$

Comment: This problem can also be considered as a $HCO_3^- - CO_3^{2-}$ buffer, and the pH calculated using Equation 17.4. The pK_a for this buffer system is 10.25 (Table 17.1).

$$pH = pK_a + \log\frac{[CO_3^{2-}]}{[HCO_3^-]} = 10.25 + \log\frac{0.050}{0.050} = 10.25 + \log 1 = 10.25$$

Notice that the result is the same. This shows that buffers are really a special case of the common ion effect.

17.42 (a) The K_a's of ascorbic acid are: $K_{a_1} = 7.9 \times 10^{-5}$, $K_{a_2} = 1.6 \times 10^{-12}$. Since K_{a_1} is considerably greater than K_{a_2}, the concentration of H^+ ion can be calculated from the first ionization step alone.

Concentration Summary:

Equation:	$H_2C_6H_6O_6(aq) \rightleftharpoons$	$H^+(aq)$ +	$HC_6H_6O_6^-(aq)$
Initial concentrations, mol/L	0.10	0	0
Concentration changes, mol/L	$-x$	$+x$	$+x$
Equilibrium concentrations, mol/L	$0.10 - x$	x	x
Approximate concentrations, mol/L	0.10	x	x

Substituting the approximate concentrations and K_{a_1} value in the K_{a_1} expression gives

$$K_{a_1} = [H^+][HC_6H_6O_6^-]/[H_2C_6H_6O_6]$$

$$7.9 \times 10^{-5} = \frac{(x)(x)}{0.10} \text{ and } x = [H^+] = 2.8 \times 10^{-3} \text{ M}$$

Since ascorbic acid is a weak diprotic acid, the concentration of ascorbate ion is equal to K_{a_2}, or $[C_6H_6O_6^{2-}] = K_{a_2} = 1.6 \times 10^{-12}$ M.

(b) Since HCl is a strong acid, virtually all of the H^+ ion in solution comes from the HCl. Therefore, the $[H^+] = 0.010$ M.

The concentration of ascorbate ion can be best or most conveniently calculated using the expression that results when the K_{a_1} expression is multiplied by the K_{a_2} expression, since then all the concentrations except that of the ascorbate ion are known. The calculation proceeds as follows:

The K_a expressions for the two ionization steps are:

$$\frac{[H^+][HC_6H_6O_6^-]}{[H_2C_6H_6O_6]} = K_{a_1} = 7.9 \times 10^{-5}$$

$$\frac{[H^+][C_6H_6O_6^{2-}]}{[HC_6H_6O_6^-]} = K_{a_2} = 1.6 \times 10^{-12}$$

The $[HC_6H_6O_6^-]$ is unknown and not wanted, and can be eliminated by multiplying the two K_a expressions together:

$$\frac{[H^+]^2[C_6H_6O_6^{2-}]}{[H_2C_6H_6O_6]} = K_{a_1} \times K_{a_2} = (7.9 \times 10^{-5})(1.6 \times 10^{-12}) = 1.3 \times 10^{-16}$$

Solving for $[C_6H_6O_6^{2-}]$ and substituting $[H_2C_6H_6O_6] = 0.10$ M and $[H^+] = 0.010$ M into the resulting expression gives

$$[C_6H_6O_6^{2-}] = \frac{(1.3 \times 10^{-16})[H_2C_6H_6O_6]}{[H^+]^2} = \frac{(1.3 \times 10^{-16})(0.10)}{(0.010)^2} = 1.3 \times 10^{-13} \text{ mol/L}$$

Comment: Notice that $[C_6H_6O_6^{2-}]$ is not equal to K_{a_2} in this case. That result applies only when the weak diprotic acid is the only acid in solution. Here, the solution also contains the strong acid HCl.

17.43   (a) Added hydrogen ions will be consumed by benzoate ions

$H^+(aq) + C_6H_5COO^-(aq) \longrightarrow C_6H_5COOH(aq)$

Added hydroxide ions will be consumed by molecular benzoic acid

$C_6H_5COOH(aq) + OH^-(aq) \longrightarrow C_6H_5COO^-(aq) + H_2O(l)$

(b) Added hydrogen ions will be consumed by CH_3NH_2

$H^+(aq) + CH_3NH_2(aq) \longrightarrow CH_3NH_3^+(aq)$

Added hydroxide ions will be consumed by $CH_3NH_3^+$

$CH_3NH_3^+(aq) + OH^-(aq) \longrightarrow CH_3NH_2(aq) + H_2O(l)$

(c) Added hydrogen ions will be consumed by CO_3^{2-}

$CO_3^{2-}(aq) + H^+(aq) \longrightarrow HCO_3^-(aq)$

Added hydroxide ions will be consumed by HCO_3^-

$HCO_3^-(aq) + OH^-(aq) \longrightarrow CO_3^{2-}(aq) + H_2O(l)$

17.45 $NH_3(aq) + H_2O(l) \rightleftharpoons NH_4^+(aq) + OH^-(aq)$

$K_b = [NH_4^+][OH^-]/[NH_3]$

$$[OH^-] = K_b \; x \; \frac{[NH_3]}{[NH_4^+]}$$

Dividing both sides into K_w gives

$$\frac{K_w}{[OH^-]} = \frac{K_w}{K_b} \; x \; \frac{[NH_4^+]}{[NH_3]}$$

Since $[H^+] = K_w/[OH^-]$ and $K_a = K_w/K_b$, the last equation can be rewritten as

$$[H^+] = K_a \; x \; \frac{[NH_4^+]}{[NH_3]}$$

Taking the negative logarithm of both sides gives

$$-\log[H^+] = -\log K_a - \log \frac{[NH_4^+]}{[NH_3]} \quad \text{and} \quad pH = pK_a + \log \frac{[NH_3]}{[NH_4^+]}$$

17.47   (a) No change occurs.   (b) No change occurs.
Dilution changes the concentrations of the acid and its conjugate base by the same factor; therefore, there is no change in the buffer ratio or pH of the solution.

17.48   (a) $[H^+]$ should be equal to K_a.   (d) The pOH should be equal to pK_b.
(b) The pH should be equal to pK_a.   (e) The concentrations of conjugate acid and
(c) $[OH^-]$ should be equal to K_b.   conjugate base should be equal.

17.52   (a) Since the buffer ratio is unity, the pH equals the pK_a of barbituric acid; $pH = pK_a = 4.01$ (Table 17.1).
(b) The buffer ratio is 1/2. Substituting 1/2 for the buffer ratio and $pK_a = 4.01$ into Equation 17.4 gives

$$pH = pK_a + \log \frac{[C_4H_3N_2O_3^-]}{[HC_4H_3N_2O_3]} = 4.01 + \log \frac{1}{2} = 3.71$$

17.54   The pK_a for this ammonia-ammonium chloride buffer is 9.248 (Example 17.14).

$$pH = pK_a + \log \frac{[NH_3]}{[NH_4^+]}; \quad 8.50 = 9.248 + \log \frac{[NH_3]}{[NH_4^+]}$$

$$\log \frac{[NH_3]}{[NH_4^+]} = 8.50 - 9.248 = -0.75$$

and $\dfrac{[NH_3]}{[NH_4^+]} = antilog(-0.75) = 10^{-0.75} = 0.18$

The concentration of NH_3 is 0.200 M. Hence, the concentration of NH_4^+ must be

$$[NH_4^+] = \frac{[NH_3]}{0.18} = \frac{0.200 \text{ M}}{0.18} = 1.1 \text{ M}$$

The number of grams of NH_4Cl that must be added to 1.00 L of the solution is

$$1.00 \text{ L} \times \frac{1.1 \text{ mol}}{1 \text{ L}} \times \frac{53.49 \text{ g } NH_4Cl}{1 \text{ mol}} = 58.8 \text{ g } NH_4Cl$$

17.56   The number of moles of HCl added to each solution is

$$1.00 \text{ mL} \times \frac{1 \text{ L}}{1000 \text{ mL}} \times \frac{10.0 \text{ mol HCl}}{1 \text{ L}} = 0.0100 \text{ mol HCl}$$

(a) The pH of the original HCl solution is

$pH = -\log[H^+] = -\log(1.76 \times 10^{-5}) = 4.754$

The HCl ionizes completely. The new H^+ concentration is

$(0.0100 \text{ mol} + 0.100 \text{ L} \times 1.76 \times 10^{-5} \text{ mol/L})/0.101 \text{ L} = 0.0990 \text{ M}$

The new pH is $pH = -\log[H^+] = -\log 0.0990 = 1.004$

The change in pH is from 4.754 to 1.004, a decrease of 3.750 units.

(b) Since the buffer ratio is initially unity, the pH of the original acetic acid–sodium acetate buffer is equal to pK_a, of $pH = pK_a = 4.754$ (Table 17.1). The added HCl reacts completely with the basic component of the buffer; 0.0100 mol HCl will convert 0.0100 mol CH_3COO^- to 0.0100 mol CH_3COOH.

$CH_3COO^-(aq) + H^+(aq) \longrightarrow CH_3COOH(aq)$

The new mole quantities are:

CH_3COO^-: 0.100 mol – 0.0100 mol = 0.090 mol
CH_3COOH: 0.100 mol + 0.0100 mol = 0.110 mol

The new pH calculated from Equation 17.4 is

$$pH = pK_a + \log \frac{[CH_3COO^-]}{[CH_3COOH]} = 4.754 + \log \frac{0.090}{0.110} = 4.67$$

The change in pH is from 4.754 to 4.67, a decrease of 0.08 units.

17.58 (a) Since the buffer ratio is initially unity, the pH of the original acetic acid–sodium acetate buffer is equal to pK_a, or $pH = pK_a = 4.754$ (Table 17.1). The added NaOH reacts completely with the acid component of the buffer; x mol NaOH will convert x mol CH_3COOH to x mol CH_3COO^-

$$CH_3COOH(aq) + OH^-(aq) \longrightarrow CH_3COO^-(aq)$$

The pH of the new solution must satisfy the Henderson–Hasselbalch equation; that is

$$pH = pK_a + \log \frac{[CH_3COO^-]}{[CH_3COOH]}$$

$$5.754 = 4.754 + \log \frac{0.100 + x}{0.100 - x}$$

$$\log \frac{0.100 + x}{0.100 - x} = 5.754 - 4.754 = 1.000$$

$$\frac{0.100 + x}{0.100 - x} = antilog\ 1.000 = 10^{+1.000} = 10.0$$

$0.100 + x = 1.00 - 10.0x$ and $x = 0.90/11.0 = 0.082$ mol = mol NaOH added

The number of milliliters of NaOH that must be added to 1.00 L of the solution is

$$0.082\ mol\ \times \frac{1000\ mL}{10.0\ mol} = 8.2\ mL$$

(b) The added NaOH reacts completely with the HCl, x mol NaOH will convert x mol HCl to x mol H_2O

$$H^+(aq) + OH^-(aq) \longrightarrow H_2O(l)$$

The $[H^+]$ in the new solution is

$[H^+] = antilog(-5.754) = 10^{-5.754} = 1.76 \times 10^{-6}$ M

The change in mol H^+ is 1.76×10^{-5} mol $- 1.76 \times 10^{-6}$ mol $= 1.58 \times 10^{-5}$ mol

Therefore, 1.58×10^{-5} mol NaOH was added to the solution. The number of milliliters of NaOH added is

$$1.58 \times 10^{-5}\ mol\ \times \frac{1000\ mL}{10.0\ mol} = 1.58 \times 10^{-3}\ mL$$

17.60 The added HCl reacts completely with the sodium acetate; x mol HCl will convert x mol CH_3COO^- to x mol CH_3COOH

$$CH_3COO^-(aq) + H^+(aq) \longrightarrow CH_3COOH(aq)$$

The pK_a for this acetic acid–sodium acetate buffer is 4.75. Since the pH of the desired buffer is equal to the pK_a, the buffer ratio must be unity, which means that the moles of CH_3COO^- must be equal to the moles of CH_3COOH. Therefore, half of the original number of moles of sodium acetate have to be converted to acetic acid. The number of milliliters of HCl required to convert half the sodium acetate over to acetic acid is

$$0.500\ L\ \times \frac{0.50\ mol\ CH_3COONa}{1\ L} \times \frac{1}{2} \times \frac{1\ mol\ HCl}{1\ mol\ CH_3COONa} \times \frac{1\ L\ HCL}{12.0\ mol\ HCl}$$

$$= 0.010\ L\ or\ 10\ mL\ HCl$$

17.63   The pH of this solution at equivalence will be greater than 7, because CN^- is a weak base:

$$CN^-(aq) + H_2O(l) \rightleftharpoons HCN(aq) + OH^-(aq)$$

The number of moles of HCN at the beginning of the titration is

$$0.0250 \text{ L} \times \frac{0.15 \text{ mol}}{1 \text{ L}} = 3.75 \times 10^{-3} \text{ mol (carry an extra significant figure)}$$

From the neutralization equation

$$HCN(aq) + NaOH(aq) \longrightarrow NaCN(aq) + H_2O(l)$$

we see that 3.75×10^{-3} mol of HCN will react with 3.75×10^{-3} mol of NaOH to form 3.75×10^{-3} mol of CN^-. The volume of 0.10 M NaOH required to reach equivalence is

$$3.75 \times 10^{-3} \text{ mol NaOH} \times \frac{1 \text{ L}}{0.10 \text{ mol NaOH}} = 0.0375 \text{ L} = 37.5 \text{ mL}$$

The total volume of the solution at the equivalence point is

25.0 mL + 37.5 mL = 62.5 mL = 0.0625 L

The molarity of CN^- at equivalence is initially

$$\frac{3.75 \times 10^{-3} \text{ mol}}{0.0625 \text{ L}} = 0.060 \text{ M}$$

but some of this reacts with water to form hydroxide ions. Using a concentration summary similar to the one in Exercise 17.33 and substituting the approximate concentrations and $K_b = 2.03 \times 10^{-5}$ (Exercise 17.33) into the K_b expression gives

$$K_b = [HCN][OH^-]/[CN^-]$$

$$2.03 \times 10^{-5} = \frac{x^2}{0.060}$$

$x = [OH^-] = 1.1 \times 10^{-3} \text{ M}$

$pOH = -\log[OH^-] = -\log(1.1 \times 10^{-3}) = 2.96$ and $pH = 14.00 - pOH = 14.00 - 2.96 = 11.04$

17.65   The pH's at the various points are:
(a) Before acid is added:

$pOH = -\log[OH^-] = -\log 0.200 = 0.699$ and $pH = 14.00 - pOH = 14.00 - 0.699 = 13.30$

(b) At the equivalence point: All of the NaOH is neutralized. The solution contains NaCl, a neutral salt, so its pH is 7.
(c) At the half-neutralization point: The pH depends on the concentration of unreacted NaOH remaining in the solution.

initial moles of NaOH = 0.0500 L × 0.200 mol/L = 0.0100 mol

moles of NaOH neutralized = moles of HCl added = 0.0100 mol/2 = 0.0050 mol

$$\text{volume of HCl added} = 0.0050 \text{ mol} \times \frac{1 \text{ L}}{0.100 \text{ mol}} = 0.050 \text{ L}$$

concentration of NaOH = moles of NaOH remaining/final solution volume

     = 0.0050 mol/(0.0500 L + 0.050 L) = 0.050 M

$pOH = -\log[OH^-] = -\log 0.050 = 1.30$ and $pH = 14.00 - pOH = 14.00 - 1.30 = 12.70$

(d) At some point before equivalence: The volume of HCl needed for complete neutralization is

$$0.0100 \text{ mol } \times \frac{1 \text{ L}}{0.100 \text{ mol}} = 0.100 \text{ L} = 100 \text{ mL}$$

Therefore, we have to calculate the concentration of unreacted NaOH remaining in the solution after 99 mL of HCl has been added.

moles of NaOH neutralized = moles of HCl added = 0.099 L x 0.100 mol/L = 0.0099 mol

moles of NaOH remaining = initial moles – moles neutralized = 0.0100 – 0.0099 = 0.0001 mol

concentration of NaOH = moles of NaOH remaining/final solution volume

$$= 0.0001 \text{ mol}/(0.0500 \text{ L} + 0.099 \text{ L}) = 7 \times 10^{-4} \text{ M}$$

pOH = –log[OH⁻] = –log (7 x 10⁻⁴) = 3.2 and pH = 14.00 – pOH = 14.00 – 3.2 = 10.8

(e) After the equivalence point: The NaOH is gone and only the excess HCl determines the pH. 101 mL of HCl is added, the pH is calculated as follows:

moles of excess HCl = volume of excess HCl x molarity = 0.001 L x 0.100 mol/L = 1 x 10⁻⁴ mol

concentration of excess HCl = moles of excess HCl/final solution volume

$$= 1 \times 10^{-4} \text{ mol}/(0.0500 \text{ L} + 0.101 \text{ L}) = 7 \times 10^{-4} \text{ M and pH} = -\log[H^+] = -\log(7 \times 10^{-4}) = 3.2$$

Make a pH versus milliliters added HCl sketch using these pH values.

17.68   To solve this problem, we first calculate the pH of the solution at the equivalence point. An indicator whose transition interval contains this calculated pH value is then selected. At the equivalence point we have a 0.050 M $C_{15}H_{15}N_2COONa$ solution. The pH of the weak base $C_{15}H_{15}N_2COO^-$ is calculated in the usual manner. Using the usual weak base concentration summary and substituting the approximate concentrations and $K_b = K_w/K_a$ = 1.00 x 10⁻¹⁴/6.3 x 10⁻⁴ = 1.6 x 10⁻¹¹ into the K_b expression gives

$$K_b = [C_{15}H_{15}N_2COOH][OH^-]/[C_{15}H_{15}N_2COO^-]$$

$$1.6 \times 10^{-11} = \frac{(x)(x)}{0.050}$$

$$x = [OH^-] = 8.9 \times 10^{-7} \text{ M}$$

pOH = –log[OH⁻] = –log(8.9 x 10⁻⁷) = 6.05 and pH = 14.00 – pOH = 14.00 – 6.05 = 7.95

The indicator should change color around pH 7.95. Table 17.3 shows that phenol red (6.8–8.4) can be used.

Comment: In general, the pH's of weak acids and weak bases do not change a great deal with concentration. For instance, if $[C_{15}H_{15}N_2COO^-]$ = 1.00 M, then pH = 8.60; if $[C_{15}H_{15}N_2COO^-]$ = 0.10 M, then pH = 8.10; and if $[C_{15}H_{15}N_2COO^-]$ = 0.010 M, then pH = 7.60. Therefore, for purposes of picking a titration indicator, choosing an approximate value for the concentration is usually sufficient when no specific concentrations are given or known.

17.71   If only the contribution of the HCl to the acidity of the solution were considered, then the concentration of H⁺ ion would be 1.0 x 10⁻⁸ M and the pH would be greater than 7, pH = –log[H⁺] = –log(1.0 x 10⁻⁸) = 8. This cannot be correct, since the solution of an acid cannot have a pH greater than pure water alone. To solve the problem correctly, the H⁺ ion contribution from the self–ionization of water must be included. The concentration summary will be based on this reaction

$$H_2O(l) \rightleftharpoons H^+(aq) + OH^-(aq)$$

Since HCl is a strong acid, the initial concentration of H⁺ ion before self–ionization is 1.0 x 10⁻⁸ M.

Concentration Summary:

Equation:	$H_2O(1)$	$\rightleftharpoons$	$H^+(aq)$	$+$	$OH^-(aq)$
Initial concentrations, mol/L			1.0×10^{-8}		0
Concentration changes, mol/L			$+x$		$+x$
Equilibrium concentrations, mol/L			$1.0 \times 10^{-8} + x$		x

Substituting the equilibrium concentrations and $K_w = 1.00 \times 10^{-14}$ into the K_w expression gives

$K_w = [H^+][OH^-]$

$1.00 \times 10^{-14} = (1.0 \times 10^{-8} + x)(x)$

$x^2 + 1.0 \times 10^{-8}x - 1.00 \times 10^{-14} = 0$ and $x = 9.5 \times 10^{-8}$ M

The $[H^+]$ is therefore $[H^+] = (1.0 \times 10^{-8} \text{ M} + x) = (1.0 \times 10^{-8} \text{ M} + 9.5 \times 10^{-8} \text{ M}) = 1.05 \times 10^{-7}$ M and pH $= -\log[H^+] = -\log(1.05 \times 10^{-7}) = 6.98$.

17.73   The molar mass of aspirin is 180.2 g. The initial concentration of aspirin is

$$\frac{0.325 \text{ g}}{0.100 \text{ L}} \times \frac{1 \text{ mol}}{180.2 \text{ g}} = 1.80 \times 10^{-2} \text{ mol/L}$$

The initial $[H^+]$ of the 100 mL sample of gastric juice is

$[H^+] = \text{antilog}(-1.20) = 10^{-1.20} = 6.3 \times 10^{-2}$ M

Concentration Summary:

Equation:	$C_8H_7O_2COOH(aq)$	$\rightleftharpoons$	$H^+(aq)$	$+$	$C_8H_7O_2COO^-(aq)$
Initial concentrations, mol/L	0.0180		0.063		0
Concentration changes, mol/L	$-x$		$+x$		$+x$
Equilibrium concentrations, mol/L	$0.0180 - x$		$0.063 + x$		x
Approximate concentrations, mol/L	0.0180		0.063		x

Substituting the approximate concentrations and $K_a = 3.3 \times 10^{-4}$ into the K_a expression gives

$K_a = [H^+][C_8H_7O_2COO^-]/[C_8H_7O_2COOH]$

$3.3 \times 10^{-4} = \dfrac{(0.063)(x)}{0.0180}$ and $x = 9.4 \times 10^{-5}$ M $= [C_8H_7O_2COO^-]$

The number of moles of aspirin ionized per liter is equal to x, so the percent ionization is

$$\% \text{ ionization} = 100\% \times \frac{\text{moles of aspirin ionized per liter}}{\text{initial moles of aspirin per liter}}$$

$$= 100\% \times \frac{9.4 \times 10^{-5} \text{ M}}{0.0180 \text{ M}} = 0.52\%$$

17.75   (a) CO_3^{2-}. CO_3^{2-} with its double negative charge is better able to attract and hold onto protons than HCO_3^- with its single negative charge.
   (b) Since CO_3^{2-} is a much stronger base than HCO_3^-; only the first hydrolysis step of CO_3^{2-} need be considered.

Concentration Summary:

Equation:	$CO_3^{2-}(aq)$	$+$	$H_2O(1)$	$\rightleftharpoons$	$HCO_3^-(aq)$	$+$	$OH^-(aq)$
Initial concentrations, mol/L	0.050				0		0
Concentration changes, mol/L	$-x$				$+x$		$+x$
Equilibrium concentrations, mol/L	$0.050 - x$				x		x
Approximate concentrations, mol/L	0.050				x		x

Substituting the approximate concentrations and $K_b = K_w/K_{a_2} = 1.00 \times 10^{-14}/5.61 \times 10^{-11} = 1.78 \times 10^{-4}$ into the K_b expression gives

$$K_b = [HCO_3^-][OH^-]/[CO_3^{2-}]$$

$$1.78 \times 10^{-4} = \frac{(x)(x)}{0.050}$$

$x = 3.0 \times 10^{-3} \text{ M} = [OH^-]$

$pOH = -\log[OH^-] = -\log(3.0 \times 10^{-3}) = 2.52$ and $pH = 14.00 - pOH = 14.00 - 2.52 = 11.48$

17.77 (a)

$$pH = pK_a + \log \frac{[HCO_3^-]}{[CO_2]}$$

$$\log \frac{[HCO_3^-]}{[CO_2]} = pH - pK_a = 7.4 - 6.10 = 1.3$$

$$\frac{[HCO_3^-]}{[CO_2]} = \text{antilog } 1.3 = 10^{+1.3} = 20$$

(b) HCO_3^-. The bicarbonate concentration is approximately 20 times greater than that of dissolved CO_2.

(c) $[HCO_3^-] = 20 \times [CO_2]$

$[HCO_3^-] + [CO_2] = 1.2 \times 10^{-3} \text{ M}$

$20[CO_2] + [CO_2] = 1.2 \times 10^{-3} \text{ M}$ and $[CO_2] = 1.2 \times 10^{-3} \text{ M}/21 = 5.7 \times 10^{-5} \text{ M}$

$[HCO_3^-] = 1.2 \times 10^{-3} \text{ M} - 5.7 \times 10^{-5} \text{ M} = 1.1 \times 10^{-3} \text{ M}$

17.79 (a) Falls. The pK_a of $HHbO_2$ is somewhat smaller than that of HHb. Therefore, $HHbO_2$ is a stronger acid than HHb and the $[H^+]$ should increase somewhat.

(b) Let x equal the equilibrium concentration of HbO_2^-. First find the buffer ratio.

$$pH = pK_a + \log \frac{[HbO_2^-]}{[HHbO_2]}$$

$$\log \frac{[HbO_2^-]}{[HHbO_2]} = pH - pK_a = 7.40 - 6.68 = 0.72$$

$$\frac{[HbO_2^-]}{[HHbO_2]} = \text{antilog } 0.72 = 10^{+0.72} = 5.2$$

Substituting $[HbO_2^-] = x$ and $[HHbO_2] = 2.50 \times 10^{-3} - x$ into the buffer ratio gives

$$\frac{x}{0.00250 - x} = 5.2 \text{ and } x = 0.013/6.2 = 2.1 \times 10^{-3} \text{ M} = [HbO_2^-]$$

$[HHbO_2] = 2.50 \times 10^{-3} \text{ M} - 2.1 \times 10^{-3} \text{ M} = 4 \times 10^{-4} \text{ M}$

17.81   The $C_6H_4NO_2^-$ is produced by adding NaOH to the $HC_6H_4NO_2$.

$$HC_6H_4NO_2(aq) + NaOH(aq) \longrightarrow NaC_6H_4NO_2(aq) + H_2O(l)$$

Let x equal the moles of NaOH added. Then x also equals the moles of $C_6H_4NO_2^-$ produced, and $0.0100 - x =$ moles of $HC_6H_4NO_2$ remaining. The pK_a of this buffer system is 4.85 (Table 17.1). Then

$$pH = pK_a + \log \frac{[C_6H_4NO_2^-]}{[HC_6H_4NO_2]} = pK_a + \log \frac{mol\ C_6H_4NO_2^-}{mol\ HC_6H_4NO_2}$$

$$5.00 = 4.85 + \log \frac{x}{0.0100 - x}$$

$$\log \frac{x}{0.0100 - x} = 5.00 - 4.85 = 0.15$$

$$\frac{x}{0.0100 - x} = antilog(0.15) = 10^{+0.15} = 1.4$$

and $x = 0.014/2.4 = 5.8 \times 10^{-3}$ mol $C_6H_4NO_2^- = 5.8 \times 10^{-3}$ mol NaOH

The volume of NaOH required is

$$5.8 \times 10^{-3}\ mol\ NaOH \times \frac{1000\ mL}{1.00\ mol\ NaOH} = 5.8\ mL$$

17.83 $HCl(aq) + NaOH(aq) \longrightarrow NaCl(aq) + H_2O(l)$

The initial pH is $pH = -\log[H^+] = -\log(1.000) = 0.0000$. The initial number of moles of HCl is 1 L $\times$ 1.000 mol/L = 1.000 mol. The molar mass of NaOH is 40.0 g.

(1) 0.0 g or 0.0 mol NaOH added: pH = 0.0000.

(2) 4.0 g or 0.10 mol NaOH added: The moles of HCl remaining are 1.000 – 0.10 = 0.90 mol. Hence, $[H^+] = 0.90$ mol/L and pH = $-\log 0.90 = 0.046$.

(3) 20.0 g or 0.500 mol NaOH added: The moles of HCl remaining are 1.000 – 0.500 = 0.500 mol. Hence, $[H^+] = 0.500$ mol/L and pH = $-\log 0.500 = 0.30$.

(4) 36.0 g or 0.900 mol NaOH added: The moles of HCl remaining are 1.000 – 0.900 = 0.100 mol. Hence, $[H^+] = 0.100$ mol/L and pH = $-\log 0.100 = 1.00$.

(5) 39.0 g or 0.975 mol NaOH added: The moles of HCl remaining are 1.000 - 0.975 = 0.025 mol. Hence, $[H^+] = 0.025$ mol/L and pH = $-\log 0.025 = 1.60$.

(6) 39.9 g or 0.998 mol NaOH added: The moles of HCl remaining are 1.000 – 0.998 = 0.002 mol. Hence, $[H^+] = 0.002$ mol/L and pH = $-\log 0.002 = 2.7$.

(7) 40.0 g or 1.00 mol NaOH added: The HCl is completely neutralized and only a NaCl solution remains; the pH is 7.00.

(a) Total pH changes = final pH – initial pH = 7.00 – 0.00 = 7.00.

(b) The addition of 0.500 mol of NaOH brought the pH up to 0.30 from 0.00. Hence,

$$fraction\ of\ total\ pH\ change = \frac{0.30}{7.00} = 0.043$$

(c) From the pH versus mole NaOH graph we see that approximately 0.999 mol of NaOH is needed.

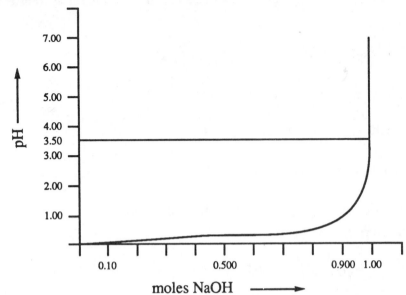

17.84 (a) The endpoint and the equivalence point for the strong acid–strong base titration described in Fig. 17.3 will not be appreciably different, since the transition interval of methyl orange (3.1 – 4.4) falls within the pH range of the steep rise in the titration curve.

(b) The endpoint and the equivalence point for the weak acid–strong base titration described in Fig. 17.4 will be appreciably different, since the transition interval of methyl orange (3.1 – 4.4) does not fall within the pH range of the steep pH rise in the titration curve. If the endpoint is signaled at pH 3.75, the midpoint of the methyl orange transition interval, then from Fig. 17.4 we see that approximately 3 mL of NaOH was added before the endpoint was reached. From the figure we see that 25 mL of NaOH has to be added in order to reach the equivalence point. Therefore, the titration will be in error by approximately 25 – 3 = 22 mL.

CHAPTER 18
SOLUBILITY AND
COMPLEX ION EQUILIBRIA

Solutions To Practice Exercises

PE 18.3   The K_{sp} for AgCl is $K_{sp} = [Ag^+][Cl^-]$.

The molar mass of AgCl is 143.3 g, therefore 8.9×10^{-4} g/L is

$$\frac{8.9 \times 10^{-4} \text{ g}}{1 \text{ L}} \times \frac{1 \text{ mol}}{143.3 \text{ g}} = 6.2 \times 10^{-6} \text{ mol/L}$$

One mole of AgCl provides 1 mol of Ag^+ ions and 1 mol of Cl^- ions. The ionic concentrations in 6.2×10^{-6} M AgCl are therefore

$[Ag^+] = 6.2 \times 10^{-6}$ mol/L and $[Cl^-] = 6.2 \times 10^{-6}$ mol/L

Substituting the concentrations into the K_{sp} expression gives

$K_{sp} = [Ag^+][Cl^-] = (6.2 \times 10^{-6})(6.2 \times 10^{-6}) = 3.8 \times 10^{-11}$

PE 18.4 $K_{sp} = [Ag^+]^2 [SO_4^{2-}]$

$1.4 \times 10^{-5} = (2x)^2 (x) = 4x^3$ and $x = 1.5 \times 10^{-2}$ mol/L $= [SO_4^{2-}]$

The equilibrium concentration of SO_4^{2-}, 1.5×10^{-2} mol/L, is also the molar solubility of Ag_2SO_4. The molar mass of Ag_2SO_4 is 311.8 g; hence, its solubility in grams per liter is

$$\frac{1.5 \times 10^{-2} \text{ mol}}{1 \text{ L}} \times \frac{311.8 \text{ g}}{1 \text{ mol}} = 4.7 \text{ g/L}$$

The amount of Ag_2SO_4 dissolved in 500 mL = 0.500 L of water is 0.500 L x 4.7 g/L = 2.3 g. The grams of Ag_2SO_4 that remain undissolved: $3.0 - 2.3 = 0.7$ g.

PE 18.5 (a) Less soluble. The OH^- ions present will repress the solubility of $Ba(OH)_2$.
(b) Let x stand for the molarity of the sodium hydroxide solution.

Concentration Summary:

Equation: $\qquad\qquad\qquad$ $Ba(OH)_2(s) \rightleftharpoons Ba^{2+}(aq) + 2OH^-(aq)$

Initial concentrations, mol/L $\qquad\qquad\qquad$ 0 $\qquad\qquad$ x

Concentration changes, mol/L $\qquad\qquad\qquad$ +0.010 $\qquad$ +0.020

Equilibrium concentrations, mol/L $\qquad\qquad\qquad$ 0.010 $\qquad$ 0.020 + x

Substituting the equilibrium concentrations into the K_{sp} expression and assuming that 0.020 + x is approximately equal to x gives

$K_{sp} = [Ba^{2+}][OH^-]^2$

$5 \times 10^{-3} = (0.010)(x)^2$ and $x = 0.7$ M = $[OH^-]$

Answer: A 0.7 M NaOH solution will dissolve 0.010 mol of $Ba(OH)_2$ per liter.

PE 18.6 $\qquad$ The quantities of each ion are:

Ca^{2+}: 0.050 L x 0.050 mol/L= 0.0025 mol

$CrO_4{}^{2-}$: 0.050 L x 0.050 mol/L = 0.0025 mol

The final volume is 50 mL + 50 mL = 100 mL = 0.100 L. The concentrations after mixing are:

Ca^{2+}: 0.0025 mol/0.100 L = 0.025 mol/L

$CrO_4{}^{2-}$: 0.0025 mol/0.100L = 0.025 mol/L

Substituting the concentrations into the ion product expression gives

$Q = [Ca^{2+}][CrO_4{}^{2-}] = (0.025)(0.025) = 6.2 \times 10^{-4}$

The ion product Q is less than the K_{sp} value of 7.1×10^{-4}, so $CaCrO_4$ will not precipitate.

PE 18.7 $\qquad$ $K_{sp} = [Pb^{2+}][Cl^-]^2 = 1.7 \times 10^{-5}$

$(1.0 \times 10^{-3})[Cl^-]^2 = 1.7 \times 10^{-5}$ and $[Cl^-] = 0.13$ M

If the HCl, which is completely ionized, is maintained at 0.13 M or greater, the concentration of lead ion will not exceed 1.0×10^{-3} M. However, a high $[Cl^-]$ must be avoided, since the soluble complex ion $PbCl_4{}^{2-}$ forms in the presence of a large excess of chloride ions.

PE 18.8 $\qquad$ The K_{sp}'s are: $Mg(OH)_2$, 7.1×10^{-12}; $Ca(OH)_2$, 6.5×10^{-6}. The optimum hydroxide concentration occurs when the solution is just barely saturated with respect to $Ca(OH)_2$. This concentration is obtained by substituting $[Ca^{2+}] = 0.10$ M into the K_{sp} expression for $Ca(OH)_2$:

$K_{sp} = [Ca^{2+}][OH^-]^2$

$6.5 \times 10^{-6} = (0.10)[OH^-]^2$ and $[OH^-] = 8.1 \times 10^{-3}$ M

The maximum separation occurs when the NaOH concentration is 8.1×10^{-3} M.

PE 18.9 (a) $\quad K_{sp} = [Mg^{2+}][OH^-]^2$

$7.1 \times 10^{-12} = [Mg^{2+}](8.1 \times 10^{-3})^2$ and $[Mg^{2+}] = 1.1 \times 10^{-7}$ M

(b) Yes. Most of the magnesium ions are in the precipitate; all of the calcium ions are in the solution.

PE 18.10 $\qquad$ $K_{sp} = [Al^{3+}][OH^-]^3$

$3 \times 10^{-34} = (0.10)[OH^-]^3$ and $[OH^-] = 1 \times 10^{-11}$ M

$pOH = -\log[OH^-] = -\log(1 \times 10^{-11}) = 11.0$ and $pH = 14.00 - 11.0 = 3.0$

Answer: The pH would have to be lowered to 3.0.

PE 18.11 The concentration of hydroxide ions in a saturated solution of $Mg(OH)_2$ containing 0.20 M Mg^{2+} is

$K_{sp} = [Mg^{2+}][OH^-]^2 = 7.1 \times 10^{-12}$

$(0.20)\,[OH^-]^2 = 7.1 \times 10^{-12}$ and $[OH^-] = 6.0 \times 10^{-6}$ M

Substituting $[OH^-] = 6.0 \times 10^{-6}$ M and $[NH_3] = 0.050$ M into the K_b expression for ammonia gives

$K_b = [NH_4^+][OH^-]/[NH_3]$

$1.8 \times 10^{-5} = \dfrac{[NH_4^+](6.0 \times 10^{-6})}{(0.050)}$ and $[NH_4^+] = 0.15$ M

Magnesium hydroxide will not precipitate if the concentration of ammonium ions is greater than or equal to 0.15 M .

PE 18.12 Only mixture (b). Mixture (a) cannot be separated, since neither $Cu(OH)_2$ nor $Fe(OH)_2$ is amphoteric. Mixture (c) cannot be separated, since both $Pb(OH)_2$ and $Zn(OH)_2$ are amphoteric.

PE 18.15 Substituting $K_{a1} \times K_{a2} = 1 \times 10^{-20}$, $[H_2S] = 0.10$ M, and $[S^{2-}] = 1.0 \times 10^{-15}$ M into the combined equilibrium constant expression for H_2S gives

$1 \times 10^{-20} = \dfrac{[H^+]^2(1.0 \times 10^{-15})}{0.10}$ and $[H^+] = 1 \times 10^{-3}$ M

The pH must therefore be maintained at pH $= -\log[H^+] = -\log(1 \times 10^{-3}) = 3.0$.

PE 18.16 First calculate the concentration of oxalate ions present in the solution.

$K_{a1} \times K_{a2} = \dfrac{[H^+]^2[C_2O_4^{2-}]}{[H_2C_2O_4]}$

Substituting $K_{a1} = 5.9 \times 10^{-2}$, $K_{a2} = 6.4 \times 10^{-5}$, $[H^+] = 0.50$ M, and $[H_2C_2O_4] = 0.20$ M gives

$(5.9 \times 10^{-2})(6.4 \times 10^{-5}) = \dfrac{(0.50)^2[C_2O_4^{2-}]}{0.20}$ and $[C_2O_4^{2-}] = 3.0 \times 10^{-6}$ M.

Substituting $[C_2O_4^{2-}] = 3.0 \times 10^{-6}$ M and $[Ba^{2+}] = 0.050$ M into the ion product expression gives

$Q = [Ba^{2+}][C_2O_4^{2-}] = (3.0 \times 10^{-6})(0.050) = 1.5 \times 10^{-7}$

The ion product Q is smaller than the K_{sp} value of 1.6×10^{-7}, so BaC_2O_4 will not precipitate.

PE 18.17 No. The K_{sp}'s are: CuS, 8×10^{-37}; HgS, 5×10^{-54}. HgS has a smaller K_{sp} and will precipitate at a lower sulfide ion concentration than CuS. We will therefore first calculate the highest sulfide ion concentration that will leave the copper ion in solution. Substituting $[Cu^{2+}] = 0.10$ M into the K_{sp} expression for CuS gives

$[Cu^{2+}][S^{2-}] = K_{sp}$

$(0.10)[S^{2-}] = 8 \times 10^{-37}$ and $[S^{2-}] = 8 \times 10^{-36}$ M

CuS will not precipitate if the $[S^{2-}]$ is kept at 1×10^{-36} M or less. The pH that provides this sulfide concentration is found by substituting $K_{a1} \times K_{a2} = 1 \times 10^{-20}$, $[S^{2-}] = 8 \times 10^{-36}$ M, and $[H_2S] = 0.10$ M into the combined equilibrium constant expression for H_2S :

$1 \times 10^{-20} = \dfrac{[H^+]^2(8 \times 10^{-36})}{(0.10)}$ and $[H^+] = 1 \times 10^7$ M

Such a high concentration of HCl cannot be realistically obtained, and, therefore, it is not possible to precipitate the HgS by itself. Therefore, the answer is no.

PE 18.18   The K_f's are: $Cd(NH_3)_4^{2+}$, 1×10^7; $Fe(SCN)^{2+}$, 1.2×10^2; HgI_4^{2-}, 1.9×10^{30}. The larger the formation constant, the more stable the ion; therefore, HgI_4^{2-} with $K_f = 1.9 \times 10^{30}$ is the most stable and $Fe(SCN)^{2+}$ with $K_f = 1.2 \times 10^2$ is the least stable.

PE 18.19   Because the K_f of $Zn(OH)_4^{2-}$ is large, 2.2×10^{16}, and because hydroxide ion is present in excess, most of the zinc will be in the form of $Zn(OH)_4^{2-}$. We will therefore assume that all of the zinc is initially in the form of the complex, which then breaks down to form x moles of zinc ion at equilibrium. So, initially $[Zn(OH)_4^{2-}] = 0.10$ M. The formation of this complex reduces the concentration of OH^- by 0.4 M, since each $Zn(OH)_4^{2-}$ ion contains four OH^- ions. Therefore, the initial $[OH^-]$ is

$$[OH^-] = 2.0 \text{ M} - 0.40 \text{ M} = 1.6 \text{ M}$$

Concentration Summary:

Equation:	$Zn(OH)_4^{2-}(aq)$	$\rightleftharpoons$	$Zn^{2+}(aq)$	$+$	$4OH^-(aq)$
Initial concentrations, mol/L	0.10		0		1.6
Concentration changes, mol/L	$-x$		$+x$		$+4x$
Equilibrium concentrations, mol/L	$0.10 - x$		x		$1.6 + 4x$
Approximate concentrations, mol/L	0.10		x		1.6

Substituting the approximate concentrations and $K_d = 4.5 \times 10^{-17}$ into the K_d expression gives

$$\frac{[Zn^{2+}][OH^-]^4}{[Zn(OH)_4^{2-}]} = K_d$$

$$\frac{(x)(1.6)^4}{(0.10)} = 4.5 \times 10^{-17} \text{ and } x = 6.9 \times 10^{-19} \text{ M} = [Zn^{2+}]$$

PE 18.21   Let x be the molar solubility of AgCl.

Concentration Summary:

Equation:	$AgCl(s)$	$+$	$2NH_3(aq)$	$\rightleftharpoons$	$Ag(NH_3)_2^+(aq)$	$+$	$Cl^-(aq)$
Initial concentrations, mol/L			2.0		0		0
Concentration changes, mol/L			$-2x$		$+x$		$+x$
Equilibrium concentrations, mol/L			$2.0 - 2x$		x		x

Substituting $K_{sp} = 1.8 \times 10^{-10}$, $K_f = 1.6 \times 10^7$, and the equilibrium concentrations into the combined equilibrium constant expression gives

$$\frac{[Ag(NH_3)_2^+][Cl^-]}{[NH_3]^2} = K_{sp} \times K_f$$

$$\frac{(x)(x)}{(2.0 - 2x)^2} = (1.8 \times 10^{-10})(1.6 \times 10^7) = 2.9 \times 10^{-3}$$

The equation is simplified by taking the sqaure root of both sides:

$$\frac{x}{2.0 - 2x} = 5.4 \times 10^{-2} \text{ and } x = 9.7 \times 10^{-2} \text{ M}$$

The solubility of AgCl in 2.0 M NH_3 is 9.7×10^{-2} M.

Solutions To Final Exercises

18.4　(a) The molar mass of Sb_2S_3 is 339.7 g, therefore 0.00175 g/L is

$$\frac{0.00175 \text{ g}}{1 \text{ L}} \times \frac{1 \text{ mol}}{339.7 \text{ g}} = 5.15 \times 10^{-6} \text{ mol/L}$$

$[Sb^{3+}] = 2 \times 5.15 \times 10^{-6} \text{ M} = 10.3 \times 10^{-6} \text{ M}$ and $[S^{2-}] = 3 \times 5.15 \times 10^{-6} \text{ M} = 15.4 \times 10^{-6} \text{ M}$.

$K_{sp} = [Sb^{3+}]^2 [S^{2-}]^3 = (10.3 \times 10^{-6})^2 (15.4 \times 10^{-6})^3 = 3.87 \times 10^{-25}$

(b) The molar mass of $CdWO_4$ is 360.3 g, therefore 0.05 g/100 mL is

$$\frac{0.05 \text{ g}}{100 \text{ mL}} \times \frac{1000 \text{ mL}}{1 \text{ L}} \times \frac{1 \text{ mol}}{360.3 \text{ g}} = 1.4 \times 10^{-3} \text{ mol/L (carry extra significant figure)}$$

$[Cd^{2+}] = 1.4 \times 10^{-3} \text{ M}$ and $[WO_4^{2-}] = 1.4 \times 10^{-3} \text{ M}$.

$K_{sp} = [Cd^{2+}] [WO_4^{2-}] = (1.4 \times 10^{-3}) (1.4 \times 10^{-3}) = 2 \times 10^{-6}$

(c) The molar mass of $Ba_3(AsO_4)_2$ is 689.8 g, therefore 0.055 g/100 mL is

$$\frac{0.055 \text{ g}}{100 \text{ mL}} \times \frac{1000 \text{ mL}}{1 \text{ L}} \times \frac{1 \text{ mol}}{689.8 \text{ g}} = 8.0 \times 10^{-4} \text{ M}$$

$[Ba^{2+}] = 3 \times 8.0 \times 10^{-4} \text{ M} = 2.4 \times 10^{-3} \text{ M}$ and $[AsO_4^{3-}] = 2 \times 8.0 \times 10^{-4} \text{ M} = 1.6 \times 10^{-3} \text{ M}$

$K_{sp} = [Ba^{2+}]^3 [AsO_4^{3-}]^2 = (2.4 \times 10^{-3})^3 (1.6 \times 10^{-3})^2 = 3.5 \times 10^{-14}$

(d) The molar mass of $CuC_2O_4 \cdot 1/2H_2O$ is 160.6 g, therefore 0.00253 g/100 mL is

$$\frac{0.00253 \text{ g}}{100 \text{ mL}} \times \frac{1000 \text{ mL}}{1 \text{ L}} \times \frac{1 \text{ mol}}{160.6 \text{ g}} = 1.58 \times 10^{-4} \text{ M}$$

$[Cu^{2+}] = 1.58 \times 10^{-4} \text{ M}$ and $[C_2O_4^{2-}] = 1.58 \times 10^{-4} \text{ M}$

$K_{sp} = [Cu^{2+}] [C_2O_4^{2-}] = (1.58 \times 10^{-4})(1.58 \times 10^{-4}) = 2.50 \times 10^{-8}$

(e) The molar mass of $Ba(IO_3)_2$ is 487.1 g, therefore 0.35 g/L is

$$\frac{0.35 \text{ g}}{1 \text{ L}} \times \frac{1 \text{ mol}}{487.1 \text{ g}} = 7.2 \times 10^{-4} \text{ M}$$

$[Ba^{2+}] = 7.2 \times 10^{-4} \text{ M}$ and $[IO_3^-] = 2 \times 7.2 \times 10^{-4} \text{ M} = 1.4 \times 10^{-3} \text{ M}$

$K_{sp} = [Ba^{2+}] [IO_3^-]^2 = (7.2 \times 10^{-4})(1.4 \times 10^{-3})^2 = 1.4 \times 10^{-9}$

18.5　$K_{sp} = [Ca^{2+}] [OH^-]^2$

$6.5 \times 10^{-6} = (x)(2x)^2 = 4x^3$ and $x = 1.2 \times 10^{-2} \text{ M} = [Ca^{2+}]$

$[OH^-] = 2x = 2 \times 1.2 \times 10^{-2} \text{ M} = 2.4 \times 10^{-2} \text{ M}$

$pOH = -\log[OH^-] = -\log(2.4 \times 10^{-2}) = 1.62$ and $pH = 14.00 - pOH = 14.00 - 1.62 = 12.38$

18.7　(a) $K_{sp} = [Sr^{2+}] [CO_3^{2-}]$

$9.3 \times 10^{-10} = (x)(x) = x^2$ and $x = 3.0 \times 10^{-5} \text{ M} = [Sr^{2+}] = [CO_3^{2-}]$

The equilibrium concentration of Sr^{2+}, 3.0×10^{-5} mol/L, is also the molar solubility of $SrCO_3$. The molar mass of $SrCO_3$ is 147.6 g; hence, its solubility in grams per 100 mL is

$$\frac{3.0 \times 10^{-5} \text{ mol}}{1 \text{ L}} \times \frac{0.10 \text{ L}}{100 \text{ mL}} \times \frac{147.6 \text{ g}}{1 \text{ mol}} = 4.4 \times 10^{-4} \text{ g/100 mL}$$

(b) $K_{sp} = [Pb^{2+}][I^-]^2$

$7.9 \times 10^{-9} = (x)(2x)^2 = 4x^3$ and $x = 1.3 \times 10^{-3}$ M $= [Pb^{2+}]$

The equilibrium concentration of Pb^{2+}, 1.3×10^{-3} mol/L, is also the molar solubility of PbI_2. The molar mass of PbI_2 is 461.0 g; hence, its solubility in grams per 100 mL is

$$\frac{1.3 \times 10^{-3} \text{ mol}}{1 \text{ L}} \times \frac{0.10 \text{ L}}{100 \text{ mL}} \times \frac{461.0 \text{ g}}{1 \text{ mol}} = 6.0 \times 10^{-2} \text{ g}/100 \text{ mL}$$

(c) $K_{sp} = [Ca^{2+}]^3[PO_4^{3-}]^2$

Let x equal the molar solubility of $Ca_3(PO_4)_2$. Then

$1.3 \times 10^{-32} = (3x)^3(2x)^2 = 108\, x^5$ and $x = 1.6 \times 10^{-7}$ M

The molar solubility of $Ca_3(PO_4)_2$ is 1.6×10^{-7} mol/L. The molar mass of $Ca_3(PO_4)_2$ is 310.2 g; hence, its solubility in grams per 100 mL is

$$\frac{1.6 \times 10^{-7} \text{ mol}}{1 \text{ L}} \times \frac{0.10 \text{ L}}{100 \text{ mL}} \times \frac{310.2 \text{ g}}{1 \text{ mol}} = 5.0 \times 10^{-6} \text{ g}/100 \text{ mL}$$

18.8 $AgCl: K_{sp} = [Ag^+][Cl^-]$

$1.8 \times 10^{-10} = (x)(x) = (x)^2$ and $x = 1.3 \times 10^{-5}$ M $= [Ag^+]$

$Ag_2CO_3: K_{sp} = [Ag^+]^2[CO_3^{2-}]$

$8.1 \times 10^{-2} = (2x)^2(x) = 4x^3$ and $x = 1.3 \times 10^{-4}$ M $= [CO_3^{2-}]$

$[Ag^+] = 2 \times [CO_3^{2-}] = 2 \times 1.3 \times 10^{-4}$ M $= 2.6 \times 10^{-4}$ M

$Ag_3PO_4: K_{sp} = [Ag^+]^3[PO_4^{3-}]$

$1.8 \times 10^{-18} = (3x)^3(x) = 27x^4$ and $x = 1.6 \times 10^{-5}$ M $= [PO_4^{3-}]$

$[Ag^+] = 3 \times [PO_4^{3-}] = 3 \times 1.6 \times 10^{-5}$ M $= 4.8 \times 10^{-5}$ M

Answer: The saturated Ag_2CO_3 solution has the highest Ag^+ concentration.

18.10   (a) The molar solubility of Ag_2SO_4 in water is 1.5×10^{-2} mol/L (Practice Exercise 18.4).
(b) Let x equal the molar solubility of Ag_2SO_4.

Concentration Summary:

Equation:	$Ag_2SO_4(s) \rightleftharpoons$	$2Ag^+(aq)$ +	$SO_4^{2-}(aq)$
Initial concentrations, mol/L		0	0.20
Concentration changes, mol/L		$+2x$	$+x$
Equilibrium concentrations, mol/L		$2x$	$0.20 + x$
Approximate concentrations, mol/L		$2x$	0.20

Substituting the approximate concentrations and $K_{sp} = 1.4 \times 10^{-5}$ into the K_{sp} expression gives

$K_{sp} = [Ag^+]^2[SO_4^{2-}]$

$1.4 \times 10^{-5} = (2x)^2(0.20)$ and $x = 4.2 \times 10^{-3}$ mol/L

The molar solubility of Ag_2SO_4 in 0.20 M Na_2SO_4 is 4.2×10^{-3} mol/L.

(c) Let x equal the molar solubility of Ag_2SO_4.

Concentration Summary:

Equation:	$Ag_2SO_4(s) \rightleftharpoons$	$2Ag^+(aq)$	$+ SO_4^{2-}(aq)$
Initial concentrations, mol/L		0.10	0
Concentration changes, mol/L		$+2x$	$+x$
Equilibrium concentrations, mol/L		$0.10 + 2x$	x
Approximate concentrations, mol/L		0.10	x

Substituting the approximate concentrations and K_{sp} value into the K_{sp} expression gives

$1.4 \times 10^{-5} = (0.10)^2(x)$ and $x = 1.4 \times 10^{-3}$ mol/L

The molar solubility of Ag_2SO_4 in 0.10 M $AgNO_3$ is 1.4×10^{-3} mol/L.

18.12 (a) $K_{sp} = [Ca^{2+}] [CO_3^{2-}]$

$4.5 \times 10^{-9} = (x)(x) = x^2$ and $x = 6.7 \times 10^{-5}$ mol/L $= [Ca^{2+}] = [CO_3^{2-}]$

The equilibrium concentration of Ca^{2+}, 6.7×10^{-5} mol/L, is also the molar solubility of $CaCO_3$. The molar mass of $CaCO_3$ is 100.1 g; hence, the number of grams of $CaCO_3$ that will dissolve in 10.0 L of pure water is

$10.0 \text{ L} \times \dfrac{6.7 \times 10^{-5} \text{ mol}}{1 \text{ L}} \times \dfrac{100.1 \text{ g}}{1 \text{ mol}} = 6.7 \times 10^{-2}$ g

(b) Let x equal the molar solubility of $CaCO_3$.

Concentration Summary:

Equation:	$CaCO_3(s) \rightleftharpoons$	$Ca^{2+}(aq)$	$+ CO_3^{2-}(aq)$
Initial concentrations, mol/L		0.50	0
Concentration changes, mol/L		$+x$	$+x$
Equilibrium concentrations, mol/L		$0.50 + x$	x
Approximate concentrations, mol/L		0.50	x

Substituting the approximate concentrations and K_{sp} value into the K_{sp} expression gives

$4.5 \times 10^{-9} = (0.50)(x)$ and $x = 9.0 \times 10^{-9}$ mol/L

The molar solubility of $CaCO_3$ in 0.50 M $CaCl_2$ is 9.0×10^{-9} mol/L. The number of grams of $CaCO_3$ that will dissolve in 10.0 L of this solution is

$10.0 \text{ L} \times \dfrac{9.0 \times 10^{-9} \text{ mol}}{1 \text{ L}} \times \dfrac{100.1 \text{ g}}{1 \text{ mol}} = 9.0 \times 10^{-6}$ g

18.13 The molar mass of TlCl is 239.8 g. The concentration of Tl^+ in 0.10 M NaCl solution is

$\dfrac{0.98 \text{ g TlCl}}{0.500 \text{ L}} \times \dfrac{1 \text{ mol Tl}^+}{239.8 \text{ g TlCl}} = 8.2 \times 10^{-3} \text{ mol Tl}^+/\text{L} = [Tl^+]$

The concentration of Cl^- in solution is 0.10 M + 0.0082 M = 0.11 M. Substituting these concentrations into the K_{sp} expression gives

$K_{sp} = [Tl^+] [Cl^-] = (8.2 \times 10^{-3})(0.11) = 9.0 \times 10^{-4}$

18.15 (a) The molar mass of $Ca(OH)_2$ is 74.1 g. The molar solubility of $Ca(OH)_2$ at $0°C$ is therefore

$$\frac{0.185 \text{ g}}{100 \text{ mL}} \times \frac{1000 \text{ mL}}{1 \text{ L}} \times \frac{1 \text{ mol}}{74.1 \text{ g}} = 2.50 \times 10^{-2} \text{ mol/L}$$

$[Ca^{2+}] = 2.50 \times 10^{-2}$ M and $[OH^-] = 2 \times 2.50 \times 10^{-2}$ M $= 5.00 \times 10^{-2}$ M. Substituting these concentrations into the K_{sp} expression gives

$K_{sp} = [Ca^{2+}][OH^-]^2 = (2.50 \times 10^{-2})(5.00 \times 10^{-2})^2 = 6.25 \times 10^{-5}$

(b) Decreases. The K_{sp} at $25°C$, 6.5×10^{-6}, is smaller than that at $0°C$, 6.25×10^{-5}.

18.17 The concentrations in the mixed solution are: $[Pb^{2+}] = 1.0 \times 10^{-3}$ M and $[Cl^-] = 1.0 \times 10^{-3}$ M. Substituting these concentrations into the Q expression gives

$Q = [Pb^{2+}][Cl^-]^2 = (1.0 \times 10^{-3})(1.0 \times 10^{-3})^2 = 1.0 \times 10^{-9}$

The ion product Q is smaller than the K_{sp} value of 1.7×10^{-5}, so $PbCl_2$ will not precipitate.

18.18 (a) The concentrations just after mixing are:

mol $Pb^{2+} = 0.050$ L x 0.20 mol/L $= 0.010$ mol

mol $Cl^- = 0.080$ L x 0.020 mol/L $= 0.0016$ mol

$[Pb^{2+}] = 0.010$ mol/(0.050 L + 0.080 L) $= 0.077$ M

$[Cl^-] = 0.0016$ mol/(0.050 L + 0.080 L) $= 0.012$ M

and $Q = [Pb^{2+}][Cl^-]^2 = (0.077)(0.012)^2 = 1.1 \times 10^{-5}$

The ion product Q is smaller than the K_{sp} value of 1.7×10^{-5}, so $PbCl_2$ will not precipitate.

(b) The concentrations just after mixing are:

mol $Pb^{2+} = 0.075$ L x 0.0010 mol/L $= 7.5 \times 10^{-5}$ mol

mol $I^- = 0.050$ L x 0.0020 mol/L $= 1.0 \times 10^{-4}$ mol

$[Pb^{2+}] = 7.5 \times 10^{-5}$ mol/(0.075 L + 0.050 L) $= 6.0 \times 10^{-4}$ M

$[I^-] = 1.0 \times 10^{-4}$ mol/(0.075 L + 0.050 L) $= 8.0 \times 10^{-4}$ M

and $Q = [Pb^{2+}][I^-]^2 = (6.0 \times 10^{-4})(8.0 \times 10^{-4})^2 = 3.8 \times 10^{-10}$

The ion product Q is smaller than the K_{sp} value of 7.9×10^{-9}, so PbI_2 will not precipitate.

(c) The concentrations just after mixing are:

mol $Pb^{2+} = 1.0$ L x 0.10 mol/L $= 0.10$ mol

mol $OH^- = 0.0010$ L x 0.0010 mol/L $= 1.0 \times 10^{-6}$ mol

$[Pb^{2+}] = 0.10$ mol/(1.0 L + 0.001 L) $= 0.10$ M

$[OH^-] = 1.0 \times 10^{-6}$ mol/(1.0 L + 0.001 L) $= 1.0 \times 10^{-6}$ M

and $Q = [Pb^{2+}][OH^-]^2 = (0.10)(1.0 \times 10^{-6})^2 = 1.0 \times 10^{-13}$

The ion product Q is greater than the K_{sp} value of 1.2×10^{-15}, so $Pb(OH)_2$ will precipitate.

18.20 (a) The concentrations just after mixing are:

mol $Ca^{2+} = 0.100$ L x 0.020 mol/L $= 2.0 \times 10^{-3}$ mol

mol $CrO_4^{2-} = 0.100$ L x 0.020 mol/L $= 2.0 \times 10^{-3}$ mol

$[Ca^{2+}] = 2.0 \times 10^{-3}$ mol/(0.100 L + 0.100 L) $= 0.010$ M

$[CrO_4^{2-}] = 2.0 \times 10^{-3}$ mol/(0.100 L + 0.100 L) = 0.010 M

and $Q = [Ca^{2+}][CrO_4^{2-}]$ = (0.010)(0.010) = 1.0 $\times 10^{-4}$

The ion product Q is smaller than the K_{sp} value of 7.1 $\times 10^{-4}$, so $CaCrO_4$ will not precipitate. The concentrations remaining in the solution are therefore

$[Ca^{2+}]$ = 0.010 M; $[Cl^-]$ = 0.020 M; $[K^+]$ = 0.020 M; and $[CrO_4^{2-}]$ = 0.010 M.

(b) The concentrations just after mixing are:

mol Ba^{2+} = 0.100 L $\times$ 0.015 mol/L = 1.5 $\times 10^{-3}$ mol

mol F^- = 0.200 L $\times$ 0.0045 mol/L = 9.0 $\times 10^{-4}$ mol

$[Ba^{2+}]$ = 1.5 $\times 10^{-3}$ mol/(0.100 L + 0.200 L) = 5.0 $\times 10^{-3}$ M

$[F^-]$ = 9.0 $\times 10^{-4}$ mol/(0.100 L + 0.200 L) = 3.0 $\times 10^{-3}$ M

and $Q = [Ba^{2+}] [F^-]^2 = (5.0 \times 10^{-3})(3.0 \times 10^{-3})^2 = 4.5 \times 10^{-8}$

The ion product Q is smaller than the K_{sp} value of 1.3 $\times 10^{-6}$, so BaF_2 will not precipitate. The concentrations remaining in solution are therefore

$[Ba^{2+}]$ = 5.0 $\times 10^{-3}$ M; $[Cl^-]$ = 1.0 $\times 10^{-2}$ M; $[Na^+]$ = 3.0 $\times 10^{-3}$ M; and $[F^-]$ = 3.0 $\times 10^{-3}$ M.

18.22 Since the volume doubles on mixing, the initial concentrations just after mixing are half what they were originally. If we assume that all the sulfate ion initially precipitates, then the concentration of Ba^{2+} remaining in the mixed solution is

$[Ba^{2+}]$ = 0.100 M – 0.045 M = 0.055 M

We now have to determine the molar solubility of $BaSO_4$ in 0.055 M Ba^{2+} solution.

Concentration Summary:

Equation:	$BaSO_4(s) \rightleftharpoons$	$Ba^{2+}(aq)$ +	$SO_4^{2-}(aq)$
Initial concentrations, mol/L		0.055	0
Concentration changes, mol/L		+x	+x
Equilibrium concentrations, mol/L		0.055 + x	x
Approximate concentrations, mol/L		0.055	x

Substituting the approximate concentrations and K_{sp} = 1.1 $\times 10^{-10}$ into the K_{sp} expression gives

$K_{sp} = [Ba^{2+}] [SO_4^{2-}]$

1.1 $\times 10^{-10}$ = (0.055)(x) and x = 2.0 $\times 10^{-9}$ M = $[SO_4^{2-}]$

The percent of sulfate ion that will not precipitate is

$\dfrac{2.0 \times 10^{-9}}{0.045}$ $\times$ 100% = 4.4 $\times 10^{-6}$%

18.23 (a) The K_{sp}'s are: Hg_2Cl_2, 1.3 $\times 10^{-18}$; $PbCl_2$, 1.7 $\times 10^{-5}$. The optimum chloride concentration occurs when the solution is just barely saturated with respect to $PbCl_2$. This concentration is obtained by susbstituting $[Pb^{2+}]$ = 0.050 M into the K_{sp} expression for $PbCl_2$:

$K_{sp} = [Pb^{2+}] [Cl^-]^2$

1.7 $\times 10^{-5}$ = (0.050)$[Cl^-]^2$ and $[Cl^-]$ = 1.8 $\times 10^{-2}$ M

The maximum separation occurs when the NaCl concentration is 1.8 $\times 10^{-2}$ M.

(b) All of the Pb^{2+} ions are still in solution, therefore $[Pb^{2+}] = 0.050$ M. The concentration of Hg_2^{2+} can be obtained from the K_{sp} expression.

$K_{sp} = [Hg_2^{2+}][Cl^-]^2$

$1.3 \times 10^{-18} = [Hg_2^{2+}](1.8 \times 10^{-2})^2$ and $[Hg_2^{2+}] = 4.0 \times 10^{-15}$ M

18.26 (a) The H^+ and OH^- concentrations are each 1.0×10^{-7} M at pH 7.00.

Fe^{3+}: $K_{sp} = [Fe^{3+}][OH^-]^3$

$1.6 \times 10^{-39} = [Fe^{3+}](1.0 \times 10^{-7})^3$ and $[Fe^{3+}] = 1.6 \times 10^{-18}$ M

Pb^{2+}: $K_{sp} = [Pb^{2+}][OH^-]^2$

$1.2 \times 10^{-15} = [Pb^{2+}](1.0 \times 10^{-7})^2$ and $[Pb^{2+}] = 0.12$ M

(b) $K_{sp} = [Al^{3+}][OH^-]^3$

$3 \times 10^{-34} = (0.12)[OH^-]^3$ and $[OH^-] = 1 \times 10^{-11}$

$pH = -\log[H^+] = -\log(1 \times 10^{-3}) = 3.0$

The pH must be lowered to 3.0 from 7.00.

18.28 If 95% of the barium precipitated, then we are left with 1.500 g $- 0.95 \times 1.500$ g $= 0.075$ g Ba^{2+} in solution. The $[Ba^{2+}]$ after precipitation is

$$\frac{0.075 \text{ g } Ba^{2+}}{100 \text{ mL}} \times \frac{1000 \text{ mL}}{1 \text{ L}} \times \frac{1 \text{ mol } Ba^{2+}}{137.33 \text{ g } Ba^{2+}} = 5.5 \times 10^{-3} \text{ M } Ba^{2+}$$

The pH can be obtained from the K_{sp} expression.

$K_{sp} = [Ba^{2+}][OH^-]^2$

$5 \times 10^{-3} = (5.5 \times 10^{-3})[OH^-]^2$

$[OH^-] = 0.95$ M (carry extra significant figure) and $pH = -\log[H^+] = -\log(1.00 \times 10^{-14}/0.95) = 14.0$

18.29 The hydroxide ions come from the ionization of ammonia

$NH_3(aq) + H_2O(l) \rightleftharpoons NH_4^+(aq) + OH^-(aq)$

The $[OH^-]$ before mixing is obtained by substituting $[NH_3] = 0.50$ M and $[NH_4^+] = 0.30$ M into the K_b expression for ammonia.

$$[OH^-] = \frac{K_b[NH_3]}{[NH_4^+]} = \frac{(1.8 \times 10^{-5})(0.50)}{(0.30)} = 3.0 \times 10^{-5} \text{ M}$$

Since this is an ammonia - ammonium chloride buffer system, the $[OH^-]$ does not change upon dilution. Therefore, the concentrations initially after mixing are

$[Mn^{2+}] = [Fe^{2+}] = [Mg^{2+}] = 0.0010$ M and $[OH^-] = 3.0 \times 10^{-5}$ M

To determine if any of these ions precipitate as hydroxides, we have to calculate their ion products and compare them to their K_{sp} values.

Mn^{2+}: $Q = [Mn^{2+}][OH^-]^2 = (0.0010)(3.0 \times 10^{-5})^2 = 9.0 \times 10^{-13}$

The ion product Q is greater than the K_{sp} value of 6×10^{-14}, so $Mn(OH)_2$ will precipitate.

Fe^{2+}: $Q = [Fe^{2+}][OH^-]^2 = 9.0 \times 10^{-13}$

The ion product Q is greater than the K_{sp} value of 7.9×10^{-16}, so $Fe(OH)_2$ will precipitate.

Mg^{2+}: $Q = [Mg^{2+}][OH^-]^2 = 9.0 \times 10^{-13}$

The ion product Q is smaller than the K_{sp} value of 7.1×10^{-12}, so $Mg(OH)_2$ will not precipitate.

18.31 First calculate the $[OH^-]$ that would make the solution saturated with respect to $Pb(OH)_2$. Precipitation will not occur if the actual hydroxide ion concentration is less than or equal to this value.

$K_{sp} = [Pb^{2+}][OH^-]^2$

$(0.0010)[OH^-]^2 = 1.2 \times 10^{-15}$ and $[OH^-] = 1.1 \times 10^{-6}$ M

The ratio of NH_4^+ to NH_3 corresponding to this $[OH^-]$ is obtained by substituting $[OH^-] = 1.1 \times 10^{-6}$ M into the K_b expression for ammonia

$$\frac{[NH_4^+]}{[NH_3]} = \frac{K_b}{[OH^-]} = \frac{1.8 \times 10^{-5}}{1.1 \times 10^{-6}} = 16$$

An NH_4^+/NH_3 ratio of 16 or greater would prevent precipitation.

18.32 The acetate ion is basic and reacts with water to produce hydroxide ions. The $[OH^-]$ can be calculated using the usual weak base concentration summary and approximations ($K_b = 5.68 \times 10^{-10}$).

$K_b = [HC_2H_3O_2][OH^-] / [C_2H_3O_2^-]$

$5.68 \times 10^{-10} = \frac{x^2}{0.20}$ and $x = 1.1 \times 10^{-5}$ M $=[OH^-]$

The concentrations in solution are:

$[Mn^{2+}] = 0.010$ M and $[OH^-] = 1.1 \times 10^{-5}$ M

Substituting the concentrations into the ion product expression gives

$Q = [Mn^{2+}][OH^-]^2 = (0.010)(1.1 \times 10^{-5})^2 = 1.2 \times 10^{-12}$

The ion product Q is greater than the K_{sp} value of 6×10^{-14}, so $Mn(OH)_2$ will precipitate.

(b) First calculate the $[OH^-]$ in a saturated solution of $Mn(OH)_2$. Precipitation will not occur if the actual $[OH^-]$ is less than or equal to this value.

$K_{sp} = [Mn^{2+}][OH^-]^2$

$(0.010)[OH^-]^2 = 6 \times 10^{-14}$ and $[OH^-] = 2.4 \times 10^{-6}$ M

The moles of acetic acid per liter needed to maintain the level of hydroxide ions at 2.4×10^{-6} M is obtained by substituting $[OH^-] = 2.4 \times 10^{-6}$ M and $[C_2H_3O_2^-] = 0.20$ M into the K_b expression for acetate ion

$K_b = [HC_2H_3O_2][OH^-] / [C_2H_3O_2^-]$

$5.68 \times 10^{-10} = \frac{[HC_2H_3O_2](2.4 \times 10^{-6})}{0.20}$ and $[HC_2H_3O_2] = 4.7 \times 10^{-5}$ mol/L

$Mn(OH)_2$ will not precipitate if 4.7×10^{-5} mol or more of acetic acid is added per liter of solution.

18.36 Al^{3+} and Fe^{3+} were present.

1. $Al^{3+}(aq) + 3OH^-(aq) \longrightarrow Al(OH)_3(s)$
    $Fe^{3+}(aq) + 3OH^-(aq) \longrightarrow Fe(OH)_3(s)$ (rust red)

2. $Al(OH)_3(s) + OH^-(aq) \longrightarrow Al(OH)_4^-(aq)$

3. $Al(OH)_4^-(aq) + H^+(aq) \longrightarrow Al(OH)_3(s)$ (white) $+ H_2O(l)$

At this point we know that Cr(III) is absent, because $Cr(OH)_3$ is greenish.

4. $Al(OH)_3(s) + 3H^+(aq) \longrightarrow Al^{3+}(aq) + 3H_2O(l)$

18.42   The reactions that have to be considered are

$$CaCO_3(s) \rightleftharpoons Ca^{2+}(aq) + CO_3^{2-}(aq)$$

$$CO_3^{2-}(aq) + H_2O(l) \rightleftharpoons HCO_3^-(aq) + OH^-(aq)$$

The Ca^{2+} ion remains unchanged in solution. The molar solubility of $CaCO_3$, x, is equal to $[Ca^{2+}]$, which is also equal to the sum of the concentrations of the species containing the carbonate ion, or

$$x = [Ca^{2+}] = [CO_3^{2-}] + [HCO_3^-]$$

The ratio of $[HCO_3^-]$ to $[CO_3^{2-}]$ at this pH is ($[OH^-] = 1.0 \times 10^{-5}$ M and $K_b = 1.78 \times 10^{-4}$)

$$\frac{[HCO_3^-][OH^-]}{[CO_3^{2-}]} = K_b \text{ and } \frac{[HCO_3^-]}{[CO_3^{2-}]} = \frac{K_b}{[OH^-]} = \frac{1.78 \times 10^{-4}}{1.0 \times 10^{-5}} = 18$$

Therefore, $[HCO_3^-] = 18\,[CO_3^{2-}]$

$[CO_3^{2-}] + 18\,[CO_3^{2-}] = x$ and $[CO_3^{2-}] = x/19$

Substituting in the K_{sp} expression gives

$[Ca^{2+}][CO_3^{2-}] = K_{sp}$

$$(x)\left[\frac{x}{19}\right] = 4.5 \times 10^{-9} \text{ and } x = 2.9 \times 10^{-4} \text{ M}$$

18.44   The reactions that have to be considered are

$$MgC_2O_4(s) \rightleftharpoons Mg^{2+}(aq) + C_2O_4^{2-}(aq) \quad (1)$$

$$C_2O_4^{2-}(aq) + H^+(aq) \rightleftharpoons HC_2O_4^-(aq) \quad (2)$$

$$HC_2O_4^-(aq) + H^+(aq) \rightleftharpoons H_2C_2O_4(aq) \quad (3)$$

The Mg^{2+} ion remains unchanged in solution. The $[Mg^{2+}]$ is equal to the molar solubility of MgC_2O_4, 0.010 M, which is also equal to the sum of the concentrations of the species containing the oxalate ion, or

$$[Mg^{2+}] = [C_2O_4^{2-}] + [HC_2O_4^-] + [H_2C_2O_4] = 0.010 \text{ M} \quad (4)$$

Since the solution is saturated with MgC_2O_4, the $[C_2O_4^{2-}]$ can be obtained from the K_{sp} expression

$[Mg^{2+}][C_2O_4^{2-}] = 8.6 \times 10^{-5}$

$(0.010)[C_2O_4^{2-}] = 8.6 \times 10^{-5}$ and $[C_2O_4^{2-}] = 8.6 \times 10^{-3}$ M

To solve the problem we will first establish a relationship between H^+ and $HC_2O_4^-$ using the equilibrium constant expression for Equation (2), and then substitute this relationship, and the relationship between H^+ and $H_2C_2O_4$ obtained using Equation (4), into the equilibrium constant expression for Equation (3):

$$K_{a2} = [H^+][C_2O_4^{2-}]/[HC_2O_4^-]$$

$$\frac{[H^+]}{[HC_2O_4^-]} = \frac{K_{a2}}{[C_2O_4^{2-}]} = \frac{6.40 \times 10^{-5}}{8.6 \times 10^{-3}} = 7.44 \times 10^{-3}$$

and $[H^+] = 0.00744[HC_2O_4^-]$ or $[HC_2O_4^-] = [H^+]/0.00744$

From Equation (4) we have

$$[H_2C_2O_4] = -[HC_2O_4^-] + 0.010 - 0.0086 = \frac{-[H^+]}{0.00744} + 0.0014 = -134.4[H^+] + 0.0014$$

Substituting these expressions for $[H_2C_2O_4]$ and $[HC_2O_4^-]$ into the equilibrium constant expression for Equation (3) gives

$$K_{a1} = [H^+][HC_2O_4^-] / [H_2C_2O_4]$$

$$5.90 \times 10^{-2} = \frac{[H^+] \times 134.4[H^+]}{-134.4[H^+] + 0.0014}$$

$$134.4[H^+]^2 + 7.93[H^+] - 8.26 \times 10^{-5} = 0 \text{ and } [H^+] = 1.0 \times 10^{-5} \text{ M}$$

Comment: This problem can also be worked out by assuming that only the first protonation of $C_2O_4^{2-}$ [Equation (2)] has to be considered, solving the problem using this assumption, and checking to see if the assumption is valid. If the assumption is valid, nothing further has to be done. If the assumption is invalid, then the complete treatment used above has to be employed. Using this assumption, the problem would have the following solution:

$$[Mg^{2+}] = [C_2O_4^{2-}] + [HC_2O_4^-] = 0.010 \text{ M}$$

$$[C_2O_4^{2-}] = 8.6 \times 10^{-3} \text{ M (as before) and } [HC_2O_4^-] = 0.010 - [C_2O_4^{2-}]$$

$$= 0.010 - 0.0086 = 0.0014 \text{ M (carry an extra significant figure)}$$

Substituting $[C_2O_4^{2-}] = 0.0086$ M and $[HC_2O_4^-] = 0.0014$ M into the equilibrium constant expression for Equation (2) gives

$$[H^+] = K_{a2} \times \frac{[HC_2O_4^-]}{[C_2O_4^{2-}]} = \frac{(6.40 \times 10^{-5})(0.0014)}{(0.0086)} = 1.0 \times 10^{-5} \text{ M}$$

The assumption can be tested by calculating the amount of $H_2C_2O_4$ present at equilibrium. The amount of $H_2C_2O_4$ can be obtained from the combined equilibrium constant expression for oxalic acid.

$$[H_2C_2O_4] = \frac{[H^+]^2[C_2O_4^{2-}]}{K_{a1} \times K_{a2}} = \frac{(1.0 \times 10^{-5})^2(8.6 \times 10^{-3})}{(5.90 \times 10^{-2})(6.40 \times 10^{-5})} = 2.3 \times 10^{-7} \text{ M}$$

The amount of $H_2C_2O_4$ is indeed quite small and the assumption is valid. This shows that assumptions, hopefully based on sound chemical principles, can possibly simplify the solutions to problems considerably. However, the validity of the assumptions must always be confirmed; exceptions being those cases where the standard approximations are always made.

18.48   (a) Substituting $K_{a1} \times K_{a2} = 1 \times 10^{-20}$, $[H_2S] = 0.10$ M, and $[S^{2-}] = 3.0 \times 10^{-18}$ M into the combined equilibrium constant expression for H_2S gives

$$1 \times 10^{-20} = \frac{[H^+]^2(3.0 \times 10^{-18})}{0.10} \text{ and } [H^+] = 0.02 \text{ M}$$

   (b) Cu^{2+}: Yes. Substituting $[S^{2-}] = 3.0 \times 10^{-18}$ M and $[Cu^{2+}] = 0.10$ M into the ion product expression gives

$$Q = [Cu^{2+}][S^{2-}] = (0.10)(3.0 \times 10^{-18}) = 3.0 \times 10^{-19}$$

The ion product Q is greater than the K_{sp} value of 8×10^{-37}, so CuS will precipitate.

Mn^{2+}: No. The ion product $Q = [Mn^{2+}][S^{2-}] = 3.0 \times 10^{-19}$ is smaller than the K_{sp} value of 2.5×10^{-13}, so MnS will not precipitate.

Answer: A precipitate of CuS will appear.

18.49   The K_{sp}'s are: PbS, 3×10^{-28}; NiS, 4×10^{-20}. PbS has a smaller K_{sp} value and will precipitate at a lower sulfide ion concentration than NiS. We will therefore first calculate the highest sulfide ion concentration that will leave the nickel ion in solution. Substituting $[Ni^{2+}] = 0.20$ M into the K_{sp} expression for NiS gives

$[Ni^{2+}] [S^{2-}] = K_{sp}$

$(0.20) [S^{2-}] = 4 \times 10^{-20}$ and $[S^{2-}] = 2 \times 10^{-19}$ M

The maximum separation occurs when the sulfide concentration is 2×10^{-19} M. The pH that provides this sulfide concentration is found by substituting $K_{a1} \times K_{a2} = 1 \times 10^{-20}$, $[S^{2-}] = 2 \times 10^{-19}$ M, and $[H_2S] = 0.10$ M into the combined equilibrium constant expression for H_2S:

$$1 \times 10^{-20} = \frac{[H^+]^2 (2 \times 10^{-19})}{(0.10)}$$

$[H^+] = 0.005$ M and pH $= -\log[H^+] = -\log(0.005) = 2.3$

(b)   All of the nickel ions are in the solution. Therefore, the percent of nickel ion left in solution is 100%. The concentration of Pb^{2+} remaining in solution can be obtained by substituting $[S^{2-}] = 2 \times 10^{-19}$ M into the K_{sp} expression.

$[Pb^{2+}] [S^{2-}] = 3 \times 10^{-28}$

$[Pb^{2+}] (2 \times 10^{-19}) = 3 \times 10^{-28}$ and $[Pb^{2+}] = 2 \times 10^{-9}$ M

The percent Pb^{2+} remaining in solution is therefore

$$\frac{2 \times 10^{-9} \text{ M}}{0.20 \text{ M}} \times 100\% = 1 \times 10^{-6}\%$$

18.55   Substituting $[SCN^-] = 0.010$ M, $[Fe(SCN)^{2+}] = 1 \times 10^{-4}$ M, and $K_f = 1.2 \times 10^2$ into the K_f expression for $Fe(SCN)^{2+}$ gives

$$\frac{[Fe(SCN)^{2+}]}{[Fe^{3+}][SCN^-]} = K_f$$

$$\frac{(1 \times 10^{-4})}{[Fe^{3+}](0.010)} = 1.2 \times 10^2 \text{ and } [Fe^{3+}] = 8 \times 10^{-5} \text{ M}$$

This concentration is added to the Fe^{3+} that entered the complex.

$[Fe^{3+}] + [Fe(SCN)^{2+}] = 0.8 \times 10^{-4}$ M $+ 1 \times 10^{-4}$ M $= 1.8 \times 10^{-4}$ M or 2×10^{-4} M.

Fe^{3+} can be detected down to a concentration of 2×10^{-4} M.

18.56   (1) $ZnS(s) \rightleftharpoons Zn^{2+}(aq) + S^{2-}(aq)$ $K_{sp} = 1 \times 10^{-21}$

   (2) $Zn^{2+}(aq) + 4NH_3(aq) \rightleftharpoons Zn(NH_3)_4^{2+}(aq)$ $K_f = 2.9 \times 10^9$

The net reaction is the sum of steps (1) and (2)

$ZnS(s) + 4NH_3(aq) \rightleftharpoons Zn(NH_3)_4^{2+}(aq) + S^{2-}(aq)$ and the combined equilibrium constant is

$$\frac{[Zn(NH_3)_4^{2+}][S^{2-}]}{[NH_3]^4} = K_{sp} \times K_f = (1 \times 10^{-21})(2.9 \times 10^9) = 2.9 \times 10^{-12}$$

Let x be the molar solubility of ZnS.

Concentration Summary:

Equation:	$ZnS(s)$ + $4NH_3(aq)$ $\rightleftharpoons$	$Zn(NH_3)_4{}^{2+}(aq)$	+ $S^{2-}(aq)$
Initial concentrations, mol/L	1.00	0	0
Concentration changes, mol/L	$-4x$	$+x$	$+x$
Equilibrium concentrations, mol/L	$1.00 - 4x$	x	x

Substituting the equilibrium concentrations into the combined equilibrium constant expression gives

$$\frac{(x)(x)}{(1.00 - 4x)^4} = 2.9 \times 10^{-12}$$

Since the combined equilibrium constant is so small, we can assume that $4x$ is small compared to 1.00 and approximate $(1.00 - 4x)$ by 1.00. Then,

$x^2 = 2.9 \times 10^{-12}$ and $x = 1.7 \times 10^{-6}$ M

The assumption is valid, since x is indeed small compared to 1.00. Therefore, the molar solubility of ZnS in 1.00 M NH_3 is 1.7×10^{-6} M.

18.57 Because the K_f of $Zn(NH_3)_4{}^{2+}$ is large, 2.9×10^9, and because ammonia is present in excess, most of the zinc will be in the form of $Zn(NH_3)_4{}^{2+}$. To solve the problem we will therefore assume that all the zinc is initially in the form of the complex, which then breaks down to form x moles of zinc ion at equilibrium. The initial concentration of the complex is

$$\frac{1.0 \text{ g } ZnCl_2}{0.500 \text{ L}} \times \frac{1 \text{ mol } ZnCl_2}{136.3 \text{ g } ZnCl_2} \times \frac{1 \text{ mol } Zn(NH_3)_4{}^{2+}}{1 \text{ mol } ZnCl_2} = 0.015 \text{ M } Zn(NH_3)_4{}^{2+}$$

The formation of this complex reduces the concentration of NH_3 by 0.060 M, since each $Zn(NH_3)_4{}^{2+}$ ion contains four NH_3 molecules. Therefore, the initial $[NH_3]$ is

$[NH_3] = 0.50 \text{ M} - 0.060 \text{ M} = 0.44 \text{ M}$

Concentration Summary:

Equation:	$Zn(NH_3)_4{}^{2+}(aq)$ $\rightleftharpoons$	$Zn^{2+}(aq)$	+ $4NH_3(aq)$
Initial concentrations, mol/L	0.015	0	0.44
Concentration changes, mol/L	$-x$	$+x$	$+4x$
Equilibrium concentrations, mol/L	$0.015 - x$	x	$0.44 + 4x$
Approximate concentrations, mol/L	0.015	x	0.44

Substituting $K_d = 1/K_f = 1/(2.9 \times 10^9) = 3.4 \times 10^{-9}$ and the approximate concentrations into the K_d expression gives

$$\frac{[Zn^{2+}][NH_3]^4}{[Zn(NH_3)_4{}^{2+}]} = K_d$$

$$\frac{(x)(0.44)^4}{(0.015)} = 3.4 \times 10^{-9} \text{ and } x = 1.4 \times 10^{-9} \text{ M}$$

The equilibrium concentrations are:

$[Zn(NH_3)_4{}^{2+}] = 0.015 - x = 0.015 \text{ M} - 1.4 \times 10^{-9} \text{ M} = 0.015 \text{ M}$

$[Zn^{2+}] = x = 1.4 \times 10^{-9} \text{ M}$

$[NH_3] = 0.44 + 4x = 0.44 \text{ M} + 5.6 \times 10^{-9} \text{ M} = 0.44 \text{ M}$

18.60   Substituting $[SCN^-] = 2.0$ M, $[Fe(SCN)^{2+}] = 0.25$ M, and $K_f = 1.2 \times 10^2$ into the K_f expression for $Fe(SCN)^{2+}$ gives

$$\frac{[Fe(SCN)^{2+}]}{[Fe^{3+}][SCN^-]} = K_f$$

$$\frac{(0.25)}{[Fe^{3+}](2.0)} = 1.2 \times 10^2 \text{ and } [Fe^{3+}] = 1.0 \times 10^{-3} \text{ M}$$

18.62 $Ag^+(aq) + 2CN^-(aq) \rightleftharpoons Ag(CN)_2^- \qquad K_f = 1 \times 10^{21}$

Because K_f is very large, virtually all of the silver will be present as the complex; therefore it is reasonable to take the $[Ag(CN)_2^-] = 0.0750$ M. Substituting $[Ag(CN)_2^-] = 0.0750$ M, $[Ag^+] = 1.0 \times 10^{-10}$ M, and the K_f value into the K_f expression gives

$$\frac{[Ag(CN)_2^-]}{[Ag^+][CN^-]^2} = K_f$$

$$\frac{(0.0750)}{(1.0 \times 10^{-10})[CN^-]^2} = 1 \times 10^{21} \text{ and } [CN^-] = 9 \times 10^{-7} \text{ M}$$

The number of moles of free CN^- is $0.250 \text{ L} \times 9 \times 10^{-7} \text{ mol/L} = 2 \times 10^{-7}$ mol. However, we also have

$$0.250 \text{ L} \times \frac{0.0750 \text{ mol } Ag(CN)_2^-}{1 \text{ L}} \times \frac{2 \text{ mol } CN^-}{1 \text{ mol } Ag(CN)_2^-} = 0.0375 \text{ mol } CN^-$$

combined in the complex. Consequently, the total number of moles of KCN that must be added to the solution is $0.0375 + 2 \times 10^{-7} = 0.0375$ mol, to three significant figures.

18.64   (1) $Zn(OH)_2(s) \rightleftharpoons Zn^{2+}(aq) + 2OH^-(aq) \qquad K_{sp} = 4.5 \times 10^{-17}$

(2) $Zn^{2+}(aq) + 4OH^-(aq) \rightleftharpoons Zn(OH)_4^{2-}(aq) \qquad K_f = 2.2 \times 10^{16}$

The net reaction is the sum of steps (1) and (2)

$Zn(OH)_2(s) + 2OH^-(aq) \rightleftharpoons Zn(OH)_4^{2-}(aq)$

and the combined equilibrium constant is

$$\frac{[Zn(OH)_4^{2-}]}{[OH^-]^2} = K_{sp} \times K_f = (4.5 \times 10^{-17})(2.2 \times 10^{16}) = 0.99$$

Let x be the molar solubililty of $Zn(OH)_2$.

Concentration Summary:

Equation:	$Zn(OH)_2(s)$	$+\ 2OH^-(aq)$	$\rightleftharpoons$	$Zn(OH)_4^{2-}(aq)$
Initial concentrations, mol/L		1.0		0
Concentration changes, mol/L		$-2x$		$+x$
Equilibrium concentrations, mol/L		$1.0 - 2x$		x

Substituting the equilibrium concentrations into the combined equilibrium constant expression gives

$$\frac{x}{(1.0 - 2x)^2} = 0.99$$

$4x^2 - 4.96x + 1.0 = 0$ and $x = 0.25$ M

The positive square root is rejected, since it would lead to a negative $[OH^-]$ at equilibrium. Therefore, the molar solubility of $Zn(OH)_2$ in 1.0 M NaOH is 0.25 M.

18.66   The overall reaction is

$FeS(s) + 6CN^-(aq) \rightleftharpoons Fe(CN)_6^{4-}(aq) + S^{2-}(aq)$

The combined equilibrium constant is

$$\frac{[Fe(CN)_6^{4-}][S^{2-}]}{[CN^-]^6} = K_{sp} \times K_f = (8 \times 10^{-19})(1.0 \times 10^{24}) = 8 \times 10^5$$

0.010 mol of Fe goes into solution where it is present as either free Fe^{2+} or $Fe(CN)_6^{4-}$. Because K_f is very large, virtually all of the iron will be present as the complex; therefore $[Fe(CN)_6^{4-}] = 0.010$ M. Substituting $[Fe(CN)_6^{4-}] = 0.010$ M and $[S^{2-}] = 0.010$ M into the combined equilibrium constant expression gives

$$\frac{(0.010)(0.010)}{[CN^-]^6} = 8 \times 10^5 \text{ and } [CN^-] = 0.02 \text{ M}$$

18.68   The molar solubility of $BaSO_4$ can be obtained from the K_{sp} expression.

$K_{sp} = [Ba^{2+}][SO_4^{2-}]$

$1.1 \times 10^{-10} = (x)(x) = x^2$ and $x = 1.0 \times 10^{-5}$ M $= [Ba^{2+}] = [SO_4^{2-}]$

The number of moles of Ba^{2+} in 250 mL = 0.250 L is 0.250 L $\times$ 1.0 $\times$ 10^{-5} mol/L = 2.5 $\times$ 10^{-6} mol. The number of grams of Ba^{2+} in 0.250 L is

$$2.5 \times 10^{-6} \text{ mol Ba}^{2+} \times \frac{137.3 \text{ g Ba}^{2+}}{1 \text{ mol Ba}^{2+}} = 3.4 \times 10^{-4} \text{ g Ba}^{2+}$$

18.70   (a) $K_{sp} = [Ag^+][Cl^-]$

$1.8 \times 10^{-10} = (x)(x) = x^2$ and $x = 1.3 \times 10^{-5}$ M $= [Ag^+]$

(b) $[Ag^+]^2[CrO_4^{2-}] = K_{sp}$

$[Ag^+]^2(0.0020) = 1.2 \times 10^{-12}$ and $[Ag^+] = 2.4 \times 10^{-5}$ M

Ag_2CrO_4 will start precipitating when the concentration of Ag^+ exceeds 2.4×10^{-5} M.

(c) Before the equivalence point the maximum concentration of Ag^+ is 1.3×10^{-5} M, which is smaller than the concentration of Ag^+ necessary to cause precipitation of Ag_2CrO_4.

18.72   (a) $CaO(s) + H_2O(l) \longrightarrow Ca(OH)_2(s)$

$Ca(OH)_2(s) \rightleftharpoons Ca^{2+}(aq) + 2OH^-(aq)$

$Mg^{2+}(aq) + 2OH^-(aq) \rightleftharpoons Mg(OH)_2(s)$

(b) The initial $[Mg^{2+}]$ is

$$\frac{1.30 \text{ g Mg}^{2+}}{1 \text{ L}} \times \frac{1 \text{ mol Mg}^{2+}}{24.3 \text{ g Mg}^{2+}} = 0.053 \text{ M Mg}^{2+}$$

The $[OH^-]$ of the seawater solution is

pOH = 14.00 − pH = 14.00 − 11.3 = 2.7 and $[OH^-]$ = antilog(−2.7) = $10^{-2.7}$ = 0.002 M

The maximum concentration of Mg^{2+} permissable when $[OH^-]$ = 0.002 M is

$$[Mg^{2+}] = \frac{K_{sp}}{[OH^-]^2} = \frac{7.1 \times 10^{-12}}{(0.002)^2} = 1.8 \times 10^{-6} \text{ M (carry extra significant figure)}$$

The percent of the Mg^{2+} not removed is $\dfrac{1.8 \times 10^{-6} \text{ M}}{0.053 \text{ M}} \times 100\% = 3 \times 10^{-3}\%$

(c)

$$1000 \text{ L} \times \frac{1.30 \text{ g Mg}}{1 \text{ L}} \times 0.99997 = 1.30 \times 10^3 \text{ g Mg} = 1.30 \text{ kg Mg}$$

(to three significant figures)

18.75 The reactions that have to be considered are

$BaF_2(s) \rightleftharpoons Ba^{2+}(aq) + 2F^-(aq)$

$F^-(aq) + H^+(aq) \rightleftharpoons HF(aq)$

The Ba^{2+} ion remains unchanged in solution. The molar solubility of BaF_2, x, is equal to $[Ba^{2+}]$, which is also equal to half the sum of the concentrations of the species containing the fluoride ion, or

$$x = \frac{[F^-] + [HF]}{2} \text{ and } [F^-] + [HF] = 2x$$

The ratio of [HF] to $[F^-]$ at this pH is ($[H^+]$ = 3.5 × 10^{-3} M and K_a = 3.53 × 10^{-4})

$$\frac{[HF]}{[F^-][H^+]} = \frac{1}{K_a} \text{ and } \frac{[HF]}{[F^-]} = \frac{[H^+]}{K_a} = \frac{3.5 \times 10^{-3}}{3.53 \times 10^{-4}} = 9.9$$

Therefore, [HF] = 9.9$[F^-]$; $[F^-]$ + 9.9$[F^-]$ = 2x and $[F^-] = \dfrac{2x}{10.9}$

Substituting in the K_{sp} expression gives

$[Ba^{2+}][F^-]^2 = K_{sp}$

$$(x)\left[\frac{2x}{10.9}\right]^2 = 1.3 \times 10^{-6} \text{ and } x = 3.4 \times 10^{-2} \text{ M}$$

The molar solubility of BaF_2 in a solution buffered at pH 2.46 is 3.4 × 10^{-2} mol/L.

18.76 The reactions that have to be considered are

$CH_3COOAg(s) \rightleftharpoons CH_3COO^-(aq) + Ag^+(aq)$

$CH_3COO^-(aq) + H^+(aq) \rightleftharpoons CH_3COOH(aq)$

The Ag^+ ion remains unchanged in solution. The $[Ag^+]$ is equal to the molar solubility of CH_3COOAg, 0.50 M, which is also equal to the sum of the concentrations of the species containing the acetate ion, or

$[Ag^+] = [CH_3COO^-] + [CH_3COOH] = 0.50$ M

Since the solution is saturated with CH_3COOAg, the $[CH_3COO^-]$ can be obtained from the K_{sp} expression

$$[CH_3COO^-][Ag^+] = K_{sp} \quad \text{and} \quad [CH_3COO^-] = \frac{K_{sp}}{[Ag^+]} = \frac{2.5 \times 10^{-3}}{0.50} = 5.0 \times 10^{-3} \text{ M}$$

The $[CH_3COOH]$ is therefore

$$[CH_3COOH] = 0.50 \text{ M} - [CH_3COO^-] = 0.50 \text{ M} - 0.0050 \text{ M} = 0.50 \text{ M}$$

Substituting in the K_a expression gives

$$\frac{[CH_3COO^-][H^+]}{[CH_3COOH]} = K_a$$

$$[H^+] = K_a \frac{[CH_3COOH]}{[CH_3COO^-]} = \frac{(1.76 \times 10^{-5})(0.50)}{(0.0050)} = 1.8 \times 10^{-3} \text{ M}$$

and $pH = -\log[H^+] = -\log(1.8 \times 10^{-3}) = 2.74$

18.77   (a) Using a concentration summary similar to that in Practice Exercise 18.21 gives

$$AgCl: \frac{[Ag(NH_3)_2^+][Cl^-]}{[NH_3]^2} = K_{sp} \times K_f$$

$$\frac{(x)(x)}{(1.0 - 2x)^2} = (1.8 \times 10^{-10})(1.6 \times 10^7) = 2.9 \times 10^{-3}$$

$$\frac{x}{1.0 - 2x} = 5.4 \times 10^{-2} \quad \text{and} \quad x = 0.049 \text{ M}$$

The molar solubility of $AgCl$ in 1.0 M NH_3 is 0.049 M.

$$AgBr: \frac{[Ag(NH_3)_2^+][Br^-]}{[NH_3]^2} = K_{sp} \times K_f$$

$$\frac{(x)(x)}{(1.0 - 2x)^2} = (5.0 \times 10^{-13})(1.6 \times 10^7) = 8.0 \times 10^{-6}$$

$$\frac{x}{1.0 - 2x} = 2.8 \times 10^{-3} \quad \text{and} \quad x = 0.0028 \text{ M}$$

The molar solubility of $AgBr$ in 1.0 M NH_3 is 0.0028 M.

$$AgI: \frac{[Ag(NH_3)_2^+][I^-]}{[NH_3]^2} = K_{sp} \times K_f$$

$$\frac{(x)(x)}{(1.0 - 2x)^2} = (8.3 \times 10^{-17})(1.6 \times 10^7) = 1.3 \times 10^{-9}$$

$$\frac{x}{1.0 - 2x} = 3.6 \times 10^{-5} \quad \text{and} \quad x = 3.6 \times 10^{-5} \text{ M}$$

The molar solubility of AgI in 1.0 M NH_3 is 3.6 x 10^{-5} M.

Aqueous NH_3 serves as a fairly good solvent for $AgCl$ and $AgBr$.

(b) Using a similar concentration summary as that in Example 18.18 gives

AgBr: $\dfrac{[Ag(S_2O_3)_2{}^{3-}][Br^-]}{[S_2O_3{}^{2-}]^2} = K_{sp} \times K_f$

$\dfrac{(x)(x)}{(1.0 - 2x)^2} = (5.0 \times 10^{-13})(1.7 \times 10^{13}) = 8.5$

$\dfrac{x}{1.0 - 2x} = 2.9$ and $x = 0.43$ M

The molar solubility of AgBr in 1.0 M $Na_2S_2O_3$ is 0.43 M.

AgI: $\dfrac{[Ag(S_2O_3)_2{}^{3-}][I^-]}{[S_2O_3{}^{2-}]^2} = K_{sp} \times K_f$

$\dfrac{(x)(x)}{(1.0 - 2x)^2} = (8.3 \times 10^{-17})(1.7 \times 10^{13}) = 1.4 \times 10^{-3}$

$\dfrac{x}{1.0 - 2x} = 3.7 \times 10^{-2}$ and $x = 0.034$ M

The molar solubility of AgI in 1.0 M $Na_2S_2O_3$ is 0.034 M.

Yes. The results show that both AgBr and AgI are considerably more soluble in $Na_2S_2O_3$ than in aqueous NH_3.

(c) Yes. The $Ag(CN)_2{}^-$ K_f of 1×10^{21} is considerably greater than the $Ag(NH_3)_2{}^+$ K_f of 1.6×10^7 and the $Ag(S_2O_3)_2{}^{3-}$ K_f of 1.7×10^{13}. Therefore, the complexing agent CN^- should be more effective for dissolving AgI.

CHAPTER S3

A SURVEY OF THE ELEMENTS 3:
THE REMAINING NONMETALS

Solutions To Practice Exercises

PE S3.1 Draw a horizontal line from left to right at 1 atm pressure to intersect the rhombic-monoclinic transformation curve. Then draw a vertical line down to the temperature scale. The phases are in equilibrium under 1 atm pressure at approximately 95°C.

PE S3.4 Refer to Fig. S3.12.
   (a) Each oxygen atom has four VSEPR pairs (two bonding and two lone pairs) and, therefore, is sp³ hybridized. According to this model one would expect the P-O-P bond angles to be slightly less than 109.5°, because of some lone pair-lone pair repulsion. (Note: The observed angle is 127°.)
   (b) Predicted angle same as (a). (Note: The observed angle is 123°.)

   Comment: VSEPR predictions are not universally correct.

Solutions to Final Exercises

S3.4 (a) See Fig. S3.4 and answer to Final Exercise 10.50.
   (b) Each S atom has four VSEPR pairs (two bonding and two lone pairs) and, therefore, is sp³ hybridized. Consequently, the bond angles should be approximately 109.5°.
   (c) The S-S-S tetrahedral bond angles force the ring to take on a puckered shape, since that shape has the least potential energy associated with it.

S3.5 (a) Refer to Occurrence, Preparation, Properties and Uses of the Elements in Section S3.1 for details about each type of sulfur.

$$S_8(\text{rhombic}) \underset{}{\overset{95.5\,°C}{\rightleftharpoons}} S_8(\text{monoclinic}) \underset{}{\overset{119.0\,°C}{\rightleftharpoons}} S_8(l) \underset{\text{to } 190\,°C}{\overset{\text{heat}}{\rightleftharpoons}} \text{viscous}$$

$$\text{sulfur} \underset{>190\,°C}{\overset{\text{heat}}{\rightleftharpoons}} \text{mobile sulfur} \overset{447.7\,°C}{\rightleftharpoons} \text{gaseous sulfur} \overset{1000\,°C}{\rightleftharpoons} S_2(g)$$

Sudden cooling of liquid sulfur produces plastic sulfur.

(b) Refer to figures in the textbook.

S3.7   (a) Sulfur has the same outer or valence electronic configuration as oxygen. They are both Group 6A elements. Therefore, sulfur can participate in the same kind of bonding as oxygen.

(b) Sulfur replacement should diminish the strength of an oxo acid, since sulfur is less electronegative than oxygen and, therefore, the O–H bond should not be as polar.

S3.8   Some of the resonance structures are:

(a)

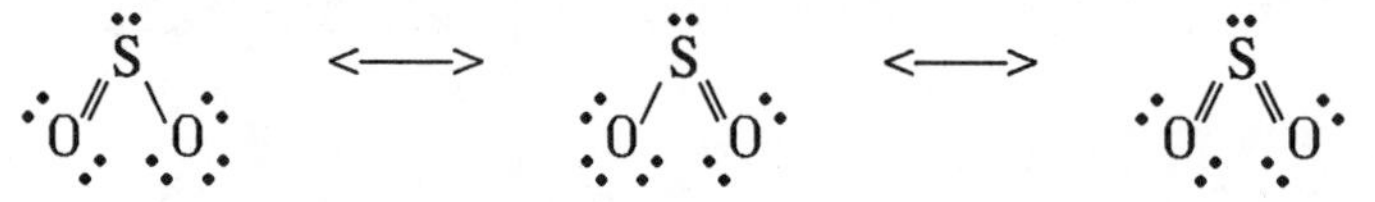

(b)

(c)

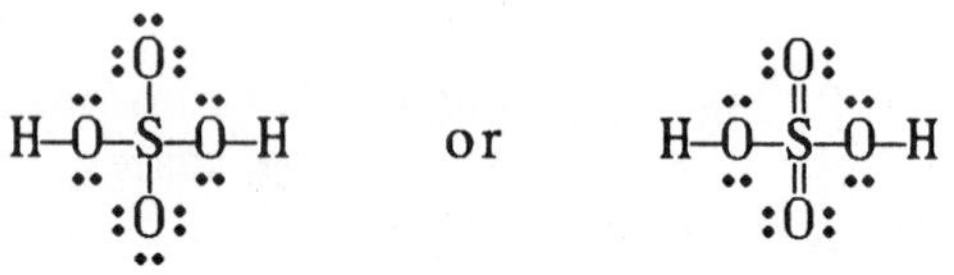

        or

(d)

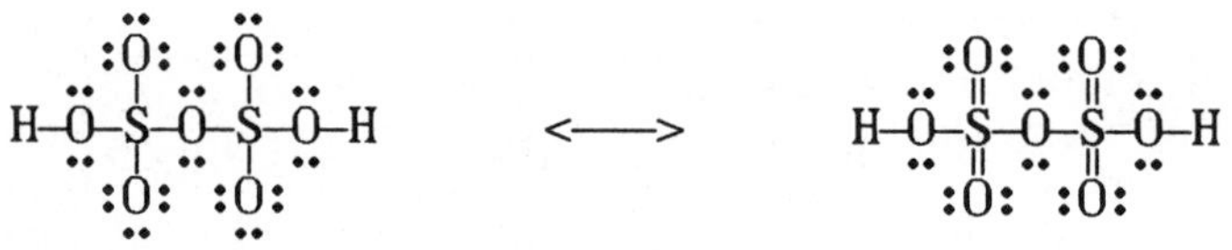

(e)

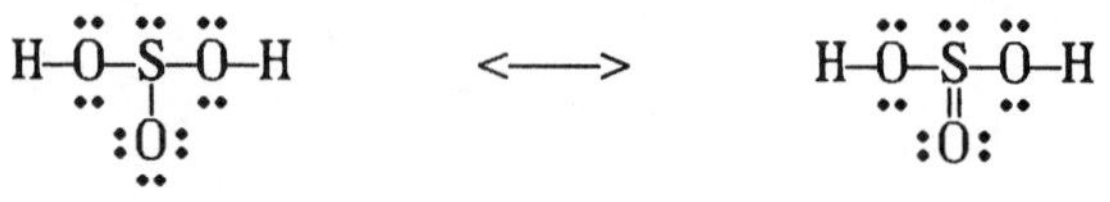

(f)

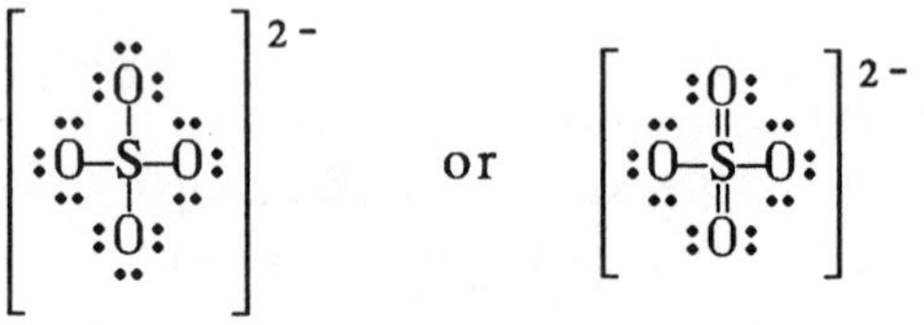

        or   resonance hybrid

(g)

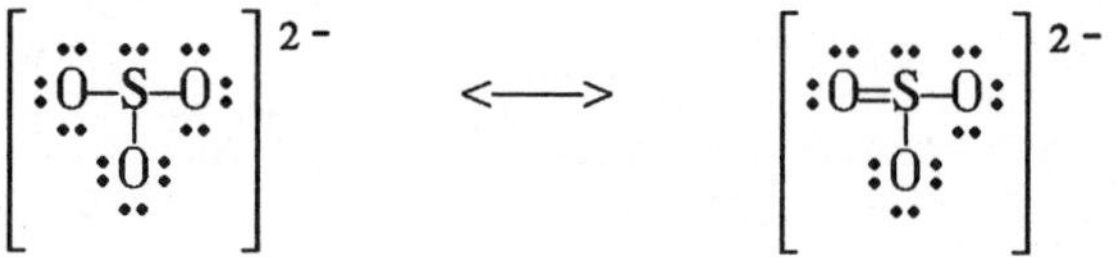

        resonance hybrid

(h)

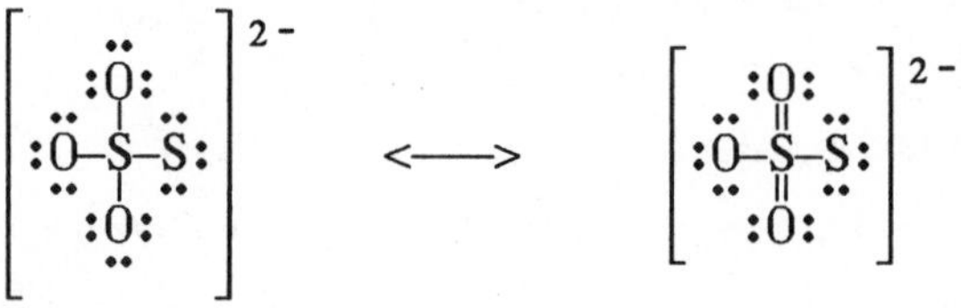

Comment: In Lewis structures any of the $S-\overset{\cdot\cdot}{\underset{\cdot\cdot}{O}}:$ bonds can be written as $S=\overset{\cdot\cdot}{O}$ and vice versa. Some chemists prefer one form over the other, depending on their viewpoint.

S3.10 (a) Sulfur, being in the third period, has empty d orbitals in the valence shell that can be involved in bonding and it is therefore known to form as many as six bonds. Oxygen, on the other hand, being in the second period has only two vacancies in its valence shell and can form only two bonds.

(b) The sulfur atom in SF_4 has a lone pair of electrons in its valence shell that can participate in further bonding, while all the sulfur valence electrons in SF_6 are already involved in bonding.

S3.14 (a) Wood is made up largely of cellulose $(C_6H_{10}O_5)_n$, a polymer in which the unit $C_6H_{10}O_5$ is repeated n times. H_2SO_4 chars wood by removing the hydrogen and oxygen from the cellulose.

$$(C_6H_{10}O_5)_n(s) + 5nH_2SO_4(98\%) \longrightarrow 6nC(s) + 5nH_2SO_4 \cdot H_2O(l)$$

(b) The concentrated sulfuric acid dehydrates the $CuSO_4 \cdot 5H_2O$ forming $CuSO_4$, which is a white powder.

$$CuSO_4 \cdot 5H_2O(s) + 5H_2SO_4(98\%) \longrightarrow CuSO_4(s) + 5H_2SO_4 \cdot H_2O(l)$$

(c) The concentrated sulfuric acid oxidizes the bromide ion to bromine, which is a red brown liquid (see Hydrogen Halides and Their Salts in Section S2.3 in the textbook).

$$2NaBr(s) + 3H_2SO_4(98\%) \longrightarrow Br_2(l) + 2NaHSO_4(s) + SO_2(g) + 2H_2O(l)$$

(d) The concentrated sulfuric acid oxidizes the copper.

$$Cu(s) + 2H_2SO_4(aq)(concentrated) \longrightarrow CuSO_4(aq) + SO_2(g) + 2H_2O(l)$$

S3.15 (a) Add a strong acid like HCl to the test tube containing the solid. If it's calcium sulfite, an acrid-smelling gas, SO_2, will be given off. If it's $CaSO_4$, no reaction will take place.

(b) Add some solid AgCl or AgBr to the solution. If the solution is sodium thiosulfate, then the solid will dissolve as $Ag(S_2O_3)_2^{3-}$ forms. If the solution is sodium sulfite, then no reaction will occur. Alternately, the addition of a strong acid like HCl will distinguish between them, since a yellow precipitate will form in the thiosulfate solution; namely,

$$\underset{\text{smell}}{Na_2SO_3(aq) + 2H^+(aq) \longrightarrow 2Na^+(aq) + SO_2(g) + H_2O(l)}$$

$$Na_2S_2O_3(aq) + 2H^+(aq) \longrightarrow 2Na^+(aq) + \underset{\text{yellow ppt}}{S(s)} + \underset{\text{smell}}{SO_2(g)} + H_2O(l)$$

S3.16 (a) $Na_2SO_3(aq) + 2HCl(aq) \longrightarrow 2NaCl(aq) + SO_2(g) + H_2O(l)$

(b) $AgBr(s) + 2Na_2S_2O_3(aq) \longrightarrow Na_3Ag(S_2O_3)_2(aq) + NaBr(aq)$

(c) $5S_2O_3^{2-}(aq) + 8MnO_4^-(aq) + 14H^+(aq) \longrightarrow 8Mn^{2+}(aq) + 10SO_4^{2-}(aq) + 7H_2O(l)$

(d) $2S_2O_3^{2-}(aq) + I_2(s) \longrightarrow S_4O_6^{2-}(aq) + 2I^-(aq)$

(e) $3(S^{2-}(aq) \longrightarrow S(s) + 2e^-)$ oxidation

$\underline{2(CrO_4^{2-}(aq) + 4H_2O(l) + 3e^- \longrightarrow Cr(OH)_4^-(aq) + 4OH^-(aq))}$ reduction

$3S^{2-}(aq) + 2CrO_4^{2-}(aq) + 8H_2O(l) \longrightarrow 3S(s) + 2Cr(OH)_4^-(aq) + 8OH^-(aq)$

(f) $H_2S(aq) + 4H_2O(l) \longrightarrow H_2SO_4(aq) + 8H^+(aq) + 8e^-$ oxidation

$\underline{8(HNO_3(aq) + H^+(aq) + e^- \longrightarrow NO_2(g) + H_2O(l))}$ reduction

$H_2S(aq) + 8HNO_3(aq, conc) \longrightarrow H_2SO_4(aq) + 8NO_2(g) + 4H_2O(l)$

(g) $K_2S(aq) + S(s) \overset{heat}{\longrightarrow} K_2S_2(aq)$

(h) $Na_2SO_3(aq) + S(s) \overset{heat}{\longrightarrow} Na_2S_2O_3(aq)$

S3.20   First salt: NaCl

$$NaCl(s) + H_2SO_4(aq) \longrightarrow NaHSO_4(aq) + HCl(g)$$
       hot, conc.

$$AgNO_3(aq) + HCl(aq) \longrightarrow AgCl(s) + HNO_3(aq)$$
                                    white

Second salt: $NaNO_3$

$$NaNO_3(s) + H_2SO_4(aq) \longrightarrow NaHSO_4(aq) + HNO_3(g)$$
        hot, conc.

$$Cu(s) + 4HNO_3(aq) \longrightarrow Cu(NO_3)_2(aq) + 2NO_2(g) + 2H_2O(l)$$
                                        brown gas

S3.23   (a) CuS. The electronegativity decreases in going down the group.
   (b) H_2Te. The atomic radius increases in going down the group. Therefore, TeH^- is a larger ion with greater charge diffusion (weaker basicity) than SH^-.
   (c) H_2SO_3. The atomic radius increases in going down the group causing $(HO)SO_2^-$ to have greater charge dispersal (weaker basicity), due to more effective p-d π bonding, than $(HO)TeO_2^-$.

S3.25   (a) White phosphorus is composed of P_4 molecules. Red phosphorus has a variable covalent network structure.
   (b) White phosphorus is a volatile waxy solid. Red phosphorus is a less volatile, less soluble, more dense, mulberry-colored solid. White phosphorus is soluble in CS_2, while red phosphorus is not.
   (c) Both undergo the same chemical reactions, but red phosphorus is less reactive than white phosphorus.
   (d) White phosphorus is very toxic. Red phosphorus is realatively nonpoisonous.

   The lower volatility, lower solubility, greater density, and lower reactivity of red phosphorus are all related to the extended polymeric structure of red phosphorus. The relatively weak intramolecular forces between the P_4 molecules in white phosphorus allows them to be easily separated, while the covalent bonding between the P atoms in red phosphorus lowers their reactivity.

S3.28   (a) Refer to Figs. S3.7 and S3.12.
   (b) P_4O_6 is related to P_4 by having an oxygen atom inserted in each of the six edges of the P_4 tetrahedron. P_4O_{10} is related to P_4O_6 by having another oxygen atom added or bonded to each of the four phosphorus atoms.

S3.29   (a)

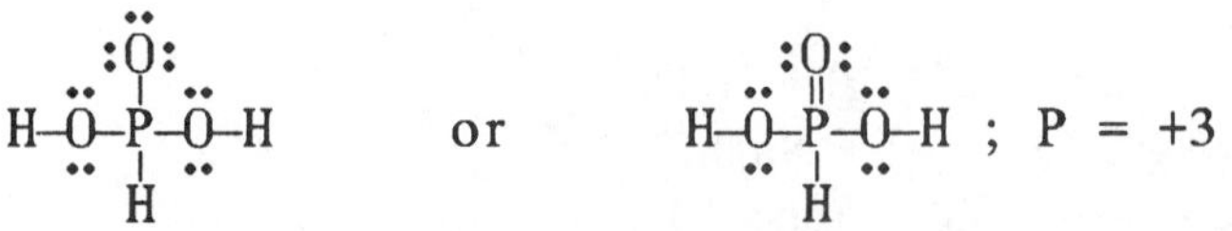

   (b)

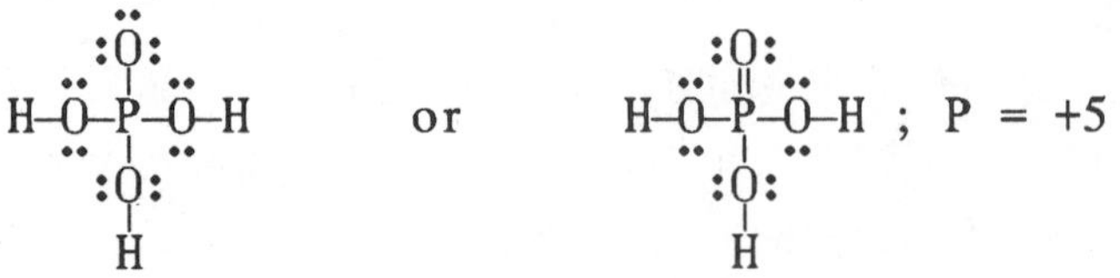

   (c)

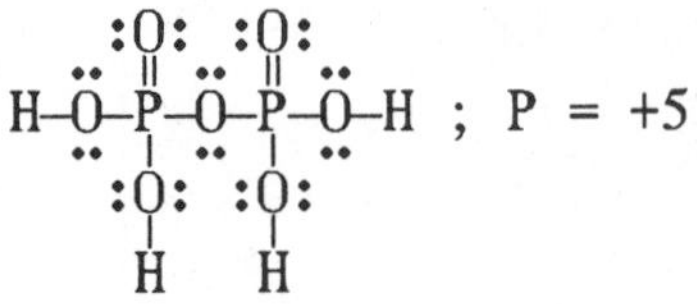

Comment: In Lewis structures any of the P–O̤: bonds can be written as P=O̤ and

vice versa. Some chemists prefer one form over the other, depending on their viewpoint.

S2.30 Refer to the Lewis structures in S3.29. In H_3PO_4 each H atom is attached to an oxygen atom and is therefore acidic. In H_3PO_3, on the other hand, only two of the H atoms are attached to oxygen atoms, the third H atom is attached to phosphorus, and therefore, only two of the H atoms are acidic.

S3.37 (a) $Ca_3(PO_4)_2(s) + H_2SO_4(aq) \longrightarrow 2CaHPO_4(aq) + CaSO_4(aq)$
(b) $Ca_3(PO_4)_2(s) + 2H_2SO_4(aq) \longrightarrow Ca(H_2PO_4)_2(s) + 2CaSO_4(s)$

These products make better fertilizer becasue they are more soluble than the original phosphate rock.

S3.39 This illustrates the trend in main periodic groups of favoring the lower of two positive oxidation states toward the bottom of the group. Both As and P are in +5 oxidation states. But As lies below P in Group 5A and, therefore, its +5 oxidation state will be somewhat less stable, and consequently, more reactive than phosphorus's +5 oxidation state, everything else being equal.

S3.40 (a) $H_3AsO_4 < H_3PO_4 < HNO_3$. The strength of these acids is primarily determined by the atomic radius of the central atom, which increases in going down the group. The smaller the central atom, the more effective the charge dispersal through extended π bonding in the conjugate base. (The greater the charge dispersal, the weaker the base). Another factor is the electronegativity of the central atom. The greater the electronegativity, the greater the O–H bond polarity and the greater the strength. And the electronegativity decreases as you go down the group.
(b) NH_3. NH_3 is a stronger base, since As has a considerably larger atomic radius than N, which leads to greater charge diffusion on AsH_3. Evidence for this lies in the fact that NH_3 forms NH_4^+, but AsH_3 does not form AsH_4^+.

S3.45 (a) $2C(s) + O_2(g) \longrightarrow 2CO(g)$
(b) $C(s) + O_2(g) \longrightarrow CO_2(g)$
Limited oxygen supply and/or temperatures above $500°C$ favor the formation of CO.

S3.47 (a) $C(s) + 2H_2O(g) \longrightarrow CO_2(g) + 4H^+(aq) + 4e^-$ balanced oxidation
$NO_3^-(aq) + 2H^+(aq) + e^- \longrightarrow NO_2(g) + H_2O(g)$ balanced reduction
(b) $C(s) + 2H_2O(g) \longrightarrow CO_2(g) + 4H^+(aq) + 4e^-$ balanced oxidation
$SO_4^{2-}(aq) + 4H^+(aq) + 2e^- \longrightarrow SO_2(g) + 2H_2O(g)$ balanced reduction

S3.48 The sizes of silicon and germanium do not allow them to form strong pi bonds with oxygen, while the much smaller carbon can form strong pi bonds with oxygen.

S3.55 (a) $:N≡N:$; $:C≡O:$; $[:C≡N:]^-$; $[:C≡C:]^{2-}$
(b) They are all isoelectronic. They all contain a triple bond and lone pairs of electrons.
(c) They are all Lewis bases.

S3.60 (a)   (b)

(c) Water glass is a saturated solution of sodium silicate (Na_4SiO_4).

S3.67 (a) The reaction in terms of the tetraborate ion, $B_4O_7^{2-}$, portion of borax, $Na_2B_4O_7 \cdot 10H_2O$, is

$$B_4O_7^{2-} + \underset{(strong \; acid)}{2H^+(aq)} + 5H_2O(l) \Longrightarrow 4H_3BO_3(aq)$$

(b) $B(OH)_3(aq) + H_2O(l) \Longrightarrow B(OH)_4^-(aq) + H^+(aq)$

(c) $2H_3BO_3(s) \xrightarrow{heat} B_2O_3(s) + 3H_2O(g)$

S3.68 Refer to Section S3.5 in the textbook. Boric acid is monoprotic, and not tripotic, because it acts as a Lewis acid and not a Brönsted acid.

S3.70 (a) In a hydrogen bridge bond there is one pair of electrons that holds three atoms together, with hydrogen being the middle atom in the extended covalent bond. In a hydrogen bond, on the other hand, the hydrogen atom, which is very small, is the link between two highly electronegative atoms; the three linked atoms sharing two pairs of electrons in a unique type of bond that combines both covalent bonding and electrostatic attraction elements.

(b) Hydrogen bridge bonds are found in electron-deficient compounds; compounds in which the atoms possess too few valence electrons for them to be held together by ordinary covalent bonds.

S3.73 (a) brimstone: S, sulfur
(b) epsom salts: $MgSO_4 \cdot 7H_2O$, magnesium sulfate heptahydrate
(c) gypsum: $CaSO_4 \cdot 2H_2O$, calcium sulfate dihydrate
(d) oil of vitrol: H_2SO_4, sulfuric acid
(e) oleum: $H_2S_2O_7$, pyrosulfuric acid
(f) phosphoric anhydride: P_4O_{10}, phosphorus pentoxide
(g) silica gel: SiO_2, silicon dioxide (with some hydration)
(h) talc: $Mg_2(Si_2O_5)_2 \cdot Mg(OH)_2$, sheet silicate
(i) borax: $Na_2B_4O_7 \cdot 10H_2O$, hydrated sodium tetraborate.

S3.75 We have to determine if the ion product Q exceeds the solubility product constant K_{sp}. If $Q > K_{sp}$, then a precipitate forms. If $Q \leq K_{sp}$, then all the ions remain in solution.

(a)
$$[Pb^{2+}] = \frac{10 \; mL \; x \; 0.1 \; mmol/mL}{11 \; mL} = 0.09 \; M$$

$$[SO_4^{2-}] = \frac{1 \; mL \; x \; 0.1 \; mmol/mL}{11 \; mL} = 0.009 \; M$$

Substituting these concentrations into the ion product expression gives

$Q = [Pb^{2+}][SO_4^{2-}] = (0.09)(0.009) = 8.1 \; x \; 10^{-4}$

The ion product Q is greater than the K_{sp} value of $6.3 \; x \; 10^{-7}$, so $PbSO_4$ will precipitate.

Answer: A white precipitate will form.

(b) $[Pb^{2+}] = 0.09$ M and $[S^{2-}] = 0.009$ M. Substituting these concentrations into the ion product expression gives

$Q = [Pb^{2+}][S^{2-}] = (0.09)(0.009) = 8.1 \; x \; 10^{-4}$

The ion product Q is greater than the K_{sp} value of $3 \; x \; 10^{-28}$, so PbS will precipitate.

Answer: A black precipitate will form.

(c) The $Pb(NO_3)_2$-Na_2S mixture, since the PbS solubility constant is much smaller than that of $PbSO_4$.

S3.76 (a) $2CaCO_3(s) + 2S(s) + 3O_2(g) \longrightarrow 2CaSO_4(s) + 2CO_2(g)$

The other product is CO_2, which escapes into the atmosphere.

(b) The mass of sulfur in the coal is 1000 kg x 0.035 = 35 kg or 3.5×10^4 g. The steps in the calculation are: g S $\longrightarrow$ mol S $\longrightarrow$ mol $CaCO_3$ $\longrightarrow$ g $CaCO_3$.

$$3.5 \times 10^4 \text{ g S} \times \frac{1 \text{ mol S}}{32 \text{ g S}} \times \frac{2 \text{ mol } CaCO_3}{2 \text{ mol S}} \times \frac{100 \text{ g } CaCO_3}{1 \text{ mol } CaCO_3}$$

$= 1.1 \times 10^5$ g or 110 kg $CaCO_3$

S3.78 (a) $Si_3H_8(g) + 5O_2(g) \longrightarrow 3SiO_2(s) + 4H_2O(l)$

The enthalpy change is the sum of the enthalpy changes for the following steps:

$\underline{\Delta H°}$

1. Breaking 2 mol of Si-Si bonds:	2 x +222 kJ =	+444 kJ
2. Breaking 8 mol of Si-H bonds:	8 x +318 kJ =	+2544 kJ
3. Breaking 5 mol of O=O bonds:	5 x +498.3 kJ =	+2491.5 kJ
4. Forming 12 mol of Si-O bonds:	12 x -452 kJ =	-5424 kJ
5. Forming 8 mol of O-H bonds:	8 x -463 kJ =	-3704 kJ

$\Delta H_c° = $ Sum $= -3,648$ kJ

The enthalpy of combustion of Si_3H_8 is –3,648 kJ/mol.

(b) The enthalpy of combustion of C_3H_8 is –2,219.9 kJ/mol (see Table 6.2). The enthalpy of combustion of Si_3H_8 is considerably greater than that of C_3H_8.

(c) Propane is much more stable than Si_3H_8. Therefore, propane can be safely handled, transported, and stored, while Si_3H_8 cannot.

S3.79 (a) $4P(s) + 5O_2(g) \longrightarrow P_4O_{10}(s)$
white

$\Delta H° = \Delta H_f°(P_4O_{10}) - 4 \times \Delta H_f°(P_{white}) - 5 \times \Delta H_f°(O_2)$

$= -2,984.0$ kJ $- 4 \times 0$ kJ $- 5 \times 0$ kJ $= -2,984.0$ kJ

(b) $4P(s) + 5O_2(g) \longrightarrow P_4O_{10}(s)$
red

$\Delta H° = \Delta H_f°(P_4O_{10}) - 4 \times \Delta H_f°(P_{red}) - 5 \times \Delta H_f°(O_2)$

$= -2,984.0$ kJ $- 4 \times -17.6$ kJ $- 0$ kJ $= -2,913.6$ kJ

S3.80 (a) S_2: $(\sigma_{3s})^2(\sigma_{3s}^*)^2(\sigma_{3px})^2(\pi_{3py})^2(\pi_{3pz})^2(\pi_{3py}^*)^1(\pi_{3pz}^*)^1$
O_2: $(\sigma_{2s})^2(\sigma_{2s}^*)^2(\sigma_{2px})^2(\pi_{2py})^2(\pi_{2pz})^2(\pi_{2py}^*)^1(\pi_{2pz}^*)^1$

They differ mainly in that sulfur uses orbitals from the third shell, while oxygen uses orbitals from the second shell.

(b) The size of sulfur does not allow the 3p orbitals to overlap sufficiently to form strong pi bonds.

(c) S_2 has essentially a single σ bond, the σ_{3px} bond, holding it together, since the net pi bond is weak. Therefore, any structure, like the S_8 ring structure, that has two σ bonds per sulfur atom would be more stable at room temperature.

S3.81 (a) Substituting d = 1.09 g/L, T = 298 K, and P = 0.500 atm into Equation 5.10 gives

$$M = \frac{dRT}{P} = \frac{1.09 \text{ g}}{1 \text{ L}} \times \frac{0.0821 \text{ L atm/mol K} \times 298 \text{ K}}{0.500 \text{ atm}} = 53.3 \text{ g/mol}$$

(b) The molar mass of boron is 10.811 g. Therefore, there can be at most four boron atoms in the molecule. Three boron atoms is not acceptable, however, since then we would have to exceed the maximum number of hydrogen atoms allowed, which is nine. Therefore, the molecule must contain four boron atoms. The number of hydrogen atoms in the molecule is

$$(53.3 - 43.2) \text{ g H} \times \frac{1 \text{ mol H atoms}}{1.01 \text{ g H}} = 10 \text{ mol H atoms}$$

or 10 H atoms per molecule. A reasonable molecular formula is therefore B_4H_{10}.

S3.82 The balanced equation for the reaction is

$2(MnO_4^-(aq) + 8H^+(aq) + 5e^- \longrightarrow Mn^{2+}(aq) + 4H_2O(l))$ reduction
$5(2S_2O_3^{2-}(aq) \longrightarrow S_4O_6^{2-}(aq) + 2e^-)$ oxidation

---

$2MnO_4^-(aq) + 10S_2O_3^{2-}(aq) + 16H^+(aq) \longrightarrow 2Mn^{2+}(aq) + 5S_4O_6^{2-}(aq) + 8H_2O(l)$

The steps in the calculation are: g $Na_2S_2O_3$ $\longrightarrow$ mol $Na_2S_2O_3$ $\longrightarrow$ mol $KMnO_4$ $\longrightarrow$ molarity $KMnO_4$.

$$3.16 \text{ g } Na_2S_2O_3 \times \frac{1 \text{ mol } Na_2S_2O_3}{158.1 \text{ g } Na_2S_2O_3} \times \frac{2 \text{ mol } KMnO_4}{10 \text{ mol } Na_2S_2O_3} = 4.00 \times 10^{-3} \text{ mol } KMnO_4$$

The molarity of the $KMnO_4$ solution is

$$\frac{4.00 \times 10^{-3} \text{ mol}}{0.0241 \text{ L}} = 0.166 \text{ M}$$

S3.83 All of the $KMnO_4$ originally present is consumed in converting the iodide ion to iodine. Therefore, the amount of iodine produced is a measure of the amount of $KMnO_4$ originally present. The reaction between $Na_2S_2O_3$ and I_2 is (in the presence of iodide ion, molecular iodine is mostly in the form of the triiodide ion and we will write the reaction in that form):

$I_3^-(aq) + 2S_2O_3^{2-}(aq) \longrightarrow 3I^-(aq) + S_4O_6^{2-}(aq)$

The steps in the calculation are: V x M ($Na_2S_2O_3$) $\longrightarrow$ mol $Na_2S_2O_3$ $\longrightarrow$ mol I_2 $\longrightarrow$ mol $KMnO_4$ $\longrightarrow$ molarity $KMnO_4$.

$$0.02970 \text{ L} \times \frac{0.1010 \text{ mol } Na_2S_2O_3}{1 \text{ L}} \times \frac{1 \text{ mol } I_2}{2 \text{ mol } Na_2S_2O_3} \times \frac{2 \text{ mol } KMnO_4}{5 \text{ mol } I_2}$$

$$= 5.999 \times 10^{-4} \text{ mol } KMnO_4$$

The molarity of the $KMnO_4$ solution is

$$\frac{5.999 \times 10^{-4} \text{ mol}}{0.02500 \text{ L}} = 0.02400 \text{ M}$$

CHAPTER 19
FREE ENERGY, ENTROPY, AND
THE SECOND LAW OF THERMODYNAMICS

Solutions To Practice Exercises

PE 19.4 (a)

$$H_2O(l) \longrightarrow H_2O(g)$$

$\Delta G_f^o(kJ):\quad -237.129 \qquad -228.572$

$\Delta G^o = -228.572 \text{ kJ} - (-237.129 \text{ kJ}) = +8.6 \text{ kJ}$

(b) The water vapor condenses to liquid water.

PE 19.5 $\Delta G^o = 2 \times \Delta G_f^o(NO) + \Delta G_f^o(Cl_2) - 2 \times \Delta G_f^o(NOCl) = 2 \times 86.55 \text{ kJ} + 0 \text{ kJ} - 2 \times 66.08 \text{ kJ}$
$= +40.94 \text{ kJ}$

Substituting $\Delta G_f^o = 40.94$ kJ/mol = 40,940 J/mol, R = 8.314 J/mol K, and T = 298 K into Equation 19.4 gives

$$\ln K_p = \frac{\Delta G^o}{-RT} = \frac{40,940 \text{ J/mol}}{-8.314 \text{ J/mol K} \times 298 \text{ K}} = -16.5$$

and $K_p = \text{antilog}(-16.5) = e^{-16.5} = 7 \times 10^{-8}$

PE 19.6 (a) $H_2O(l) \rightleftharpoons H_2O(g)$

$\Delta G = \Delta G^o + RT \ln Q = \Delta G^o + RT \ln P_{H_2O}$

$\Delta G = 0 + 8.314 \times 10^{-3} \text{ kJ/mol K} \times 373 \text{ K} \times \ln 2.00 = +2.15 \text{ kJ/mol}$

(b) ΔG is positive, so condensation is thermodynamically favored.

PE 19.7 (a) Warming increases the entropy; the entropy increases.
(b) Two moles of gas are more disordered than 1 mol of gas; the entropy decreases.
(c) Two moles of gas are more disordered than 1 mol of gas and 1 mol of liquid; the entropy increases.

PE 19.8   The vaporization of liquid water at 100°C and 1 atm is an equilibrium process; therefore Equation 19.8 applies. The change in enthalpy is (the vaporization takes place under standard state conditions):

$$\Delta H° = 1 \text{ mol} \times 40.7 \text{ kJ/mol} = 40.7 \text{ kJ}$$

Substituting $\Delta H° = 40.7$ kJ and T = 373 K into Equation 19.8 gives

$$\Delta S° = \frac{\Delta H°}{T} = \frac{40.7 \text{ kJ}}{373 \text{ K}} = 0.109 \text{ kJ/K} = 109 \text{ J/K}$$

PE 19.9 $1/2 N_2(g) + 3/2 H_2(g) \longrightarrow NH_3(g)$

Substituting $\Delta G_f° = -16.45$ kJ/mol, $\Delta H_f° = -46.11$ kJ/mol, and T = 298 K into Equation 19.7 gives

$$\Delta G_f° = \Delta H_f° - T\Delta S_f°$$

-16.45 kJ/mol $= -46.11$ kJ/mol $- 298$ K $\times \Delta S_f°$ and $\Delta S_f° = -0.0995$ kJ/mol K $= -99.5$ J/mol K

PE 19.11

$$\Delta S° = \frac{\Delta H° - \Delta G°}{T} = \frac{-2816 \text{ kJ} + 2870 \text{ kJ}}{298 \text{ K}} = 0.181 \text{ kJ/K}$$

Assume that the values of $\Delta H°$ and $\Delta S°$ do not change significantly between 25°C and 37°C. Substituting $\Delta H° = -2816$ kJ, $\Delta S° = 0.181$ kJ/K, and T = 310 K into Equation 19.7 gives

$$\Delta G° = \Delta H° - T\Delta S° = -2816 \text{ kJ} - 310 \text{ K} \times 0.181 \text{ kJ/K} = -2872 \text{ kJ}$$

PE 19.12 $\Delta G = \Delta G° + RT \ln Q = \Delta G° + RT \ln P_{CO_2}$ (1)

We want to find the temperature at which ΔG is zero. The $\Delta G°$ in Equation (1) is the $\Delta G°$ at that temperature. Using Equation 19.7 and assuming that the values of $\Delta H°$ and $\Delta S°$ do not change significantly with temperature gives

$$\Delta G° = \Delta H° - T\Delta S° = 178.3 \text{ kJ/mol} - T \times 0.1606 \text{ kJ/mol K}$$

Substituting $\Delta G = 0$, $\Delta G° = \Delta H° - T\Delta S°$, $\Delta H° = +178.3$ kJ/mol, $\Delta S° = +0.1606$ kJ/mol K, R = 8.314 $\times 10^{-3}$ kJ/mol K, and $P_{CO_2} = 0.10$ atm into Equation (1), and solving for T gives

$$0 = \Delta H° - T\Delta S° + RT \ln P_{CO_2}; \quad -\Delta H° = T \times (-\Delta S° + R \ln P_{CO_2})$$

$$\text{and } T = \frac{-\Delta H°}{(-\Delta S° + R \ln P_{CO_2})}$$

$$= \frac{-178.3 \text{ kJ/mol}}{(-0.1606 \text{ kJ/mol K} + 8.314 \times 10^{-3} \text{ kJ/mol K} \times \ln 0.10)} = 992 \text{ K} = 719°C$$

Solutions to Final Exercises

19.6   (a) The system is at equilibrium; therefore $\Delta G = 0$.
(b) The forward reaction is spontaneous; therefore ΔG is negative.
(c) The forward reaction is spontaneous; therefore ΔG is negative.
(d) The system is at equilibrium; therefore $\Delta G = 0$.

19.9   (a) ΔG decreases with increasing reactant concentrations.
(b) ΔG increases with increasing product concentrations.

19.10   (a) $\Delta G = \Delta G°$ whenever Q = 1; in which case $\Delta G = \Delta G° + RT \ln Q = \Delta G° + RT \ln 1 = \Delta G°$.
(b) $\Delta G = 0$ when the system is at equilibrium. At that point there is no net driving force in either direction and Q = K.

(c) $\Delta G^\circ = 0$ when the system is at equilibrium and all the reactants and products are in their standard states, since then $K = 1$; namely,

$\Delta G^\circ = -RT \ln K = -RT \ln 1 = 0$.

Such a system would be unusual.

19.11   (a) $NH_3(g) \longrightarrow 1/2N_2(g) + 3/2H_2(g)$; $\Delta G^\circ = +16.45$ kJ/mol; stable

  (b) $HNO_3(l) \longrightarrow 1/2H_2(g) + 1/2N_2(g) + 3/2O_2(g)$; $\Delta G^\circ = +80.71$ kJ/mol; stable

  (c) $N_2O(g) \longrightarrow N_2(g) + 1/2O_2(g)$; $\Delta G^\circ = -104.20$ kJ/mol; unstable

  (d) $NO(g) \longrightarrow 1/2N_2(g) + 1/2O_2(g)$; $\Delta G^\circ = -86.55$ kJ/mol; unstable

  (e) $NO_2(g) \longrightarrow 1/2N_2(g) + O_2(g)$; $\Delta G^\circ = -51.31$ kJ/mol; unstable

HNO_3 is the most stable and N_2O is the least stable.

Comment: An alternate approach is: Compounds for which ΔG_f° is negative are stable with respect to their elements under standard state conditions. These include (a) NH_3 and (b) HNO_3. Compounds for which ΔG_f° is positive are unstable with respect to their elements under standard state conditions. These include (c) N_2O, (d) NO, and (e) NO_2. HNO_3 has the lowest ΔG_f° (–80.71 kJ/mol) and is therefore the most stable. N_2O has the highest ΔG_f° (+104.20 kJ/mol) and is therefore the least stable.

19.13   (a)

$$2SO_2(g) \quad + \quad O_2(g) \quad \rightleftharpoons \quad 2SO_3(g)$$

$\Delta G_f^\circ(kJ)$:   2 x –300.19   0   2 x –371.06

$\Delta G^\circ = $ 2 x –371.06 kJ – (2 x –300.19 kJ + 0 kJ) = –141.74 kJ

Since $\Delta G^\circ < 0$, the spontaneous direction is the forward reaction.

  (b)

$$Hg_2Cl_2(s) \quad \rightleftharpoons \quad HgCl_2(s) \quad + \quad Hg(l)$$

$\Delta G_f^\circ(kJ)$:   –210.7   –178.6   0

$\Delta G^\circ = $ –178.6 kJ + 0 kJ – (–210.7 kJ) = +32.1 kJ

Since $\Delta G^\circ > 0$, the spontaneous direction is the reverse reaction.

  (c)

$$2H_2S(g) \quad + \quad 3O_2(g) \quad \rightleftharpoons \quad 2H_2O(l) \quad + \quad 2SO_2(g)$$

$\Delta G_f^\circ(kJ)$:   2 x –33.6   0   2 x –237.1   2 x –300.2

$\Delta G^\circ = $ 2 x –237.1 kJ + 2 x –300.2 kJ – (2 x –33.6 kJ + 0 kJ) = –1007.4 kJ

Since $\Delta G^\circ < 0$, the spontaneous direction is the forward reaction.

19.14

$$Zn(s) \quad + \quad HgO(s) \quad \longrightarrow \quad ZnO(s) \quad + \quad Hg(l)$$

$\Delta G_f^\circ(kJ)$:   0   –58.54   –318.30   0

$\Delta G^\circ = $ –318.30 kJ + 0 kJ – (0 kJ – 58.54 kJ) = –259.76 kJ

The limiting reagent is HgO. The moles of HgO are

$$100 \text{ mg HgO} \times \frac{1 \text{ g}}{1000 \text{ mg}} \times \frac{1 \text{ mol HgO}}{216.59 \text{ g HgO}} = 4.62 \times 10^{-4} \text{ mol HgO}$$

The maximum electrical work is

maximum electrical work = –(4.62 x 10⁻⁴ mol x –259.76 kJ/mol) = 0.120 kJ

19.16 $Br_2(l) + Cl_2(g) \rightleftharpoons 2BrCl(g)$

$\Delta G° = 2 \times \Delta G_f°(BrCl) - \Delta G_f°(Br_2) - \Delta G_f°(Cl_2) = 2 \times -0.98 \text{ kJ} - 0 \text{ kJ} - 0 \text{ kJ} = -1.96 \text{ kJ} = -1960 \text{ J}$

$\Delta G = \Delta G° + RT \ln Q = \Delta G° + RT \ln \dfrac{P^2_{BrCl}}{P_{Cl_2}}$

$\Delta G = -1960 \text{ J/mol} + 8.314 \text{ J/mol K} \times 298 \text{ K} \times \ln \dfrac{(0.10)^2}{0.0010}$

$= +3740 \text{ J/mol or } 3.74 \text{ kJ/mol}$

Since $\Delta G > 0$, the reverse direction is spontaneous under these conditions.

19.18 $NH_4Cl(s) \rightleftharpoons NH_3(g) + HCl(g)$

$\Delta G° = \Delta G_f°(NH_3) + \Delta G_f°(HCl) - \Delta G_f°(NH_4Cl)$

$= -16.45 \text{ kJ} - 95.30 \text{ kJ} + 202.87 \text{ kJ} = +91.12 \text{ kJ} = +91,120 \text{ J}$

(a) $\Delta G = \Delta G° + RT \ln Q = \Delta G° + RT \ln P_{NH_3}P_{HCl}$

$\Delta G = +91,120 \text{ J/mol} + 8.314 \text{ J/mol K} \times 298 \text{ K} \times \ln (0.25)(0.40) = +85,400 \text{ J/mol or } 85.4 \text{ kJ/mol}$

(b) $\Delta G = +91,120 \text{ J/mol} + 8.314 \text{ J/mol K} \times 298 \text{ K} \times \ln (0.30)(0.30) = +85,200 \text{ J/mol or } 85.2 \text{ kJ/mol}$

The closer ΔG is to zero, the closer the system is to equilibrium. Therefore, the reacting system will be closer to equilibrium under the set of pressures in (b).

19.20 (a) $\Delta G° = -RT \ln K$

$\ln K = \dfrac{\Delta G°}{-RT} = 0 \text{ and } K = \text{antilog } 0 = e^0 = 1$

(b) When $\Delta G° < 0$, $\ln K > 0$, and $K > 1$.
(c) When $\Delta G° > 0$, $\ln K < 0$, and $K < 1$.

19.21 (a) Substituting $K_p = 2.7 \times 10^{-2}$, $T = 773$ K, and $R = 8.314$ J/mol K into Equation 19.4 gives

$\Delta G° = -RT \ln K_p = -8.314 \text{ J/mol K} \times 773 \text{ K} \times \ln(2.7 \times 10^{-2}) = +23,200 \text{ J/mol or } 23.2 \text{ kJ/mol}$

(b)

$\Delta G = \Delta G° + RT \ln Q = \Delta G° + RT \ln \dfrac{P^2_{NO}P_{Cl_2}}{P^2_{NOCl}}$

$\Delta G = +23,200 \text{ J/mol} + 8.314 \text{ J/mol K} \times 773 \text{ K} \times \ln \dfrac{(0.50)^2(0.50)}{(0.50)^2}$

$= +18,700 \text{ J/mol or } 18.7 \text{ kJ/mol}$

(c) $\Delta G > 0$, therefore the reverse direction is spontaneous under the conditions of part (b).

19.23 (a) $\Delta G° = 2 \times \Delta G_f°(NO) - \Delta G_f°(N_2) - \Delta G_f°(O_2) = 2 \times 86.55 \text{ kJ} - 0 \text{ kJ} - 0 \text{ kJ} = +173.1 \text{ kJ}$

$\ln K_p = \dfrac{\Delta G°}{-RT} = \dfrac{173,100 \text{ J/mol}}{-8.314 \text{ J/mol K} \times 298 \text{ K}} = -69.9$

and $K_p = \text{antilog}(-69.9) = e^{-69.9} = 4 \times 10^{-31}$

(b) $\Delta G° = 2 \times \Delta G_f°(O_3) - 3 \times \Delta G_f°(O_2) = 2 \times 163.2 \text{ kJ} - 3 \times 0 \text{ kJ} = +326.4 \text{ kJ}$

$\ln K_p = \dfrac{\Delta G°}{-RT} = \dfrac{326,400 \text{ J/mol}}{-8.314 \text{ J/mol K} \times 298 \text{ K}} = -132 \text{ and } K_p = \text{antilog}(-132) = e^{-132} = 10^{-58}$

(c) $\Delta G° = \Delta G_f°(C_2H_6) - \Delta G_f°(C_2H_4) - \Delta G_f°(H_2) = -32.82\ kJ - 68.15\ kJ - 0\ kJ = -100.97\ kJ$

$$\ln K_p = \frac{\Delta G°}{-RT} = \frac{-100,970\ J/mol}{-8.314\ J/mol\ K \times 298\ K} = +40.8$$

and $K_p = antilog(+40.8) = e^{+40.8} = 5 \times 10^{17}$

(d) $\Delta G° = \Delta G_f°(CaSO_4) - \Delta G_f°(CaO) - \Delta G_f°(SO_2) - 1/2\Delta G_f°(O_2)$

$= -1321.79\ kJ + 604.03\ kJ + 300.19\ kJ - 1/2 \times 0\ kJ = -417.57\ kJ$

$$\ln K_p = \frac{\Delta G°}{-RT} = \frac{-417,570\ J/mol}{-8.314\ J/mol\ K \times 298\ K} = +169 \text{ and } K_p = antilog(+169) = e^{+169} = 10^{73}$$

(e) $\Delta G° = 2 \times \Delta G_f°(HBr) - \Delta G_f°(H_2) - \Delta G_f°(Br_2) = 2 \times -53.45\ kJ - 0\ kJ - 0\ kJ = -106.9\ kJ$

$$\ln K_p = \frac{\Delta G°}{-RT} = \frac{-106,900\ J/mol}{-8.314\ J/mol\ K \times 298\ K} = +43.1$$

and $K_p = antilog(+43.1) = e^{+43.1} = 5 \times 10^{18}$

19.24   (a) $H_2O(l) \rightleftharpoons H_2O(g)$

$K_p = P_{H_2O} = 17.5\ torr/760\ torr = 2.30 \times 10^{-2}$

$\Delta G° = -RT \ln K_p = -8.314\ J/mol\ K \times 293\ K \times \ln(2.30 \times 10^{-2}) = 9,190\ J/mol = +9.19\ kJ/mol$

(b) The vapor pressure at the normal boiling point of water is 760 torr = 1 atm.

$K_p = P_{H_2O} = 1; \Delta G° = -RT \ln K_p = -RT \ln 1 = 0$

19.26   (a) $K_a = 1.76 \times 10^{-5}$

$\Delta G° = -RT \ln K_a = -8.314\ J/mol\ K \times 298\ K \times \ln(1.76 \times 10^{-5}) = 27,100\ J/mol = +27.1\ kJ/mol$

(b) $K_f = 1.2 \times 10^2$

$\Delta G° = -RT \ln K_f = -8.314\ J/mol\ K \times 298\ K \times \ln(1.2 \times 10^2) = -11,900\ J/mol = -11.9\ kJ/mol$

(c) $K_b = 1.77 \times 10^{-5}$

$\Delta G° = -RT \ln K_b = -8.314\ J/mol\ K \times 298\ K \times \ln(1.77 \times 10^5) = 27,100\ J/mol = +27.1\ kJ/mol$

(d) $K_{a2} = 1 \times 10^{-13}$

$\Delta G° = -RT \ln K_{a2} = -8.314\ J/mol\ K \times 298\ K \times \ln(1 \times 10^{-13}) = 74,200\ J/mol = +74.2\ kJ/mol$

(e) $K_{sp} = 1.8 \times 10^{-10}$. Reversing the direction of the reaction just changes the sign of $\Delta G°$, so

$\Delta G° = +RT \ln K_{sp} = +8.314\ J/mol\ K \times 298\ K \times \ln(1.8 \times 10^{-10}) = -55,600\ J/mol = -55.6\ kJ/mol$

19.29   (a) The entropy increases. A gas is more disordered than a solid.
(b) The entropy increases. Expansion reduces orderliness and increases chaos.
(c) The entropy increases. Warming increases chaos and reduces orderliness.
(d) The entropy increases. Mixing reduces orderliness.
(e) The entropy decreases. Separating increases orderliness, and decreasing the number of moles of particles decreases the entropy.

19.30   (a) The entropy increases. A gas is evolved.
(b) The entropy decreases. A gas is consumed.
(c) The entropy decreases. Three moles of products, one of which is a solid, have less disorder than 3 mol of mixed reactants in solution.
(d) The entropy increases. Two moles of gaseous products has more disorder than 1 mol of gaseous and 1 mol of solid reactants.

19.34   (a) The kinetic energy of the gas increases when it is warmed and as a consequence the movements of the gas molecules become more chaotic.

(b) The volume of the gas increases when it expands, the gas molecules spread out, and as a consequence the orderliness of the gas molecules decreases and the randomness increases.

19.36   Negative. A solid substance has a greater order, lower entropy, than a solution of the substance. This is especially true if the substance dissociates, which increases disorder, in solution.

19.38   The melting of benzene at 5.4°C and 1 atm is an equilibrium process, therefore Equation 19.8 applies. The change in enthalpy is (the melting takes place under standard state conditions):

$$\Delta H° = 1 \text{ mol} \times \frac{78.1 \text{ g}}{1 \text{ mol}} \times \frac{126 \text{ J}}{1 \text{ g}} = 9{,}840 \text{ J}$$

Substituting $\Delta H° = 9{,}840$ J and $T = 278.6$ K into Equation 19.8 gives

$$\Delta S° = \frac{\Delta H°}{T} = \frac{9{,}840 \text{ J}}{278.6 \text{ K}} = 35.3 \text{ J/K}$$

19.40   The vaporization of liquid ethanol at 78.5°C and 1 atm is an equilibrium process; therefore Equation 19.8 applies. The change in enthalpy is (the vaporization takes place under standard state conditions):

$$\Delta H° = 45.0 \text{ g} \times \frac{1 \text{ mol}}{46.1 \text{ g}} \times \frac{38.6 \text{ kJ}}{1 \text{ mol}} = 37.7 \text{ kJ}$$

Substituting $\Delta H° = 37.7$ kJ and $T = 351.7$ K into Equation 19.8 gives

$$\Delta S° = \frac{\Delta H°}{T} = \frac{37.7 \text{ kJ}}{351.7 \text{ K}} = 0.107 \text{ kJ/K} = 107 \text{ J/K}$$

19.42 $T = 298$ K for each reaction.

(a) $\Delta G_f°(CO_2) = -394.359$ kJ and $\Delta H_f°(CO_2) = -393.509$ kJ

$$\Delta S_f° = \frac{\Delta H_f° - \Delta G_f°}{T} = \frac{-393.509 \text{ kJ} + 394.359 \text{ kJ}}{298 \text{ K}} = 2.85 \times 10^{-3} \text{ kJ/K} = +2.85 \text{ J/K}$$

(b) $\Delta G_f°(N_2O) = 104.20$ kJ and $\Delta H_f°(N_2O) = 82.05$ kJ

$$\Delta S_f° = \frac{\Delta H_f° - \Delta G_f°}{T} = \frac{82.05 \text{ kJ} - 104.20 \text{ kJ}}{298 \text{ K}} = -0.0743 \text{ kJ/K} = -74.3 \text{ J/K}$$

(c) $\Delta G_f°(ZnO) = -318.30$ kJ and $\Delta H_f°(ZnO) = -348.28$ kJ

$$\Delta S_f° = \frac{-348.28 \text{ kJ} + 318.30 \text{ kJ}}{298 \text{ K}} = -0.101 \text{ kJ/K} = -101 \text{ J/K}$$

(d) $\Delta G_f°(Hg(g)) = 31.82$ kJ and $\Delta H_f°(Hg(g)) = 61.32$ kJ

$$\Delta S_f° = \frac{61.32 \text{ kJ} - 31.82 \text{ kJ}}{298 \text{ K}} = 0.0990 \text{ kJ/K} = +99.0 \text{ J/K}$$

(e) $\Delta G_f°(CH_4) = -50.72$ kJ and $\Delta H_f°(CH_4) = -74.81$ kJ

$$\Delta S_f° = \frac{-74.81 \text{ kJ} + 50.72 \text{ kJ}}{298 \text{ K}} = -0.0808 \text{ kJ/K} = -80.8 \text{ J/K}$$

19.45   (a), (b), and (d) would have zero entropy at zero Kelvin, since they are either pure, perfectly crystalline elements or compounds. (c) and (e) would not, since (c) is a noncrystalline mixture and (e) is a mixture.

19.52 $C(graphite) \longrightarrow C(diamond)$

For this reaction at T = 298 K,

$\Delta H^° = \Delta H_f^°(diamond) - \Delta H_f^°(graphite) = 1.895 \text{ kJ} - 0 \text{ kJ} = +1.895 \text{ kJ}$

$\Delta S^° = S^°(diamond) - S^°(graphite) = 2.377 \text{ J/K} - 5.740 \text{ J/K} = -3.363 \text{ J/K}$

and $\Delta G^° = \Delta H^° - T\Delta S^° = +1.895 \text{ kJ} - 298 \text{ K} \times -3.363 \times 10^{-3} \text{ kJ/K} = +0.888 \text{ kJ}$

Therefore, the reaction is not spontaneous at 298 K, and since $\Delta H^°$ is positive and $\Delta S^°$ is negative, $\Delta G^°$ will be positive at all temperatures (see Table 19.3). Therefore, the reaction at 1 atm pressure is not spontaneous at any temperature and, consequently, diamond cannot be made from graphite at 1 atm pressure.

19.53 $\Delta G = \Delta H - T\Delta S$ (19.7)

The lower the ΔG value, the greater the net driving force for the decomposition. In general, decompositions are accompanied by an increase in entropy, $\Delta S > 0$, since they increase the number of moles of particles. From Equation 19.7 we see that for both endothermic and exothermic reactions ΔG decreases with increasing temperature when $\Delta S > 0$. Consequently, both endothermic and exothermic decompositions are thermodynamically favored by heating.

19.54 $N_2O_4(g) \rightleftharpoons 2NO_2(g)$

At 298 K,

$\Delta H^° = 2 \times \Delta H_f^°(NO_2) - \Delta H_f^°(N_2O_4) = 2 \times 33.18 \text{ kJ} - 9.16 \text{ kJ} = +57.20 \text{ kJ}$

$\Delta S^° = 2 \times S^°(NO_2) - S^°(N_2O_4) = 2 \times 240.06 \text{ J/K} - 304.29 \text{ J/K} = +175.83 \text{ J/K} = +0.17583 \text{ kJ/K}$

When each gas has a partial pressure of 1 atm, then ln Q = ln 1 = 0 and $\Delta G = \Delta G^°$. In other words, the reaction is taking place under standard state conditions. We want to find the temperature at which $\Delta G^° = 0$. Assuming that $\Delta H^°$ and $\Delta S^°$ do not change with temperature and substituting their values and $\Delta G^° = 0$ into Equation 19.7 gives

$\Delta G^° = \Delta H^° - T\Delta S^°$

$0 \text{ kJ} = +57.20 \text{ kJ} - T \times 0.17583 \text{ kJ/K}$ and $T = 325 \text{ K} = 52°C$

19.55   (a) $Ag_2O(s) \longrightarrow 2Ag(s) + 1/2 \ O_2(g)$
        $\Delta G_f^°(kJ):$ -11.20 0 0

$\Delta G^° = 0 \text{ kJ} + 0 \text{ kJ} - (-11.20 \text{ kJ}) = +11.20 \text{ kJ}$

Since $\Delta G > 0$, the spontaneous direction is the reverse reaction. Therefore, under these conditions of temperature (25°C) and O_2 partial pressure (1 atm), Ag_2O is thermodynamically stable with respect to its elements.

(b) At 298 K,

$\Delta H^° = 2 \times \Delta H_f^°(Ag) + 1/2 \times \Delta H_f^°(O_2) - \Delta H_f^°(Ag_2O)$

$= 2 \times 0 \text{ kJ} + 1/2 \times 0 \text{ kJ} - (-31.05 \text{ kJ}) = +31.05 \text{ kJ}$

$\Delta S^° = 2 \times S^°(Ag) + 1/2 \times S^°(O_2) - S^°(Ag_2O)$

$= 2 \times 42.55 \text{ J/K} + 1/2 \times 205.138 \text{ J/K} - 121.3 \text{ J/K} = +66.4 \text{ J/K}$

A value for $\Delta G°$ at $180°C$ can be obtained from Equation 19.7 if we assume that $\Delta H°$ and $\Delta S°$ do not change with temperature. Substituting $\Delta H° = 31.05$ kJ, $\Delta S° = 0.0644$ kJ/K, and $T = 453$ K into Equation 19.7 gives

$$\Delta G° = \Delta H° - T\Delta S° = 31.05 \text{ kJ/K} - 453 \text{ K} \times 0.0664 \text{ kJ/K} = +0.97 \text{ kJ}$$

Since $\Delta G > 0$, the spontaneous direction is the reverse reaction. Therefore, under these conditions of temperature $(180°C)$ and O_2 partial pressure (1 atm), Ag_2O is thermodynamically stable with respect to its elements.

19.56   (a) $Ag_2O(s) \longrightarrow 2Ag(s) + 1/2 O_2(g)$

$$\Delta G = \Delta G° + RT \ln Q = \Delta G° + RT \ln P_{O_2}^{1/2}$$

Substituting $\Delta G° = +11.20$ kJ/mol (see Exercise 19.55), $R = 8.314 \times 10^{-3}$ kJ/mol K, $T = 298$ K, and $P_{O_2} = 0.2$ atm into the above equation gives

$$\Delta G = +11.20 \text{ kJ/mol} + 8.314 \times 10^{-3} \text{ kJ/mol K} \times 298 \text{ K} \times \ln\sqrt{0.2} = +9 \text{ kJ/mol}$$

Since $\Delta G > 0$, the spontaneous direction is the reverse reaction. Therefore, at $25°C$ Ag_2O is thermodynamically stable with respect to its elements when exposed to the atmosphere.

(b) Substituting $\Delta G° = +0.97$ kJ/mol (see Exercise 19.55), $R = 8.314 \times 10^{-3}$ kJ/mol K, $T = 453$ K, and $P_{O_2} = 0.2$ atm into the above equation gives

$$\Delta G = +0.97 \text{ kJ/mol} + 8.314 \times 10^{-3} \text{ kJ/mol K} \times 453 \text{ K} \times \ln\sqrt{0.2} = -2 \text{ kJ/mol}$$

Since $\Delta G < 0$, the spontaneous direction is the forward reaction. Therefore, at $180°C$ Ag_2O is thermodynamically unstable with respect to its elements when exposed to the atmosphere.

19.57   (1) $2NO_2(g) \longrightarrow 2NO(g) + O_2(g)$

(a) $\Delta G° = 2 \times \Delta G_f°(NO) + \Delta G_f°(O_2) - 2 \times \Delta G_f°(NO_2)$

$= 2 \times 86.55 \text{ kJ} + 0 \text{ kJ} - 2 \times 51.31 \text{ kJ} = +70.48 \text{ kJ}$

Since $\Delta G > 0$, the reaction is not spontaneous at $25°C$ when each substance is in its standard state.

(b) At 298 K,

$\Delta H° = 2 \times \Delta H_f°(NO) + \Delta H_f°(O_2) - 2 \times \Delta H_f°(NO_2) = 2 \times 90.25 \text{ kJ} + 0 \text{ kJ} - 2 \times 33.18 \text{ kJ} = +114.14 \text{ kJ}$

$\Delta S° = 2 \times S°(NO) + S°(O_2) - 2 \times S°(NO_2)$

$= 2 \times 210.76 \text{ J/K} + 205.138 \text{ J/K} - 2 \times 240.06 \text{ J/K} = +146.54 \text{ J/K}$

Since both $\Delta H°$ and $\Delta S°$ are positive, the reaction can be reversed by raising the temperature.

(2) $Fe_2O_3(s) + 2Al(s) \longrightarrow Al_2O_3(s) + 2Fe(s)$

(a) $\Delta G° = \Delta G_f°(Al_2O_3) + 2 \times \Delta G_f°(Fe) - \Delta G_f°(Fe_2O_3) - 2 \times \Delta G_f°(Al)$

$= -1582.3 \text{ kJ} + 2 \times 0 \text{ kJ} + 742.2 \text{ kJ} - 2 \times 0 \text{ kJ} = -840.1 \text{ kJ}$

Since $\Delta G < 0$, the reaction is spontaneous under these conditions.

(b) At 298 K,

$\Delta H° = \Delta H_f°(Al_2O_3) + 2 \times \Delta H_f°(Fe) - \Delta H_f°(Fe_2O_3) - 2 \times \Delta H_f°(Al)$

$= -1675.7 \text{ kJ} + 2 \times 0 \text{ kJ} + 824.2 \text{ kJ} - 2 \times 0 \text{ kJ} = -851.5 \text{ kJ}$

$\Delta S° = S°(Al_2O_3) + 2 \times S°(Fe) - S°(Fe_2O_3) - 2 \times S°(Al)$

$= 50.92 \text{ J/K} + 2 \times 27.28 \text{ J/K} - 87.40 \text{ J/K} - 2 \times 28.33 \text{ J/K} = -38.58 \text{ J/K}$

Since both $\Delta H°$ and $\Delta S°$ are negative, the reaction can be reversed by raising the temperature.

(3) C(gr) ——> C(d)

    (a) $\Delta G^\circ = \Delta G_f^\circ(C(d)) - \Delta G_f^\circ(C(gr)) = 2.900 \text{ kJ} - 0 \text{ kJ} = +2.900 \text{ kJ}$

    Since $\Delta G > 0$, the reaction is not spontaneous under these conditions.

    (b) At 298 K,

    $\Delta H^\circ = \Delta H_f^\circ(C(d)) - \Delta H_f^\circ(C(gr)) = 1.895 \text{ kJ} - 0 \text{ kJ} = +1.895 \text{ kJ}$

    $\Delta S^\circ = S^\circ(C(d)) - S^\circ(C(gr)) = 2.377 \text{ J/K} - 5.740 \text{ J/K} = -3.363 \text{ J/K}$

    Since ΔH° and ΔS° have different signs, the reaction cannot be reversed by raising the temperature.

(4) $C_2H_2(g) + H_2(g)$ ——> $C_2H_4(g)$

    (a) $\Delta G^\circ = \Delta G_f^\circ(C_2H_4) - \Delta G_f^\circ(C_2H_2) - \Delta G_f^\circ(H_2) = 68.15 \text{ kJ} - 209.20 \text{ kJ} - 0 \text{ kJ} = -141.05 \text{ kJ}$

    Since $\Delta G < 0$, the reaction is spontaneous under these conditions.

    (b) At 298 K,

    $\Delta H^\circ = \Delta H_f^\circ(C_2H_4) - \Delta H_f^\circ(C_2H_2) - \Delta H_f^\circ(H_2) = 52.26 \text{ kJ} - 226.73 \text{ kJ} - 0 \text{ kJ} = -174.47 \text{ kJ}$

    $\Delta S^\circ = S^\circ(C_2H_4) - S^\circ(C_2H_2) - S^\circ(H_2) = 219.56 \text{ J/K} - 200.94 \text{ J/K} - 130.684 \text{ J/K} = -112.06 \text{ J/K}$

    Since both ΔH° and ΔS° are negative, the reaction can be reversed by raising the temperature.

19.58   (a) Substituting $K_p = 50.3$, T= 731 K, and R = 8.314 J/mol K into Equation 19.4 gives

    $\Delta G^\circ = -RT \ln K_p = -8.314 \text{ J/mol K} \times 731 \text{ K} \times \ln 50.3 = -23,800 \text{ J/mol} = -23.8 \text{ kJ/mol}$

    (b) ΔS° can be obtained by substituting $\Delta G^\circ = -23.8 \text{ kJ}$, $\Delta H^\circ = 51.9 \text{ kJ}$, and T = 731 K into Equation 19.7

$$\Delta S^\circ = \frac{\Delta H^\circ - \Delta G^\circ}{T} = \frac{51.9 \text{ kJ} + 23.8 \text{ kJ}}{731 \text{ K}} = 0.104 \text{ kJ/K}$$

    Assuming that ΔH° and ΔS° do not change with temperature, the ΔG° value at 400°C can be obtained by substituting $\Delta H^\circ = 51.9 \text{ kJ}$, $\Delta S^\circ = 0.104 \text{ kJ/K}$, and T = 673 K into Equation 19.7.

    $\Delta G^\circ = \Delta H^\circ - T\Delta S^\circ = 51.9 \text{ kJ} - 673 \text{ K} \times 0.104 \text{ kJ/K} = -18.1 \text{ kJ}$

    K_p at 400°C can be obtained by substituting $\Delta G^\circ = -18.1 \text{ kJ/mol}$, T = 673 K, and R = 8.314 x 10^{-3} kJ/mol K into Equation 19.4

$$\ln K_p = \frac{\Delta G^\circ}{-RT} = \frac{-18.1 \text{ kJ/mol}}{-8.314 \times 10^{-3} \text{ kJ/mol K} \times 673 \text{ K}} = 3.23$$

    and $K_p = \text{antilog } 3.23 = e^{+3.23} = 25$

19.60   A positive ΔG° value means that a reaction is not spontaneous in the forward direction when each reactant and each product is present in their standard states. Since the partial pressure of $Br_2(g)$ is much lower than 1 atm, essentially zero, the ΔG° value doesn't apply to this situation. Under these conditions we must use the $\Delta G = \Delta G^\circ + RT \ln Q$ value, and since $\ln Q$ ——> $-\infty$ as Q ——> 0, the ΔG value will be negative under these conditions. In other words, under atmospheric conditions the decomposition of AgBr is thermodynamically spontaneous. The photons from sunlight initiate the reaction by supplying the necessary activation energy.

19.61   (a) The performance of useful work decreases the amount of heat evolved during a reaction.
    (b) $\Delta G = -\text{maximum useful work}$

    Since this an equilibrium process, $\Delta G = 0$ and none of the evolved energy can be obtained as useful work. Therefore, the answer is zero.

19.63 (a) I.

$$4HCl(g) \quad + \quad O_2(g) \quad \longrightarrow \quad 2Cl_2(g) \quad + \quad 2H_2O(g)$$

ΔG_f°(kJ): $\quad$ 4 x –95.30 $\qquad$ 0 $\qquad\qquad$ 0 $\qquad\qquad$ 2 x –228.572

ΔG° = 0 kJ + 2 x –228.572 kJ – (4 x –95.30 kJ + 0 kJ) = –75.9 kJ

Substituting ΔG° = –75.9 kJ/mol, T = 298 K, and R = 8.314 x 10⁻³ kJ/mol K into Equation 19.4 gives

$$\ln K_p = \frac{\Delta G^\circ}{-RT} = \frac{-75.9 \ kJ/mol}{-8.314 \ x \ 10^{-3} \ kJ/mol \ K \ x \ 298 \ K} = 30.6$$

and K_p = antilog 30.6 = $e^{+30.6}$ = 2 x 10¹³

II. At 298 K,

$\Delta H^\circ = 2 \ x \ \Delta H_f^\circ(Cl_2) + 2 \ x \ \Delta H_f^\circ(H_2O) - 4 \ x \ \Delta H_f^\circ(HCl) - \Delta H_f^\circ(O_2)$

$\quad$ = 2 x 0 kJ + 2 x –241.818 kJ – 4 x –92.30 kJ – 0 kJ = –114.6 kJ

$\Delta S^\circ = 2 \ x \ S^\circ(Cl_2) + 2 \ x \ S^\circ(H_2O) - 4 \ x \ S^\circ(HCl) - S^\circ(O_2)$

$\quad$ = 2 x 223.07 J/K + 2 x 188.825 J/K – 4 x 186.91 J/K – 205.138 J/K = –129.0 J/K

A value for ΔG° at 400°C can be obtained using Equation 19.7 if we assume that ΔH° and ΔS° do not change with temperature. Substituting ΔH° = –114.6 kJ, ΔS° = –0.1290 kJ/K, and T = 673 K into Equation 19.7 gives

$\Delta G^\circ = \Delta H^\circ - T\Delta S^\circ$ = –114.6 kJ – 673 K x –0.1290 kJ/K = –27.8 kJ

Substituting ΔG° = –27.8 kJ/mol, T = 673 K, and R = 8.314 x 10⁻³ kJ/mol K into Equation 19.4 gives

$$\ln K_p = \frac{\Delta G^\circ}{-RT} = \frac{-27.8 \ kJ}{-8.314 \ x \ 10^{-3} \ kJ/mol \ K \ x \ 673 \ K} = 4.97$$

and K_p = antilog 4.97 = $e^{+4.97}$ = 140

(b) The reaction at 25°C must be very slow compared to that at 400°C. In other words, at 25°C it would take too long to obtain a substantial amount of product, while at 400°C a substantial amount of product can be obtained in a reasonable amount of time, even though the equilibrium conditions are many orders of magnitude less favorable.

19.64 (a) Substituting ΔG° = –31 kJ/mol, T = 298 K, and R = 8.314 x 10⁻³ kJ/mol K into Equation 19.4 gives

$$\ln K_H = \frac{\Delta G^\circ}{-RT} = \frac{-31 \ kJ}{-8.314 \ x \ 10^{-3} \ kJ/mol \ K \ x \ 298 \ K} = 13$$

and K_H = antilog 13 = e^{+13} = 1 x 10⁵

(b)

$$\Delta G = \Delta G^\circ + RT \ \ln Q = \Delta G^\circ + RT \ \ln \frac{[ADP][phosphate]}{[ATP]}$$

$$\Delta G = -31 \ kJ/mol + 8.314 \ x \ 10^{-3} \ kJ/mol \ K \ x \ 298 \ K \ x \ \ln \frac{(0.01)(0.01)}{(0.01)} = -42 \ kJ/mol$$

Since $\Delta G < 0$, the forward reaction is spontaneous and, therefore, capable of providing useful work.

19.66

(1) $2ZnS(s) + 3O_2(g) \longrightarrow 2ZnO(s) + 2SO_2(g)$

$\Delta H° = 2 \times \Delta H_f°(ZnO) + 2 \times \Delta H_f°(SO_2) - 2 \times \Delta H_f°(ZnS) - 3 \times \Delta H_f°(O_2)$

$= 2 \times -348.28 \text{ kJ} + 2 \times -296.83 \text{ kJ} - 2 \times -205.98 \text{ kJ} - 3 \times 0 \text{ kJ} = -878.26 \text{ kJ}$

$\Delta S° = 2 \times S°(ZnO) + 2 \times S°(SO_2) - 2 \times S°(ZnS) - 3 \times S°(O_2)$

$= 2 \times 43.64 \text{ J/K} + 2 \times 248.22 \text{ J/K} - 2 \times 57.7 \text{ J/K} - 3 \times 205.138 \text{ J/K} = -147.1 \text{ J/K}$

Since both $\Delta H°$ and $\Delta S°$ are negative, $\Delta G°$ changes from negative to positive above $T = \Delta H°/\Delta S°$. Therefore, the reaction will be spontaneous in the forward direction until

$$T = \frac{\Delta H°}{\Delta S°} = \frac{-878.26 \text{ kJ}}{-0.1471 \text{ kJ/K}} = 5,970 \text{ K} = 5,697°C$$

Since the temperature of the reduction reaction never gets this high, we can assume that the reaction is always spontaneous in the forward direction under the circumstances of the actual reaction.

(2) $ZnO(s) + C(gr) \longrightarrow Zn(g) + CO(g)$

$\Delta H° = \Delta H_f°(Zn) + \Delta H_f°(CO) - \Delta H_f°(ZnO) - \Delta H_f°(C)$

$= 130.73 \text{ kJ} - 110.525 \text{ kJ} + 348.28 \text{ kJ} - 0 \text{ kJ} = +368.48 \text{ kJ}$

$\Delta S° = S°(Zn) + S°(CO) - S°(ZnO) - S°(C)$

$= 160.98 \text{ J/K} + 197.67 \text{ J/K} - 43.64 \text{ J/K} - 5.740 \text{ J/K} = +309.27 \text{ J/K}$

Since both $\Delta H°$ and $\Delta S°$ are positive, $\Delta G°$ will change from positive to negative above $T = \Delta H°/\Delta S°$. Therefore, the reaction will be spontaneous in the forward direction above

$$T = \frac{\Delta H°}{\Delta S°} = \frac{368.48 \text{ kJ}}{0.30927 \text{ kJ/K}} = 1,191 \text{ K} = 918°C$$

Answer: The first two steps are spontaneous above $918°C$.

CHAPTER 20
ELECTROCHEMISTRY

Solutions To Practice Exercises

PE 20.4   Substituting $Q = 1.00 \times 10^{-7}$ C/s $\times 600$ s $= 6.00 \times 10^{-5}$ C and $E = 1.35$ V $= 1.35$ J/C into Equation 20.1 gives

maximum electrical work $= 6.00 \times 10^{-5}$ C $\times 1.35$ J/C $= 8.10 \times 10^{-5}$ J

PE 20.5   The oxidation of 2 mol of Al atoms by Cu^{2+} ions requires the transfer of 6 mol of electrons. Substituting $n = 6$ mol e^-, $F = 96,485$ C/mol e^-, and $\Delta G^\circ = -1166$ kJ into Equation 20.5b gives

$$E^\circ = \frac{\Delta G^\circ}{-nF} = \frac{-1166 \text{ kJ}}{-6 \text{ mol } e^- \times 96,485 \text{ C/mol } e^-} = 2.01 \times 10^{-3} \text{ kJ/C} = 2.01 \text{ J/C} = 2.01 \text{ V}$$

PE 20.7   The standard reduction potentials are:

$Co^{2+}(aq) + 2e^- \longrightarrow Co(s)$ $E^\circ = -0.282$ V

$Cr^{3+}(aq) + 3e^- \longrightarrow Cr(s)$ $E^\circ = -0.74$ V

An aqueous solution of Co^{2+} ions has a more positive reduction potential and a greater tendency to accept electrons than an aqueous solution of Cr^{3+} ions; the Co^{2+} ion will be more easily reduced.

PE 20.8   The standard oxidation potentials are:

$2Cl^-(aq) \longrightarrow Cl_2(g) + 2e^-$ $E^\circ_{oxid} = -1.360$ V

$2I^-(aq) \longrightarrow I_2(s) + 2e^-$ $E^\circ_{oxid} = -0.535$ V

I^- has a higher (more positive) oxidation potential and a greater tendency to give up eletrons than Cl^-; I^- is more easily oxidized.

PE 20.9   One of the reactions listed in Table 20.1 is

$NO_3^-(aq) + 4H^+(aq) + 3e^- \rightleftharpoons NO(g) + 2H_2O(l)$ $E^\circ = 0.964$ V

(a) No. From Table 20.1 we have

$$Br_2(l) + 2e^- \rightleftharpoons 2Br^-(aq) \qquad\qquad E^\circ = 1.078 \text{ V}$$

Since the aqueous nitric acid reduction potential of 0.964 V is lower than the Br_2 reduction potential of 1.078 V, aqueous nitric acid cannot force the bromide reaction to go in reverse and, consequently, aqueous nitric acid cannot oxidize bromide ions.

(b) Yes. From Table 20.1 we have

$$I_2(s) + 2e^- \rightleftharpoons 2I^-(aq) \qquad\qquad E^\circ = 0.535 \text{ V}$$

Since the $HNO_3(aq)$ reduction potential of 0.964 V is greater than the I_2 reduction potential of 0.535 V, $HNO_3(aq)$ can force the iodine reaction to go in reverse and, consequently, $HNO_3(aq)$ can oxidize iodide ions.

PE 20.10 (a) The reduction potentials from Table 20.1 are

$$MnO_4^-(aq) + 8H^+(aq) + 5e^- \rightleftharpoons Mn^{2+}(aq) + 4H_2O(l) \quad E^\circ = 1.512 \text{ V}$$

$$I_2(s) + 2e^- \rightleftharpoons 2I^-(aq) \qquad\qquad\qquad\qquad\qquad E^\circ = 0.535 \text{ V}$$

The permanganate ion half-reaction has the more positive reduction potential; it will go forward as a reduction and the iodine half-reaction will go in reverse as an oxidation. The half-reactions are

oxidation: $2I^-(aq) \longrightarrow I_2(s) + 2e^- \qquad E^\circ_{oxid} = -0.535 \text{ V}$

reduction: $MnO_4^-(aq) + 8H^+(aq) + 5e^- \longrightarrow Mn^{2+}(aq) + 4H_2O(l) \qquad E^\circ_{red} = 1.512 \text{ V}$

(b) The cell voltage is obtained by substituting $E^\circ_{oxid} = -0.535$ V and $E^\circ_{red} = 1.512$ V into Equation 20.6:

$$E^\circ = E^\circ_{oxid} + E^\circ_{red} = -0.535 \text{ V} + 1.512 \text{ V} = 0.977 \text{ V}$$

PE 20.11 The reaction is the sum of the following half-reactions:

$$Cu(s) \longrightarrow Cu^{2+} (1 \text{ M}) + 2e^- \qquad\qquad E^\circ_{oxid} = -E^\circ_{red} = -0.339 \text{ V}$$

$$2Ag^+ (1 \text{ M}) + 2e^- \longrightarrow 2Ag(s) \qquad\qquad E^\circ_{red} = 0.799 \text{ V}$$

The total voltage is

$$E^\circ = -0.339 \text{ V} + 0.799 \text{ V} = 0.460 \text{ V} = 0.460 \text{ J/C}$$

Two moles of electrons are transferred per mole of Cu oxidized; $n = 2$ mol e^-. Substituting in Equation 20.5 gives

$$\Delta G^\circ = -nFE^\circ = -2 \text{ mol } e^- \times \frac{96,485 \text{ C}}{1 \text{ mol } e^-} \times \frac{0.460 \text{ J}}{1 \text{ C}} = -8.88 \times 10^{-4} \text{ J} = -88.8 \text{ kJ}$$

PE 20.12 The cell reaction and standard voltage are

$$Br_2(l) + 2Fe^{2+}(aq) \longrightarrow 2Fe^{3+}(aq) + 2Br^-(aq) \qquad\qquad E^\circ = 0.31 \text{ V}$$

The reaction quotient is

$$Q = \frac{[Fe^{3+}]^2[Br^-]^2}{[Fe^{2+}]^2} = \frac{(0.10)^2(0.050)^2}{(0.10)^2} = 2.5 \times 10^{-3}$$

Two moles of electrons are transferred per mole of Br_2 reduced, therefore $n = 2$. Substituting the values for Q, n, and E° into the Nernst equation gives

$$E = 0.31 \text{ V} - \frac{0.0592 \text{ V}}{2} \times \log(2.5 \times 10^{-3}) = 0.39 \text{ V}$$

PE20.13 The half-reaction and standard reduction potential are

$$2H^+(aq) + 2e^- \longrightarrow H_2(g) \qquad\qquad E^\circ = 0.000 \text{ V}$$

The reaction quotient is

$$Q = \frac{P_{H_2}}{[H^+]^2} = \frac{1.00}{(10^{-7})^2} = 1.00 \times 10^{+14}$$

Two moles of electrons are transferred per mole of H_2 formed, therefore n = 2. Substituting the values for Q, n, and E° into the Nernst equation gives

$$E = 0.000 \text{ V} - \frac{0.0592 \text{ V}}{2} \times \log(1.00 \times 10^{+14}) = -0.414 \text{ V}$$

PE 20.14 (a)

The oxidation numbers change by 2, therefore n = 2. Substituting the values for n and K into Equation 20.8b gives

$$E^\circ = \frac{0.0592 \text{ V}}{2} \times \log(1.9 \times 10^4) = 0.127 \text{ V}$$

(b)

$$\Delta G^\circ = -nFE^\circ = -2 \text{ mol } e^- \times \frac{96,485 \text{ C}}{1 \text{ mol } e^-} \times \frac{0.127 \text{ J}}{1 \text{ C}} = -24,500 \text{ J} = -24.5 \text{ kJ}$$

PE 20.15 $Zn^{2+}(aq) + 4NH_3(aq) \rightleftharpoons Zn(NH_3)_4^{2+}(aq)$

This is not a redox reaction, but it can be written as the sum of two half-reactions whose potentials can be found in Table 20.1

$$Zn(s) + 4NH_3(aq) \longrightarrow Zn(NH_3)_4^{2+}(aq) + 2e^- \qquad E^\circ_{oxid} = -E^\circ_{red} = 1.015 \text{ V}$$

$$Zn^{2+}(aq) + 2e^- \longrightarrow Zn(s) \qquad\qquad\qquad\qquad\quad E^\circ_{red} = -0.762 \text{ V}$$

The sum of the half-cell voltages is

$$E^\circ = E^\circ_{oxid} + E^\circ_{red} = 1.015 \text{ V} - 0.762 \text{ V} = 0.253 \text{ V}$$

Substituting n = 2 and $E^\circ = 0.253$ V into Equation 20.8b gives

$$0.253 \text{ V} = \frac{0.0592 \text{ V}}{2} \times \log K$$

log K = 8.55 and K = antilog 8.55 = $10^{8.55}$ = 3.5 x 10^8

PE 20.17 $AuCl_4^-(aq) + 3e^- \longrightarrow Au(s) + 4Cl^-(aq)$

The equation for the electrode reaction shows that 1 mol (196.97 g) of gold metal is deposited by 3 mol of electrons, or 3 x 96,485 C. The steps in the calculation are:
5000 C $\longrightarrow$ mol Au $\longrightarrow$ g Au.

$$5000 \text{ C} \times \frac{1 \text{ mol Au}}{3 \times 96,485 \text{ C}} \times \frac{196.97 \text{ g}}{1 \text{ mol Au}} = 3.40 \text{ g}$$

PE 20.18   The number of coulombs that passes through the circuit is the same as the number of coulombs produced by the zinc electrode. The electrode reaction, $Zn(s) \longrightarrow Zn^{2+}(aq) + 2e^-$, shows that 1 mol (65.4 g) of zinc dissolves producing 2 mol of electrons, or $2 \times 96,485$ C. The steps in the calculation are: 350 mg Zn $\longrightarrow$ mol Zn $\longrightarrow$ C.

$$350 \text{ mg Zn} \times \frac{1 \text{ g}}{1000 \text{ mg}} \times \frac{1 \text{ mol Zn}}{65.4 \text{ g Zn}} \times \frac{2 \times 96,485 \text{ C}}{1 \text{ mol Zn}} = 1.03 \times 10^3 \text{ C}$$

PE 20.20   The current is 15.0 A = 15.0 C/s. The electrode equation, $2Cl^- \longrightarrow Cl_2(g) + 2e^-$, shows that 2 mol of electrons, or $2 \times 96,485$ C, produces 1 mol of chlorine. At STP (1.00 atm and 0°C), 1 mol of gas occupies approximately 22.4 L. The steps in the calculation are: C/s $\longrightarrow$ C/min $\longrightarrow$ mol Cl_2/min $\longrightarrow$ L/min.

$$\frac{15.0 \text{ C}}{1 \text{ s}} \times \frac{60 \text{ s}}{1 \text{ min}} \times \frac{1 \text{ mol } Cl_2}{2 \times 96,485 \text{ C}} \times \frac{22.4 \text{ L}}{1 \text{ mol } Cl_2} = 0.104 \text{ L/min}$$

Solutions to Final Exercises

20.5   (c)

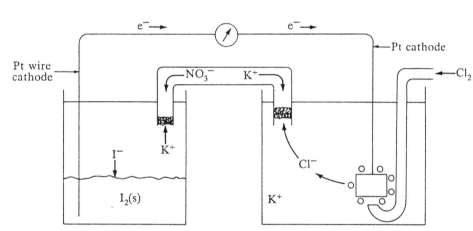

The half-reactions are

$2I^-(aq) \longrightarrow I_2(s) + 2e^-$ anode, oxidation

$Cl_2(g) + 2e^- \longrightarrow 2Cl^-(aq)$ cathode, reduction

(d)

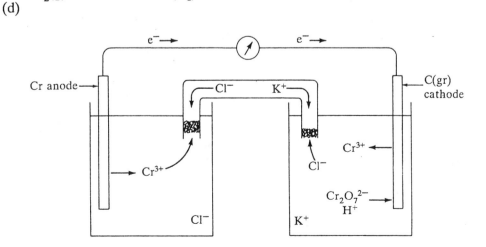

The half-reactions are

$$Cr(s) \longrightarrow Cr^{3+}(aq) + 3e^- \qquad \text{anode, oxidation}$$

$$Cr_2O_7^{2-}(aq) + 14H^+(aq) + 6e^- \longrightarrow 2Cr^{3+}(aq) + 7H_2O(l) \qquad \text{cathode, reduction}$$

(e)

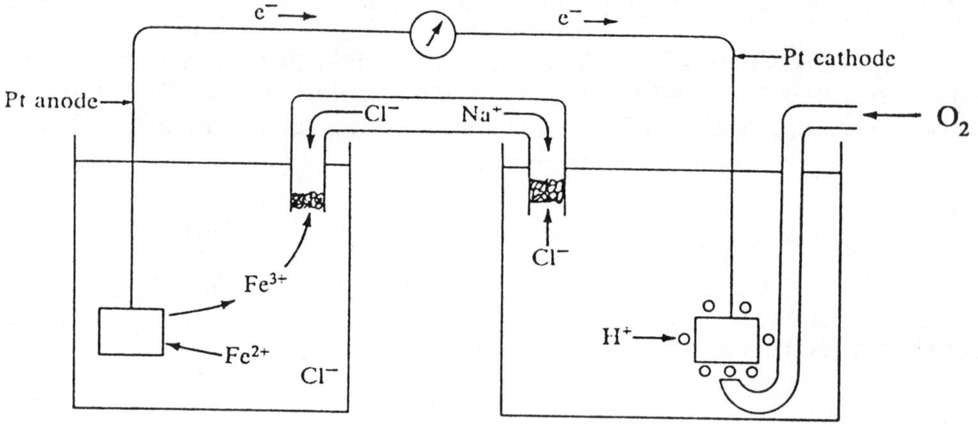

The half-reactions are

$$Fe^{2+}(aq) \longrightarrow Fe^{3+}(aq) + e^- \qquad \text{anode, oxidation}$$

$$O_2(g) + 4H^+(aq) + 4e^- \longrightarrow 2H_2O(l) \qquad \text{cathode, reduction}$$

20.6 (a) $Fe(s) \mid Fe^{2+}(aq) \parallel Sn^{2+}(aq) \mid Sn(s)$

(b) $Pt \mid H_2(g) \mid H^+(aq) \parallel Br^-(aq) \mid Br_2(l) \mid C(gr)$

(c) $Pt \mid I_2(s) \mid I^-(aq) \parallel Cl^-(aq) \mid Cl_2(g) \mid Pt$

(d) $Cr(s) \mid Cr^{3+}(aq) \parallel Cr^{3+}(aq), Cr_2O_7^{2-}(aq), H^+(aq) \mid C(gr)$

(e) $Pt \mid Fe^{2+}(aq), Fe^{3+}(aq) \parallel H^+(aq) \mid O_2(g) \mid Pt$

20.7 (a) $3Ag(s) + NO_3^-(aq) + 4H^+(aq) \longrightarrow 3Ag^+(aq) + NO(g) + 2H_2O(l)$

$Ag(s) \mid Ag^+ (1\ M) \parallel H^+ (1\ M), NO_3^- (1\ M) \mid NO (1\ atm) \mid Pt$

(b) The half-reactions are

$$Zn(s) + 4NH_3(aq) \longrightarrow Zn(NH_3)_4^{2+}(aq) + 2e^- \quad \text{anode, oxidation}$$

$$Ag(NH_3)_2^+(aq) + e^- \longrightarrow Ag(s) + 2NH_3(aq) \quad \text{cathode, reduction}$$

$$Zn(s) \mid Zn(NH_3)_4^{2+} (1\ M), NH_3 (1\ M) \parallel NH_3 (1\ M), Ag(NH_3)_2^+ (1\ M) \mid Ag(s)$$

(c) The cell notation for the formation of water from its elements depends on how the reaction is performed.

In basic solution: The half-reactions are

$$H_2(g) + 2OH^-(aq) \longrightarrow 2H_2O(l) + 2e^- \qquad \text{anode, oxidation}$$

$$O_2(g) + 2H_2O(l) + 4e^- \longrightarrow 4OH^-(aq) \qquad \text{cathode, reduction}$$

$$Pt \mid H_2 (1\ atm) \mid OH^- (1\ M) \mid O_2 (1\ atm) \mid Pt$$

In acidic solution: The half-reactions are

$H_2(g) \longrightarrow 2H^+(aq) + 2e^-$ anode, oxidation

$O_2(g) + 4H^+(aq) + 4e^- \longrightarrow 2H_2O(l)$ cathode, reduction

$Pt \mid H_2 \text{ (1 atm)} \mid H^+ \text{ (1 M)} \mid O_2 \text{ (1 atm)} \mid Pt$

Reverse of neutral electrolysis - considered a formation in neutral solution:
The half-reactions are

$H_2(g) + 2OH^-(aq) \longrightarrow 2H_2O(l) + 2e^-$ anode, oxidation

$O_2(g) + 4H^+(aq) + 4e^- \longrightarrow 2H_2O(l)$ cathode, reduction

$Pt \mid H_2 \text{ (1 atm)} \mid OH^- \text{ (1 M)} \parallel H^+ \text{ (1 M)} \mid O_2 \text{ (1 atm)} \mid Pt$

20.8 $Zn(s) + 2MnO_2(s) + 2NH_4^+(aq) \longrightarrow Zn^{2+}(aq) + Mn_2O_3(s) + 2NH_3(aq) + H_2O(l)$

The oxidation of 1 mol of Zn atoms by MnO_2 requires the transfer of 2 mol of electrons.
Substituting n = 2 mol e^-, F = 96,485 C/mol e^-, and E = 0.35 V = 0.35 J/C into
Equation 20.5a gives

$$\Delta G = -nFE = -2 \text{ mol } e^- \times \frac{96,485 \text{ C}}{1 \text{ mol } e^-} \times \frac{0.35 \text{ J}}{1 \text{ C}} = -6.8 \times 10^4 \text{ J} = -68 \text{ kJ}$$

20.9 $Hg^{2+}(aq) + Hg(l) \longrightarrow Hg_2^{2+}(aq)$

$$\Delta G^\circ = \Delta G_f^\circ(Hg_2^{2+}) - \Delta G_f^\circ(Hg^{2+}) - \Delta G_f^\circ(Hg) = 153.5 \text{ kJ} - 164.4 \text{ kJ} - 0 \text{ kJ} = -10.9 \text{ kJ}$$

From the half-reaction

$2Hg(l) \longrightarrow Hg_2^{2+}(aq) + 2e^-$ anode, oxidation

we see that the oxidation of 1 mol of Hg atoms by Hg^{2+} ions requires the transfer of 1 mol of
electrons. Substituting n = 1 mol e^-, F = 96,485 C/mol e^-, and ΔG° = –10.9 kJ = –10,900 kJ into
Equation 20.5b gives

$$E^\circ = \frac{\Delta G^\circ}{-nF} = \frac{-10,900 \text{ J}}{-1 \text{ mol } e^- \times 96,485 \text{ C/mol } e^-} = 0.113 \text{ J/C} = 0.113 \text{ V}$$

20.11   (a) $H_2(g) + 1/2 O_2(g) \longrightarrow H_2O(l)$

From the half-reaction

$H_2(g) + 2OH^-(aq) \longrightarrow 2H_2O(l) + 2e^-$ anode, oxidation

we see that the oxidation of 1 mol of H_2 by O_2 requires the transfer of 2 mol of electrons.
Substituting n = 2 mol e^-, F = 96,485 C/mol e^-, and ΔG° = –237.13 kJ = –237,130 J into Equation
20.5b gives

$$E^\circ = \frac{\Delta G^\circ}{-nF} = \frac{-237,130 \text{ J}}{-2 \text{ mol } e^- \times 96,485 \text{ C/mol } e^-} = 1.23 \text{ J/C} = 1.23 \text{ V}$$

(b)   Since we have a standard cell

maximum electrical work = $-\Delta G^\circ$ = 237.13 kJ/mol

The maximum electrical work obtainable from 1.00 kg H_2 is therefore

$$1.00 \times 10^3 \text{ g } H_2 \times \frac{1 \text{ mol } H_2}{2.02 \text{ g } H_2} \times \frac{237.13 \text{ kJ}}{1 \text{ mol } H_2} = 1.17 \times 10^5 \text{ kJ}$$

20.15   (a) Ni^{2+}. The higher the reduction potential the greater the tendency to accept electrons.

(b)   Cd. Since the reduction potential for Cd^{2+} ion is lower than that for Ni^{2+} ion, the oxidation
potential for Cd metal is higher than that for Ni metal; and the higher the oxidation potential,
the more easily the oxidation takes place.

20.17   (a) Potassium. Potassium's standard oxidation potential (2.936 V) is greater than sodium's (2.714 V).
     (b) Barium. Barium's standard oxidation potential (2.906 V) is greater than magnesium's (2.357 V).

20.19   The standard reduction potentials from Table 20.1a are:

$$Cl_2(g) + 2e^- \longrightarrow 2Cl^-(aq) \qquad\qquad E^\circ = 1.360 \text{ V}$$

$$MnO_4^-(aq) + 8H^+(aq) + 5e^- \longrightarrow Mn^{2+}(aq) + 4H_2O(l) \qquad E^\circ = 1.512 \text{ V}$$

An acidified solution of potassium permanganate has a more positive reduction potential than chlorine water; therefore the permanganate solution will be the stronger oxidizing agent.

20.20   Only acidified $KMnO_4$. From Table 20.1 we have

$$MnO_2(s) + 4H^+(aq) + 2e^- \longrightarrow Mn^{2+}(aq) + 2H_2O(l) \qquad E^\circ = 1.229 \text{ V}$$

$$MnO_4^-(aq) + 2H_2O(l) + 3e^- \longrightarrow MnO_2(s) + 4OH^-(aq) \qquad E^\circ = 0.597 \text{ V}$$

$$S(s) + 2H^+(aq) + 2e^- \longrightarrow H_2S(aq) \qquad E^\circ = 0.144 \text{ V}$$

$$Hg^{2+}(aq) + 2e^- \longrightarrow 2Hg(l) \qquad E^\circ = 0.796 \text{ V}$$

$$Fe^{3+}(aq) + e^- \longrightarrow Fe^{2+}(aq) \qquad E^\circ = 0.769 \text{ V}$$

$$MnO_4^-(aq) + 8H^+(aq) + 5e^- \longrightarrow Mn^{2+}(aq) + 4H_2O(l) \qquad E^\circ = 1.512 \text{ V}$$

To chemically oxidize Mn^{2+} to MnO_2, we need an oxidizing agent with a reduction potential greater than that of MnO_2, whose $E^\circ = 1.229$ V. H_2S can be eliminated immediately, since H_2S is not an oxidizing agent; the sulfur atom in H_2S is already reduced. Hg^{2+}, Fe^{3+}, and MnO_4^- by itself, are all oxidizing agents, but their standard reduction potentials are all below that of MnO_2. Only an acidified solution of $KMnO_4$ has a greater standard reduction potential than that of MnO_2. Therefore, only the acidified $KMnO_4$ is worth trying.

20.22   (a) 1. $Zn^{2+}(aq) + 2e^- \longrightarrow Zn(s) \qquad E^\circ = -0.762$ V

               $2H^+(aq) + 2e^- \longrightarrow H_2(g) \qquad E^\circ = 0.000$ V

The hydrogen half-reaction has the more positive reduction potential; therefore hydrochloric acid will oxidize zinc metal. The equation for the reaction is

$$Zn(s) + 2H^+(aq) \longrightarrow Zn^{2+}(aq) + H_2(g)$$

      2. $Cu^{2+}(aq) + 2e^- \longrightarrow Cu(s) \qquad E^\circ = 0.339$ V

               $2H^+(aq) + 2e^- \longrightarrow H_2(g) \qquad E^\circ = 0.000$ V

The copper half-reaction has the more positive reduction potential; therefore no reaction occurs.

   (b) 1. $Ag^+(aq) + e^- \longrightarrow Ag(s) \qquad\qquad\qquad E^\circ = 0.799$ V

           $NO_3^-(aq) + 4H^+(aq) + 3e^- \longrightarrow NO(g) + 2H_2O(l) \qquad E^\circ = 0.964$ V

The nitric acid half-reaction has the more positive reduction potential; therefore nitric acid will oxidize silver metal. The equation for the reaction is

$$3Ag(s) + NO_3^-(aq) + 4H^+(aq) \longrightarrow 3Ag^+(aq) + NO(g) + 2H_2O(l)$$

      2. $Au^+(aq) + e^- \longrightarrow Au(s) \qquad E^\circ = 1.691$ V

   or $Au^{3+}(aq) + 3e^- \longrightarrow Au(s) \qquad E^\circ = 1.498$ V

           $NO_3^-(aq) + 4H^+(aq) + 3e^- \longrightarrow NO(g) + 2H_2O(l) \qquad E^\circ = 0.964$ V

The gold half-reaction has the more positive potential; therefore no reaction occurs.

(c) $Cl_2(g) + 2e^- \longrightarrow 2Cl^-(aq)$ $\qquad\qquad$ $E^\circ = 1.360$ V

$\quad\ \ F_2(g) + 2e^- \longrightarrow 2F^-(aq)$ $\qquad\qquad$ $E^\circ = 2.889$ V

The fluorine half-reaction has the more positive reduction potential; therefore no reaction occurs.

(d) $Cl_2(g) + 2e^- \longrightarrow 2Cl^-(aq)$ $\qquad\qquad$ $E^\circ = 1.360$ V

$\quad\ \ Br_2(l) + 2e^- \longrightarrow 2Br^-(aq)$ $\qquad\qquad$ $E^\circ = 1.078$ V

The chlorine half-reaction has the more positive reduction potential; therefore chlorine gas will oxidize bromide ions. The equation for the reaction is

$$Cl_2(g) + 2Br^-(aq) \longrightarrow 2Cl^-(aq) + Br_2(l)$$

(e) $Fe^{3+}(aq) + e^- \longrightarrow Fe^{2+}(aq)$ $\qquad\qquad$ $E^\circ = 0.769$ V

$\quad\ \ Cr_2O_7^{2-}(aq) + 14H^+(aq) + 6e^- \longrightarrow 2Cr^{3+}(aq) + 7H_2O(l)$ $\quad$ $E^\circ = 1.33$ V

The dichromate half-reaction has a more positive reduction potential than that of iron(III); therefore the acidified dichromate solution will oxidize Fe^{2+} to Fe^{3+}. The equation for the reaction is

$$6Fe^{2+}(aq) + Cr_2O_7^{2-}(aq) + 14H^+(aq) \longrightarrow 6Fe^{3+}(aq) + 2Cr^{3+}(aq) + 7H_2O(l)$$

(f) 1. (a) Can H_2O_2 reduce I_2?

$\quad I_2(s) + 2e^- \longrightarrow 2I^-(aq)$ $\qquad\qquad$ $E^\circ_{red} = 0.535$ V

$\quad H_2O_2(aq) \longrightarrow O_2(g) + 2H^+(aq) + 2e^-$ $\qquad$ $E^\circ_{oxid} = -0.695$ V

The sum is negative, therefore no reaction occurs.

(b) Can H_2O_2 oxidize I_2?

$\quad I_2(s) + 6H_2O(l) \longrightarrow 2IO_3^-(aq) + 12H^+(aq) + 10e^-$ $\qquad$ $E^\circ_{oxid} = -1.196$ V

$\quad H_2O_2(aq) + 2H^+(aq) + 2e^- \longrightarrow 2H_2O(l)$ $\qquad\qquad$ $E^\circ_{red} = 1.763$ V

The sum is positive, therefore I_2 is oxidized. The equation for the reaction is

$$I_2(s) + 5H_2O_2(aq) \longrightarrow 2IO_3^-(aq) + 2H^+(aq) + 4H_2O(l)$$

2. Ag^+ can only be reduced. Can H_2O_2 reduce Ag^+?

$\quad Ag^+(aq) + e^- \longrightarrow Ag(s)$ $\qquad\qquad\qquad\qquad$ $E^\circ_{red} = 0.799$ V

$\quad H_2O_2(aq) \longrightarrow O_2(g) + 2H^+(aq) + 2e^-$ $\qquad\qquad$ $E^\circ_{oxid} = -0.695$ V

The sum is positive, therefore Ag^+ is reduced. The equation for the reaction is

$$2Ag^+(aq) + H_2O_2(aq) \longrightarrow 2Ag(s) + O_2(g) + 2H^+(aq)$$

3. (a) Can H_2O_2 reduce Fe^{2+}?

E°_{red} for Fe^{2+} is negative (-0.409 V) and E°_{oxid} for H_2O_2 is also negative (-0.695 V), therefore no reaction occurs.

(b) Can H_2O_2 oxidize Fe^{2+}?

$\quad Fe^{2+}(aq) \longrightarrow Fe^{3+}(aq) + e^-$ $\qquad\qquad\qquad$ $E^\circ_{oxid} = -0.769$ V

$\quad H_2O_2(aq) + 2H^+(aq) + 2e^- \longrightarrow 2H_2O(l)$ $\qquad$ $E^\circ_{red} = 1.763$ V

The sum is positive, therefore Fe^{2+} is oxidized. The equation for the reaction is

$$2Fe^{2+}(aq) + H_2O_2(aq) + 2H^+(aq) \longrightarrow 2Fe^{3+}(aq) + 2H_2O(l)$$

20.23   (a) oxidation: $Fe(s) \longrightarrow Fe^{2+}(aq) + 2e^-$ $E^{\circ}_{oxid} = 0.409$ V

         reduction: $Sn^{2+}(aq) + 2e^- \longrightarrow Sn(s)$ $E^{\circ}_{red} = -0.14$ V

         $E^{\circ} = E^{\circ}_{oxid} + E^{\circ}_{red} = 0.409$ V $- 0.14$ V $= 0.27$ V

         Substituting $n = 2$ mol e^-, $F = 96,485$ C/mol e^-, and $E^{\circ} = 0.27$ J/C into Equation 20.5 gives

$$\Delta G^{\circ} = -nFE^{\circ} = -2 \text{ mol } e^- \times \frac{96,485 \text{ C}}{1 \text{ mol } e^-} \times \frac{0.27 \text{ J}}{1 \text{ C}} = -5.2 \times 10^4 \text{ J} = -52 \text{ kJ}$$

  (b) oxidation: $H_2(g) \longrightarrow 2H^+(aq) + 2e^-$ $E^{\circ}_{oxid} = 0.000$ V

         reduction: $Br_2(l) + 2e^- \longrightarrow 2Br^-(aq)$ $E^{\circ}_{red} = 1.078$ V

         $E^{\circ} = E^{\circ}_{oxid} + E^{\circ}_{red} = 0.000$ V $+ 1.078$ V $= 1.078$ V

         Substituting $n = 2$ mol e^-, $F = 96,485$ C/mol e^-, and $E^{\circ} = 1.078$ J/C into Equation 20.5 gives

$$\Delta G^{\circ} = -nFE^{\circ} = -2 \text{ mol } e^- \times \frac{96,485 \text{ C}}{1 \text{ mol } e^-} \times \frac{1.078 \text{ J}}{1 \text{ C}} = -2.08 \times 10^5 \text{ J} = -208 \text{ kJ}$$

  (c) oxidation: $2I^-(aq) \longrightarrow I_2(s) + 2e^-$ $E^{\circ}_{oxid} = -0.535$ V

         reduction: $Cl_2(g) + 2e^- \longrightarrow 2Cl^-(aq)$ $E^{\circ}_{red} = 1.360$ V

         $E^{\circ} = E^{\circ}_{oxid} + E^{\circ}_{red} = -0.535$ V $+ 1.360$ V $= 0.825$ V

$$\Delta G^{\circ} = -nFE^{\circ} = -2 \text{ mol } e^- \times \frac{96,485 \text{ C}}{1 \text{ mol } e^-} \times \frac{0.825 \text{ J}}{1 \text{ C}} = -1.59 \times 10^5 \text{ J} = -159 \text{ kJ}$$

  (d) oxidation: $Cr(s) \longrightarrow Cr^{3+}(aq) + 3e^-$ $E^{\circ}_{oxid} = 0.74$ V

         reduction: $Cr_2O_7^{2-}(aq) + 14H^+(aq) + 6e^- \longrightarrow 2Cr^{3+}(aq) + 7H_2O(l)$ $E^{\circ}_{red} = 1.33$ V

         $E^{\circ} = E^{\circ}_{oxid} + E^{\circ}_{red} = 0.74$ V $+ 1.33$ V $= 2.07$ V

         While E is independent of the form of the reaction equation, ΔG and n are not. For the reaction written in the approved form (no fractional coefficients)

         $2Cr(s) + Cr_2O_7^{2-}(aq) + 14H^+(aq) \longrightarrow 4Cr^{3+}(aq) + 7H_2O(l)$

         $n = 6$ mol e^-, and ΔG° is

$$\Delta G^{\circ} = -nFE^{\circ} = -6 \text{ mol } e^- \times \frac{96,485 \text{ C}}{1 \text{ mol } e^-} \times \frac{2.07 \text{ J}}{1 \text{ C}} = -1.20 \times 10^6 \text{ J} = -1.20 \times 10^3 \text{ kJ}$$

  (e) oxidation: $Fe^{2+}(aq) \longrightarrow Fe^{3+}(aq) + e^-$ $E^{\circ}_{oxid} = -0.769$ V

         reduction: $O_2(g) + 4H^+(aq) + 4e^- \longrightarrow 2H_2O(l)$ $E^{\circ}_{red} = 1.229$ V

         $E^{\circ} = E^{\circ}_{oxid} + E^{\circ}_{red} = -0.769$ V $+ 1.229$ V $= 0.460$ V

         For the reaction written in the form

         $4Fe^{2+}(aq) + O_2(g) + 4H^+(aq) \longrightarrow 4Fe^{3+}(aq) + 2H_2O(l)$

         $n = 4$ mol e^-, and ΔG° is

$$\Delta G^{\circ} = -nFE^{\circ} = -4 \text{ mol } e^- \times \frac{96,485 \text{ C}}{1 \text{ mol } e^-} \times \frac{0.460 \text{ J}}{1 \text{ C}} = -1.78 \times 10^5 \text{ J} = -178 \text{ kJ}$$

20.27   (a) The cell reaction and standard voltage are

         $Cu(s) + 2Ag^{2+}(aq) \longrightarrow Cu^{2+}(aq) + 2Ag(s)$

         $E^{\circ} = E^{\circ}_{oxid} + E^{\circ}_{red} = -0.339$ V $+ 0.799$ V $= 0.460$ V

The reaction quotient is

$$Q = \frac{[Cu^{2+}]}{[Ag^+]^2} = \frac{1.5}{(1.0)^2} = 1.5$$

Substituting Q = 1.5, n = 2, and E° = 0.460 V into Equation 20.7b gives

$$E = 0.460 \text{ V} - \frac{0.0592 \text{ V}}{2} \times \log 1.5 = 0.45 \text{ V}$$

(b) This is an example of a concentration cell, a cell in which there is no net chemical reaction, only an equalization of the concentrations in the two cell compartments. Concentration cells harness the spontaneous mixing process. When the concentrations become equal, $\Delta G = 0$ and the current stops. The cell reaction and standard voltage are

oxidation:	$Cd(s) \longrightarrow Cd^{2+}(0.0030 \text{ M}) + 2e^-$	$E^\circ_{oxid} = 0.402 \text{ V}$
reduction:	$Cd^{2+}(1.2 \text{ M}) + 2e^- \longrightarrow Cd(s)$	$E^\circ_{red} = -0.402 \text{ V}$
net reaction:	$Cd^{2+}(1.2 \text{ M}) \longrightarrow Cd^{2+}(0.0030 \text{ M})$	$E^\circ = 0.000 \text{ V}$

The reaction quotient is

$$Q = \frac{[Cd^{2+}]_{anode\ compartment}}{[Cd^{2+}]_{cathode\ compartment}} = \frac{0.0030}{1.2} = 0.0025$$

Substituting Q = 0.0025, n = 2, and E° = 0.000 V into Equation 20.7b gives

$$E = 0.000 \text{ V} - \frac{0.0592 \text{ V}}{2} \times \log 0.0025 = 0.077 \text{ V}$$

20.29 (a)
$$Q = \frac{[Cr^{3+}]^2}{[Cr_2O_7^{2-}][H^+]^{14}} = \frac{(0.50)^2}{(0.30)(1.0)^{14}} = 0.83$$

Substituting n = 6, E° = 1.33 V, and Q = 0.83 into the Nernst equation gives

$$E = 1.33 \text{ V} - \frac{0.0592 \text{ V}}{6} \times \log 0.83 = 1.33 \text{ V}$$

(b)
$$Q = \frac{1}{P_{O_2}[H^+]^4} = \frac{1}{(1)(1 \times 10^{-7})^4} = 1 \times 10^{28}$$

Substituting n = 4, E° = 1.229 V, and Q = 1 x 10^{28} into the Nernst equation gives

$$E = 1.229 \text{ V} - \frac{0.0592 \text{ V}}{4} \times \log(1 \times 10^{28}) = 0.815 \text{ V}$$

(c)
$$Q = \frac{[Fe^{2+}]}{[Fe^{3+}]} = \frac{(0.50)}{(0.50)} = 1$$

Log Q = 0, therefore E = E° = 0.769 V

20.31 (a) $2I^-(aq) \longrightarrow I_2(s) + 2e^-$ $\qquad E^\circ_{oxid} = -0.535 \text{ V}$

$O_2(g) + 4H^+(aq) + 4e^- \longrightarrow 2H_2O(l)$ $\qquad E^\circ_{red} = 1.229 \text{ V}$

$E^\circ = E^\circ_{oxid} + E^\circ_{red} = -0.535 \text{ V} + 1.229 \text{ V} = 0.694 \text{ V}$

Substituting $E° = 0.694$ V and $n = 4$ into Equation 20.8b gives

$$\log K = \frac{nE°}{0.0592} = \frac{4 \times 0.694 \text{ V}}{0.0592 \text{ V}} = 46.9 \text{ and } K = \text{antilog } 46.9 = 10^{46.9} = 8 \times 10^{46}$$

(b) $Zn(s) \longrightarrow Zn^{2+}(aq) + 2e^-$ $E°_{oxid} = 0.762$ V

$Zn(NH_3)_4^{2+}(aq) + 2e^- \longrightarrow Zn(s) + 4NH_3(aq)$ $E°_{red} = -1.015$ V

$E° = E°_{oxid} + E°_{red} = 0.762 \text{ V} - 1.015 \text{ V} = -0.253$ V

Substituting $E° = -0.253$ V and $n = 2$ into Equation 20.8b gives

$$\log K = \frac{nE°}{0.0592} = \frac{2 \times -0.253 \text{ V}}{0.0592 \text{ V}} = -8.55$$

and $K = \text{antilog}(-8.55) = 10^{-8.55} = 2.8 \times 10^{-9}$

(c) $Ag(s) + I^-(aq) \longrightarrow AgI(s) + e^-$ $E°_{oxid} = 0.152$ V

$I_2(s) + 2e^- \longrightarrow 2I^-(aq)$ $E°_{red} = 0.535$ V

$E° = E°_{oxid} + E°_{red} = 0.152 \text{ V} + 0.535 \text{ V} = 0.687$ V

Substituting $E° = 0.687$ V and $n = 1$ into Equation 20.8b gives

$$\log K = \frac{nE°}{0.0592} = \frac{1 \times 0.687 \text{ V}}{0.0592 \text{ V}} = 11.6 \text{ and } K = \text{antilog}(11.6) = 10^{11.6} = 4 \times 10^{11}$$

(d)

$H_2(g) \longrightarrow$ $2H^+(aq) + 2e^-$ $E°_{oxid} = 0.000$ V

$2H_2O(1) + 2e^- \longrightarrow H_2(g) + 2OH^-(aq)$ $E°_{red} = -0.828$ V

$2H_2O(1) \rightleftharpoons$ $2H^+(aq) + 2OH^-(aq)$ $E° = -0.828$ V

Using the half-reactions in Table 20.1 gives a reaction that is double the desired one. To obtain the desired reaction, we have to multiply each half-reaction by one half (1/2). This does not affect the potentials, but makes $n = 1$ instead of 2. Substituting $E° = -0.828$ V and $n = 1$ into Equation 20.8b gives

$$\log K = \frac{nE°}{0.0592} = \frac{1 \times (-0.828 \text{ V})}{0.0592 \text{ V}} = -14.0 \text{ and } K = \text{antilog}(-14.0) = 10^{-14.0} = 1 \times 10^{-14}$$

20.34   First we have to find the equilibrium constant for the reaction

$Cu(s) + 2Ag^+(aq) \longrightarrow Cu^{2+}(aq) + 2Ag(s)$

From Table 20.1 we have

$Cu(s) \longrightarrow Cu^{2+}(aq) + 2e^-$ $E°_{oxid} = -0.339$ V

$Ag^+(aq) + e^- \longrightarrow Ag(s)$ $E°_{red} = 0.799$ V

and $E° = E°_{oxid} + E°_{red} = -0.339 \text{ V} + 0.799 \text{ V} = 0.460$ V

Substituting $E° = 0.460$ V and $n = 2$ into Equation 20.8b gives

$$\log K = \frac{nE°}{0.0592} = \frac{2 \times 0.460 \text{ V}}{0.0592 \text{ V}} = 15.5 \text{ and } K = \text{antilog}(15.5) = 10^{15.5} = 3 \times 10^{15}$$

Since K is so large, virtually all of the Ag^+ will be converted to Ag, so long as there is a sufficient amount of copper metal present to react with all the Ag^+ ions present. Therefore, the $[Cu^{2+}] = 0.005$ M and the $[Ag^+]$ is calculated as follows:

$$\frac{[Cu^{2+}]}{[Ag^+]^2} = \frac{0.005}{x^2} = 3 \times 10^{15}; \quad x = [Ag^+] = 1 \times 10^{-9} \text{ M}$$

20.39 (a) From the half-cell reactions we see that 5 mol of ions are consumed and 1 mol of ions is produced, leading to an overall reduction of 4 mol of ions for every 2 mol of electrons that pass through the circuit. Therefore, the molality of the electrolyte in a discharged lead storage battery is considerably lower than that in a fully charged one and, consequently, the electrolyte in a discharged battery freezes at a higher temperature.

(b) Shaking and sudden shock can dislodge the solid lead sulfate from the electrodes. Once dislodged it falls to the bottom of the cell and can no longer be converted back to lead and lead dioxide. This diminishes the amount of reactants and can cause a short circuit if enough builds up so that the sheets of lead and lead dioxide come in contact with one another.

20.43 Advise against. Copper has a lower oxidation potential than iron; therefore if the iron and copper are in contact, the iron will behave as the anode and the copper as the cathode in any galvanic situation that occurs. Hence, the presence of the copper enhances the corrosion of the iron pipe, which is not desireable.

20.44 (a) No. The tin plating is only a tough and adhesive protective coating. In order for the tin plating to work, the entire piece must be covered and the tin surface must be intact.

(b) Tin has a lower oxidation potential than iron; therefore the iron will behave as the anode and the tin as the cathode in any galvanic situation that occurs. When the tin can is damaged, a galvanic system can start up, i.e., corrosion can begin, and the presence of the tin, acting now as a large cathode instead of a protective coating, enhances or promotes the corrosion of the tin can. Consequently, a damaged tin can will rust more rapidly than an unplated steel can.

20.50 To obtain an active metal from its compounds by chemical reduction, a stronger reducing agent than the metal must be used. Since active metals are strong reducing agents themselves, there are few reducing agents available that can do the job and the cost of obtaining them is usually prohibitive. Therefore, cost and availability are limiting factors. On the other hand, all active metals can be electrolytically reduced by the application of a sufficient voltage.

20.51 (a) Since the reduction potential of water is considerably higher than that of potassuim ion, the water would be reduced in preference to the potassium ion. This holds for other active metals as well.

(b) If water gets into the cell, hydrogen would be produced at the cathode instead of the active metal.

20.58 $2H_2O(l) + 2e^- \longrightarrow H_2(g) + 2OH^-(aq)$

(a) The equation for the electrode reaction shows that 2 mol (2 x 18.0 g = 36.0 g) of water are decomposed by the passage of 2 mol of electrons, or 2 x 96,485 C. The steps in the calculation are: 15,000 C $\longrightarrow$ mol H_2O $\longrightarrow$ g H_2O.

$$15,000 \text{ C} \times \frac{2 \text{ mol } H_2O}{2 \times 96,485 \text{ C}} \times \frac{18.0 \text{ g}}{1 \text{ mol } H_2O} = 2.80 \text{ g}$$

(b) The equation for the electrode reaction shows that 1 mol of hydrogen is produced by the passage of 2 mol of electrons, or 2 Faradays. The steps in the calculation are: 1.25 F $\longrightarrow$ mol H_2 $\longrightarrow$ L H_2.

$$1.25 \text{ F} \times \frac{1 \text{ mol } H_2}{2 \text{ F}} = 0.625 \text{ mol } H_2$$

Substituting n = 0.625 mol, P = 1.00 atm, T = 298 K, and R = 0.0821 L atm/mol K into the ideal gas equation gives

$$V = \frac{nRT}{P} = \frac{0.625 \text{ mol} \times 0.0821 \text{ L atm/mol K} \times 298 \text{ K}}{1.00 \text{ atm}} = 15.3 \text{ L}$$

20.60 $Pb^{2+}(aq) + 2e^- \longrightarrow Pb(s)$

The equation for the electrode reaction shows that 1 mol (207.2 g) of lead metal is deposited by 2 mol of electrons, or 2 x 96,485 C. The steps in the calculation are:
$I \times t \longrightarrow C \longrightarrow$ mol Pb $\longrightarrow$ g Pb.

$$\frac{0.15 \text{ C}}{1 \text{ s}} \times 3600 \text{ s} \times \frac{1 \text{ mol Pb}}{2 \times 96,485 \text{ C}} \times \frac{207.2 \text{ g}}{1 \text{ mol Pb}} = 0.58 \text{ g}$$

20.63   nickel compound + $ne^- \longrightarrow Ni(s)$

The oxidation state of the Ni compound is equal to n, and n is equal to the number of Faradays required to produce 1 mol of Ni. The steps in the calculation are:
$I \times t \longrightarrow C \longrightarrow$ C/g Ni $\longrightarrow$ C/mol Ni $\longrightarrow$ F/mol Ni $\longrightarrow$ n $\longrightarrow$ oxidation state.

$$\frac{0.0500 \text{ C}}{1 \text{ s}} \times 6.00 \text{ h} \times \frac{3600 \text{ s}}{1 \text{ h}} \times \frac{1}{0.328 \text{ g Ni}} \times \frac{58.7 \text{ g Ni}}{1 \text{ mol Ni}} \times \frac{1 \text{ F}}{96,485 \text{ C}} = 2 \text{ F/mol Ni}$$

Since n = 2, the nickel in the compound is in the +2 oxidation state.

20.65   The oxidation state of chromium in CrO_4^{2-} is +6. Therefore, 6 Faradays, or 6 x 96,485 C = 578,910 C, are required to deposit 1 mol of chromium from an acidified solution of CrO_4^{2-}.

20.68 $2H_2O(l) \longrightarrow 4H^+(aq) + O_2(g) + 4e^-$ anode, oxidation

$2H_2O(l) + 2e^- \longrightarrow H_2(g) + 2OH^-(aq)$ cathode, reduction

(a) The current is 80 x 10^{-3} A = 0.080 C/s. The electrode equation shows that 4 mol of electrons, or 4 x 96,485 C, will liberate 1 mol of oxygen. The steps in the calculation are:
mol $O_2 \longrightarrow C \longrightarrow$ t.

$$0.0030 \text{ mol } O_2 \times \frac{4 \times 96,485 \text{ C}}{1 \text{ mol } O_2} \times \frac{1 \text{ s}}{0.080 \text{ C}} \times \frac{1 \text{ h}}{3600 \text{ s}} = 4.0 \text{ h}$$

(b) From the electrode equations we see that for every mole of oxygen liberated, 2 mol of hydrogen are liberated. Therefore, 6.0 mmol of hydrogen is liberated along with the oxygen.

20.70 $Ca^{2+} + 2e^- \longrightarrow Ca(s)$ cathode, reduction

$2Cl^- \longrightarrow Cl_2(g) + 2e^-$ anode, oxidation

(a) The electrode equation shows that 2 mol of electrons, or 2 x 96,485 C, will produce 1 mol (40.1 g) of calcium. The steps in the calculation are: 1.00 kg Ca $\longrightarrow$ mol Ca $\longrightarrow$ C $\longrightarrow$ I.

$$1000 \text{ g Ca} \times \frac{1 \text{ mol Ca}}{40.1 \text{ g Ca}} \times \frac{2 \times 96,485 \text{ C}}{1 \text{ mol Ca}} \times \frac{1}{10.0 \text{ days}} \times \frac{1 \text{ day}}{24 \text{ h}} \times \frac{1 \text{ h}}{3600 \text{ s}}$$

$$= 5.57 \text{ C/s} = 5.57 \text{ A}$$

(b) From the electrode equations, we see that 1 mol of chlorine is produced for every mole of calcium. The moles of chlorine produced are

$$1000 \text{ g Ca} \times \frac{1 \text{ mol Ca}}{40.1 \text{ g Ca}} \times \frac{1 \text{ mol Cl}_2}{1 \text{ mol Ca}} = 24.9 \text{ mol Cl}_2$$

The volume of chlorine gas is obtained by substituting n = 24.9 mol, P = 710 torr/760 torr = 0.934 atm, T = 303 K, and R = 0.0821 L atm/mol K into the ideal gas equation

$$V = \frac{nRT}{P} = \frac{24.9 \text{ mol} \times 0.0821 \text{ L atm/mol K} \times 303 \text{ K}}{0.934 \text{ atm}} = 663 \text{ L}$$

20.72   (a) The relevant half-reactions are

$$Cu^{2+}(aq) + 2e^- \longrightarrow Cu(s) \qquad\qquad E^\circ = 0.339 \text{ V}$$

$$NO_3^-(aq) + 4H^+(aq) + 3e^- \longrightarrow NO(g) + 2H_2O(l) \qquad E^\circ = 0.964 \text{ V}$$

$$2H^+(aq) + 2e^- \longrightarrow H_2(g) \qquad\qquad E^\circ = 0.000 \text{ V}$$

Only the nitric acid has a reduction potential greater than that of copper; therefore only nitric acid can oxidize copper metal and thus dissolve it.

(b) From Table 20.1 we have

$$Fe(s) \longrightarrow Fe^{2+}(aq) + 2e^- \qquad\qquad E^\circ_{oxid} = 0.402 \text{ V}$$

$$\underline{2Fe^{3+}(aq) + 2e^- \longrightarrow 2Fe^{2+}(aq)} \qquad\qquad \underline{E^\circ_{red} = 0.769 \text{ V}}$$

$$Fe(s) + 2Fe^{3+}(aq) \longrightarrow 3Fe^{2+}(aq) \qquad\qquad E^\circ = 1.171 \text{ V}$$

Since $E^\circ > 0$, $\Delta G^\circ < 0$ and this reaction is spontaneous in the forward direction. Hence, the presence of metallic iron in an aqueous Fe^{2+} solution will reduce any Fe^{3+} formed by atmospheric oxidation back to Fe^{2+}.

(c) From Table 20.1 we have

$$Cu^+(aq) \longrightarrow Cu^{2+}(aq) + e^- \qquad\qquad E^\circ_{oxid} = -0.161 \text{ V}$$

$$\underline{Cu^+(aq) + e^- \longrightarrow Cu(s)} \qquad\qquad \underline{E^\circ_{red} = 0.518 \text{ V}}$$

$$2Cu^+(aq) \longrightarrow Cu^{2+}(aq) + Cu(s) \qquad\qquad E^\circ = 0.357 \text{ V}$$

Since $E^\circ > 0$, $\Delta G^\circ < 0$ and this reaction is spontaneous in the forward direction. Therefore, Cu^+ will disproportionate in aqueous solution.

20.76   The half-cell reactions are

$$Cd(s) + 2OH^-(aq) \longrightarrow Cd(OH)_2(s) + 2e^- \qquad\qquad E^\circ_{oxid} = 0.82 \text{ V}$$

$$NiO_2(s) + 2H_2O(l) + 2e^- \longrightarrow Ni(OH)_2(s) + 2OH^-(s) \qquad\qquad E^\circ_{red} = 0.49 \text{ V}$$

From the half-cell reactions we see that the cell voltage is independent of the hydroxide ion concentration, since the KOH electrolyte is common to both half-cells and, therefore, cancels out in the overall reaction quotient expression. Consequently, the cell voltage equals the standard cell voltage E°.

$$E = E^\circ = E^\circ_{oxid} + E^\circ_{red} = 0.82 \text{ V} + 0.49 \text{ V} = 1.31 \text{ V}$$

This assumes that the small change in the water concentration, since this is not a dilute solution, can be ignored.

20.77   (a) $SO_3^{2-}(aq) + 2OH^-(aq) \longrightarrow SO_4^{2-}(aq) + H_2O(l) + 2e^- \qquad\qquad E^\circ_{oxid} = 0.936 \text{ V}$

$MnO_4^-(aq) + 2H_2O(l) + 3e^- \longrightarrow MnO_2(s) + 4OH^-(aq) \qquad\qquad E^\circ_{red} = 0.597 \text{ V}$

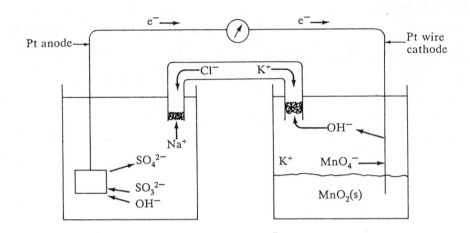

(b) $E° = E°_{oxid} + E°_{red} = 0.936$ V $+ 0.597$ V $= 1.533$ V

Substituting $E° = 1.533$ V $= 1.533$ J/C, n $= 6$ mol e^-, and F $= 96,485$ C/mol e^- in Equation 20.5b gives

$$\Delta G° = -nFE° = -6 \text{ mol } e^- \times \frac{96,485 \text{ C}}{1 \text{ mol } e^-} \times \frac{1.533 \text{ J}}{1 \text{ C}} = -8.87 \times 10^5 \text{ J} = -887 \text{ kJ}$$

Substituting $E° = 1.533$ V and n $= 6$ into Equation 20.8b gives

$$\log K = \frac{nE°}{0.0592} = \frac{6 \times 1.533 \text{ V}}{0.0592 \text{ V}} = 155 \text{ and } K = \text{antilog } 155 = 10^{155}$$

(c)

$$Q = \frac{[SO_4^{2-}]^3[OH^-]^2}{[MnO_4^-]^2[SO_3^{2-}]^3} = \frac{(0.10)^3(0.10)^2}{(0.10)^2(0.10)^3} = 1$$

Since Q $= 1$, E $= E° = 1.533$ V

20.79 (a) $Sn^{2+}(aq) \longrightarrow Sn^{4+}(aq) + 2e^-$ $\qquad E°_{oxid} = -0.154$ V

$Sn^{2+}(aq) + 2e^- \longrightarrow Sn(s)$ $\qquad E°_{red} = -0.14$ V

$E° = E°_{oxid} + E°_{red} = -0.154$ V $- 0.14$ V $= -0.29$ V

Substituting $E° = -0.29$ V and n $= 2$ into Equation 20.8b gives

$$\log K = \frac{nE°}{0.0592} = \frac{2 \times -0.29 \text{ V}}{0.0592 \text{ V}} = -9.8 \text{ and } K = \text{antilog}(-9.8) = 10^{-9.8} = 2 \times 10^{-10}$$

(b)

$$K = \frac{[Sn^{4+}]}{[Sn^{2+}]^2} = 2 \times 10^{-10} \text{ and } [Sn^{4+}] = 2 \times 10^{-10}[Sn^{2+}]^2$$

Since K is very small we can assume that the concentration of Sn^{2+} doesn't change; so $[Sn^{2+}] = 1.0$ M. Hence,

$[Sn^{4+}] = 2 \times 10^{-10} \times (1.0)^2 = 2 \times 10^{-10}$ M and the fraction of Sn^{2+} converted to Sn^{4+} is

$$\frac{2 \times 10^{-10} \text{ M}}{1.0 \text{ M}} = 2 \times 10^{-10}$$

20.81 (a) The current I $= 0.10$ μA $= 1.0 \times 10^{-7}$ A $= 1.0 \times 10^{-7}$ C/s. The time t $= 1$ h $= 3600$ s. Substituting I and t into Equation 20.9 gives

$Q = I \times t = 1.0 \times 10^{-7}$ C/s $\times 3600$ s $= 3.6 \times 10^{-4}$ C

(b) $HgO(s) + H_2O(l) + 2e^- \longrightarrow Hg(l) + 2OH^-(aq)$

The electrode equation shows that 1 mol (200.6 g) of mercury is formed when 2 mol of electrons, or 2 x 96,485 C, passes through the circuit. The steps in the calculation are: C $\longrightarrow$ mol Hg $\longrightarrow$ g Hg.

$$3.6 \times 10^{-4} \text{ C} \times \frac{1 \text{ mol Hg}}{2 \times 96,485 \text{ C}} \times \frac{200.6 \text{ g Hg}}{1 \text{ mol Hg}} = 3.7 \times 10^{-7} \text{ g Hg}$$

(c) Substituting $Q = 3.6 \times 10^{-4}$ C and $E = 1.35$ V = 1.35 J/C into Equation 20.1 gives

maximum electrical work = $Q \times E = 3.6 \times 10^{-4}$ C x 1.35 J/C = 4.9×10^{-4} J

20.83 (a) The total volume of silver to be plated is equal to a hundred times the difference in volume between two spheres with radii of 2.520 cm and 2.500 cm. Since $V_{sphere} = 4\pi r^3/3$ and $\pi = 3.142$, we have

$$\text{total Ag volume} = 100 \times \frac{4 \times 3.142}{3} \times ((2.520 \text{ cm})^3 - (2.500 \text{ cm})^3) = 158.4 \text{ cm}^3$$

The grams of silver needed to plate the spheres is therefore

$$158.4 \text{ cm}^3 \times \frac{10.5 \text{ g}}{1 \text{ cm}^3} = 1.66 \times 10^3 \text{ g or } 1.66 \text{ kg}$$

(b) $Ag(CN)_2^-(aq) + e^- \longrightarrow Ag(s) + 2CN^-(aq)$

The electrode equation shows that 1 mol of electrons, or 96,485 C, will deposit 1 mol (107.9 g) of silver. The steps in the calculation are: g Ag $\longrightarrow$ mol Ag $\longrightarrow$ C $\longrightarrow$ I.

$$1660 \text{ g Ag} \times \frac{1 \text{ mol Ag}}{107.9 \text{ g Ag}} \times \frac{96,485 \text{ C}}{1 \text{ mol Ag}} \times \frac{1}{5.00 \text{ h}} \times \frac{1 \text{ h}}{3600 \text{ s}} = 82.5 \text{ A}$$

(c) Let x stand for the actual current needed. Then,

x x 0.95 = 82.5 A and x = 82.5 A/0.95 = 87 A

CHAPTER 21
METALS AND COORDINATION CHEMISTRY

Solutions To Practice Exercises

PE 21.1 VCl_3. In VCl_3 vanadium has a +3 oxidation state, while in VCl_2 it is only +2.

PE 21.2 (a) In_2O_3. Indium lies just below gallium in Group 3A; therefore, In_2O_3 should be more basic than Ga_2O_3.

(b) $Fe(OH)_2$. In $Fe(OH)_2$ iron has a +2 oxidation state, while in $Fe(OH)_3$ it has a +3 oxidation state.

PE 21.3   The complex ion is the bracketed portion, $Co(CN)_5NO^{2-}$. (The charge is 2– because the two Na^+ ions have a total charge of 2+.) Therefore, the sum of the oxidation numbers in the complex is –2. Each CN^- has a charge of 1– and Co(III) has an oxidation number of +3, so

$$+3 + 5 \times (-1) + x_{NO} = -2 \text{ and } x_{NO} = 0$$

The charge on the nitrosyl ligand, NO, is zero.

PE 21.8 (a)

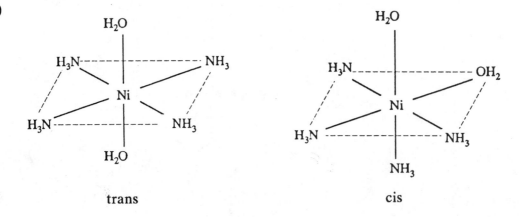

trans   cis

(c)

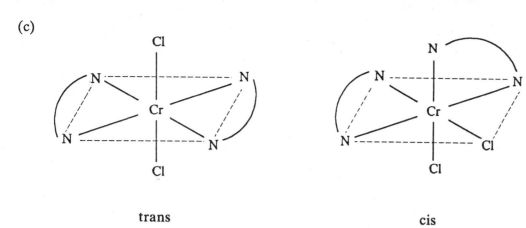

trans   cis

PE 21.9

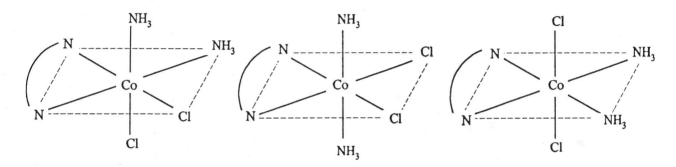

(a) chiral (optically active)   (b) Each of the above structural isomers is achiral
                                          (optically inactive)

PE 21.10 $Ni(EN)_3^{2+}$. Ethylenediamine (EN) is a stronger ligand than NH_3 (see Table 21.8). Therefore, the orbital splitting energy, Δ, should be greater in $Ni(EN)_3^{2+}$ and $Ni(EN)_3^{2+}$ should absorb higher frequency light.

PE 21.11 Fe^{2+} has 6 d electrons. The high- and low-spin configurations are

$\frac{\uparrow}{}$ $\frac{\uparrow}{}$ $\frac{}{}$ $\frac{}{}$

$\underset{\text{high spin}}{\frac{\uparrow\downarrow}{}\;\frac{\uparrow}{}\;\frac{\uparrow}{}}$ $\underset{\text{low spin}}{\frac{\uparrow\downarrow}{}\;\frac{\uparrow\downarrow}{}\;\frac{\uparrow\downarrow}{}}$

Fe^{3+} has 5 d electrons. The high- and low-spin configurations are

$\frac{\uparrow}{}$ $\frac{\uparrow}{}$ $\frac{}{}$ $\frac{}{}$

$\underset{\text{high spin}}{\frac{\uparrow}{}\;\frac{\uparrow}{}\;\frac{\uparrow}{}}$ $\underset{\text{low spin}}{\frac{\uparrow\downarrow}{}\;\frac{\uparrow\downarrow}{}\;\frac{\uparrow}{}}$

The only configuration that has one unpaired d electron is the Fe^{3+} low-spin one; therefore the oxidation state of the iron is +3.

Solutions to Final Exercises

21.6   (a) The melting point of a metal depends on the strength of the metallic bond, which in turn depends on the atomic size and number of valence electrons. The strength of the metallic bond decreases with increasing atomic size. Since the atomic size increases in going down a representative group and the number of valence electrons remains constant, the melting points of representative metals should decrease in going down such a group.

    (b) The strength of the metallic bond increases with the number of valence electrons available for metallic bonding and decreases with increasing atomic size. In many transition groups the atomic size does not change very much, but the number of valence electrons that becomes available for metallic bonding increases going down the group, because the underlying d electrons are further from the nucleus and therefore more easily delocalized. Consequently, the melting points in several transition groups increase from top to bottom, instead of decrease as in the representative groups.

21.7   The number of electrons available for bonding is roughly similar for all lanthanides because each new electron in the series is added to an inner shell (n = 4). The atomic radius, however, decreases steadily going across the series, thus the metallic bond strength increases and with it the melting point.

21.8   (a) Since the valence electrons in the metallic lattice are delocalized, the number of nearest neighbors in a metallic lattice is not restricted by the number of covalent bonds that can be formed (normally a maximum of four). Therefore, the space in a metallic lattice is more filled up and the metallic lattice is more compact.

    (b) Freezing normally decreases the size of a metal. Therefore, the expansion of bismuth indicates that it also participates in some covalent bonding.

21.10   The relevant periodic trends are: 1. Metallic character decreases in going from left to right across a period. 2. Metallic character increases in going down a group. Since these two trends oppose one another in a perpendicular manner, the changeover from metallic to nonmetallic properties follows a slanting stepwise line going from upper left to lower right.

21.12 $Ca(s) \longrightarrow Ca^{2+}(aq) + 2e^-$

    ΔH°_{ion} = 590 kJ/mol + 1145 kJ/mol = 1735 kJ/mol (Table 8.3). E°_{oxid} = 2.869 V (Table 20.1).

    (a) $\Delta H^{\circ}_{oxid} = \Delta H^{\circ}_{sub} + \Delta H^{\circ}_{ion} + \Delta H^{\circ}_{hyd}$ = 178 kJ/mol + 1735 kJ/mol − 2469 kJ/mol = −556 kJ/mol

    (b) Substituting n = 2 mol e^-, F = 96,485 C/mol e^-, and E°_{oxid} = 2.869 V = 2.869 J/C into Equation 20.5 gives

$$\Delta G^{\circ}_{oxid} = -nFE^{\circ}_{oxid} = -2 \text{ mol } e^- \times \frac{96,485 \text{ C}}{1 \text{ mol } e-} \times \frac{2.869 \text{ J}}{1 \text{ C}} = -5.536 \times 10^5 \text{ J} = -553.6 \text{ kJ}$$

    (c) $\Delta G^{\circ}_{oxid} = \Delta H^{\circ}_{oxid} - T \Delta S^{\circ}_{oxid}$

$$\Delta S^{\circ}_{oxid} = \frac{\Delta H^{\circ}_{oxid} - \Delta G^{\circ}_{oxid}}{T} = \frac{-556 \text{ kJ/mol} + 553.6 \text{ kJ/mol}}{298 \text{ K}}$$

      = −8.05 x 10^{-3} kJ/K mol or −8.05 J/K mol

21.13   (a) In the d-block, f-block, and p-block. In the transition metals (d- and f-blocks) multiple oxidation states are attributed to the ability of the metal to employ electrons from more than one shell in bonding. In the p-block representative metals it is attributed to having valence electrons in both the s- and p-subshells of the valence shell.

    (b) In Groups 1A and 2A the electrons below the valence shell are not used in bonding because their energies are too low. A Group 2A atom always loses both of its outer s electrons (never just one) because the 2+ ion is smaller and more strongly stabilized by hydration or by lattice energy.

21.15   The tendency toward covalence decreases with increasing atomic size. Li, Be, and Al being the smallest metals in their respective groups should therefore exhibit more covalent character than the other metals in their groups. Small atoms can get closer to one another thus allowing their orbitals to overlap better, which enables them to form a stronger covalent bond. Higher ionization energies also favor covalent bonding over ionic bonding, because the electrons have to be completely removed or transferred in ionic bonding. Since Li, Be, and Al are the top metals in their respective groups, they have the highest ionization energies and should therefore be less likely to form ionic bonds.

21.16   (a) Thallium(I) hydroxide: $TlOH$; thallium(III) hydroxide: $Tl(OH)_3$. The strong and soluble base should be $TlOH$, since the lower oxidation state of thallium has the more ionic bonds.

    (b) Tl(I) chloride: $TlCl$; Tl(III) chloride: $TlCl_3$. The bonds in $TlCl_3$ are more covalent than those in $TlCl$ and, therefore, $TlCl_3$ should be more molecular than $TlCl$. Therefore, $TlCl_3$ should be the lower melting chloride, the $25°C$ melting chloride, and $TlCl$ the higher melting chloride, the $430°C$ melting chloride.

21.17   (a) The reaction between $Ca(OH)_2$ and aqueous HCl involves independent OH^- ions. $Ca(OH)_2$ is a basic ionic hydroxide, while $Zn(OH)_2$, often written in its probable hydrated form as $Zn(H_2O)_2(OH)_2$, is an amphoteric covalent hydroxide.

$$OH^-(aq) + H^+(aq) \longrightarrow H_2O(l)$$

$$Zn(OH)_2(s) + 2H^+(aq) \longrightarrow Zn^{2+}(aq) + 2H_2O(l)$$

    (b) Neutralization of chloride solution: 1. The $CaCl_2$ solution is already neutral. 2. The $ZnCl_2$ solution is slightly acidic due to the hydrated zinc ion, $Zn(H_2O)_4^{2+}$. Neutralization with hydroxide ion precipitates the neutral complex $Zn(H_2O)_2(OH)_2$ or $Zn(OH)_2$.

$$[Zn(H_2O)_4]Cl_2(aq) + 2NaOH(aq) \longrightarrow Zn(H_2O)_2(OH)_2(s) + 2NaCl(aq) + 2H_2O(l)$$

Reaction with excess concentrated $NaOH$:

1. $CaCl_2(aq) + 2NaOH(aq) \longrightarrow Ca(OH)_2(s) + 2NaCl(aq)$ Note: $Ca(OH)_2$ is slightly soluble.
2. $Zn(OH)_2(s) + 2NaOH(aq) \longrightarrow Na_2[Zn(OH)_4](aq)$
or $Zn(H_2O)_2(OH)_2(s) + 2NaOH(aq) \longrightarrow Na_2[Zn(OH)_4](aq) + 2H_2O(l)$

    (c) Zn is considerably smaller than Ca (see Figure 8.8) and has a higher electronegativity than calcium (see Figure 9.11). Consequently, Zn should form bonds with more covalent character than Ca. Therefore, the metal-oxygen bond in $Zn(OH)_2$ should be more covalent than that in $Ca(OH)_2$, and that is why $Zn(OH)_2$ is an amphoteric covalent hydroxide, while $Ca(OH)_2$ is a basic ionic hydroxide.

21.19   (a) 1. Small compact atoms. 2. Most are paramagnetic. 3. Variable oxidation states. 4. The activity of the transition metals usually decreases from top to bottom in a group. 5. Most of the transition metal compounds absorb visible light.

    (b) The highest oxidation states of Zn, Cd, and Hg are the +2 states, that is, Zn, Cd, and Hg only part with their s valence electrons and their underlying d orbitals are always completely filled. Some chemists consider transition elements to be only those elements that have partially filled d orbitals in at least one observed oxidation state.

21.21   (a) Molecular orbital theory predicts that when N atomic orbitals combine they produce N molecular orbitals with a range of energies. When N is very large, however, the spacing or energy gap between the various energy levels is extremely small and we get a band, which is a collection of very closely spaced energy levels; the energy difference between any level and the next highest level being negligibly small. The foregoing holds for crystal metallic conductors. For insulators, the theory predicts that the N molecular orbitals formed will split into two bands separated by an energy gap called the forbidden zone.

(b) 1. Metallic conductors have a band that is only partly filled; called the conduction band. When a band is only partly filled, the electrons can be easily promoted into the unfilled levels of the band and thereby conduct electricity.

2. Insulators have completely filled bands that are separated from empty bands by a large energy gap called the forbidden zone. Electrons cannot move into empty molecular orbitals and can therefore not conduct electricity, i.e., there is no way for them to gain and transport energy.

3. In semiconductors the forbidden zone or energy gap is smaller than that in an insulator and some electrons from the filled lower band can be excited into the unfilled conduction band above. Semiconductors have a very low electrical conductivity compared to metals, because they have very few electrons in the conduction band.

21.22 (a) The electron configuration of sodium is Na: $1s^2\ 2s^2\ 2p^6\ 3s^1$. The electron bands formed by the 1s, 2s, and 2p atomic orbitals are completely filled. The band formed by the 3s atomic orbitals is the conduction band, since it has a maximum capacity of 2 N electrons and is only half-filled with N electrons.

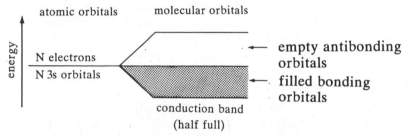

(b) All the bonding molecular orbitals are essentially filled, while all the antibonding molecular orbitals are essentially empty. Sodium is a metallic conductor because the energy levels in the band are continuous for all practical purposes and, therefore, the electrons can be very easily excited or promoted from the filled bonding orbitals into the empty antibonding orbitals of the conduction band. The promoted electrons are mobile and, therefore, can conduct electricity.

21.23 (a) The electron configuration of magnesium is Mg: $1s^2\ 2s^2\ 2p^6\ 3s^2$.

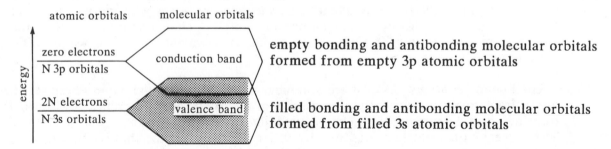

(b) The band formed from the 3s atomic orbitals is essentially full and the band formed from the 3p orbitals is essentially empty. If the 3s and 3p bands did not overlap, than Mg would have completely filled bands separated by a forbidden zone from an empty conduction band and would consequently be an insulator and not a metallic conductor. However, since the 3s and 3p bands in magnesium do overlap, there is no forbidden zone between them and excitation of electrons from the 3s valence band to the empty 3p conduction band occurs easily and, consequently, Mg is metallic in nature.

21.24 (a) The electron configuration of silicon is Si: $1s^2\ 2s^2\ 2p^6\ 3s^2\ 3p^2$. Silicon has the same crystalline structure as diamond. Each silicon atom is covalently bonded to four neighboring silicon atoms at the corners of a regular tetrahedron. Therefore, the silicon atom is sp^3 hybridized and uses sp^3 hybrid orbitals to form localized sigma bonds. However, these localized molecular orbitals further overlap to form two energy bands, because the silicon $n = 3$ valence orbitals used in the bonding are somewhat large and diffuse themselves.

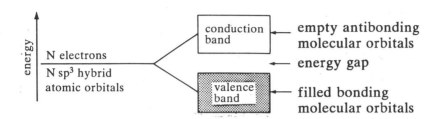

The energy bands in diamond are formed from carbon $n = 2$ sp^3 hybrid orbitals, which are much more localized than the $n = 3$ sp^3 hybrid orbitals of silicon. Furthermore, since carbon atoms are much smaller than silicon atoms, the spacing between the carbon atoms in diamond is a lot closer and the hybrid orbitals overlap better, giving diamond stronger bonds, lower energy bonding molecular orbitals and correspondingly higher energy antibonding molecular orbitals, than silicon. Consequently, the energy gap between the valence and conduction bands in diamond is considerably greater than that in silicon.

(b) Diamond is an insulator because the energy gap between the valence and conduction bands is too great for an appreciable number of valence band electrons to be excited into the conduction band. On the other hand, the energy gap in silicon is small enough for some of the valence band electrons to move into the conduction band, where they are mobile and can be made to move under the influence of an applied voltage.

21.25 The energy of a single energy gap is

$$\frac{1.06 \times 10^5\ J}{1\ mol} \times \frac{1\ mol}{6.022 \times 10^{23}\ energy\ gaps} = 1.76 \times 10^{-19}\ J/energy\ gap$$

The lowest radiation frequency that would excite an electron across the gap is

$$\nu = \frac{E}{h} = \frac{1.76 \times 10^{-19}\ J}{6.63 \times 10^{-34}\ Js} = 2.65 \times 10^{14}\ Hz$$

(b) From Figure 7.3 we see that radiation of this frequency lies in the infrared region of the spectrum that borders on the visible portion of the spectrum. Therefore, the higher frequency visible light can excite or promote electrons across the energy gap, which increases the number of electrons in the conduction band and, hence, increases the conductivity.

21.33 (a) Exercise 21.29: (a) hexamminecobalt(III) chloride; (b) potassium hexafluoroferrate(III); (c) sodium tetrachloroaluminate; (d) potassium tetrachlorocuprate(II); (e) potasssium hexacyanoferrate(II); (f) potassium hexacyanoferrate(III); (g) diammineplatinum(IV) chloride; (h) hexaaquavanadium(II) sulfate.

(b) Exercise 21.30: (a) tetrachloroplatinate(II) ion; (b) tetrahydroxoberyllate(II) ion; (c) dichloroargentate ion; (d) pentaamminecarbonatocobalt(III) ion; (e) tetraamminecopper(II) ion; (f) tetrachlorovanadate(III) ion; (g) hexaisothiocyanatochromate(III) ion.

(c) Exercise 21.31: (a) bis(ethylenediamine)platinum(II) ion; (b) aquachlorobis(ethylenediamine)cobalt(II) ion; (c) triamminediethylenetriaminenickle(II) ion; (d) hexacyanovanadate(II) ion; (e) trioxalatoaluminate(III) ion

21.36 (c)

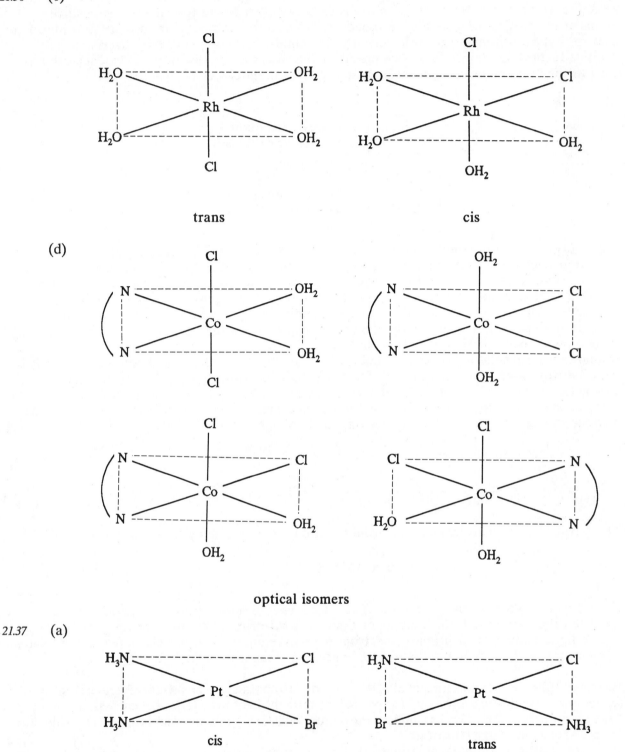

trans   cis

(d)

optical isomers

21.37 (a)

cis   trans

All other sketches can be superimposed on one of these by just rotating through 90 or 180 degrees or by flipping the sketch.

(b)

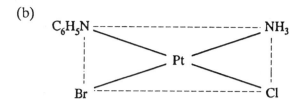

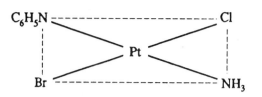

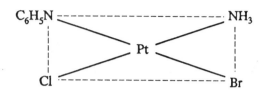

All other sketches can be superimposed on one of these.

21.38   Several of the enantiomer pairs are:

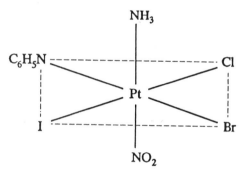

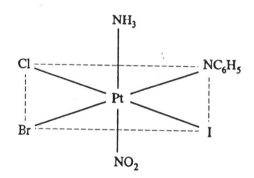

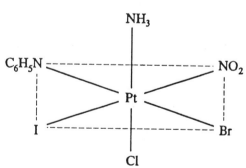

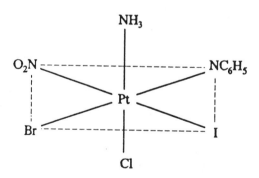

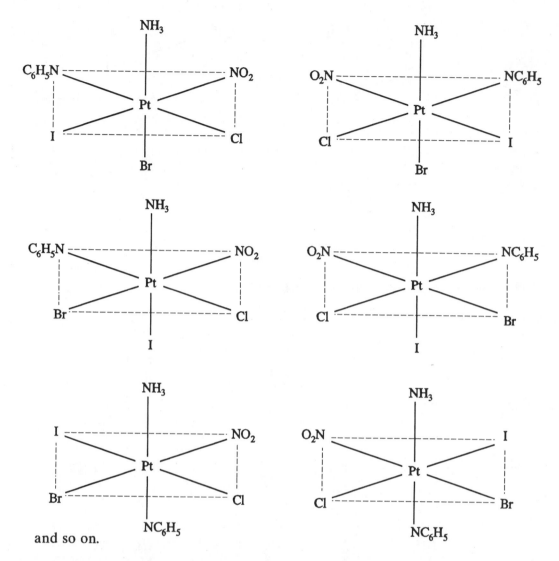

and so on.

21.41   Metal–H_2O bonds become stronger with increasing ionic charge and decreasing ionic radius, that is, with increasing charge density. And the stronger the bonds are, the larger the formation constant should be.

(a) $Be(H_2O)_4^{2+}$. Be^{2+} is much smaller than Cu^{2+}.

(b) $Fe(H_2O)_6^{3+}$. Fe^{3+} has a greater charge than Fe^{2+}.

(c) $Al(H_2O)_6^{3+}$. Al^{3+} has a greater charge and is also smaller than Ni^{2+}.

21.44   (a) The splitting of the five equal energy d orbitals on the metal atom into two sets of orbitals with different energies is caused by the nonsymmetric electrical field of the ligands. If the electrical field of the ligands were symmetrical, then the five d orbitals would be raised in energy, but not split, by the interaction with the ligands.

(b)

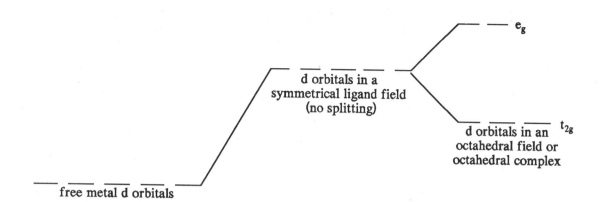

The t_{2g} orbitals are d_{xy}, d_{xz}, and d_{yz}.
The e_g orbitals are $d_{x^2-y^2}$ and d_{z^2}.

(c) By splitting, electrons can now go into or occupy the lower energy t_{2g} d orbitals, which helps stabilize the complex by giving it an overall lower energy.

21.48 (a)

Ni^{2+}: $3d^8$ ↑↓ ↑↓ ↑↓ ↑ ↑

(c)

Fe^{2+}: $3d^6$ ↑↓ ↑ ↑ ↑ ↑

(b)

Co^{2+}: $3d^7$ ↑↓ ↑↓ ↑ ↑ ↑

(d)

Fe^{3+}: $3d^5$ ↑ ↑ ↑ ↑ ↑

21.50 The electronic configuration of zinc is $[Ar]\ 3d^{10}\ 4s^2$. Zinc only forms 2+ ions; therefore, all the d orbitals in a zinc complex are filled and, consequently, no d orbital electron transitions leading to the absorption in the visible range can take place. Since zinc complexes cannot absorb light, they are colorless.

21.51 (a) two

Ni^{2+}: $3d^8$ ↑↓ ↑↓ ↑↓ ↑ ↑

(d) none

Pt^{2+}: $5d^8$ ↑↓ ↑↓ ↑↓ ↑↓

(b) none

Pt^{4+}: $5d^6$ ↑↓ ↑↓ ↑↓

(e) one

Mn^+: $3d^5$ ↑↓ ↑↓ ↑

(c) three   (f) one

— —   — —

Mo^{3+}: 4d^3 ↑ ↑ ↑   Ru^{3+}: 4d^5 ↑↓ ↑↓ ↑

21.52   (a) CoF$_6$$^{3-}$: Since the orbital splitting energy produced by F$^-$ is less than the pairing energy, CoF$_6$$^{3-}$ should be a high-spin complex.

↑ ↑

Co^{3+}: 3d^6 ↑↓ ↑ ↑

Co(NH$_3$)$_6$$^{3+}$: Since the orbital splitting energy produced by NH$_3$ is greater than the pairing energy, Co(NH$_3$)$_6$$^{3+}$ should be a low-spin complex.

— —

Co^{3+}: 3d^6 ↑↓ ↑↓ ↑↓

(b) CoF$_6$$^{3-}$ is paramagnetic and Co(NH$_3$)$_6$$^{3+}$ is not.

21.53   (a)

↑ ↑   ↑ —

Co^{2+}: 3d^7 ↑↓ ↑↓ ↑   ↑↓ ↑↓ ↑↓

high-spin   low-spin

(b) If Co^{2+} is in a high-spin state, then the removal of one paired d electron reduces the crystal field stabilization. However, if Co^{2+} is in a low-spin state, then the removal of the unpaired electron does add to the stabilization of the system, since a low-spin d^6 electron arrangement is a particularly stable arrangement. Since NH$_3$ is a stronger ligand than H$_2$O, the formation of the hexammine complex promotes spin pairing and easy loss of one electron.

21.54   (a)

Fe(H$_2$O)$_6$$^{2+}$:

↑ ↑

Fe^{2+}: 3d^6 ↑↓ ↑ ↑

Fe(H$_2$O)$_6$$^{3+}$:

↑ ↑

Fe^{3+}: 3d^5 ↑ ↑ ↑

Fe(CN)$_6$$^{4-}$:

— —

Fe^{2+}: 3d^6 ↑↓ ↑↓ ↑↓

Fe(CN)$_6$$^{3-}$:

— —

Fe^{3+}: 3d^5 ↑↓ ↑↓ ↑

(b) The Fe(H$_2$O)$_6$$^{2+}$ oxidizes because the oxidation removes the paired electron and along with it the pairing energy that was required to pair it up. Therefore, the resulting complex is more stable. Also, half-filled sets of orbitals are particularly stable.

(c) From the configurations we see that a strong field ligand produces a low–spin d^6 electron arrangement in the +2 oxidation state. This stabilizes the +2 oxidation state of iron, because the low–spin d^6 electron arrangement is a particularly stable arrangement of the d electrons.

21.57 (a) Yes. Since CN^- is a stronger ligand then NH_3 (Table 21.8), $Co(CN)_6^{3-}$ is also not paramagnetic.
(b) No. Since H_2O is a weaker ligand than NH_3 (Table 21.8), we cannot tell whether $Co(H_2O)_6^{3+}$ is paramagnetic or not.

21.60 From Table 2.3 we see that nonmetals make up approximately 83.77% of all the atoms in the earth's crust. Therefore, the approximate ratio of metal to nonmetal atoms in the earth's crust is 16.23 : 83.77 or 1:5.

21.61 The atomic radius of gold is 0.144 nm (Figure 8.8).
(a) In a simple cubic lattice the atoms are touching one another in straight rows piled one atop the other and we only have to calculate the number of gold diameters that fit into 100 nm in order to determine the number of layers of atoms. The number of layers of atoms is therefore

$$\frac{100 \text{ nm}}{0.288 \text{ nm/layer}} = 347 \text{ layers}$$

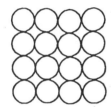

side view of simple unit packing

(b) Gold crystallizes in the face–centered cubic lattice system. In a face–centred cubic unit cell, the atoms that lie along an edge do not touch. Therefore, we will first calculate the width of three layers of atoms and then the number of layers in 100 nm.

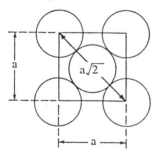

side view of a face–centered cubic unit cell

For a face-centered cubic unit cell we have

$$4r = a\sqrt{2} \text{ and } a = \frac{4r}{\sqrt{2}} = \frac{4 \times 0.144 \text{ nm}}{\sqrt{2}} = 0.407 \text{ nm}$$

The width of three layers is therefore

width three layers = a + 2r = 0.407 nm + 2 x 0.144 nm = 0.695 nm

The number of layers of atoms is therefore

$$\frac{100 \text{ nm}}{0.695 \text{ nm/3 layers}} = 432 \text{ layers}$$

21.63   If the aqueous solution of $CrCl_3$ only contained $Cr(H_2O)_6^{3+}$ ions, then the solution would appear violet, since $Cr(H_2O)_6^{3+}$ has a violet color. Therefore, the green solution of $CrCl_3$ must also contain complex ions in which some of the water is replaced by chloride ion, for example, $Cr(H_2O)_5Cl^{2+}$ and $Cr(H_2O)_4Cl_2^{+}$. According to crystal field theory, the observed color is the complimentary color of the absorbed light and the wavelength of the absorbed light depends on the size of Δ, the orbital splitting energy. From the spectrochemical series (Table 21.8), we see that Cl^- is a weaker bonding ligand than H_2O. Consequently, Δ should decrease, which means that the wavelength of the absorption should increase, when H_2O is replaced by Cl^-. From the color wheel (Figure 21.28) we see that a shift to higher wavelength absorption shifts the observed color from violet toward green. Therefore, it is likely that the aquachlorochromium(III) complex ions are green and their presence makes the solution appear green.

21.64   (a) Purple compound: The steps in the calculation are:

g AgCl ——> mol AgCl ——> mol Cl^- ions ——> mol Cl^- ions/mol compound ——> formula.

$$1.06 \text{ g AgCl} \times \frac{1 \text{ mol AgCl}}{143.32 \text{ g AgCl}} \times \frac{1 \text{ mol } Cl^- \text{ ions}}{1 \text{ mol AgCl}} = 7.40 \times 10^{-3} \text{ mol } Cl^- \text{ ions}$$

The moles of Cl^- ions per mole of compound is

$$\frac{7.40 \times 10^{-3} \text{ mol } Cl^- \text{ ions}}{0.100 \text{ L} \times 0.037 \text{ mol compound/L}} = 2 \text{ mol } Cl^- \text{ ions/mol compound}$$

A tentative formula is $[Co(NH_3)_5Cl]Cl_2 \cdot H_2O$

(b) Brick red compound:

$$4.3 \text{ g AgCl} \times \frac{1 \text{ mol AgCl}}{143.32 \text{ g AgCl}} \times \frac{1 \text{ mol } Cl^- \text{ ions}}{1 \text{ mol AgCl}} = 0.030 \text{ mol } Cl^- \text{ ions}$$

The moles of Cl^- ions per mole of compound is

$$\frac{0.030 \text{ mol } Cl^- \text{ ions}}{0.100 \text{ L} \times 0.10 \text{ mol compound/L}} = 3 \text{ mol } Cl^- \text{ ions/mol compound}$$

A tentative formula is $[Co(NH_3)_5H_2O]Cl_3$

21.65   No.

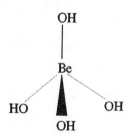

The tetrahedral symmetry properties will only allow for stereoisomerism when all four groups attached to the central atom are different, and then only of the optical kind.

CHAPTER S4

A SURVEY OF THE ELEMENTS 4:

METALS AND METALLURGY

Solutions To Practice Exercises

PE S4.2   Oxygen is the oxidizing agent:

$$O_2(g) + 2H_2O(l) + 4e^- \longrightarrow 4OH^-(aq) \qquad \text{reduction}$$

Gold is the reducing agent:

$$Au(s) + 2CN^-(aq) \longrightarrow Au(CN)_2^-(aq) + e^- \qquad \text{oxidation}$$

PE S4.4 (a)   Yes. The standard oxidation potentials are:

$$Sn^{2+}(aq) \longrightarrow Sn^{4+}(aq) + 2e^- \qquad E^\circ_{oxid} = -0.154 \text{ V}$$

$$Hg(l) \longrightarrow Hg^{2+}(aq) + 2e^- \qquad E^\circ_{oxid} = -0.852 \text{ V}$$

Sn^{2+} has a higher (less negative) oxidation potential and a greater tendency to give up electrons than Hg; therefore, $Sn(NO_3)_2$ will reduce Hg^{2+} to Hg.

(b)   No. The standard oxidation potentials are:

$$Ag(s) + Br^-(aq) \longrightarrow AgBr(s) + e^- \qquad E^\circ_{oxid} = -0.0732 \text{ V}$$

$$Sn^{2+}(aq) \longrightarrow Sn^{4+}(aq) + 2e^- \qquad E^\circ_{oxid} = -0.154 \text{ V}$$

The silver half-reaction has a higher (less negative) oxidation potential and a greater tendency to give up electrons than Sn^{2+}; therefore $Sn(NO_3)_2$ will not reduce AgBr to Ag.

PE S4.6 $K_{sp} = [Hg_2^{2+}][Cl^-]^2$

$1.3 \times 10^{-18} = (x)(2x)^2 = 4x^3$ and $x = 6.9 \times 10^{-7} \text{ M} = [Hg_2^{2+}]$

The equilibrium concentration of Hg_2^{2+}, 6.9×10^{-7} mol/L, is also the molar solubility of Hg_2Cl_2.

PE S4.7   Refer to the solution of Exercise 20.72(c). Substituting n = 1 mol e^-, F = 96,485 C/mol e^-, and E° = 0.357 V = 0.357 J/C into Equation 20.5 gives

$$\Delta G^\circ = -nFE^\circ = -1 \text{ mol } e^- \times \frac{96,485 \text{ C}}{1 \text{ mol } e^-} \times \frac{0.357 \text{ J}}{1 \text{ C}} = -3.44 \times 10^4 \text{ J}$$

PE S4.9 (a) Cl⁻ is –1; therefore the oxidation state of cobalt is +2. Hence, the central cobalt atom has 7 3d electrons.

(b) NO_2^- is –1; therefore the oxidation state of cobalt is +3. Hence, the central cobalt atom has 6 3d electrons.

(c) NH_3 is zero; therefore the oxidation state of nickel is +2. Hence, the central nickel atom has 8 3d electrons.

Solutions to Final Exercises

S4.6 To answer this exercise we have to test the thermodynamic stability of the respective oxides at 500°C.

(a) Hg: $HgO(s) \xrightarrow{500°C} Hg(g) + 1/2\ O_2(g)$

At 298 K:

$\Delta H° = \Delta H_f°(Hg(g)) + 1/2 \times \Delta H_f°(O_2) - \Delta H_f°(HgO) = 61.3\ kJ + 1/2 \times 0\ kJ - (-90.8\ kJ) = 152.1\ kJ$

$\Delta S° = S°(Hg(g)) + 1/2 \times S°(O_2) - S°(HgO) = 175.0\ J/K + 1/2 \times 205.1\ J/K - 70.3\ J/K = 207.2\ J/K$

A value for $\Delta G°$ at 500°C can be obtained from Equation 19.7 if we assume that $\Delta H°$ and $\Delta S°$ do not change significantly with temperature. Substituting $\Delta H° = 152.1\ kJ$, $\Delta S° = 0.2072\ kJ/K$, and T = 773 K into Equation 19.7 gives

$\Delta G° = \Delta H° - T\Delta S° = 152.1\ kJ - 773\ K \times 0.2072\ kJ/K = -8.1\ kJ$

Since $\Delta G < 0$, HgO is thermodynamically unstable at 500°C and O_2 partial pressure 1 atm. Therefore, Hg will form from the roasting of HgS and not HgO.

Zn: $ZnO(s) \xrightarrow{500°C} Zn(l) + 1/2\ O_2(g)$

At 298 K: For Zn(l) use the values given for Zn(s) in Table 19.2.

$\Delta H° = \Delta H_f°(Zn) + 1/2 \times \Delta H_f°(O_2) - \Delta H_f°(ZnO) = 0\ kJ + 1/2 \times 0\ kJ - (-348.3\ kJ) = +348.3\ kJ$

$\Delta S° = S°(Zn) + 1/2 \times S°(O_2) - S°(ZnO) = 41.63\ J/K + 1/2 \times 205.1\ J/K - 43.6\ J/K = 100.6\ J/K$

At 773 K: $\Delta G° = \Delta H° - T\Delta S° = 348.3\ kJ - 773\ K \times 0.1006\ kJ/K = 270.5\ kJ$

Since $\Delta G > 0$, ZnO is thermodynamically stable at 500°C and O_2 partial pressure 1 atm. (The correction for atmospheric conditions, O_2 partial pressure 0.2 atm, is slight and we will ignore it). Therefore, ZnO will form from the roasting of ZnS and not Zn.

(b) Ag:

$Ag_2O(s) \xrightarrow{500°C} 2Ag(s) + 1/2\ O_2(g)$

At 298 K: $\Delta H° = 31.05\ kJ$ and $\Delta S° = 66.4\ J/K$ (see solution to Exercise 19.55).

At 773 K: $\Delta G° = \Delta H° - T\Delta S° = 31.05\ kJ - 773\ K \times 0.0664\ kJ/K = -20.3\ kJ$

Since $\Delta G < 0$, Ag_2O is thermodynamically unstable at 500°C and O_2 partial pressure 1 atm. Therefore, Ag will form from the roasting of Ag_2S and not Ag_2O.

S4.9 (a)

$MnO_2(s) + 2CO(g) \xrightarrow{heat} Mn(l) + 2CO_2(g)$

(b)

$FeCr_2O_4(s) + 4C(s) \xrightarrow{heat} Fe(l) + 2Cr(l) + 4CO(g)$

(c)

$3Mn_3O_4(s) + 8Al(s) \longrightarrow 9Mn(l) + 4Al_2O_3(l)$

(d)

$GeO_2(s) + 2H_2(g) \longrightarrow Ge(s) + 2H_2O(g)$

(e)

$$TiCl_4(l) + 2Mg(s) \longrightarrow Ti(s) + 2MgCl_2(s)$$

S4.10 (a) $KCl(l) + Na(l) \longrightarrow NaCl(l) + K(g)$ (c) $WO_3(s) + 3H_2(g) \longrightarrow W(s) + 3H_2O(g)$

(b)

$$PbO(s) + C(s) \xrightarrow{\text{heat}} Pb(l) + CO(g) \quad \text{(d)} \ Cr_2O_3(s) + 2Al(s) \longrightarrow 2Cr(l) + Al_2O_3(l)$$

S4.12 Impurities more active than copper are found in the electrolyte. Less active impurities are found in the anode sludge. Therefore, gold and silver will be found in the anode sludge and lead and zinc in the electrolyte.

S4.13 (a) Aeration is the forcing of air through a solution or medium in order to bring about an oxidation by the oxygen in the air. In the cyanide extraction of gold, the oxygen of the air oxidizes the metallic gold to the gold(I) ion, Au^+.

(b) Cyanide is added as a complexing agent to stabilize the oxidized gold.

S4.16 The molar concentration of Mg^{2+} in seawater is

$$\frac{1000 \ mL}{1 \ L} \ \text{x} \ \frac{1.024 \ g \ seawater}{1 \ mL} \ \text{x} \ \frac{0.0013 \ g \ Mg^{2+}}{100 \ g \ seawater} \ \text{x} \ \frac{1 \ mol \ Mg^{2+}}{24.3 \ g \ Mg^{2+}}$$

$$= 5.5 \ \text{x} \ 10^{-4} \ mol \ Mg^{2+}/L \ \text{or} \ 5.5 \ \text{x} \ 10^{-4} \ M \ Mg^{2+}$$

The molar concentration of OH^- in saturated calcium hydroxide is

$$\frac{1.85 \ g \ Ca(OH)_2}{1 \ L} \ \text{x} \ \frac{1 \ mol \ Ca(OH)_2}{74.1 \ g \ Ca(OH)_2} \ \text{x} \ \frac{2 \ mol \ OH^-}{1 \ mol \ Ca(OH)_2} = 4.99 \ \text{x} \ 10^{-2} \ M \ OH^-$$

Since the OH^- is present in excess, we can assume that the Mg^{2+} is initially completely precipitated. The inital $[OH^-] = (0.0499 \ M - 2 \ \text{x} \ 0.00055 \ M)/2 = 0.0244 \ M$.

Concentration Summary:

Equation:	$Mg(OH)_2(s) \rightleftharpoons$	$Mg^{2+}(aq) \ +$	$2OH^-(aq)$
Initial concentrations. mol/L		0	0.0244
Concentration changes, mol/L		$+x$	$+2x$
Equilibrium concentrations, mol/L		x	$0.0244 + 2x$
Approximate concentrations, mol/L		x	0.0244

Substituting the approximate concentrations and $K_{sp} = 7.1 \ \text{x} \ 10^{-12}$ into the K_{sp} expression gives

$$K_{sp} = [Mg^{2+}][OH^-]^2$$

$7.1 \ \text{x} \ 10^{-12} = (x)(0.0244)^2$ and $x = 1.2 \ \text{x} \ 10^{-8} \ mol/L = [Mg^{2+}]$

The approximation is acceptable because the calculated value of $2x$ is less than 5% of 0.0489 M. The fraction of magnesium ion remaining unprecipitated is

$$\frac{1.2 \ \text{x} \ 10^{-8} \ M}{5.5 \ \text{x} \ 10^{-4} \ M} = 2.2 \ \text{x} \ 10^{-5}$$

S4.21 Aluminum is an active metal. The film of Al_2O_3 that forms when aluminum is initially exposed to the atmosphere does not allow air and water to come in contact with the aluminum metal underneath. Therefore, the Al_2O_3 film protects the Al from further atmospheric corrosion.

S4.22 (a) $2Al(s) + 6HCl(aq) \longrightarrow 2AlCl_3(aq) + 3H_2(g)$

(b) $Al_2O_3(s) + 6HCl(aq) \longrightarrow 2AlCl_3(aq) + 3H_2O(l)$

(c) $SnO(s) + 2HCl(aq) \longrightarrow SnCl_2(aq) + H_2O(l)$

(d) $SnO_2(s) + 6HCl(aq) \longrightarrow 2H^+(aq) + SnCl_6^{2-}(aq) + 2H_2O(l)$

(e) $PbO(s) + 2HCl(aq) \longrightarrow PbCl_2(s) + H_2O(l)$

(f) $Bi_2O_3(s) + 2HCl(dil) \longrightarrow 2BiOCl(s) + H_2O(l)$

$BiOCl(s) + 2HCl(conc) \longrightarrow BiCl_3(aq) + H_2O(l)$

S4.23 (a) $2Al(s) + 2NaOH(aq) + 6H_2O(l) \longrightarrow 2NaAl(OH)_4(aq) + 3H_2(g)$

(b) $Al_2O_3(s) + 2NaOH(aq) + 3H_2O(l) \longrightarrow 2NaAl(OH)_4(aq)$

(c) $SnO(s) + NaOH(aq) + H_2O(l) \longrightarrow NaSn(OH)_3(aq)$

(d) $SnO_2(s) + 2NaOH(aq) + 2H_2O(l) \longrightarrow Na_2Sn(OH)_6(aq)$

(e) $PbO(s) + NaOH(aq) + H_2O(l) \longrightarrow NaPb(OH)_3(aq)$

(f) No reaction; Bi_2O_3 is a basic oxide.

S4.28 (a) $SnCl_2$. In general, as the oxidation state increases, the bonding becomes more covalent.
(b) $SnCl_4$. Since the bonding in $SnCl_4$ is more covalent, $SnCl_4$ has more of a molecular nature and, therefore, a lower boiling point.

S4.31 Zinc, cadmium, and mercury have filled underlying d subshells (d^{10}). Since a filled subshell is very stable, the underlying d electrons are not used in bonding. Therefore, zinc, cadmium, and mercury only have the same two s electrons for use in bonding as the Group 2A elements, Ca, Sr, and Ba, which precede them in their periods.

S4.32 (a) Zn(Z=30): [Ar] $3d^{10}4s^2$; Ca(Z=20): [Ar] $4s^2$. Both have two 4s valence electrons for use in bonding.
(b) Atomic radii, nm: Zn, 0.133; Ca, 0.197 (from Fig. 8.8). Zn is considerably smaller than Ca.
(c) First ionization energies in kJ/mol: Zn, 906; Ca, 590 (from Fig. 8.9). Based on first ionization energies, Ca should be more reactive than Zn.
(d) Electronegativity (Pauling scale): Zn, 1.7; Ca, 1.0 (from Fig. 9.11). Zn has a higher electronegativity and should form bonds with more covalent character than Ca.
(e) Activity: Zn, $E^\circ_{oxid} = 0.762$ V; Ca, $E^\circ_{oxid} = 2.869$ V. Ca is considerably more active than Zn as shown by their oxidation potentials.
(f) ZnO is amphoteric and CaO is basic. This means that the Zn-O bond is much more covalent in nature than the Ca-O bond, which is essentially ionic in character.

Because Zn has ten additional underlying 3d electrons compared to Ca, it has a greater nuclear charge that draws the electrons in much closer to the nucleus, as shown by its smaller atomic radius. Therefore, the outer valence electrons are held more tightly in Zn (the attractive force on its 4s electrons is greater) and, consequently, Zn is less active than calcium, as shown by the greater ionization energy and lower activity.

S4.34 The principle quantum number of the valence shell increases by one in going from Zn to Cd and also in going from Cd to Hg. However, the nuclear charge increases by 18 in going from Zn to Cd and by 32 in going from Cd to Hg. The opposing effects on the ionization energy of increased nuclear attraction and increased valence shell level more nearly cancel in going from Zn to Cd, so these elements are similar in activity. The nuclear charge effect is more pronounced in Hg, which is therefore much less active than either Zn or Cd.

S4.37 (a) $Zn(s) + 2HCl(1\ M) \longrightarrow ZnCl_2(aq) + H_2(g)$

$Cd(s) + 2HCl(1\ M) \longrightarrow CdCl_2(aq) + H_2(g)$

Mercury is inert toward nonoxidizing acids.

(b) $4Zn(s) + 10HNO_3(6\ M) \longrightarrow NH_4NO_3(aq) + 4Zn(NO_3)_2(aq) + 3H_2O(l)$

$4Cd(s) + 10HNO_3(6\ M) \longrightarrow NH_4NO_3(aq) + 4Cd(NO_3)_2(aq) + 3H_2O(l)$

$3Hg(l) + 8HNO_3(6\ M) \xrightarrow{excess\ acid} 3Hg(NO_3)_2(aq) + 2NO(g) + 4H_2O(l)$

or $6Hg(l) + 8HNO_3(6\ M) \xrightarrow{excess\ mercury} 3Hg_2(NO_3)_2(aq) + 2NO(g) + 4H_2O(l)$

(c) $Zn(s) + 2NaOH(6\ M) + 2H_2O(l) \longrightarrow Na_2Zn(OH)_4(aq) + H_2(g)$
sodium zincate

Zinc is amphoteric and reacts with aqueous solutions of strong bases; cadmium and mercury are not amphoteric and do not react with aqueous solutions of strong bases.

S4.38 (a) $ZnO(s) + 2HCl(aq) \longrightarrow ZnCl_2(aq) + H_2O(l)$

$CdO(s) + 2HCl(aq) \longrightarrow CdCl_2(aq) + H_2O(l)$

$HgO(s) + 2HCl(aq) \longrightarrow HgCl_2(aq) + H_2O(l)$

(b) $ZnO(s) + 2NaOH(aq) + H_2O(l) \longrightarrow Na_2Zn(OH)_4(aq)$

(c) $ZnO(s) + 4NH_3(aq) + H_2O(l) \longrightarrow Zn(NH_3)_4^{2+}(aq) + 2OH^-(aq)$

$CdO(s) + 4NH_3(aq) + H_2O(l) \longrightarrow Cd(NH_3)_4^{2+}(aq) + 2OH^-(aq)$

S4.39 (a) Treat the zinc oxide with nitric acid:

$ZnO(s) + 2HNO_3(aq) \longrightarrow Zn(NO_3)_2(aq) + H_2O(l)$

(b) Treat the zinc metal with potassium hydroxide:

$Zn(s) + 2KOH(aq) + 2H_2O(l) \longrightarrow K_2Zn(OH)_4(aq) + H_2(g)$

(c) First treat the mercury with an excess of hot concentrated sulfuric acid to form $HgSO_4$. Then heat a dry mixture of mercuric sulfate and sodium chloride to form mercury(II) chloride, which sublimes.

$Hg(l) + 2H_2SO_4(aq) \xrightarrow{excess\ acid} HgSO_4(aq) + SO_2(g) + 2H_2O(l)$

$HgSO_4(s) + 2NaCl(s) \xrightarrow{heat} Na_2SO_4(s) + HgCl_2(g)$

An alternate method is:

$Hg(l) \xrightarrow[excess]{HNO_3} Hg(NO_3)_2(aq) \xrightarrow{OH^-} HgO(s) \xrightarrow{HCl} HgCl_2(aq)$

Also, $Hg(l) + Cl_2(g) \xrightarrow{\Delta} HgCl_2(s)$

(d) First dissolve excess mercury in concentrated nitric acid to form $Hg_2(NO_3)_2$, a soluble mercurous salt. Then add chloride ion to precipitate mercury(I) chloride, which is only slightly soluble.

$6Hg(l) + 8HNO_3(aq) \xrightarrow{excess\ mercury} 3Hg_2(NO_3)_2(aq) + 2NO(g) + 4H_2O(l)$

$Hg_2(NO_3)_2(aq) + 2NaCl(aq\ or\ s) \longrightarrow Hg_2Cl_2(s) + 2NaNO_3(aq)$

S4.45 (a) $Cu(s) + Cl_2(g) \longrightarrow CuCl_2(s)$

$2Ag(s) + Cl_2(g) \longrightarrow 2AgCl(s)$

$2Au(s) + 3Cl_2(g) \longrightarrow 2AuCl_3(s)$

(b) $2Cu(s) + 2H_2S(g) + O_2(g) \longrightarrow 2CuS(s) + 2H_2O(g)$

$4Ag(s) + 2H_2S(g) + O_2(g) \longrightarrow 2Ag_2S(s) + 2H_2O(g)$

(c) Concentrated HNO_3:

$$Cu(s) + 4H^+(aq) + 2NO_3^-(aq) \longrightarrow Cu^{2+}(aq) + 2NO_2(g) + 2H_2O(l)$$

$$Ag(s) + 2H^+(aq) + NO_3^-(aq) \longrightarrow Ag^+(aq) + NO_2(g) + H_2O(l)$$

S4.48 (a) (i) $CuCl(s) \rightleftharpoons Cu^+(aq) + Cl^-(aq)$

$K_{sp} = [Cu^+][Cl^-]$; $1.7 \times 10^{-7} = (x)(x) = x^2$ and $x = 4.1 \times 10^{-4}$ M $= [Cu^+]$

(ii) Concentration Summary:

Equation:	$Cu(CN)_2^-(aq) \rightleftharpoons$	$Cu^+(aq)$ +	$2CN^-(aq)$
Initial concentrations, mol/L	1.0	0	0
Concentration changes, mol/L	$-x$	$+x$	$+2x$
Equilibrium concentrations, mol/L	$1.0 - x$	x	$2x$
Approximate concentrations, mol/L	1.0	x	$2x$

Substituting the approximate concentrations and $K_d = 9.9 \times 10^{-25}$ into the dissociation constant expression gives

$$\frac{[Cu^+][CN^-]^2}{[Cu(CN)_2^-]} = K_d$$

$$\frac{(x)(2x)^2}{1.0} = 9.9 \times 10^{-25} \text{ and } x = 6.3 \times 10^{-9} \text{ M} = [Cu^+]$$

(b) (i) The net reaction for the disproportionation of CuCl is

$$2CuCl(s) \rightleftharpoons Cu(s) + Cu^{2+}(aq) + 2Cl^-(aq)$$

with the equilibrium constant

$$K = [Cu^{2+}][Cl^-]^2$$

The value of K can be obtained by breaking down the net reaction into a series of steps.

$2CuCl(s) \rightleftharpoons 2Cu^+(aq) + 2Cl^-(aq)$	K_{sp}^2
$2Cu^+(aq) \rightleftharpoons Cu(s) + Cu^{2+}(aq)$	K_c

$$2CuCl(s) \rightleftharpoons Cu(s) + Cu^{2+}(aq) + 2Cl^-(aq) \qquad K = K_{sp}^2 K_c$$

K_c is obtained from Equation 20.8b with $E^\circ = 0.357$ V and $n = 1$ [see 20.72(c)].

$$\log K_c = \frac{nE^\circ}{0.0592} = \frac{(1)(0.357 \text{ V})}{0.0592 \text{ V}} = 6.03 \text{ and } K_c = 1.1 \times 10^6$$

The equilibrium constant for the net reaction is therefore

$$K = K_{sp}^2 K_c = (1.7 \times 10^{-7})^2(1.1 \times 10^6) = 3.2 \times 10^{-8}$$

The small value of K shows that very little Cu^{2+} will be present at equilibrium, and that substantially no disproportionation occurs.

(ii) The net reaction for the disproportionation of $Cu(CN)_2^-$ is

$$2Cu(CN)_2^-(aq) \rightleftharpoons Cu(s) + Cu^{2+}(aq) + 4CN^-(aq)$$

with the equilibrium constant

$$K = \frac{[Cu^{2+}][CN^-]^4}{[Cu(CN)_2^-]^2}$$

In a similar manner to that above, we get

$K = K^2_d K_c = (9.9 \times 10^{-25})^2(1.1 \times 10^6) = 1.1 \times 10^{-42}$

The extremely low K value means that no disproportionation occurs.

S4.49   The volume of the wire is that of a cylinder 3000 m long:

$V = \pi r^2 h = 3.14 \times r^2 \times 3.00 \times 10^5 \text{ cm} = r^2 \times 9.42 \times 10^5 \text{ cm}$

where r is the radius of the cylinder and V has the units of cm³. The volume of 1 g of gold can be calculated from the density (Table S4.6):

$$\frac{1.00 \text{ g}}{19.3 \text{ g/cm}^3} = 0.0518 \text{ cm}^3$$

The radius of the wire is obtained by equating these two volumes:

$r^2 \times 9.42 \times 10^5 \text{ cm} = 0.0518 \text{ cm}^3$

$$r^2 = \frac{0.0518 \text{ cm}^3}{9.42 \times 10^5 \text{ cm}} = 5.50 \times 10^{-8} \text{ cm}^2 \text{ and } r = 2.35 \times 10^{-4} \text{ cm}$$

The diameter of the wire is therefore 4.70×10^{-4} cm or 0.00470 mm.

S4.50   (a) $CuS(l) + O_2(g) \longrightarrow Cu(l) + SO_2(g)$

$Cu_2S(l) + O_2(g) \longrightarrow 2Cu(l) + SO_2(g)$

The mass of CuS (molar mass 95.6 g) equals the mass of Cu_2S (molar mass 159.2 g); let x equal this mass. Now the number of moles of Cu produced

$$1.00 \times 10^9 \text{ g Cu} \times \frac{1 \text{ mol Cu}}{63.5 \text{ g Cu}} = 1.57 \times 10^7 \text{ mol Cu}$$

is equal to the number of moles of CuS reduced plus twice the number of moles of Cu_2S reduced. Therefore,

$$\frac{x}{95.6 \text{ g/mol}} + \frac{2x}{159.2 \text{ g/mol}} = 1.57 \times 10^7 \text{ mol and } x = 6.82 \times 10^8 \text{ g}$$

The amount of SO_2 produced when the CuS is reduced is calculated as follows:
g CuS $\longrightarrow$ mol CuS $\longrightarrow$ mol SO_2 $\longrightarrow$ g SO_2.

$$6.82 \times 10^8 \text{ g CuS} \times \frac{1 \text{ mol CuS}}{95.6 \text{ g CuS}} \times \frac{1 \text{ mol SO}_2}{1 \text{ mol CuS}} \times \frac{64.1 \text{ g SO}_2}{1 \text{ mol SO}_2} = 4.57 \times 10^8 \text{ g SO}_2$$

The amount of SO_2 produced when the Cu_2S is reduced is calculated similarly

$$6.82 \times 10^8 \text{ g Cu}_2\text{S} \times \frac{1 \text{ mol Cu}_2\text{S}}{159.2 \text{ g Cu}_2\text{S}} \times \frac{1 \text{ mol SO}_2}{1 \text{ mol Cu}_2\text{S}} \times \frac{64.1 \text{ g SO}_2}{1 \text{ mol SO}_2} = 2.75 \times 10^8 \text{ g SO}_2$$

The total mass of SO_2 evolved during the production of 1000 metric tons of copper from this ore is therefore

$4.57 \times 10^8 \text{ g} + 2.75 \times 10^8 \text{ g} = 7.32 \times 10^8 \text{ g}$

(b) The equations needed are:

$$2SO_2(g) + O_2(g) \longrightarrow 2SO_3(g)$$

$$SO_3(g) + H_2O(l) \longrightarrow H_2SO_4(aq)$$

$$CaCO_3(s) + H_2SO_4(aq) \longrightarrow CaSO_4(aq) + CO_2(aq) + H_2O(l)$$

The steps in the calculation are: g $SO_2 \longrightarrow$ mol $SO_2 \longrightarrow$ mol $H_2SO_4 \longrightarrow$ mol $CaCO_3 \longrightarrow$ g $CaCO_3 \longrightarrow$ volume $CaCO_3$.

$$7.32 \times 10^8 \text{ g } SO_2 \times \frac{1 \text{ mol } SO_2}{64.1 \text{ g } SO_2} \times \frac{1 \text{ mol } H_2SO_4}{1 \text{ mol } SO_2} \times \frac{1 \text{ mol } CaCO_3}{1 \text{ mol } H_2SO_4} \times \frac{100.1 \text{ g } CaCO_3}{1 \text{ mol } CaCO_3}$$

$$\times \frac{1 \text{ cm}^3 \text{ CaCO}_3}{2.93 \text{ g } CaCO_3} = 3.90 \times 10^8 \text{ cm}^3 \text{ CaCO}_3 \text{ or } 390 \text{ m}^3 \text{ CaCO}_3$$

S5.55 (a) Quenching leaves most of the carbon in steel in the form of cementite, which makes the steel hard and brittle.

(b) Tempering allows some of the cementite formed to revert back to iron and minute graphite crystals, which makes the steel stronger and more flexible.

(c) Cementite is iron carbide (Fe_3C).

S4.57 (a) The atomic number of iron is 26.

Fe: $1s^2 \, 2s^2 \, 2p^6 \, 3s^2 \, 3p^6 \, 3d^6 \, 4s^2$ or [Ar] $3d^6 \, 4s^2$

Fe^{2+}: $1s^2 \, 2s^2 \, 2p^6 \, 3s^2 \, 3p^6 \, 3d^6$ or [Ar] $3d^6$

Fe^{3+}: $1s^2 \, 2s^2 \, 2p^6 \, 3s^2 \, 3p^6 \, 3d^5$ or [Ar] $3d^5$

(b) The atomic number of cobalt is 27.

Co: $1s^2 \, 2s^2 \, 2p^6 \, 3s^2 \, 3p^6 \, 3d^7 \, 4s^2$ or [Ar] $3d^7 \, 4s^2$

Co^{2+}: $1s^2 \, 2s^2 \, 2p^6 \, 3s^2 \, 3p^6 \, 3d^7$ or [Ar] $3d^7$

Co^{3+}: $1s^2 \, 2s^2 \, 2p^6 \, 3s^2 \, 3p^6 \, 3d^6$ or [Ar] $3d^6$

(c) The atomic number of nickel is 28.

Ni: $1s^2 \, 2s^2 \, 2p^6 \, 3s^2 \, 3p^6 \, 3d^8 \, 4s^2$ or [Ar] $3d^8 \, 4s^2$

Ni^{2+}: $1s^2 \, 2s^2 \, 2p^6 \, 3s^2 \, 3p^6 \, 3d^8$ or [Ar] $3d^8$

S4.59 (a) Fe^{3+}. The standard reduction potentials are:

$Fe^{3+}(aq) + e^- \longrightarrow Fe^{2+}(aq)$ $\qquad E^\circ = 0.769$ V

$Fe^{2+}(aq) + 2e^- \longrightarrow Fe(s)$ $\qquad E^\circ = -0.409$ V

Fe^{3+} has a more positive reduction potential and a greater tendency to accept electrons than Fe^{2+}; Fe^{3+} should be a better oxidizing agent.

(b) Ni^{2+}. The standard reduction potentials are:

$Ni^{2+}(aq) + 2e^- \longrightarrow Ni(s)$ $\qquad E^\circ = -0.236$ V

$Fe^{2+}(aq) + 2e^- \longrightarrow Fe(s)$ $\qquad E^\circ = -0.409$ V

Ni^{2+} has a more positive (less negative) reduction potential and a greater tendency to accept electrons than Fe^{2+}; Ni^{2+} should be a better oxidizing agent.

S4.61 (a) The high positive charge of Fe^{3+} attracts and strongly binds water molecules in aqueous solution

$$Fe^{3+}(aq) + 6H_2O(l) \longrightarrow Fe(H_2O)_6^{3+}(aq)$$

The positive central iron ion in the hydrated cation draws negative charge to it and, in so doing, increases the O–H bond polarity in the bound water molecules and makes them proton donors. Up to three protons can be removed from the hydrated cation.

(b) Fe^{3+}. Fe^{3+} should be more acidic because it has a higher positive charge and, therefore, should be capable of causing a greater polarization of the O–H bond than Fe^{2+}.

S4.63 (a) Add potassium thiocyanate (KSCN) to the solution. If Fe^{3+} is present the solution will turn deep red.

$$Fe^{3+}(aq) + SCN^-(aq) \longrightarrow \underset{\text{deep red}}{Fe(SCN)^{2+}(aq)}$$

Fe^{3+} can also be identified in solution by adding potassium ferrocyanide ($K_4[Fe(CN)_6]$) to form a dark suspension of Prussian blue.

$$Fe^{3+}(aq) + K^+(aq) + Fe(CN)_6^{4-}(aq) \longrightarrow \underset{\text{dark blue}}{KFe[Fe(CN)_6](s)}$$

(b) Add potassium nitrite (KNO$_2$) to the solution. If Co^{2+} is present, a yellow precipitate will form.

$$Co^{2+}(aq) + 7KNO_2(aq) + H_2O(l) \longrightarrow \underset{\text{yellow}}{K_3[Co(NO_2)_6](s)} + 4K^+(aq) + NO(g) + 2OH^-(aq)$$

or in acid solution (pH close to neutral)

$$Co^{2+}(aq) + 7KNO_2(aq) + 2H^+(aq) \longrightarrow K_3[Co(NO_2)_6](s) + 4K^+(aq) + NO(g) + H_2O(l)$$

(c) Add dimethylglyoxime to the solution. If Ni^{2+} is present an insoluble bright red complex will form.

S4.66 (a) $\underset{\text{chromite}}{FeCr_2O_4(s)} + 4C(s) \longrightarrow \underset{\text{ferrochrome}}{Fe(s) + 2Cr(s)} + 4CO(g)$

(b) $\underset{\text{pyrolusite}}{MnO_2(s)} + 2C(s) \longrightarrow Mn(s) + 2CO(g)$

with some $Fe_2O_3(s) + 3C(s) \longrightarrow 2Fe(s) + 3CO(g)$

and $Fe_2O_3(s) + 3CO(g) \longrightarrow 2Fe(s) + 3CO_2(g)$

Comment: Manganese combines with carbon at high temperatures to form the carbide Mn_3C, similar to the reaction of iron and carbon that occurs at the high temperatures encountered in the blast furnace.

$$3Mn(s) + C(s) \rightleftharpoons Mn_3C(s)$$

(c) $Cr_2O_3(s) + 2Al(s) \longrightarrow 2Cr(l) + Al_2O_3(l)$

Ferrochrome is an iron–chromium alloy used in the production of stainless steel.

S4.70 (a) Similarities:
1. Both chromium and aluminum form oxide films that render them resistant to corrosion.
2. Their +3 oxides (Cr_2O_3 and Al_2O_3) and hydroxides ($Cr(OH)_3$ and $Al(OH)_3$) are both amphoteric.
3. The aqueous Cr^{3+} chemistry resembles that of aqueous Al^{3+}.
4. Both metals have high boiling points.

(b) Differences:

1. Chromium, being a transition metal, exhibits several oxidation states (+2, +3, and +6 being the important ones), while aluminum just has a +3 oxidation state.

2. Chromium is considerably denser than aluminum and has a much higher melting point.

S4.71 (a)

$$2CrO_4^{2-}(aq) + 2H^+(aq) \underset{base}{\overset{acid}{\rightleftharpoons}} Cr_2O_7^{2-}(aq) + H_2O(l)$$
yellow $\qquad\qquad\qquad\qquad\qquad\qquad$ orange

(b) Lowering the pH (increasing $[H^+]$) drives the reaction to the right. Therefore, the dichromate ion predominates in acidic solutions (below pH 6). Increasing the pH (decreasing $[H^+]$) drives the reaction to the left. Therefore, the chromate ion predominates in neutral and basic solutions.

S4.72 (a) $2Cr(OH)_4^-(aq) + 3H_2O_2(aq) + 2OH^-(aq) \longrightarrow 2CrO_4^{2-}(aq) + 8H_2O(l)$
chromite ion $\qquad\qquad\qquad\qquad\qquad\qquad\qquad$ chromate ion

(b) $2MnO_2(s) + 4KOH(s) + O_2(g) \overset{\Delta}{\longrightarrow} 2K_2MnO_4(s) + 2H_2O(g)$

or $2MnO_2(s) + 2K_2CO_3(s) + O_2(g) \overset{\Delta}{\longrightarrow} 2K_2MnO_4(s) + 2CO_2(g)$

(c) $3MnO_4^{2-}(aq) + 4H^+(aq) \rightleftharpoons 2MnO_4^-(aq) + MnO_2(s) + 2H_2O(l)$
green $\qquad\qquad\qquad\qquad\qquad$ purple

or $2MnO_4^{2-}(aq) + Cl_2(g) \rightleftharpoons 2MnO_4^-(aq) + 2Cl^-(aq)$
$\qquad$ manganate ion $\qquad\qquad\qquad$ permanganate ion

S4.74 (a)

$$1.00 \times 10^6 \text{ g Mg} \times \frac{100 \text{ g seawater}}{0.0013 \text{ g Mg}} \times \frac{1 \text{ mL seawater}}{1.024 \text{ g seawater}} \times \frac{1}{0.70}$$

$= 1.1 \times 10^{11}$ mL or 1.1×10^8 L seawater

(b) The equations needed are:

$CaCO_3(s) \overset{heat}{\longrightarrow} CaO(s) + CO_2(g)$
shells $\qquad\qquad$ lime

$CaO(s) + H_2O(l) \longrightarrow Ca(OH)_2(aq)$
$\qquad\qquad\qquad\qquad$ saturated solution

$Mg^{2+}(aq) + Ca(OH)_2(aq) \longrightarrow Mg(OH)_2(s) + Ca^{2+}(aq)$
seawater

The steps in the calculation are: g Mg $\longrightarrow$ mol Mg $\longrightarrow$ mol $CaCO_3$ $\longrightarrow$ theoretical g $CaCO_3$ required $\longrightarrow$ g of shells required.

$$1.00 \times 10^6 \text{ g Mg} \times \frac{1 \text{ mol Mg}}{24.3 \text{ g Mg}} \times \frac{1 \text{ mol } CaCO_3}{1 \text{ mol Mg}} \times \frac{100.1 \text{ g } CaCO_3}{1 \text{ mol } CaCO_3} \times \frac{100 \text{ g shells}}{97 \text{ g } CaCO_3}$$

$= 4.2 \times 10^6$ g shells

(c) $Mg(OH)_2(s) + 2HCl(aq) \longrightarrow MgCl_2(aq) + 2H_2O(l)$

The steps in the calculation are: g Mg $\longrightarrow$ mol Mg $\longrightarrow$ mol $Mg(OH)_2$ $\longrightarrow$ mol HCl $\longrightarrow$ volume HCl (12 M).

$$1.00 \times 10^6 \text{ g Mg} \times \frac{1 \text{ mol Mg}}{24.3 \text{ g Mg}} \times \frac{1 \text{ mol } Mg(OH)_2}{1 \text{ mol Mg}} \times \frac{2 \text{ mol HCl}}{1 \text{ mol } Mg(OH)_2} \times \frac{1 \text{ L HCl (12 M)}}{12 \text{ mol HCl}}$$

$= 6.9 \times 10^3$ L HCl (12 M)

(d) $Mg^{2+} + 2e^- \longrightarrow Mg(l)$

The equation for the electrode reaction shows that 1 mol (24.3 g) of magnesium metal is produced by the passage of 2 mol of electrons, or 2 x 96,485 C. The steps in the calculation are: g Mg $\longrightarrow$ mol Mg $\longrightarrow$ C.

$$1.00 \times 10^6 \text{ g Mg} \times \frac{1 \text{ mol Mg}}{24.3 \text{ g Mg}} \times \frac{2 \times 96,485 \text{ C}}{1 \text{ mol Mg}} \times \frac{1}{0.80} = 9.9 \times 10^9 \text{ C}$$

(e) $2CH_4(g) + 4Cl_2(g) + O_2(g) \longrightarrow 8HCl(g) + 2CO(g)$

S4.75 $Fe_2O_3(s) + 2Al(s) \longrightarrow 2Fe(s) + Al_2O_3(s)$

$\Delta H^\circ = 2 \times \Delta H_f^\circ(Fe) + \Delta H_f^\circ(Al_2O_3) - \Delta H_f^\circ(Fe_2O_3) - 2 \times \Delta H_f^\circ(Al)$

    $= 2 \times 0 \text{ kJ} - 1675.7 \text{ kJ} + 824.2 \text{ kJ} - 2 \times 0 \text{ kJ} = -851.5 \text{ kJ}$

ΔH° per mole of reaction is –851.5 kJ/mol. We want to calculate the temperature to which this amount of evolved heat can raise the products, which are 2 mol of iron and 1 mol of aluminum oxide.

$$q = n_{Fe} \times \frac{68 \text{ J}}{\text{mol K}} \times \Delta T + n_{Al_2O_3} \times \frac{124 \text{ J}}{\text{mol K}} \times \Delta T; \quad \Delta T = \frac{851.5 \times 10^3 \text{ J}}{(136 \text{ J/K} + 124 \text{ J/K})} = 3275 \text{ K}$$

and $T_{final} = 3275 \text{ K} + T_{initial} = 3275 \text{ K} + 298 \text{ K} = 3573 \text{ K or } 3300^\circ C$

S4.79   (a) $Fe_2O_3(s) + 3CO(g) \longrightarrow 2Fe(s) + 3CO_2(g)$

At $25^\circ C$: $\Delta G^\circ = 2 \times \Delta G_f^\circ(Fe) + 3 \times \Delta G_f^\circ(CO_2) - \Delta G_f^\circ(Fe_2O_3) - 3 \times \Delta G_f^\circ(CO)$

    $= 2 \times 0 \text{ kJ} + 3 \times -394.4 \text{ kJ} + 742.2 \text{ kJ} - 3 \times -137.2 \text{ kJ} = -29.4 \text{ kJ}$

(b) At $25^\circ C$:

$\Delta H^\circ = 2 \times \Delta H_f^\circ(Fe) + 3 \times \Delta H_f^\circ(CO_2) - \Delta H_f^\circ(Fe_2O_3) - 3 \times \Delta H_f^\circ(CO)$

    $= 2 \times 0 \text{ kJ} + 3 \times -393.5 \text{ kJ} + 824.2 \text{ kJ} - 3 \times -110.5 \text{ kJ} = -24.8 \text{ kJ}$

$\Delta S^\circ = 2 \times S^\circ(Fe) + 3 \times S^\circ(CO_2) - S^\circ(Fe_2O_3) - 3 \times S^\circ(CO)$

    $= 2 \times 27.28 \text{ J/K} + 3 \times 213.74 \text{ J/K} - 87.40 \text{ J/K} - 3 \times 197.67 \text{ J/K} = 15.37 \text{ J/K} = 0.01537 \text{ kJ/K}$

We will assume that the values of ΔH° and ΔS° do not change significantly between $25^\circ C$ and $1000^\circ C$ (1273 K). Substituting these values and T = 1273 K into Equation 19.7 gives

$\Delta G^\circ = \Delta H^\circ - T\Delta S^\circ = -24.8 \text{ kJ} - 1273 \text{ K} \times 0.01537 \text{ kJ/K} = -44.4 \text{ kJ}$

The standard free energy change is approximately –44.4 kJ per mole of reaction at $1000^\circ C$. The difference between ΔG° at $25^\circ C$ and $1000^\circ C$ is not that substantial. The main advantage of carrying out the smelting at high temperature is kinetic. At high temperatures the reaction proceeds very rapidly, while at low temperatures it takes too long to produce any substantial amount of product.

S4.80   (a) $BaSO_4(s) + 2C(s) + CaCl_2(s) \longrightarrow BaCl_2(s) + CaS(s) + 2CO_2(g)$
       1.00 kg   g=?

The steps in the calculation are: g $BaSO_4$ $\longrightarrow$ mol $BaSO_4$ $\longrightarrow$ mol $BaCl_2$ $\longrightarrow$ g $BaCl_2$ $\longrightarrow$ volume $80^\circ C$ H_2O.

$$1.00 \times 10^3 \text{ g } BaSO_4 \times \frac{1 \text{ mol } BaSO_4}{233.4 \text{ g } BaSO_4} \times \frac{1 \text{ mol } BaCl_2}{1 \text{ mol } BaSO_4} \times \frac{208.2 \text{ g } BaCl_2}{1 \text{ mol } BaCl_2} = 892 \text{ g } BaCl_2$$

The volume of $80°C$ water needed to dissolve 892 g $BaCl_2$ is

$$892 \text{ g } BaCl_2 \text{ x } \frac{100 \text{ mL}}{53 \text{ g } BaCl_2} = 1.7 \text{ x } 10^3 \text{ mL or } 1.7 \text{ L}$$

(b) The mass of CaS produced is calculated as follows: g $BaSO_4$ ⟶ mol $BaSO_4$ ⟶ mol CaS ⟶ g CaS.

$$1.00 \text{ x } 10^3 \text{ g } BaSO_4 \text{ x } \frac{1 \text{ mol } BaSO_4}{233.4 \text{ g } BaSO_4} \text{ x } \frac{1 \text{ mol CaS}}{1 \text{ mol } BaSO_4} \text{ x } \frac{72.1 \text{ g CaS}}{1 \text{ mol CaS}} = 309 \text{ g CaS}$$

The amount of CaS that dissolves in 1.7 L of $80°C$ H_2O is

$$1.7 \text{ x } 10^3 \text{ mL x } \frac{0.048 \text{ g CaS}}{100 \text{ mL}} = 0.82 \text{ g CaS}$$

The fraction of CaS leached out is

$$\frac{0.82 \text{ g}}{309 \text{ g}} = 2.7 \text{ x } 10^{-3}$$

CHAPTER 22
NUCLEAR CHEMISTRY

Solutions To Practice Exercises

PE 22.1 (a) The atomic number of mercury is 80. The alpha particle symbol is ^4_2He, so

$$^{187}_{80}\text{Hg} \longrightarrow \, ^4_2\text{He} + \, ^{183}_{78}\text{X}$$

Element number 78 is Pt, and the complete equation is

$$^{187}_{80}\text{Hg} \longrightarrow \, ^4_2\text{He} + \, ^{183}_{78}\text{Pt}$$

Answer: mass number = 183; atomic number = 78; symbol is $^{183}_{78}\text{Pt}$

(b) The atomic numbers of aluminum and silicon are 13 and 14, respectively. So

$$^{28}_{13}\text{Al} \longrightarrow \, ^{28}_{14}\text{Si} + \, ^{0}_{-1}\text{e}$$

PE 22.3 First calculate k using Equation 22.1. Substituting $N/N_0 = 0.908$ and $t = 48.0$ h in Equation 22.1 gives

$\ln 0.908 = -k \times 48.0$ h and $k = 2.01 \times 10^{-3}$ h^{-1}

The half-life is obtained from k using Equation 22.2:

$$t_{1/2} = \frac{0.693}{k} = \frac{0.693}{2.01 \times 10^{-3} \text{ h}^{-1}} = 345 \text{ h}$$

PE 22.4 Substituting $k = 1.21 \times 10^{-4}$ yr^{-1} (see Example 22.4) and $N/N_0 = 1/8$ into Equation 22.1 gives

$$t = \frac{\ln(N/N_0)}{-k} = \frac{\ln(1/8)}{-1.21 \times 10^{-4} \text{ yr}^{-1}} = 17,200 \text{ yr}$$

Or, since 1/8 of the radionuclides will remain after three half-lives; $t = 3 \times 5730$ yr = 17,190 yr.

PE 22.5   Substituting $N/N_0 = 10,000/10,056 = 0.99443$ and $k = \ln 2/t_{1/2} = \ln 2/(4.9 \times 10^{11} \text{ yr})$
$= 1.4 \times 10^{-12} \text{ yr}^{-1}$ into Equation 22.1 gives

$\ln 0.99443 = -1.4 \times 10^{-12} \text{ yr}^{-1} \times t$ and $t = 4.0 \times 10^9 \text{ yr}$

PE 22.6   The atomic number of rubidium is 37. Rubidium-95, with 37 protons and 58 neutrons, lies above the stability band of Figure 22.14. It will decay by a mode that decreases the n/p ratio. The most common mode for decreasing the n/p ratio is beta emission (neutron emmision is rare):

$$^{95}_{37}\text{Rb} \longrightarrow {}^{95}_{38}\text{Sr} + {}^{0}_{-1}e$$

PE 22.8 (a)   The total mass of the separate nucleons is

28 protons x 1.00728 amu/proton =   28.20384 amu
30 neutrons x 1.00866 amu/neutron = 30.25980 amu
                              Total = 58.46364 amu

mass defect = mass of separate nucleons − nuclear mass of nickle-58
   = 58.46364 amu − 57.9199 amu = 0.5437 amu

(b)   The binding energy is the energy equivalent of the mass defect or
0.5437 amu x 931.5 MeV/amu = 506.5 MeV

(c)   The binding energy per nucleon is 506.5 MeV/58 nucleons = 8.733 MeV/nucleon.

Solutions to Final Exercises

22.1   (a)   Alpha particles are the nuclei of helium atoms, beta particles are electrons moving at very high speeds, and gamma rays consist of photons with very high frequencies.
(b)   1. The emission of an alpha particle reduces the mass number of a nucleus by four units and the atomic number by two units.
2. The emission of a beta particle raises the atomic number of a nucleus by one unit and leaves the mass number unchanged.
3. The emission of a gamma-ray photon does not affect the mass number or the atomic number of a nucleus.

22.5   (a)   In order of increasing energy we have: beta particles (between 0.05 and 1 MeV) < gamma ray photons (about 1 MeV) < alpha particles (about 5 MeV).
(b)   In order of increasing penetrating ability we have:
alpha particles < beta particles < gamma ray photons.
(c)   Alpha particles have a greater mass, lower speed, and higher charge than beta particles and this makes them more likely to be absorbed by molecules along their path. Therefore, alpha particles do not penetrate as far as beta particles. Gamma rays, on the other hand, have no mass, carry no charge, and move at the speed of light, and therefore have greater penetrating abilities than alpha or beta particles.

22.9   (a)

$$^{228}_{90}\text{Th} \longrightarrow {}^{4}_{2}\text{He} + {}^{224}_{88}\text{Ra}$$

(d)

$$^{11}_{6}\text{C} \longrightarrow {}^{0}_{1}e + {}^{11}_{5}\text{B}$$

(b)

$$^{28}_{13}\text{Al} \longrightarrow {}^{0}_{-1}e + {}^{28}_{14}\text{Si}$$

(e)

$$^{90}_{36}\text{Kr} \longrightarrow {}^{1}_{0}n + {}^{89}_{36}\text{Kr}$$

(c)

$$^{82}_{37}\text{Rb} + {}^{0}_{-1}e \longrightarrow {}^{82}_{36}\text{Kr} + \text{X-ray photon}$$

22.10

$$^{238}_{92}U \longrightarrow ^{4}_{2}He + ^{234}_{90}Th$$

$$^{234}_{90}Th \longrightarrow ^{0}_{-1}e + ^{234}_{91}Pa$$

$$^{234}_{91}Pa \longrightarrow ^{0}_{-1}e + ^{234}_{92}U$$

$$^{234}_{92}U \longrightarrow ^{4}_{2}He + ^{230}_{90}Th$$

$$^{230}_{90}Th \longrightarrow ^{4}_{2}He + ^{226}_{88}Ra$$

$$^{226}_{88}Ra \longrightarrow ^{4}_{2}He + ^{222}_{86}Rn$$

$$^{222}_{86}Rn \longrightarrow ^{4}_{2}He + ^{218}_{84}Po$$

$$^{218}_{84}Po \longrightarrow ^{4}_{2}He + ^{214}_{82}Pb$$

$$^{214}_{82}Pb \longrightarrow ^{0}_{-1}e + ^{214}_{83}Bi$$

$$^{214}_{83}Bi \longrightarrow ^{0}_{-1}e + ^{214}_{84}Po$$

$$^{214}_{84}Po \longrightarrow ^{4}_{2}He + ^{210}_{82}Pb$$

$$^{210}_{82}Pb \longrightarrow ^{0}_{-1}e + ^{210}_{83}Bi$$

$$^{210}_{83}Bi \longrightarrow ^{0}_{-1}e + ^{210}_{84}Po$$

$$^{210}_{84}Po \longrightarrow ^{4}_{2}He + ^{206}_{82}Pb$$

22.12 (a)

$$^{10}_{5}B + ^{4}_{2}He \longrightarrow ^{13}_{7}N + ^{1}_{0}n$$

(b)

$$^{8}_{3}Li + ^{1}_{0}n \longrightarrow ^{9}_{3}Li$$

(c)

$$^{238}_{92}U + ^{1}_{0}n \longrightarrow ^{239}_{93}Np + ^{0}_{-1}e$$

(d)

$$^{98}_{42}Mo + ^{2}_{1}H \longrightarrow ^{99}_{43}Tc + ^{1}_{0}n$$

(e)

$$^{23}_{11}Na + ^{1}_{1}H \longrightarrow ^{21}_{12}Mg + 3\ ^{1}_{0}n$$

(f)

$$^{141}_{59}Pr + ^{12}_{6}C \longrightarrow ^{149}_{65}Tb + 4\ ^{1}_{0}n$$

22.13 (a) $^{10}B(\alpha,n)^{13}N$

(b) $^{8}Li(n,0)^{9}Li$

(c) $^{238}U(n,\beta)^{239}Np$

(d) $^{98}Mo(D,n)^{99}Tc$

(e) $^{23}Na(p,3n)^{21}Mg$

(f) $^{141}Pr(^{12}C,4n)^{149}Tb$

22.16 (a)

$$^{209}_{83}Bi + {}^{4}_{2}He \longrightarrow {}^{211}_{85}At + 2\ {}^{1}_{0}n$$

(b)

$$^{211}_{85}At + {}^{0}_{-1}e \longrightarrow {}^{211}_{84}Po + \text{X-ray photon}$$

$$^{211}_{85}At \longrightarrow {}^{4}_{2}He + {}^{207}_{83}Bi$$

22.18

$$^{239}_{94}Pu + {}^{1}_{0}n \longrightarrow {}^{240}_{94}Pu$$

$$^{240}_{94}Pu \longrightarrow {}^{240}_{95}Am + {}^{0}_{-1}e$$

$$^{240}_{95}Am + {}^{1}_{0}n \longrightarrow {}^{241}_{95}Am$$

Or, alternatively

$$^{239}_{94}Pu + 2\ {}^{1}_{0}n \longrightarrow {}^{241}_{94}Pu \longrightarrow {}^{241}_{95}Am + {}^{0}_{-1}e$$

22.22

$$k = \frac{0.693}{t_{1/2}} = \frac{0.693}{1.83\ h} = 0.379\ h^{-1}$$

Substituting k and $N/N_0 = 0.750$ into Equation 22.1 gives

$$t = \frac{\ln(N/N_0)}{-k} = \frac{\ln\ 0.750}{-0.379\ h^{-1}} = 0.759\ h\ \text{or}\ 45.5\ \text{min}$$

22.24   The rate constant, k, of carbon-14 is $1.21 \times 10^{-4}\ yr^{-1}$.
(a) $\ln(N/N_0) = -1.21 \times 10^{-4}\ yr^{-1} \times 500\ yr = -0.605$ and $N/N_0 = e^{-0.605} = 0.546$
(b) $\ln(N/N_0) = -1.21 \times 10^{-4}\ yr^{-1} \times 10,000\ yr = -1.21$ and $N/N_0 = e^{-1.21} = 0.30$
(c) $\ln(N/N_0) = -1.21 \times 10^{-4}\ yr^{-1} \times 25,000\ yr = -3.02$ and $N/N_0 = e^{-3.02} = 4.9 \times 10^{-2}$
(d) $\ln(N/N_0) = -1.21 \times 10^{-4}\ yr^{-1} \times 50,000\ yr = -6.05$ and $N/N_0 = e^{-6.05} = 2.4 \times 10^{-3}$

(e) It is not used for objects more than 50,000 years old because the activity is so low that the experimental error in the measurement either exceeds it or invalidates the measurement.

22.25

$$^{40}_{19}K + {}^{0}_{-1}e \longrightarrow {}^{40}_{18}Ar + \text{X-ray photon}$$

The rate constant is obtained from the half-life using Equation 22.2:

$$k = \frac{0.693}{t_{1/2}} = \frac{0.693}{1.25 \times 10^9\ yr} = 5.54 \times 10^{-10}\ yr^{-1}$$

Substituting k and $N/N_0 = 1.5/2.5 = 0.60$ into Equation 22.1 gives

$$t = \frac{\ln(N/N_0)}{-k} = \frac{\ln\ 0.60}{-5.54 \times 10^{-10}\ yr^{-1}} = 9.2 \times 10^8\ yr$$

22.27　The numbers of carbon-14 atoms are proportional to the disintegration rates; therefore, the fraction of carbon-14 remaining is

$$\frac{N}{N_0} = \frac{^{14}C_{\text{now}}}{^{14}C_{\text{at } t=0}} = \frac{11.0 \text{ dpm}}{15.3 \text{ dpm}} = 0.719$$

Substituting $k = 1.21 \times 10^{-4}$ yr^{-1} and $N/N_0 = 0.719$ into Equation 22.1 gives

$$t = \frac{\ln(N/N_0)}{-k} = \frac{\ln 0.719}{-1.21 \times 10^{-4} \text{ } yr^{-1}} = 2730 \text{ yr}$$

22.30　$5.0 \times 3.7 \times 10^{-2}$ disintegrations/s mL $\times$ 10 mL $\times$ 60 s/min = 110 disintegrations/min

22.32

$$k = \frac{0.693}{t_{1/2}} = \frac{0.693}{2.69 \text{ days}} = 0.258 \text{ days}^{-1}$$

Substituting k and $N/N_0 = 1/10$ into Equation 22.1 gives

$$t = \frac{\ln(N/N_0)}{-k} = \frac{\ln(1/10)}{-0.258 \text{ days}^{-1}} = 9 \text{ days}$$

(b) $\ln(N/N_0) = -0.258$ days^{-1} $\times$ 14 days $= -3.61$; $N/N_0 = e^{-3.61} = 0.027$
and $N = 0.027N_0 = (0.027)(100 \text{ mCi}) = 2.7 \text{ mCi}$

22.34　dose (in rems) = dose (in rads) x RBE
(a) RBE = 10 for alpha particles; therefore

$$\text{dose(in rads)} = \frac{\text{dose(in rems)}}{\text{RBE}} = \frac{500}{10} = 50 \text{ rads}$$

(b) RBE = 1 for gamma rays; therefore

$$\text{dose(in rads)} = \frac{500}{1} = 500 \text{ rads}$$

(c) RBE = 1 for X-rays; therefore dose (in rads) = 500 rads
(d) RBE = 10 for neutrons; therefore dose (in rads) = 50 rads
(e) RBE = 1 for beta particles; therefore dose (in rads) = 500 rads
(f) RBE = 10 for protons; therefore dose (in rads) = 50 rads

22.38

$$^{68}_{29}\text{Cu} \longrightarrow ^{68}_{30}\text{Zn} + ^{0}_{-1}\text{e}$$

(a)

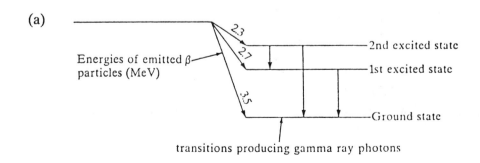

Energies of emitted β particles (MeV)

transitions producing gamma ray photons

(b) Three different gamma-ray photons will be emitted with energies of 3.5 − 2.7 = 0.8 MeV, 3.5 − 2.3 = 1.2 MeV, and 2.7 − 2.3 = 0.4 MeV.

22.41 The atomic number of strontium is 38. Strontuim-90, with 38 protons and 52 neutrons, lies above the stability band of Figure 22.14. It will decay by a mode that decreases the n/p ratio. The most common mode for decreasing the n/p ratio is beta emission (neutron emission is rare):

$$^{90}_{38}Sr \longrightarrow ^{90}_{39}Y + ^{0}_{-1}e$$

22.42 The atomic number of oxygen is 8. Oxygen-13, with 8 protons and 5 neutrons, oxygen-14, with 8 protons and 6 neutrons, and oxygen-15, with 8 protons and 7 neutrons, all lie below the stability band of Figure 22.14. They will all decay by a mode that increases the n/p ratio. Alpha emission is not common for elements with Z < 66, and proton emission rarely occurs. Therefore, the possible modes of decay are positron emission and electron capture. Since electron capture does not occur, ^{13}O, ^{14}O, and ^{15}O decay by positron emission:

$$^{13}_{8}O \longrightarrow ^{13}_{7}N + ^{0}_{1}e \qquad\qquad ^{15}_{8}O \longrightarrow ^{15}_{7}N + ^{0}_{1}e$$

$$^{14}_{8}O \longrightarrow ^{14}_{7}N + ^{0}_{1}e$$

Oxygen-19, with 8 protons and 11 neutrons, and oxygen-20, with 8 protons and 12 neutrons, both lie above the stability band of Figure 22.14. They will decay by a mode that decreases the n/p ratio. The most common mode for decreasing the n/p ratio is beta emission (neutron emission is rare):

$$^{19}_{8}O \longrightarrow ^{19}_{9}F + ^{0}_{-1}e \qquad\qquad ^{20}_{8}O \longrightarrow ^{20}_{9}F + ^{0}_{-1}e$$

22.43 (a)

$^{39}_{18}Ar$, with 18 protons and 21 neutrons, lies below the stability band of Figure 22.14.

Positron emission and electron capture are possible decay modes (Z < 66).

(b)

$^{30}_{16}S$, with 16 protons and 14 neutrons, lies below the stability band of Figure 22.14.

Positron emission and electron capture are possible decay modes (Z < 66).

(c)

$^{37}_{16}S$, with 16 protons and 21 neutrons, lies above the stability band of Figure 22.14.

Decay by beta emission is the only common possibility.

(d)

$^{56}_{25}Mn$, with 25 protons and 31 neutrons, lies below the stability band of Figure 22.14.

Positron emission and electron capture are possible decay modes (Z < 66).

(e) Zinc-69m is a metastable nucleus, i.e., a nucleus in an excited state that has a significant lifetime. Metastable nuclei decay by gamma-ray emission.

(f)

$^{69}_{30}Zn$, with 30 protons and 39 neutrons, lies above the stability band of Figure 22.14.

Decay by beta emission is the only common possibility.

(g)

$_2^6$He, with 2 protons and 4 neutrons, lies above the stability band of Figure 22.14.

Decay by beta emission is the only common possibility.

22.44   (a)

$$\frac{1 \text{ GeV}}{1 \text{ particle}} \times \frac{10^3 \text{ MeV}}{1 \text{ GeV}} \times \frac{1.6022 \times 10^{-16} \text{ kJ}}{1 \text{ MeV}} \times \frac{6.022 \times 10^{23} \text{ particles}}{1 \text{ mol}}$$

$$= 9.648 \times 10^{10} \text{ kJ/mol}$$

(b)

$$\frac{1 \text{ TeV}}{1 \text{ particle}} \times \frac{10^6 \text{ MeV}}{1 \text{ TeV}} \times \frac{1.6022 \times 10^{-16} \text{ kJ}}{1 \text{ MeV}} \times \frac{6.022 \times 10^{23} \text{ particles}}{1 \text{ mol}}$$

$$= 9.648 \times 10^{13} \text{ kJ/mol}$$

22.45

The mass equivalent of 39.35 kJ is

$$39.35 \text{ kJ} \times \frac{1 \text{ amu}}{1.492 \times 10^{-13} \text{ kJ}} \times \frac{1 \text{ g}}{6.022 \times 10^{23} \text{ amu}} = 4.380 \times 10^{-10} \text{ g}$$

22.48

$$4_1^1\text{H} \longrightarrow {}_2^4\text{He} + 2_1^0\text{e}$$

Reactant mass: $4^1\text{H} = 4.02912$ amu
Product masses: $^4\text{He} = 4.00150$ amu
                        $2^0\text{e} = \underline{0.001098}$ amu
Total product mass: 4.00260 amu

The vanished mass is 4.02912 amu − 4.00260 amu = 0.02652 amu.

(a) The energy equivalent of the vanished mass is 0.02652 amu x 1.4924 x 10^{-10} J/amu = 3.958 x 10^{-12} J. This is the energy released when one helium atom is produced.

(b) The energy released in joules per gram of helium is

$$\frac{3.958 \times 10^{-12} \text{ J}}{4.00260 \text{ amu}} \times \frac{6.022 \times 10^{23} \text{ amu}}{1 \text{ g}} = 5.955 \times 10^{11} \text{ J/g}$$

22.50

$$_{92}^{238}\text{U} \longrightarrow {}_{90}^{234}\text{Th} + {}_2^4\text{He}$$

In this reaction, a uranium nucleus and 92 electrons are converted into a thorium ion having 92 electrons (two too many) and an alpha particle. Thus, the total product mass is the sum of the masses of the neutral atoms thorium-234 and helium-4.

Reactant mass: ^{238}U atom $= 238.0508$ amu
Product masses: ^{234}Th atom $= 234.0436$ amu
                ^4He atom $= \underline{4.0026}$ amu
Total product mass: 238.0462 amu

The vanished mass is 238.0508 amu − 238.0462 amu = 0.0046 amu.

(a) The energy equivalent of the vanished mass in MeV is 0.0046 amu x 931.5 MeV/amu = 4.3 MeV. This is the energy released during the decay of one uranium atom.

(b) The energy released in joules per gram of uranium is

$$\frac{4.3 \text{ MeV}}{238.0508 \text{ amu}} \times \frac{6.022 \times 10^{23} \text{ amu}}{1 \text{ g}} \times \frac{1.6022 \times 10^{-13} \text{ J}}{1 \text{ MeV}} = 1.7 \times 10^9 \text{ J/g}$$

22.52   (a) Beryllium-9 has 4 protons and 5 neutrons. The total mass of the separate nucleons is

4 protons x 1.00728 amu/proton   = 4.02912 amu
5 neutrons x 1.00866 amu/neutron = 5.04330 amu
                         Total = 9.07242 amu

mass defect = mass of separate nucleons – nuclear mass of beryllium-9

= 9.07242 amu – 9.00998 amu = 0.06244 amu

The binding energy is the energy equivalent of the mass defect, or 0.06244 amu x 931.5 MeV/amu = 58.16 MeV. The average binding energy per nucleon is 58.16 MeV/9 nucleons = 6.462 MeV/nucleon.

(b) Boron-10 has 5 protons and 5 neutrons. The total mass of the separate nucleons is

5 protons x 1.00728 amu/proton   = 5.03640 amu
5 neutrons x 1.00866 amu/neutron = 5.04330 amu
                         Total = 10.07970 amu

mass defect = mass of separate nucleons – nuclear mass of boron-10

= 10.07970 amu – 10.0102 amu = 0.0695 amu

The binding energy is the energy equivalent of the mass defect, or 0.0695 amu x 931.5 MeV/amu = 64.7 MeV. The average binding energy per nucleon is 64.7 MeV/10 nucleons = 6.47 MeV/nucleon.

(c) Silicon-28 has 14 protons and 14 neutrons. The total mass of the separate nucleons is

14 protons x 1.00728 amu/proton   = 14.10192 amu
14 neutrons x 1.00866 amu/neutron = 14.12124 amu
                          Total = 28.22316 amu

mass defect = mass of separate nucleons – nuclear mass of silicon-28

= 28.22316 amu – 27.96925 amu = 0.25391 amu

The binding energy is 0.25391 amu x 931.5 MeV/amu = 236.5 MeV. The average binding energy per nucleon is 236.5 MeV/28 nucleons = 8.45 MeV/nucleon.

The order of increasing stability is ^{9}Be < ^{10}B < ^{28}Si

22.53   The atomic mass of iron-56, which includes the nucleus and 26 electrons, is 55.9349 amu. The nuclear mass is obtained by subtracting the mass of the 26 electrons:

nuclear mass = 55.9349 amu – 26 x 0.000549 amu = 55.9206 amu

Iron-56 has 26 protons and 30 neutrons. The total mass of the separate nucleons is

26 protons x 1.00728 amu/proton   = 26.18928 amu
30 neutrons x 1.00866 amu/neutron = 30.25980 amu
                          Total = 56.44908 amu

The mass defect is therefore 56.44908 amu – 55.9206 amu = 0.5285 amu. The binding energy is 0.5285 amu x 931.5 MeV/amu = 492.3 MeV. The binding energy per nucleon is 492.3 MeV/56 nucleons = 8.791 MeV/nucleon.

The atomic mass of iron-57, which includes the nucleus and 26 electrons, is 56.9354 amu. The nuclear mass is obtained by subtracting the mass of the 26 electrons:

nuclear mass = 56.9354 amu − 26 x 0.000549 amu = 56.9221 amu

Iron-57 has 26 protons and 31 neutrons. The total mass of the separate nucleons is

26 protons x 1.00728 amu/proton = 26.18928 amu
31 neutrons x 1.00866 amu/neutron = 31.26846 amu
Total = 57.45774 amu

The mass defect is therefore 57.45774 amu − 56.9221 amu = 0.5356 amu. The binding energy is 0.5356 amu x 931.5 MeV/amu = 498.9 MeV. The binding energy per nucleon is 498.9 MeV/57 nucleons = 8.753 MeV/nucleon.

Iron-56 is the more stable because it has a greater binding energy per nucleon than iron-57.

22.56 (a)

$$^{235}_{92}U + ^1_0n \longrightarrow ^{90}_{37}Rb + ^{144}_{55}Cs + 2\ ^1_0n$$

(d)

$$^{235}_{92}U + ^1_0n \longrightarrow ^{97}_{39}Y + ^{137}_{53}I + 2\ ^1_0n$$

(b)

$$^{235}_{92}U + ^1_0n \longrightarrow ^{90}_{38}Sr + ^{143}_{54}Xe + 3\ ^1_0n$$

(e)

$$^{235}_{92}U + ^1_0n \longrightarrow ^{137}_{52}Te + ^{97}_{40}Zr + 2\ ^1_0n$$

(c)

$$^{235}_{92}U + ^1_0n \longrightarrow ^{90}_{38}Sr + ^{144}_{54}Xe + 2\ ^1_0n$$

22.59 The energy released when 1 g of uranium-235 undergoes fission is

$$\frac{200\ MeV}{235.0439\ amu} \times \frac{6.022 \times 10^{23}\ amu}{1\ g} \times \frac{1.6022 \times 10^{-16}\ kJ}{1\ MeV} = 8.21 \times 10^7\ kJ/g$$

The tons of TNT equivalent to this amount of energy is

$$8.21 \times 10^7\ kJ \times \frac{1\ g}{2.8\ kJ} \times \frac{1\ ton}{9.072 \times 10^5\ g} = 32\ tons$$

22.63

$$^2_1H + ^3_1H \longrightarrow ^4_2He + ^1_0n$$

(a) Reactant masses:
^2H = 2.01355 amu
^3H = 3.01550 amu
Total reactant mass: 5.02905 amu

(b) Product masses:
^4He = 4.00150 amu
^1n = 1.00866 amu
Total product mass: 5.01016 amu

The vanished mass is 5.02905 amu − 5.01016 amu = 0.01889 amu. The energy equivalent of the vanished mass in MeV is 0.01889 amu x 931.5 MeV/amu = 17.60 MeV. This is the energy released during the production of one helium atom.

(b) The energy released in kilojoules per mole of product is

$$\frac{17.60\ MeV}{1\ atom} \times \frac{1.6022 \times 10^{-16}\ kJ}{1\ MeV} \times \frac{6.022 \times 10^{23}\ atoms}{1\ mol} = 1.698 \times 10^9\ kJ/mol$$

22.64

$$^2_1H + ^3_1H \longrightarrow ^4_2He + ^1_0n + 17.6 \text{ MeV}$$

(a) The energy released when 1 g of deuterium fuses with tritium is

$$\frac{17.6 \text{ MeV}}{2.01410 \text{ amu}} \times \frac{6.022 \times 10^{23} \text{ amu}}{1 \text{ g}} \times \frac{1.6022 \times 10^{-16} \text{ kJ}}{1 \text{ MeV}} = 8.43 \times 10^8 \text{ kJ/g}$$

(b) The tons of TNT equivalent to this amount of energy is

$$8.43 \times 10^8 \text{ kJ} \times \frac{1 \text{ g}}{2.8 \text{ kJ}} \times \frac{1 \text{ ton}}{9.072 \times 10^5 \text{ g}} = 330 \text{ tons}$$

22.71　(a)

$$^{10}B(n,\alpha)^7Li; \quad ^{10}_5B + ^1_0n \longrightarrow ^4_2He + ^7_3Li$$

(b)

$$^9Be(n,p)^9Li; \quad ^9_4Be + ^1_0n \longrightarrow ^9_3Li + ^1_1H$$

(c)

$$^{238}U(n,2\beta)^{239}Pu; \quad ^{238}_{92}U + ^1_0n \longrightarrow ^{239}_{94}Pu + 2_{-1}^0e$$

(d)

$$^{98}Mo(D,n)^{99}Tc; \quad ^{98}_{42}Mo + ^2_1H \longrightarrow ^{99}_{43}Tc + ^1_0n$$

(e)

$$^{23}Na(p,3n)^{21}Mg; \quad ^{23}_{11}Na + ^1_1H \longrightarrow ^{21}_{12}Mg + 3\ ^1_0n$$

(f)

$$^{141}Pr(^{12}C,4n)^{149}Tb; \quad ^{141}_{59}Pr + ^{12}_6C \longrightarrow ^{149}_{65}Tb + 4\ ^1_0n$$

22.74

$$^{235}_{92}U \text{ decays to } ^{207}_{82}Pb$$

There are three natural decay series and each isotope in these series decays by either alpha particle or beta particle emission. Alpha particle emission lowers the mass number by four and the atomic number by two, but beta particle emission only raises the atomic numer by one, it does not affect the mass number at all. Therefore, the mass number is only affected by the alpha particle emissions, and the number of alpha particles emitted is equal to the difference in the mass numbers of uranium-235 and lead-207 divided by four:

$$\text{alpha particles emitted} = \frac{235 - 207}{4} = 7$$

The emission of seven alpha particles lowers the atomic number to $92 - 2 \times 7 = 78$. To bring the atomic number back up to 82, four beta particles must be emitted. Therefore, seven alpha particles and four beta particles are emitted during the sequence.

22.76　(a) The total energy radiated by the sun per second is

$(50 \times 10^9)(173,000 \times 10^{12} \text{ J/s}) = 8.65 \times 10^{27} \text{ J/s}$ (carry extra significant figure)

The mass equivalent of this amount of energy is

$$8.65 \times 10^{27} \text{ J} \times \frac{1 \text{ amu}}{1.4924 \times 10^{-10} \text{ J}} \times \frac{1 \text{ g}}{6.022 \times 10^{23} \text{ amu}} = 9.6 \times 10^{13} \text{ g}$$

Therefore, the sun loses approximately 9.6×10^{13} g per second.

(b) The mass converted to energy every 100 years is

$$\frac{9.6 \times 10^{13} \text{ g}}{1 \text{ s}} \times \frac{3600 \text{ s}}{1 \text{ h}} \times \frac{24 \text{ h}}{1 \text{ day}} \times \frac{36525 \text{ days}}{100 \text{ yr}} = 3.0 \times 10^{23} \text{ g}/100 \text{ yr}$$

The percent of the sun's mass converted to energy every 100 years is

$$\frac{3.0 \times 10^{23} \text{ g}}{1.99 \times 10^{33} \text{ g}} \times 100\% = 1.5 \times 10^{-8}\%$$

22.78 (a)

$$k = \frac{0.693}{t_{1/2}} = \frac{0.693}{15.0 \text{ h}} = 0.0462 \text{ h}^{-1}$$

Substituting k and t = 2 h into Equation 22.1 gives

$\ln(N/N_0) = -kt = -0.0462 \text{ h}^{-1} \times 2 \text{ h} = -0.0924$ and $N/N_0 = e^{-0.0924} = 0.912$

(b) $N = 0.912N_0 = (0.912)(4.0 \text{ } \mu\text{Ci}) = 3.6 \text{ } \mu\text{Ci}$

22.80

The rate constant for the radioactive decay is

$$k_1 = \frac{0.693}{t_{1/2}} = \frac{0.693}{45.1 \text{ days}} = 0.0154 \text{ days}^{-1}$$

The rate constant for the biological elimination is

$$k_2 = \frac{0.693}{t_{1/2}} = \frac{0.693}{60 \text{ days}} = 0.012 \text{ days}^{-1}$$

The rate constant for the overall process is equal to the sum of the rate constants of the individual processes:

$k = k_1 + k_2 = 0.0514 \text{ days}^{-1} + 0.012 \text{ days}^{-1} = 0.027 \text{ days}^{-1}$

Substituting $k = 0.027 \text{ days}^{-1}$ and t = 7 days into Equation 22.1 gives

$\ln(N/N_0) = -kt = -0.027 \text{ days}^{-1} \times 7 \text{ days} = -0.19$ and $N/N_0 = e^{-0.19} = 0.83$

CHAPTER 23
ORGANIC CHEMISTRY
AND THE CHEMICALS OF LIFE

Solutions To Practice Exercises

PE 23.3   No. The carbon atom at the right of the double-bond does not have two different substituents.

PE 23.9 (a) Not chiral. None of the carbon atoms has four different substituents.
       (b) Chiral. The middle carbon atom has four different substituents; $CH_3\overset{*}{C}HClCH_2OH$.

Solutions to Final Exercises

23.3   No. Since each carbon atom is tetrahedrally bonded, the C–C–C bond angle is actually 109.5°, not 180°, and, therefore, the carbon chain is actually zig-zag in nature. Furthermore, free rotation about the C–C single bonds leads to a variety of convoluted chains or shapes.

23.9 (a)

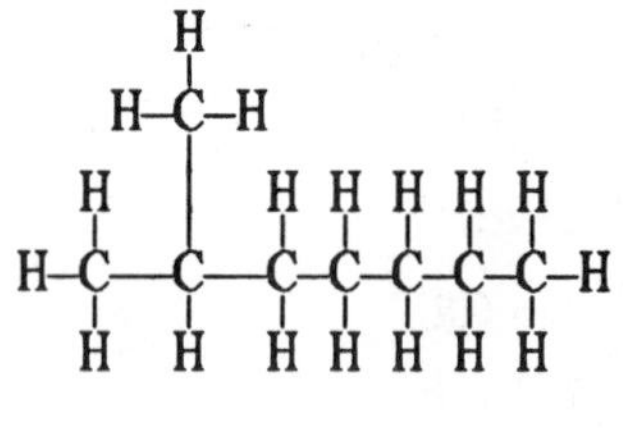

C_8H_{18}

    (b)

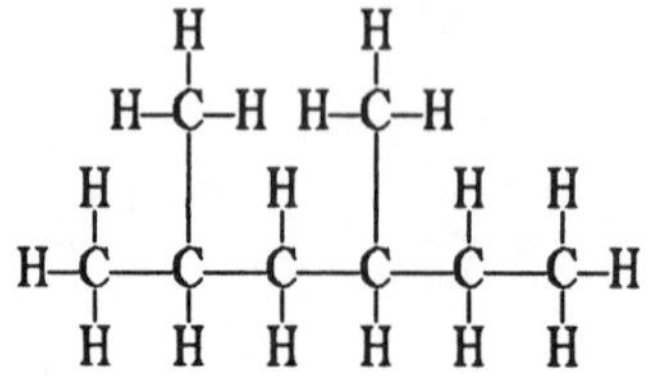

C_8H_{18}

(c)

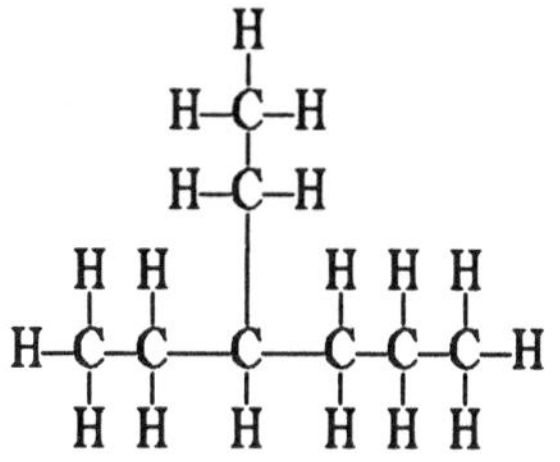

$$C_8H_{18}$$

(d)

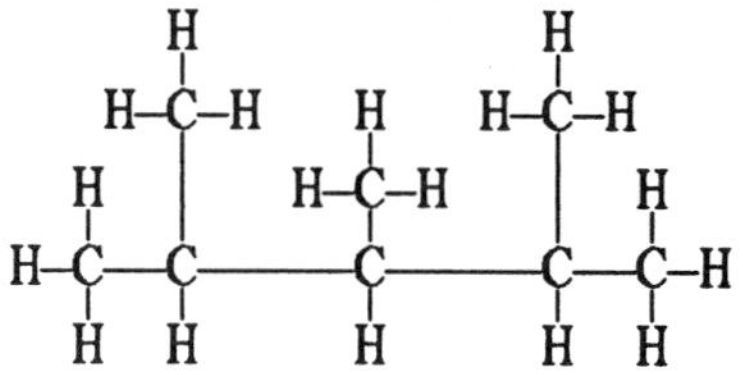

$$C_8H_{18}$$

(e)

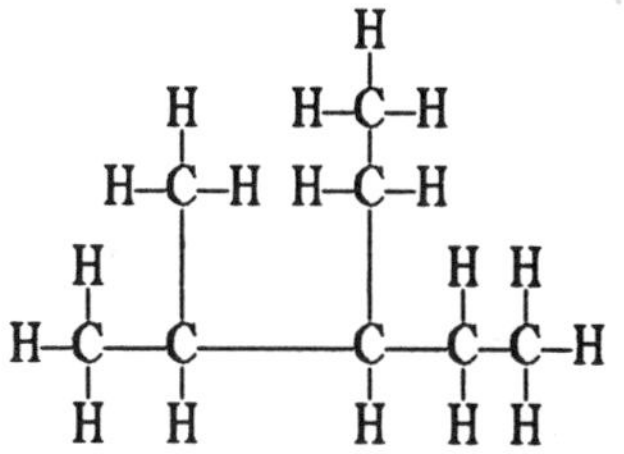

$$C_8H_{18}$$

They are all structural isomers of the molecular formula C_8H_{18}.

23.11

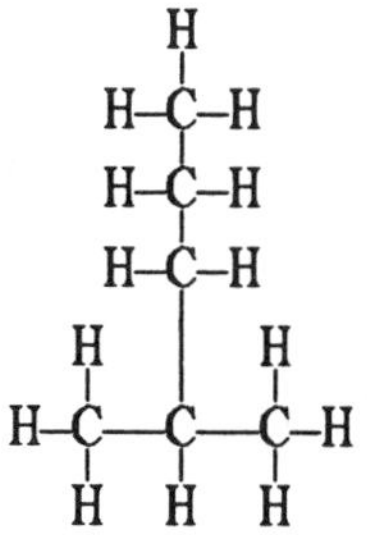

2-methylpentane

23.14   (a) 17

(b)

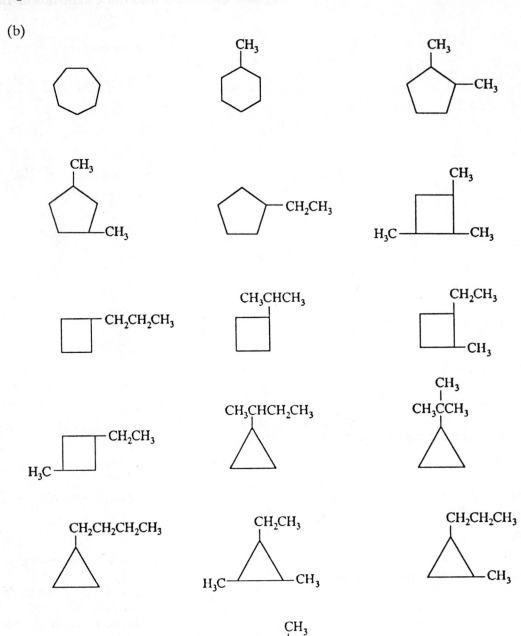

23.16   Step 1. $CH_4 + Cl_2 \xrightarrow{h\nu} CH_3Cl + HCl$

Step 2. $CH_3Cl + Cl_2 \xrightarrow{h\nu} CH_2Cl_2 + HCl$

Step 3. $CH_2Cl_2 + Cl_2 \xrightarrow{h\nu} CHCl_3 + HCl$

Step 4. $CHCl_3 + Cl_2 \xrightarrow{h\nu} CCl_4 + HCl$

The other product is hydrogen chloride.

23.18   (a) Let X_2 stand for a halogen molecule (F_2, Cl_2, or Br_2; I_2 does not react) and RH for a hydrocarbon. Then,

$X_2 \xrightarrow{light} 2X\cdot$ initiation step

$X\cdot + RH \longrightarrow HX + R\cdot$

$R\cdot + X_2 \longrightarrow RX + X\cdot$ propagation steps

repeated over-and-over again until

$X\cdot + \cdot X \longrightarrow X_2$
or
$R\cdot + \cdot R \longrightarrow R\text{-}R$ termination steps
or
$R\cdot + \cdot X \longrightarrow RX$

For the specific reaction of ethane with chlorine, X_2 is Cl_2, $X\cdot$ is $Cl\cdot$, RH is C_2H_6, $R\cdot$ is $C_2H_5\cdot$ (ethyl radical), RX is C_2H_5Cl, and R-R is C_4H_{10} (butane).

(b) 1. If only one hydrogen atom on ethane is replaced by a chlorine atom, then chloroethane is produced.
2. If two hydrogen atoms on one of the ethane's carbon atoms are replaced by chlorine atoms, then 1,1-dichloroethane is produced.
3. If one hydrogen atom on each of the ethane's carbon atoms is replaced by a chlorine atom, then 1,2-dichloroethane is produced.
4. Trichloroethane is produced if three of ethane's hydrogen atoms are replaced by chlorine atoms.
5. Butane is formed when two ethyl radicals ($CH_3CH_2\cdot$) combine in a chain terminating step.
6. Chlorobutane can form if a chloroethyl radical, like $CH_2ClCH_2\cdot$, and an ethyl radical ($CH_3CH_2\cdot$) combine in a chain terminating step or if butane is produced and subsequently monochlorinated.

23.19   (a) C_nH_{2n} (d) C_nH_{2n-2}
(b) C_nH_{2n-2} (e) C_nH_{2n-4}
(c) C_nH_{2n-4} (f) C_nH_{2n-2}

23.21

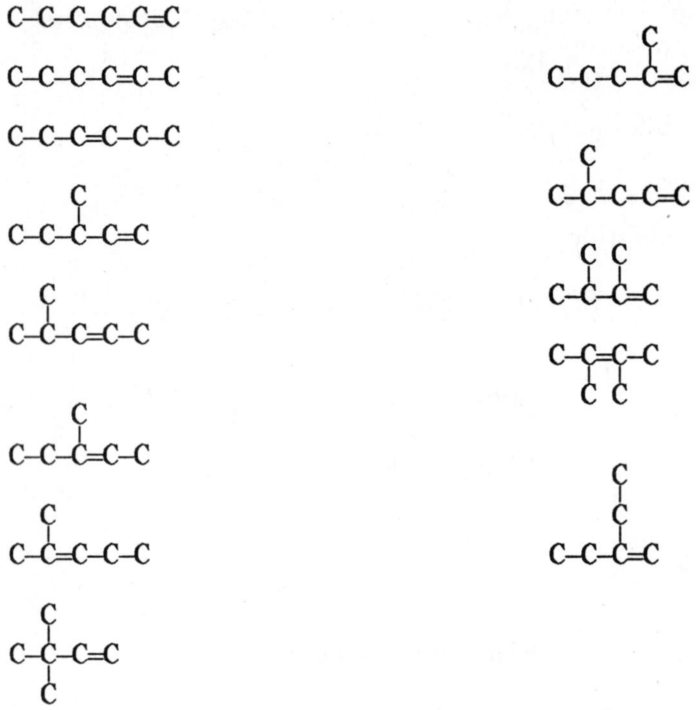

C–C–C–C–C=C

C–C–C–C≡C–C

C–C–C≡C–C–C

$\underset{\displaystyle C}{\overset{\displaystyle C}{C-C-C-C=C}}$

$\underset{\displaystyle C}{\overset{\displaystyle C}{C-C-C=C-C}}$

$\underset{\displaystyle C}{\overset{\displaystyle C}{C-C-C=C-C}}$

$\underset{\displaystyle C}{\overset{\displaystyle C}{C-C=C-C-C}}$

$\underset{\displaystyle C}{\overset{\displaystyle C}{C-C-C=C}}$

$\overset{\displaystyle C}{C-C-C-C=C}$

$\overset{\displaystyle C}{C-C-C-C=C}$

$\overset{\displaystyle C\ \ C}{C-C-C=C}$

$\underset{\displaystyle C\ \ C}{\overset{\displaystyle C\ \ C}{C-C=C-C}}$

$\overset{\displaystyle \overset{C}{C}}{C-C-C=C}$

23.24 (a) No.

H–C=C–C–C–C–H

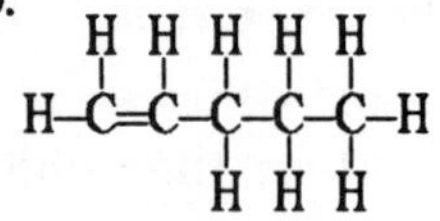

(b) No.

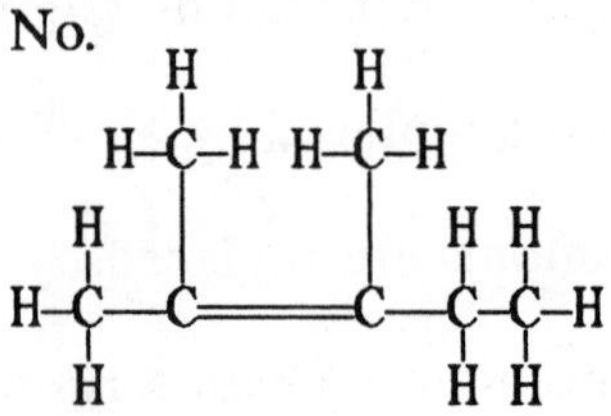

(c) No.

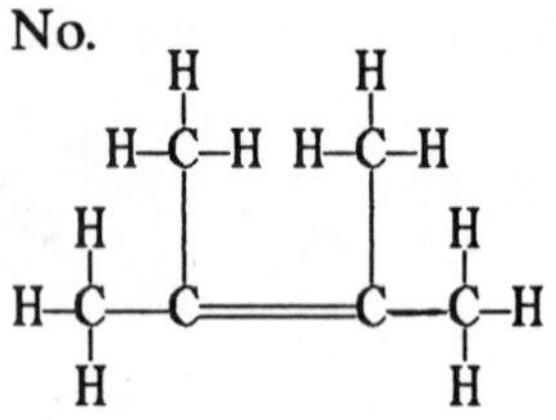

(d) Yes.

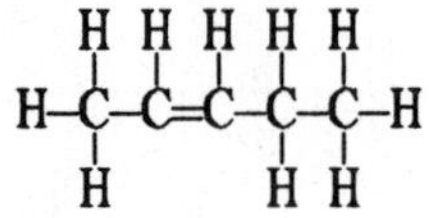

(e) No.

H–C=C–C=C–H

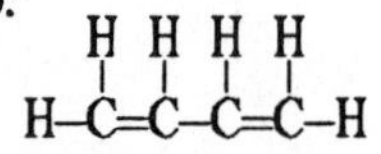

23.28 (a) 1,2-dibromobenzene or o-dibromobenzene
     (b) 1,3-dibromobenzene or m-dibromobenzene
     (c) 1,4-dibromobenzene or p-dibromobenzene
     (d) 3-ethyltoluene or 1-methyl-3-ethylbenzene

     (e) 1-methyl-3-chlorohexane
     (f) 1-methyl-4-chlorohexane

23.29 (a)

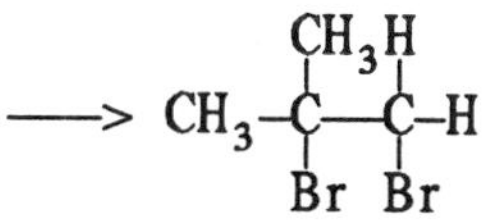

$$\longrightarrow \quad CH_3-\overset{\overset{\displaystyle CH_3}{|}}{\underset{\underset{\displaystyle Br}{|}}{C}}-\overset{\overset{\displaystyle H}{|}}{\underset{\underset{\displaystyle Br}{|}}{C}}-H$$

(b)

$$\longrightarrow \quad CH_3-CH_2-\overset{\overset{\displaystyle Br}{|}}{\underset{\underset{\displaystyle Br}{|}}{C}}-\overset{\overset{\displaystyle Br}{|}}{\underset{\underset{\displaystyle Br}{|}}{C}}-H$$

(c)

$$\longrightarrow \quad CH_3-CH_2-\overset{\overset{\displaystyle Br}{|}}{\underset{\underset{\displaystyle Br}{|}}{C}}-CH_3$$

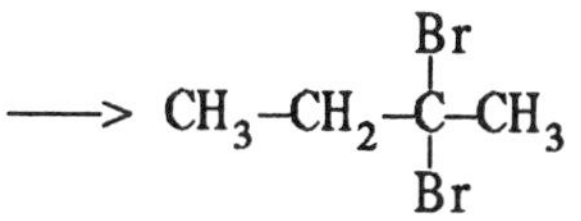

(d)

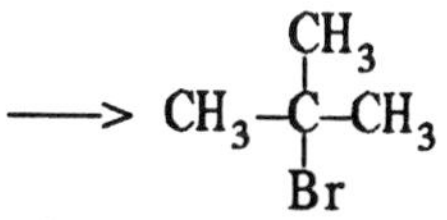

$$\longrightarrow \quad CH_3-\overset{\overset{\displaystyle CH_3}{|}}{\underset{\underset{\displaystyle Br}{|}}{C}}-CH_3$$

(e)

$$\longrightarrow \quad CH_3-\overset{\overset{\displaystyle CH_3}{|}}{\underset{\underset{\displaystyle H}{|}}{C}}-CH_3$$

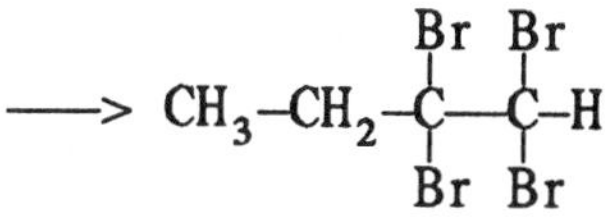

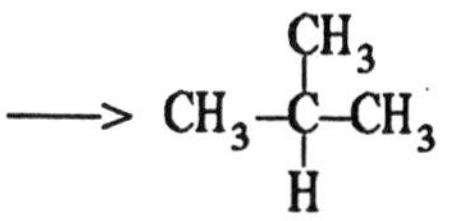

(f) $\longrightarrow CH_3-CH_2-CH_2-CH_3$

23.31 (a)

(b)

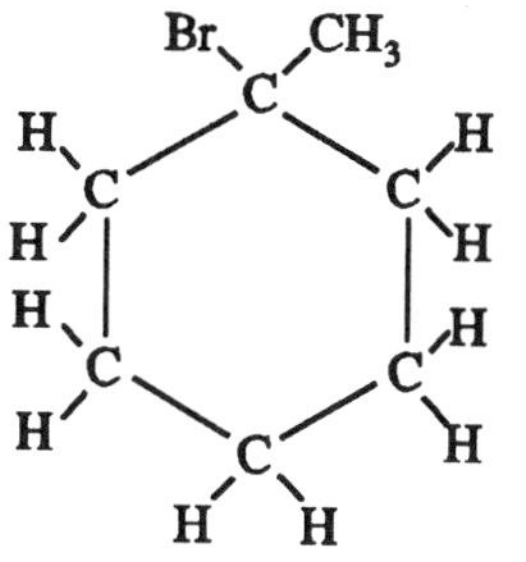

(c)

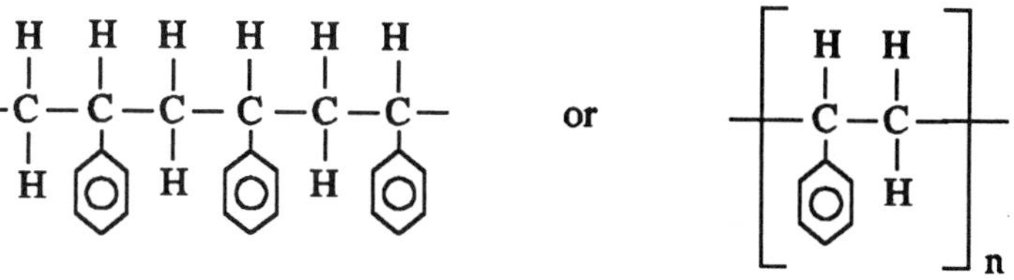

or

23.32 (a)

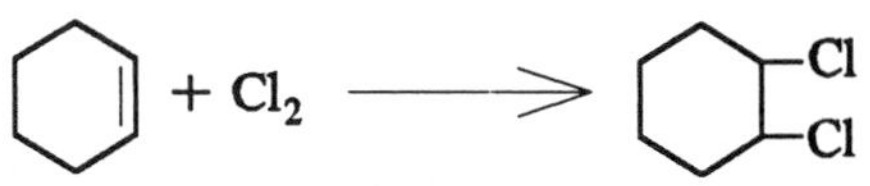

(b)

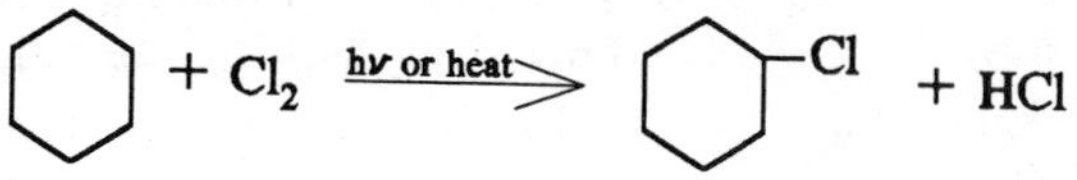

$$\text{cyclohexane} + Cl_2 \xrightarrow{\text{h}\nu\text{ or heat}} \text{chlorocyclohexane} + HCl$$

(c)

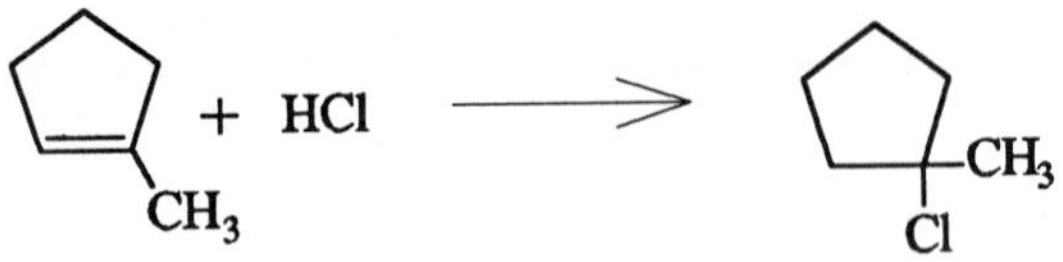

$$+ \ HCl \longrightarrow$$

(d)

$$+ \ 2H_2 \xrightarrow{\text{Pt}}$$

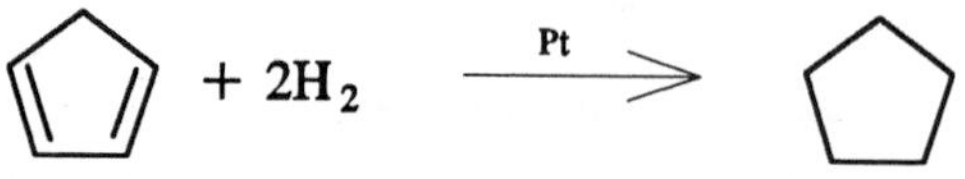

(e)

$$CH_3CH_2CH_2-C\equiv C-H \ + \ 2H_2 \xrightarrow{\text{P t}} \text{pentane}$$

or

$$H_2C=CHCH_2CH=CH_2 \ + \ 2H_2 \xrightarrow{\text{P t}} \text{pentane}$$

(f) $H-C\equiv C-CH_2CH_2CH_3 + 2Br_2 \longrightarrow 1,1,2,2\text{-tetrabromopentane}$

(g) $H-C\equiv C-CH_2CH_2CH_3 + 2HBr \longrightarrow 2,2\text{-dibromopentane}$

23.33   Localized pi bonds are sites of relatively high energy and electron density and easily attract electron seeking species, called electrophiles. These electrophiles are electron deficient and readily form covalent bonds with energetic localized pi bond electrons. Aromatic compounds, on the other hand, contain delocalized pi bonds. The pi electrons are spread out in space and do not present a region of high electron density for attracting electrophiles. The delocalized pi bond is also a relatively stable or low energy electron arrangement, since spreading the electrons or electron density over a greater volume has the effect of lowering the energy. Therefore, the delocalized pi electrons are much less likely to react and show no tendency to take part in addition reactions.

23.39   (a) carbonyl group, double bond, and carboxyl group
        (b) hydroxyl group, double bond, and carboxyl group
        (c) aldehyde group, double bond, and double bond

23.40

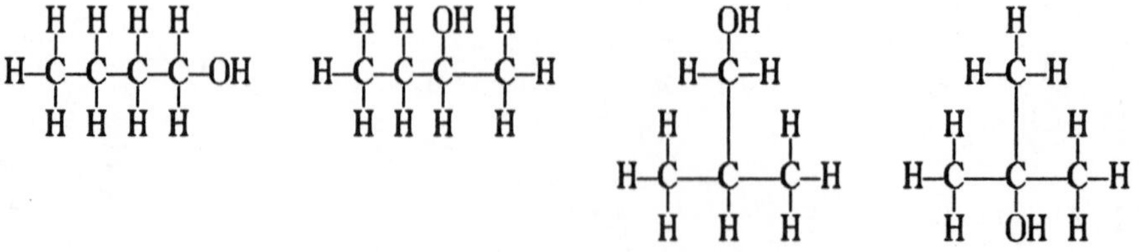

23.45   (a) Alcohols are soluble in water because they are capable of forming hydrogen bonds with water. However, the effectiveness of the hydrogen bonding decreases with the size, which is proportional to the molar mass of the alcohol. Therefore, the solubility of alcohols in water decreases with molar mass.

(b) Acetone is not capable of forming hydrogen bonds with itself, since it does not have a hydrogen atom or proton attached to the oxygen atom. Therefore, the forces binding the acetone molecules together are very weak, which accounts for the fact that acetone is very volatile. However, acetone can form hydrogen bonds with water, and that is why acetone is very soluble in water.

(c) Paper is made of cellulose, which contains many hydroxyl groups, and the glycol can form hydrogen bonds with these hydroxyl groups and thus make the ink adherent to the paper. The glycol also hydrogen bonds with moisture, which helps keep the ink from drying in the pen.

23.46 (a) Aqueous hydroxides convert phenols into their salts.

$$C_6H_5OH(l \text{ or } aq) + NaOH(aq) \longrightarrow C_6H_5ONa(aq) + H_2O(l)$$

(b) In phenol the aromatic ring withdraws electron density from the O–H bond and this makes the O–H bond more polar, while in ethyl alcohol the alkyl group does not.

23.47 The COOH group is more acidic or a better proton donor because the highly electronegative double-bonded oxygen increases the polarity of the O–H bond by drawing electron density from the O–H bond.

23.48 (a) oxidation
(b) neither; this is an elimination reaction
(c) reduction
(d) neither; this is an internal rearrangement
(e) oxidation; this type of reaction is better known as a substitution reaction, but is also an oxidation reaction because H is replaced by a more electronegative atom

23.53 (a)

$$CH_3-O-\overset{\displaystyle O}{\overset{\|}{C}}-CH_2CH_2CH_3$$

(b)

(c)

$$H_2C-O-\overset{\displaystyle O}{\overset{\|}{C}}-CH_2CH_3$$
$$HC-O-\overset{\displaystyle O}{\overset{\|}{C}}-CH_2CH_3$$
$$H_2C-O-\overset{}{\underset{\displaystyle O}{\overset{\|}{C}}}-CH_2CH_3$$

23.55 ethylene glycol: $HO-CH_2-CH_2-OH$; oxalic acid: $HOOC-COOH$

$$HO-\overset{\displaystyle O}{\overset{\|}{C}}-\overset{\displaystyle O}{\overset{\|}{C}}-O-CH_2CH_2-O-\overset{\displaystyle O}{\overset{\|}{C}}-\overset{\displaystyle O}{\overset{\|}{C}}-O-CH_2CH_2-OH$$

↑ another alcohol can condense here   ↑ another acid can condense here

or

$$\sim\!\!\sim\!\!\sim\overset{\displaystyle O}{\overset{\|}{C}}-\overset{\displaystyle O}{\overset{\|}{C}}-O-CH_2CH_2-O-\overset{\displaystyle O}{\overset{\|}{C}}-\overset{\displaystyle O}{\overset{\|}{C}}-O-CH_2CH_2-O\!\!\sim\!\!\sim\!\!\sim$$

23.56

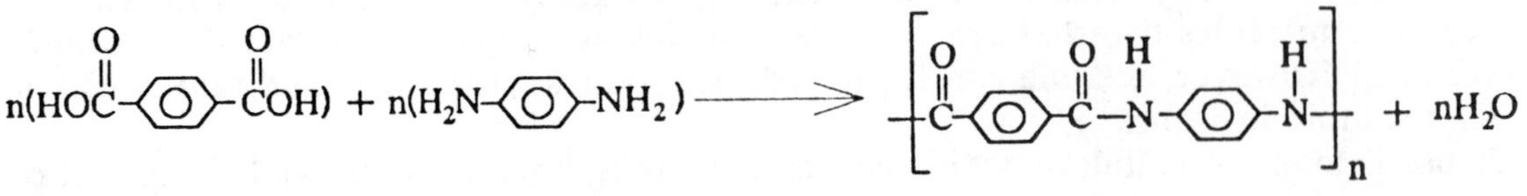

$$n(HO\overset{O}{\underset{||}{C}}-\langle O \rangle-\overset{O}{\underset{||}{C}}OH) + n(H_2N-\langle O \rangle-NH_2) \longrightarrow \left[\overset{O}{\underset{||}{C}}-\langle O \rangle-\overset{O}{\underset{||}{C}}-\overset{H}{\underset{}{N}}-\langle O \rangle-\overset{H}{\underset{}{N}} \right]_n + nH_2O$$

terephthalic acid   p-diaminobenzene   Kevlar

23.58 (a) The melting point decreases as the degree of unsaturation increases.
      (b) The melting point of the fat depends on how closely the fat molecules fit together. A closer fit leads to stronger intermolecular forces and a higher melting point. Saturated fatty acids have a linear extension and fit together very well. However, cis–unsaturated fatty acids have a bend at the double bond and do not fit together very well with other fatty acids. Therefore, the greater the unsaturation, the weaker the intermolecular forces and the lower the melting point of the fat.
      (c) Oils are hydrogenated in order to make them into solids.

23.59

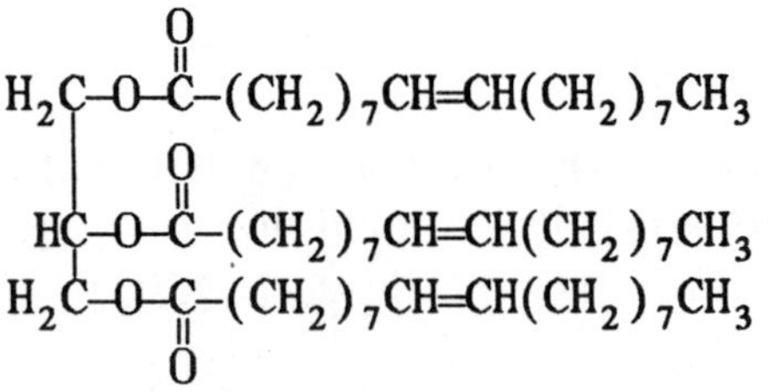

$$H_2C-O-\overset{O}{\underset{||}{C}}-(CH_2)_7CH=CH(CH_2)_7CH_3$$
$$HC-O-\overset{O}{\underset{||}{C}}-(CH_2)_7CH=CH(CH_2)_7CH_3$$
$$H_2C-O-\underset{||}{\overset{}{C}}-(CH_2)_7CH=CH(CH_2)_7CH_3$$
$$O$$

(a)

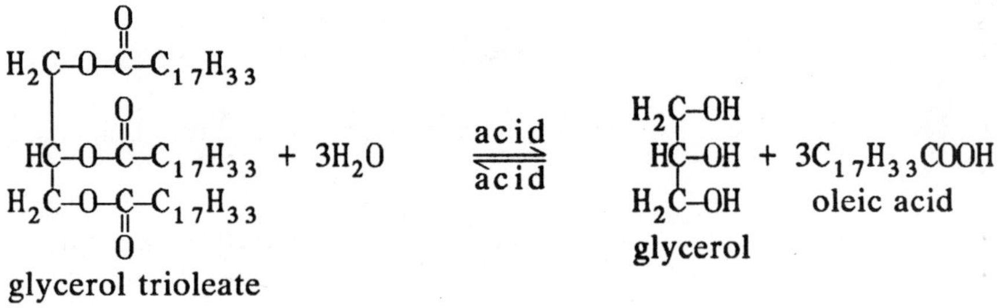

$$H_2C-O-\overset{O}{\underset{||}{C}}-C_{17}H_{33}$$
$$HC-O-\overset{O}{\underset{||}{C}}-C_{17}H_{33} + 3H_2O \quad \underset{acid}{\overset{acid}{\rightleftharpoons}} \quad \begin{matrix} H_2C-OH \\ HC-OH + 3C_{17}H_{33}COOH \\ H_2C-OH \quad \text{oleic acid} \\ \text{glycerol} \end{matrix}$$
$$H_2C-O-\underset{||}{\overset{}{C}}-C_{17}H_{33}$$
$$O$$
glycerol trioleate

(b)

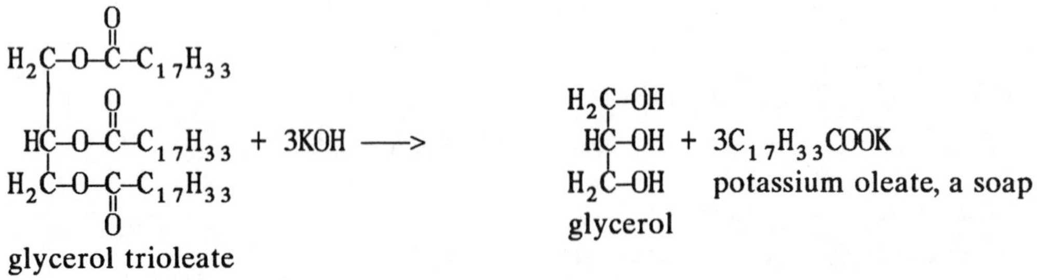

$$H_2C-O-\overset{O}{\underset{||}{C}}-C_{17}H_{33}$$
$$HC-O-\overset{O}{\underset{||}{C}}-C_{17}H_{33} + 3KOH \longrightarrow \begin{matrix} H_2C-OH \\ HC-OH + 3C_{17}H_{33}COOK \\ H_2C-OH \quad \text{potassium oleate, a soap} \\ \text{glycerol} \end{matrix}$$
$$H_2C-O-\underset{||}{\overset{}{C}}-C_{17}H_{33}$$
$$O$$
glycerol trioleate

23.63 (a) $CH_3-\overset{*}{C}H-COOH$
                NH_2

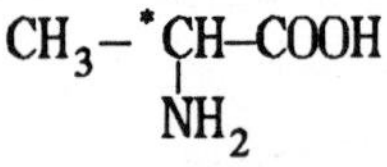

(b)

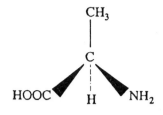

D-amino acid
D-alanine

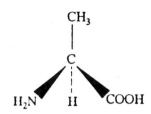

L-amino acid
L-alanine

(c) Only the L enantiomer.

23.68 (a)

$$n(HO-\overset{O}{\overset{\|}{C}}-R-\overset{O}{\overset{\|}{C}}-OH) + n(H_2N-R'-NH_2) \longrightarrow \left[\overset{O}{\overset{\|}{C}}-R-\overset{O}{\overset{\|}{C}}-\overset{H}{\overset{|}{N}}-R'-\overset{H}{\overset{|}{N}}\right]_n + nH_2O$$

(b) Refer to Polyamides in Section 23.8 in the textbook.

(c)

$$n(HO-\overset{O}{\overset{\|}{C}}-(CH_2)_4-\overset{O}{\overset{\|}{C}}-OH) + n(H_2N-(CH_2)_4-NH_2) \longrightarrow \left[\overset{O}{\overset{\|}{C}}-(CH_2)_4-\overset{O}{\overset{\|}{C}}-\overset{H}{\overset{|}{N}}-(CH_2)_4-\overset{H}{\overset{|}{N}}\right]_n + nH_2O$$

adipic acid   1,4-diaminobutane   Nylon 46

23.73 (a) hydrogen bonding: Ser, Gln, Tyr, Asn, and Thr.
(b) ionic interactions: His, Asp, Glu, Lys, and Arg. These amino acids have charged R groups at physiological pH.
(c) hydrophobic interactions: Gly, Ala, Val, Leu, Ile, Met, Phe, Pro, and Trp. These amino acids have nonpolar R groups.

23.74 (a) The disulfide bridge is a true covalent bond, while the other interactions are not.
(b) Only cysteine is involved in sulfide bridge formation.

23.75 (a)   before stretching

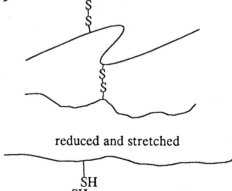

reduced and stretched

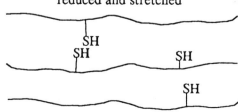

oxidized

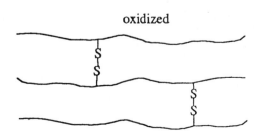

(b) The oxidizing agent forms disulfide bridges between the polypeptide chains.

(c)

$$R-S-H + H-S-R' \xrightarrow{\text{oxidizing agent [O]}} R-S-S-R' + H_2O$$

$$R-S-S-R' \xrightarrow{\text{reducing agent [H]}} R-SH + R'-SH$$

23.76 (a) Hexose – a monosaccharide containing 6 carbon atoms
(b) Pentose – a monosaccharide containing 5 carbon atoms
(c) Aldose – a monosaccharide containing an aldehyde functional group
(d) Ketose – a monosaccharide containing a ketone functional group

Glucose is a hexose and an aldose, i.e., an aldohexose. Fructose is a hexose and a ketose, i.e., a ketohexose.

23.79 (a) Starch, glycogen, and cellulose are all polymers of glucose.
(b) Starch is a condensation product of α-D-glucose, while cellulose is a condensation product of β-D-glucose. α-D-glucose and β-D-glucose are the two different cyclic forms of open–chain D-glucose (see Figure 23.43). Glycogen is similar to starch but has more branching in the polymer chains.
(c) Starch and cellulose are found in plants. Glycogen is found in animals.

23.81 Enzyme active sites can only accommodate molecules that have the correct shape. The glycosidic linkage in cellulose, which is a condensation product of β-D-glucose, has a different shape than the glycosidic linkage in starch, which is a condensation product of α-D-glucose. The enzyme active sites in humans cannot accommodate the shape of the glycosidic linkage in cellulose, only that in starch, and, consequently, humans cannot digest cellulose.

23.86 The fact that all DNA samples yield equal amounts of adenine and thymine and equal amounts of guanine and cytosine indicates that the adenine and thymine exist as hydrogen bonded pairs, and the guanine and cytosine also exist as hydrogen bonded pairs in DNA. For this to be so, the DNA structure would have to consist of two interacting polymer strands, and not one or three.

23.90 (a) Carbon has four valence electrons and with few exceptions forms four covalent bonds in compounds. Combining carbon's bonding capacity with its ability to form strong bonds with other carbon atoms allows for an unending array of straight and branched chains of varying lengths and complexity and rings (simple, multiple, and substituted) of different sizes. The small size of the carbon atom also permits its p orbitals to participate in π bonding, forming both double, C=C, and triple, C≡C, bonds with other carbon atoms, thus allowing for whole new categories of compounds containing these unsaturated bonds.
(b) The bonds formed between the silicon atoms are not nearly as strong as those between carbon atoms. This severly limits the length and complexity of silicon chains and rings. Also, the larger size of the silicon atom doesn't allow it to participate in π bonding with its p orbitals.

23.91 (a)

isohexane or 2-methylpentane

(b)

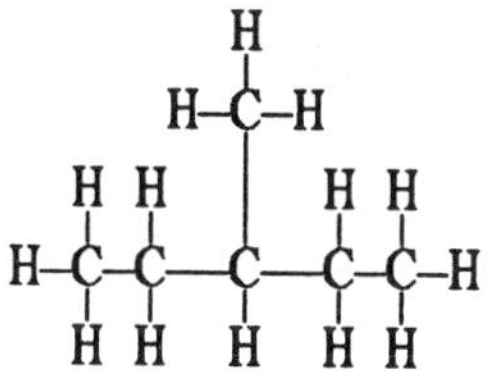

3-methylpentane

(c)

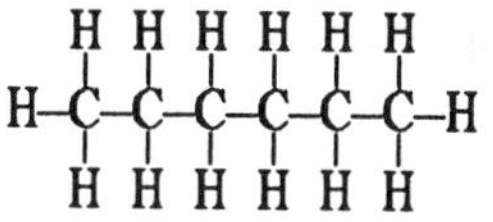

n–hexane

or

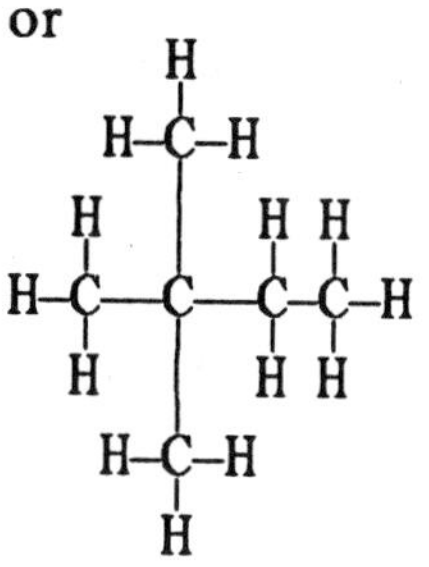

2,2-dimethylbutane

(d)

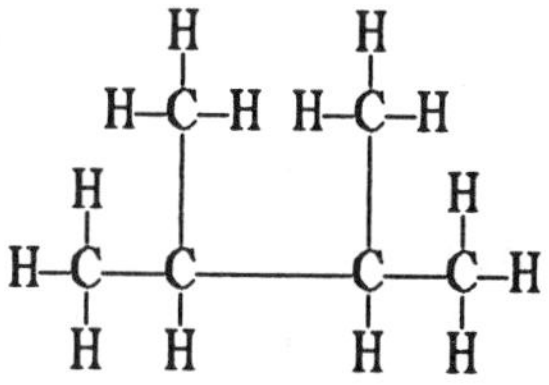

2,3-dimethylbutane

23.92   Since each carbon can have no more than three hydrogen atoms, the formula for the hydrocarbon must be C_5H_{12}. The only saturated hydrocarbon with this formula that gives one monobromo derivative is

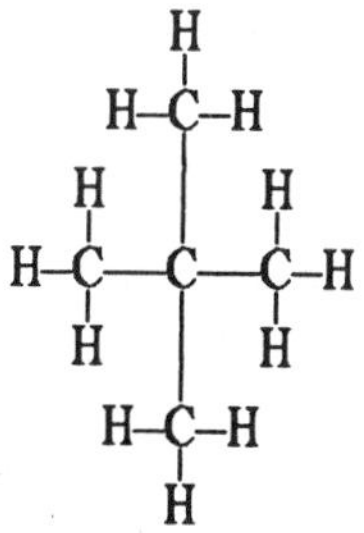

23.93   Ketones are not easily oxidized and their oxidation requires the breaking of a C–C bond; therefore, the original compound is not a ketone. Both aldehydes and alcohols can be easily oxidized, but there are too many hydrogens for the compound to be an aldehyde (as well as a ketone for that matter); namely,

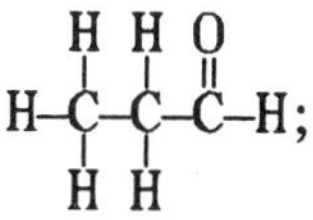

only 6 H's

Therefore, the original compound must be an alcohol. The product (C_3H_6O) must be a ketone, because it is not oxidized further. Therefore, the original compound must be a secondary alcohol and not a primary alcohol, since secondary alcohols oxidize to ketones.

Original compound: H–C–C—C–H;   2-propanol or isopropyl alcohol

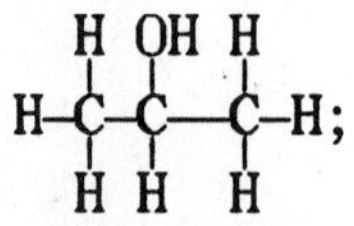

Oxidation product: H–C–C–C–H;   acetone

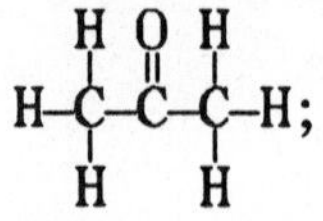

23.94 (a) Glyceryl trioleate has three double bonds per molecule or 3 mol of double bonds per mole of fat. Each mole of double bonds consumes 1 mol of iodine (I_2). The molar mass of glyceryl trioleate ($C_{57}H_{104}O_6$) is 885 g. The road map is: 100 g fat ——> mol fat ——> mol double bonds ——> mol I_2 ——> g I_2 ——> iodine number.

$$100 \text{ g fat} \times \frac{1 \text{ mol fat}}{885 \text{ g fat}} \times \frac{3 \text{ mol double bonds}}{1 \text{ mol fat}} \times \frac{1 \text{ mol } I_2}{1 \text{ mol double bonds}} \times \frac{253.8 \text{ g } I_2}{1 \text{ mol } I_2}$$

$= 86 \text{ g } I_2$

Answer: The iodine number is 86.

(b) Glyceryl trilinoleate has six double bonds per molecule or 6 mol of double bonds per mole of fat. Its molar mass ($C_{57}H_{98}O_6$) is 879 g.

$$100 \text{ g fat} \times \frac{1 \text{ mol fat}}{879 \text{ g fat}} \times \frac{6 \text{ mol double bonds}}{1 \text{ mol fat}} \times \frac{1 \text{ mol } I_2}{1 \text{ mol double bonds}} \times \frac{253.8 \text{ g } I_2}{1 \text{ mol } I_2}$$

$= 173 \text{ g } I_2$

Answer: The iodine number is 173.

(c) Stearin contains no double bonds. Therefore, its iodine number is zero.